Test Bank
for Stewart's
Calculus
Concepts and Contexts ◆ 3E

William Tomhave
Xueqi Zeng
CONCORDIA COLLEGE

THOMSON

BROOKS/COLE

Australia • Canada • Mexico • Singapore • Spain

United Kingdom • United States

THOMSON

BROOKS/COLE

Mathematics Editor □ *Bob Pirtle*

Assistant Editor □ *Stacy Green*

Cover Designer □ *Denise Davidson*

Print/Media Buyer □ *Lisa Claudeanos*

Cover Image □ *Tom Bonner*

Compositor □ *Andy Bulman-Fleming*

Text and Cover Printer □ *Thomson/West*

For more information about our products, contact us at:
Thomson Learning Academic Resource Center
1-800-423-0563

ISBN-13: 978-0-534-41031-5
ISBN-10: 0-534-41031-6

Thomson Higher Education
10 Davis Drive
Belmont, CA 94002-3098
USA

Asia
Thomson Learning
5 Shenton Way
#01-01 UIC Building
Singapore 068808

Australia/New Zealand
Nelson Thomson Learning
102 Dodds Street
Southbank, Victoria 3006
Australia

Canada
Thomson Nelson
1120 Birchmount Road
Toronto, Ontario M1K 5G4
Canada

UK/Europe/Middle East/South Africa
Thomson Learning
High Holborn House
50/51 Bedford Row
London WC1R 4LR
United Kingdom

Latin America
Thomson Learning
Seneca, 53
Colonia Polanco
11560 Mexico
D.F. Mexico

Spain (includes Portugal)
Thomson Paraninfo
Calle/Magallanes, 25
28015 Madrid
Spain

Preface

These test items were designed to accompany *Calculus: Concepts and Contexts, Third Edition* by James Stewart. The test items include both multiple choice and free-response questions, and approach calculus from four viewpoints: descriptive, algebraic, numeric, and graphic. They are designed to help instructors assess students' conceptual understanding of the material as well as their manipulative skills. It is our hope that you will find enough variety in both difficulty and approach to allow you substantial flexibility in designing examinations and quizzes that meet your needs and those of your students.

This project could not have been completed without the assistance of several associates. We would especially like to thank Charles Heuer for his careful checking and amazing turnaround times, Andy Bulman-Fleming for his work related to page layout and design, and Stacy Green for persuasion, support, and encouragement throughout this writing process. A sincere thanks again goes to James Stewart for providing us with the opportunity to be part of this project. Finally, we extend our deepest gratitude to Lois and Wentong, our spouses, who have been incredibly supportive as we carried out the work involved in this project.

William K. Tomhave
Xueqi Zeng

Table of Contents

Functions and Models

1.1 | Four Ways to Represent a Function

1. Find the smallest value in the domain of the function $f(x) = \sqrt{2x - 5}$.

   (A) 2 (B) $\frac{5}{2}$ (C) 5 (D) $\frac{2}{5}$

   (E) -2 (F) 1 (G) 0 (H) -5

   Answer: (B)

2. Find the largest value in the range of the function $f(x) = 3 - 2x^2$.

   (A) $-\frac{2}{3}$ (B) $\frac{2}{3}$ (C) 3 (D) -2

   (E) -3 (F) $-\frac{3}{2}$ (G) 2 (H) $\frac{3}{2}$

   Answer: (C)

3. The range of the function $f(x) = \sqrt{20 + 8x - x^2}$ is a closed interval $[a, b]$. Find its length $b - a$.

   (A) 1 (B) 2 (C) 3 (D) 4

   (E) 5 (F) 6 (G) 7 (H) 9

   Answer: (F)

4. Find the smallest value in the range of the function $f(x) = |2x| + |2x + 3|$.

   (A) 2 (B) 3 (C) 5 (D) $\frac{1}{2}$

   (E) $\frac{3}{2}$ (F) $\frac{5}{2}$ (G) 0 (H) 1

   Answer: (B)

5. Find the largest value in the domain of the function $f(x) = \sqrt{\dfrac{3 - 2x}{4 + 3x}}$.

   (A) $-\frac{3}{2}$ (B) $-\frac{2}{3}$ (C) 0 (D) 2

   (E) $\frac{2}{3}$ (F) $\frac{3}{2}$ (G) 3 (H) No largest value

   Answer: (F)

6. Find the domain of the function $f(x) = \sqrt[3]{\dfrac{2 - x}{x - 3}}$.

   (A) $(-\infty, 3)$ (B) $(-\infty, 3) \cup (3, \infty)$ (C) $(-\infty, -3)$ (D) $(-\infty, 2) \cup (2, \infty)$

   (E) $[2, 3)$ (F) $(3, \infty)$ (G) $(-3, 3)$ (H) $(-\infty, 2) \cup (3, \infty)$

   Answer: (B)

1

7. Find the range of the function $f(x) = |x - 1| + x - 1$.

(A) $[1, \infty)$ (B) $(1, \infty)$ (C) $[0, \infty)$ (D) $(0, \infty)$

(E) $[-1, \infty)$ (F) $(-1, \infty)$ (G) $[0, 1]$ (H) $\mathbb{R}$

Answer: **(C)**

8. The function $f(x) = \sqrt{\dfrac{x - 1}{x}}$ has as its domain all values of x such that

(A) $x > 0$ (B) $x \geq 1$ (C) $x \leq 0$ (D) $x \leq 1$

(E) $0 < x \leq 1$ (F) $x \geq 1$ or $x < 0$ (G) $x \geq -1$ (H) $-1 \leq x < 0$

Answer: **(F)**

9. Find the range of the function $f(x) = \dfrac{x - 1}{2x}$.

(A) $(-\infty, 0) \cup (0, \infty)$ (B) $\left(-\infty, \frac{1}{2}\right) \cup \left(\frac{1}{2}, \infty\right)$

(C) $(-\infty, 1) \cup (1, \infty)$ (D) $(0, 1]$

(E) $\left(\frac{1}{2}, 1\right]$ (F) $\frac{1}{2}$

(G) 1 (H) 2

Answer: **(B)**

10. Which of the following are graphs of functions?

I   II   III

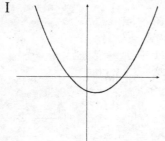 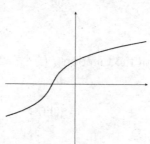 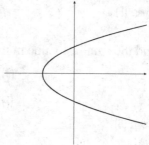

IV   V

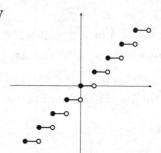 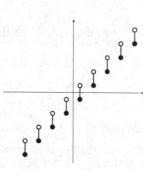

(A) I only   (B) II only   (C) III only   (D) I and II only

(E) I and III only   (F) I, II, and IV only   (G) II and V only   (H) I, II, and III only

Answer: **(F)**

11. Each of the functions in the table below is increasing, but each increases in a different way. Select the graph from those given below which best fits each function:

t	1	2	3	4	5	6
$f(t)$	26	34	41	46	48	49
$g(t)$	16	24	32	40	48	56
$h(t)$	36	44	53	64	77	93

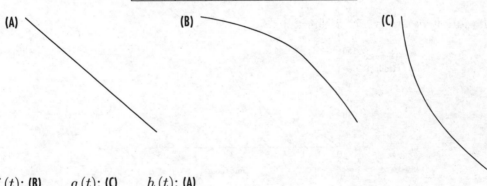

(A)　　　　　　　　**(B)**　　　　　　　　**(C)**

Answer: $f(t)$: **(B)**　　$g(t)$: **(A)**　　$h(t)$: **(C)**

12. Each of the functions in the table below is decreasing, but each decreases in a different way. Select the graph from those given below which best fits each function:

t	1	2	3	4	5	6
$f(t)$	98	91	81	69	54	35
$g(t)$	80	71	63	57	53	52
$h(t)$	78	69	60	51	42	33

(A)　　　　　　　　**(B)**　　　　　　　　**(C)**

Answer: $f(t)$: **(B)**　　$g(t)$: **(C)**　　$h(t)$: **(A)**

13. Suppose a pet owner decides to wash her dog in the laundry tub. She fills the laundry tub with warm water, puts the dog into the tub and shampoos it, removes the dog from the tub to towel it, then pulls the plug to drain the tub. Let t be the time in minutes, beginning when she starts to fill the tub, and let $h(t)$ be the water level in the tub at time t. If the total time for filling and draining the tub and washing the dog was 40 minutes, sketch a possible graph of $h(t)$.

Answer: (One possible answer — answers will vary.)

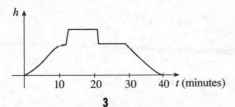

14. A homeowner mowed her lanw on June 1, cutting it to a uniform height of 3″. She mowed the lawn at one-week intervals after that until she left for a vacation on June 30. A local lawn service put fertilizer on her lawn shortly after she mowed on June 15, causing the grass to grow more rapidly. She returned from her vacation on July 13 to find that the neighborhood boy whom she had hired to mow the lawn while she was away had indeed mowed on June 22 and on June 29, but had forgotten to mow on July 6. Sketch a possible graph of the height of the grass as a function of time over the time period from June 1 through July 13.

Answer: (One possible answer — answers will vary.)

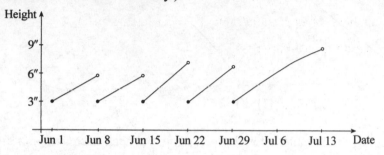

15. A professor left the college for a professional meeting, a trip that was expected to take 4 hours. The graph below shows the distance $D(t)$ that the professor has traveled from the college as a function of the time t, in hours. Refer to the graph and answer the questions which follow.

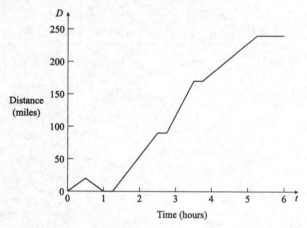

(a) Describe what might have happened at $D(0.5)$.

(b) Describe what might have happened at $D(1.0)$.

(c) Describe what might have happened at $D(1.2)$.

(d) Describe what might have happened at $D(2.5)$.

(e) Describe what might have happened at $D(3.5)$.

(f) Describe what might have happened at $D(3.75)$.

(g) Describe what might have happened at $D(4.0)$.

(h) Describe what might have happened at $D(5.25)$.

Answer:

(a) He was traveling to the meeting.

(b) He returned to the college (maybe he forgot something.)

(c) He left the college for the meeting again.

(d) He stopped to rest.

(e) He stopped for a second time after traveling at a relatively high rate of speed, perhaps at the request of a highway patrol officer.

(f) He continued on his trip but at a substantially lower rate of speed.

(g) He was traveling to the meeting.

(h) He arrived at his destination.

16. Let $f(x) = 4 - x^2$. Find

(a) the domain of f.

(b) the range of f.

Answer: (a) $(-\infty, \infty)$ (b) $(-\infty, 4]$

17. Let $f(x) = \sqrt{2x + 5}$. Find

(a) the domain of f.

(b) the range of f.

Answer: (a) $\left[-\frac{2}{5}, \infty\right)$ (b) $[0, \infty)$

18. Let $f(x) = \sqrt{16 - x^2}$. Find

(a) the domain of f.

(b) the range of f.

Answer: (a) $[-4, 4]$ (b) $[0, 4]$

19. Let $f(x) = \dfrac{1}{\sqrt{x^2 - 16}}$. Find

(a) the domain of f.

(b) the range of f.

Answer: (a) $(-\infty, -4) \cup (4, \infty)$ (b) $(0, \infty)$

20. Express the area A of a circle as a function of its circumference C.

Answer: $A = \dfrac{C^2}{4\pi}$

21. Let $f(x) = \begin{cases} x^2 + 3 & \text{if } x \leq -1 \\ \dfrac{2 + 3x}{6} & \text{if } x > -1 \end{cases}$ Find

(a) the domain of f.

(b) the range of f.

Answer: (a) $(-\infty, \infty)$ (b) $\left(-\frac{1}{6}, \infty\right)$

5

22. A function has domain $[-2, 2]$ and a portion of its graph is shown.

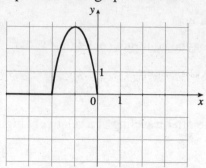

(a) Complete the graph of f if it is known that f is an even function.

(b) Complete the graph of f if it is known that f is an odd function.

Answer: (a)

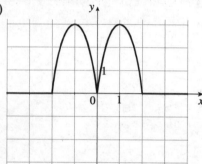

(b)

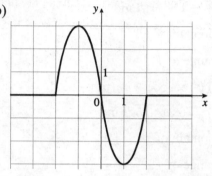

23. A function has domain $[-4, 4]$ and a portion of its graph is shown.

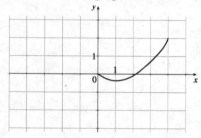

(a) Complete the graph of f if it is known that f is an even function.

(b) Complete the graph of f if it is known that f is an odd function.

Answer:

(a)

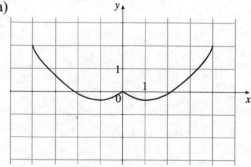

(b)

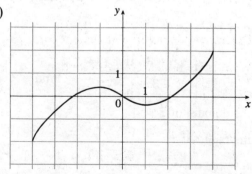

24. Given the graph of $y = f(x)$:

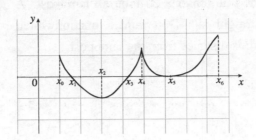

Find all values of x where:

(a) f is increasing.

(b) f is decreasing.

Answer: (a) (x_2, x_4) and (x_5, x_6) (b) (x_0, x_2) and (x_4, x_5)

25. An observer atop a cliff sees a speedboat approaching a dock located at the base of the cliff directly below the observer. Express the distance from the observer to the boat as a function of the distance from the boat to the dock, if the cliff is 150 feet high.

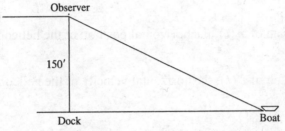

Answer: Let d be the distance from the observer to the boat in feet and let x be the distance from the observer to the dock. Then $d = \sqrt{150^2 + x^2}$.

26. A tank used for portland cement consists of a cylinder mounted on top of a cone, with its vertex pointing downward. The cylinder is 30 feet high, both the cylinder and the cone have radii of 4 feet, and the cone is 6 feet high.

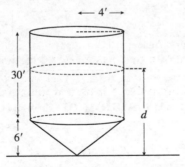

(a) Determine the volume of cement contained in the tank as a function of the depth d of the cement.

(b) What is the domain of this function?

Answer:

(a) $V(d) = \begin{cases} \dfrac{4\pi d^3}{27} & \text{if } 0 \le d \le 6 \\ 16\pi d - 64\pi & \text{if } 6 < d \le 36 \end{cases}$ (b) $d \subset [0, 36]$

7

27. A parking lot light is mounted on top of a 20-foot tall lamppost. A person T feet tall is walking away from the lamppost along a straight path. Determine a function which expresses the length of the person's shadow in terms of the person's distance from the lamppost.

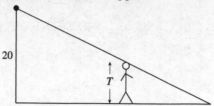

Answer: Let L be the length of the person's shadow and x be the person's distance from the lamppost. Then $L = \dfrac{Tx}{(20 - T)}$.

28. A medical helicopter leaves a hospital for an accident scene 24 miles due east of the hospital. At the scene the paramedics pick up two accident victims and then the helicopter returns directly to the hospital helipad. The round trip takes a total of 30 minutes.

   (a) Sketch a possible graph of $x(t)$, the horizontal position of the helicopter at time t.

   (b) Sketch a possible graph of $v(t)$, the horizontal velocity of the helicopter at time t.

Answer:

(a)
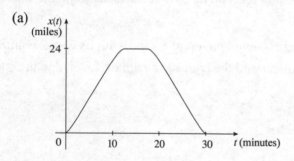

(b)
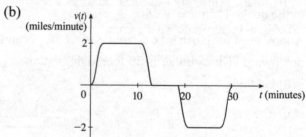

1.2 Mathematical Models: A Catalog of Essential Functions

1. Classify the function $f(x) = \dfrac{x^2 + \pi}{x}$.

   (A) Power function

   (B) Root function

   (C) Polynomial function

   (D) Rational function

   (E) Algebraic function

   (F) Trigonometric function

   (G) Exponential function

   (H) Logarithmic function

   Answer: (D)

2. Classify the function $f(x) = x^{3/2} + 2x^{1/2} + 4$.

(A) Power function   (B) Root function

(C) Polynomial function   (D) Rational function

(E) Algebraic function   (F) Trigonometric function

(G) Exponential function   (H) Logarithmic function

Answer: (E)

3. Classify the function $f(x) = \sin(5)x^2 + \sin(3)x$.

(A) Power function   (B) Root function

(C) Polynomial function   (D) Rational function

(E) Algebraic function   (F) Trigonometric function

(G) Exponential function   (H) Logarithmic function

Answer: (C)

4. The data in this problem concern the gross domestic product (GDP) for the United States. The GDP is defined as the total market value of all the goods and services produced by a country during one year.

Year	1950	1960	1970	1980	1990	2000
Gross Domestic Product 1996 Dollars (billions)	1686.6	2376.7	3578.0	4900.9	6707.9	9191.4

Source: Bureau of Economic Analysis, U.S. Department of Commerce website

(a) Make a scatter plot of these data.

(b) Fit a linear model to the data.

(c) Fit an exponential model to the data.

(d) Fit a quadratic model to the data.

(e) Use your equations to make a table showing the predicted 2002 GDP for each model, rounded to one decimal place.

(f) The actual value for the GDP in 2002 was 9439.9. Which model was closest? Which model was second-closest?

Answer:

(a)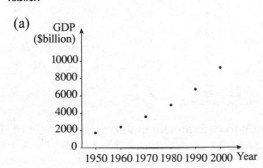

(b) $y = 148.12x + 1046.0$

(c) $y = 1725.187434e^{1.034599687}$

(d) $y = 2.033893857x^2 + 46.4249713x + 1719.1237925$

(e) Linear: 8748.2
Exponential: 10,115.9
Quadratic: 9632.9

(f) Closest: quadratic. Second-closest: exponential

9

5. Consider the data below:

t	1	2	3	4	5	6
y	2.4	19	64	152	295	510

(a) Fit both an exponential curve and a third-degree polynomial to the data.

(b) Which of the models appears to be a better fit? Defend your choice.

Answer:

(a)

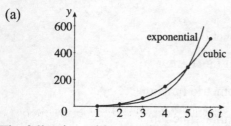

(b) A third degree polynomial, for example, $y = 2.40t^3$, appears to be the better fit.

6. The following table contains United States population data for the years 1981–1990, as well as estimates based on the 1990 census.

Year	U. S. Population (millions)
1981	229.5
1982	231.6
1983	233.8
1984	235.8
1985	237.9
1986	240.1
1987	242.3
1988	244.4
1989	246.8
1990	249.5
1991	252.2
1992	255.0
1993	257.8
1994	260.3
1995	262.8
1996	265.2
1997	267.8
1998	270.2
1999	272.7
2000	275.1

Source: U.S. Census Bureau website

(a) Make a scatter plot for the data and use your scatter plot to determine a mathematical model of the U.S. population.

(b) Use your model to predict the U.S. population in 2003.

Answer:

(a)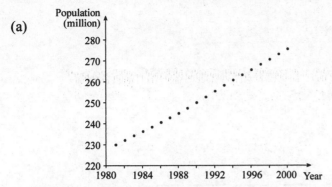

(b) $P(22) \approx 282.3$

A linear model seems appropriate. Taking $t = 0$ in 1981, we obtain the model $P(t) = 2.4455t + 228.5$.

7. The following table contains United States population data for the years 1790–2000 at intervals of 10 years.

Year	Years since 1790	U.S. Population (millions)
1790	0	3.9
1800	10	5.2
1810	20	7.2
1820	30	9.6
1830	40	12.9
1840	50	17.1
1850	60	23.2
1860	70	31.4
1870	80	39.8
1880	90	50.2
1890	100	62.9
1900	110	76.0
1910	120	92.0
1920	130	105.7
1930	140	122.8
1940	150	131.7
1950	160	150.7
1960	170	178.5
1970	180	202.5
1980	190	225.5
1990	200	248.7
2000	210	281.4

(a) Make a scatter plot for the data and use your scatter plot to determine a mathematical model of the U.S. population.

(b) Use your model to predict the U.S. population in 2005.

Answer:

(a)

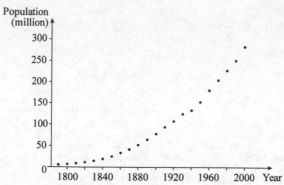

Answers will vary, but a quadratic or cubic model is most appropriate.

Linear model: $P(t) = 1.28545t - 40.47668$; quadratic model: $P(t) = 0.006666t^2 - 0.1144t + 5.9$;

cubic model: $P(t) = (6.6365 \times 10^{-6}) t^3 + 0.004575t^2 + 0.057155t + 3.7$;

exponential model: $P(t) = 6.04852453 \times 1.020407795^t$

(b) Linear model: $P(215) \approx 235.9$; quadratic model: $P(215) \approx 289.4$; cubic model: $P(215) \approx 293.4$;
exponential model: $P(215) \approx 465.6$

8. Refer to your models from Problems 6 and 7 above. Why do the two data sets produce such different models?

Answer: Problem 6 covers a much shorter time span, so its data exhibit local linearity, while Problem 7 shows nonlinear population growth over a longer time span.

1.3 | New Functions From Old Functions

1. Let $f(x) = \sqrt{x^2 + 9}$ and $g(x) = x - 3$, then $(f + g)(x)$ is equal to

(A) $2x$ (B) $2x + 6$ (C) $x^2 + x + 6$ (D) $\sqrt{x^2 + 9} + x - 3$

(E) $\sqrt{x^2 + 9}\, x - 3$ (F) $x^2 + 2x + 6$ (G) $x^2 + 9x + 9$ (H) $\sqrt{x^2 + 6}$

Answer: (D)

2. Let $f(x) = \sqrt{x^2 + 4}$ and $g(x) = -\sqrt{x^2 - 4}$. Find the domain of $(g \circ f)(x)$.

(A) $(-\infty, 0]$ (B) $(2, \infty)$ (C) $(-\infty, -2)$ (D) $(-\infty, 2) \cup (2, \infty)$

(E) $[-2, \infty)$ (F) $(-\infty, -2]$ (G) $(-\infty, -2] \cup [2, \infty)$ (H) $\mathbb{R}$

Answer: (H)

3. Let $f(x) = \sqrt{x - 1}$ and $g(x) = \sqrt{9 - x^2}$. Find the domain of $\left(\dfrac{g}{f}\right)(x)$.

(A) $(-\infty, -3] \cup (1, 3]$ (B) $(-\infty, -3] \cup [3, \infty)$ (C) $(-\infty, -3] \cup [1, \infty)$ (D) $(-\infty, 1] \cup [3, \infty)$

(E) $[3, \infty)$ (F) $(-\infty, -1) \cup [3, \infty)$ (G) $(1, 3)$ (H) $[-3, 1) \cup [3, \infty)$

Answer: (A)

4. Let $f(x) = 3x - 2$ and $g(x) = 2 - 3x$. Find the value of $(f + g)(x)$ when $x = 5$.

(A) 13   (B) 26   (C) 0   (D) $6x + 4$

(E) -5 (F) -13 (G) -26 (H) $4 - 6x$

Answer: (C)

5. Let $f(x) = 3x - 2$ and $g(x) = 2 - 3x$. Find the value of $(f \circ g)(x)$ when $x = 3$.

(A) -23 (B) -9 (C) -6 (D) -3

(E) 3   (F) 6   (G) 9   (H) 23

Answer: (A)

6. Let $f(x) = 2 - x^3$ and $g(x) = 3 + x$. Find the value of $(f \circ g)(x)$ when $x = -5$.

(A) -510 (B) -5 (C) -2 (D) 0

(E) 5   (F) 10   (G) 127   (H) 130

Answer: (F)

7. Let $f(x) = \frac{1}{2}x$ and $(f \circ g)(x) = x^2$. Find $g(2)$.

(A) 0   (B) 1   (C) 2   (D) 4

(E) 8   (F) 16   (G) 32   (H) 64

Answer: (E)

8. Relative to the graph of $y = x^2 + 2$, the graph of $y = (x - 2)^2 + 2$ is changed in what way?

(A) Shifted 2 units upward   (B) Compressed vertically by a factor of 2

(C) Compressed horizontally by a factor of 2   (D) Shifted 2 units to the left

(E) Shifted 2 units to the right   (F) Shifted 2 units downward

(G) Stretched vertically by a factor of 2   (H) Stretched horizontally by a factor of 2

Answer: (E)

9. Relative to the graph of $y = x^2$, the graph of $y = x^2 - 2$ is changed in what way?

(A) Shifted 2 units downward   (B) Stretched horizontally by a factor of 2

(C) Shifted 2 units to the right   (D) stretched vertically by a factor of 2

(E) Compressed horizontally by a factor of 2   (F) Compressed vertically by a factor of 2

(G) Stretched vertically by a factor of 2   (H) Stretched horizontally by a factor of 2

Answer: (A)

10. Relative to the graph of $y = x^3$, the graph of $y = \frac{1}{2}x^3$ is changed in what way?

(A) Compressed horizontally by a factor of 2   (B) Shifted 2 units downward

(C) Stretched vertically by a factor of 2   (D) Stretched horizontally by a factor of 2

(E) Shifted 2 units upward   (F) Compressed vertically by a factor of 2

(G) Shifted 2 units to the right   (H) Shifted 2 units to the left

Answer: (F)

11. Relative to the graph of $y = x^2 + 2$, the graph of $y = 4x^2 + 2$ is changed in what way?

   (A) Compressed vertically by a factor of 2

   (B) Stretched horizontally by a factor of 2

   (C) Compressed horizontally by a factor of 2

   (D) Shifted 2 units upward

   (E) Shifted 2 units to the right

   (F) stretched vertically by a factor of 2

   (G) Shifted 2 units to the left

   (H) Shifted 2 units downward

   Answer: (C)

12. Relative to the graph of $y = \sin x$, the graph of $y = 3 \sin x$ is changed in what way?

   (A) Compressed horizontally by a factor of 3

   (B) Shifted 3 units to the right

   (C) Compressed vertically by a factor of 3

   (D) Shifted 3 units upward

   (E) Shifted 3 units to the left

   (F) Stretched vertically by a factor of 3

   (G) Shifted 3 units downward

   (H) Stretched horizontally by a factor of 3

   Answer: (F)

13. Relative to the graph of $y = x^2$, the graph of $y = 4x^2$ can be thought of as expanded vertically by a factor of 4. In what other way can it be thought of as being changed?

   (A) Shifted 2 units downward

   (B) Shifted 4 units downward

   (C) Stretched horizontally by a factor of 2

   (D) Compressed horizontally by a factor of 4

   (E) Shifted 2 units upward

   (F) Shifted 4 units upward

   (G) Compressed horizontally by a factor of 2

   (H) Stretched horizontally by a factor of 4

   Answer: (G)

14. Relative to the graph of $y = \sin x$, where x is in radians, the graph of $y = \sin x$, where x is in degrees, is changed in what way?

   (A) Stretched vertically by a factor of $\frac{180}{\pi}$

   (B) Compressed horizontally by a factor of $\frac{180}{\pi}$

   (C) Compressed horizontally by a factor of $\frac{90}{\pi}$

   (D) Stretched horizontally by a factor of $\frac{90}{\pi}$

   (E) Compressed vertically by a factor of $\frac{90}{\pi}$

   (F) Stretched vertically by a factor of $\frac{90}{\pi}$

   (G) Stretched horizontally by a factor of $\frac{180}{\pi}$

   (H) Compressed vertically by a factor of $\frac{180}{\pi}$

   Answer: (G)

15. Let $f(x) = 4 - x^2$. Find each of the following:

   (a) $f(0) + f(-2)$
   (b) $f(x + 2)$
   (c) $[f(x)]^2$
   (d) $f(x^2)$

   Answer:

   (a) 4
   (b) $-x^2 - 4x$
   (c) $16 - 8x^2 + x^4$
   (d) $4 - x^4$

16. Let $f(x) = \sqrt{2x + 5}$. Find each of the following:

   (a) $f(0) + f(-2)$
   (b) $f(x + 2)$
   (c) $[f(x)]^2$
   (d) $f(x^2)$

   Answer:

   (a) $f(0) + f(-2) = \sqrt{5} + \sqrt{1} = \sqrt{5} + 1$

   (b) $f(x + 2) = \sqrt{2(x + 2) + 5} = \sqrt{2x + 9}$

14

(c) $[f(x)]^2 = 2x + 5, \; x \geq -\frac{5}{2}$ \hfill (d) $f(x^2) = \sqrt{2x^2 + 5}$

17. Let $f(x) = \sqrt{16 - x^2}$. Find each of the following:

(a) $f(0) + f(-2)$ \hfill (b) $f(x + 2)$ \hfill (c) $[f(x)]^2$ \hfill (d) $f(x^2)$

Answer:

(a) $f(0) + f(-2) = \sqrt{16} + \sqrt{12} = 4 + 2\sqrt{3} \approx 7.46$

(b) $f(x + 2) = \sqrt{16 - (x + 2)^2} = \sqrt{16 - (x^2 + 4x + 4)} = \sqrt{12 - 4x - x^2}, \; -6 \leq x \leq 2$

(c) $[f(x)]^2 = 16 - x^2, \; -4 \leq x \leq 4$

(d) $f(x^2) = \sqrt{16 - (x^2)^2} = \sqrt{16 - x^4}, \; 0 \leq x \leq 2$

18. Let $f(x) = \sqrt{\dfrac{1}{x - 6}}$. Find each of the following:

(a) $f(8) + f(7)$ \hfill (b) $f(x^2 + 6)$ \hfill (c) $f(x^2) + 6$ \hfill (d) $[f(x + 6)]^2$

Answer:

(a) $f(8) + f(7) = \sqrt{\dfrac{1}{2}} + \sqrt{\dfrac{1}{1}} = \dfrac{\sqrt{2}}{2} + 1 = \dfrac{2 + \sqrt{2}}{2}$

(b) $f(x^2 + 6) = \sqrt{\dfrac{1}{(x^2 + 6) - 6}} = \sqrt{\dfrac{1}{x^2}} = \dfrac{1}{|x|}, \; x \neq 0$

(c) $f(x^2) + 6 = \sqrt{\dfrac{1}{x^2 - 6}} + 6, \; x > \sqrt{6} \text{ or } x < -\sqrt{6}$

(d) $[f(x + 6)]^2 = \sqrt{\dfrac{1}{(x + 6) - 6}} = \dfrac{1}{x}, \; x > 0$

19. Evaluate the difference quotient $\dfrac{f(x) - f(a)}{x - a}$ for $f(x) = \dfrac{1}{x^2}$.

Answer: $\dfrac{f(x) - f(a)}{x - a} = \dfrac{\dfrac{1}{x^2} - \dfrac{1}{a^2}}{x - a} = -\dfrac{a + x}{a^2 x^2}$

20. Given the graph of $y = f(x)$:

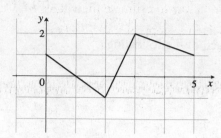

Sketch the graph of each of the following functions:

(a) $-f(x)$

(b) $f(-x)$

(c) $f(2x)$

(d) $2f(x)$

(e) $-f(-x)$

(f) $f\left(\frac{1}{2}x\right)$

(g) $\frac{1}{2}f(x)$

(h) $f(x+1)$

(i) $f(x+1)$

(j) $1 - f(x)$

Answer:

(a)

(b)

(c)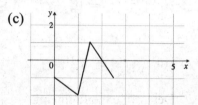

(d)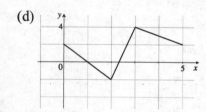

(e)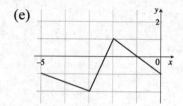

(f)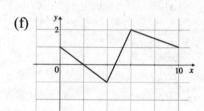

(g)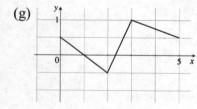

(h)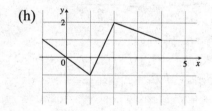

(i)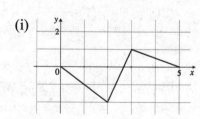

(j)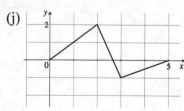

21. Use the graphs of f and g given below to estimate the values of $f(g(x))$ for $x = -3, -2, -1, 0, 1, 2,$ and 3, and use these values to sketch a graph of $y = f(g(x))$.

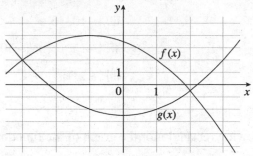

Answer:

x	-3	-2	-1	0	1	2	3
$f(g(x))$	-0.5	3.88	3.50	2.88	3.50	3.88	-0.5

22. f and g are functions defined by the following table.

x	-3	-2	-1	0	1	2	3
$f(x)$	1	0	1	2	3	4	5
$g(x)$	7	2	-1	-2	-1	2	7

Determine the following:

(a) $(f+g)(-1)$ 　　　　　　(b) $(f-g)(2)$ (c) $(f \cdot g)(-2)$ (d) $(f/g)(-3)$

(e) $(f \circ g)(0)$ 　　　　　　(f) $(f \circ f)(0)$ (g) $(g \circ f)(1)$

Answer: (a) 0 　　　(b) 2 　　　(c) 0 　　　(d) $\frac{1}{7}$ 　　　(e) 0 　　　(f) 4 　　　(g) 7

23. Find functions f and g such that $F(x) = 1 - 2\cos^2 x = (f \circ g)(x)$.
   Answer: $f(x) = 1 - 2x^2$, $g(x) = \cos x$ is one possible answer. Answers will vary.

24. Find functions f and g such that $F(x) = \sec^2 x = (f \circ g)(x)$.
   Answer: $f(x) = x^2$, $g(x) = \sec x$ is one possible answer. Answers will vary.

25. Find functions f and g such that $F(x) = e^{\sin x} = (f \circ g)(x)$.
   Answer: $f(x) = e^x$, $g(x) = \sin x$ is one possible answer. Answers will vary.

1.4 Graphing Calculators and Computers

1. Determine an appropriate viewing rectangle for the graph of the function $f(x) = 6x^2 + x - 10$.

   (A) $[-50, 50] \times [-50, 50]$ 　　　　　　(B) $[0, 10] \times [0, 10]$

   (C) $[-5, 10] \times [-10, 50]$ 　　　　　　(D) $[-5, 5] \times [-5, 5]$

   (E) $[-5, 5] \times [-10, 10]$ 　　　　　　(F) $[-50, 10] \times [-10, 100]$

   (G) $[-5, 50] \times [-5, 10]$ 　　　　　　(H) $[-10, 10] \times [-5, 5]$

   Answer: (E)

17

2. Determine an appropriate viewing rectangle for the graph of the function $f(x) = \sqrt{98 + 5x - x^2}$.

   (A) $[-7, 7] \times [0, 10]$ **(B)** $[-10, 10] \times [0, 7]$

   (C) $[-10, 10] \times [-15, 15]$ **(D)** $[-10, 10] \times [-7, 7]$

   (E) $[-15, 15] \times [-15, 15]$ **(F)** $[-15, 15] \times [-10, 10]$

   (G) $[-10, 10] \times [-10, 10]$ **(H)** $[-1, 1] \times [-1, 1]$

   Answer: **(E)**

3. Determine an appropriate viewing rectangle for the graph of the function $f(x) = \dfrac{3x}{x^4 + 75}$.

   (A) $[-10, 10] \times [-10, 10]$ **(B)** $[-1, 1] \times [-1, 1]$

   (C) $[-10, 10] \times [-1, 1]$ **(D)** $[-100, 100] \times [-1, 1]$

   (E) $[-100, 100] \times [-10, 10]$ **(F)** $[-5, 5] \times [-5, 5]$

   (G) $[-5, 5] \times [-0.5, 0.5]$ **(H)** $[-1, 1] \times [-10, 10]$

   Answer: **(C)**

4. Determine an appropriate viewing rectangle for the graph of the function $f(x) = 6\sin(20x + 10)$.

   (A) $[-10, 10] \times [-10, 10]$ **(B)** $[-5, 5] \times [-5, 5]$

   (C) $[-100, 100] \times [-5, 5]$ **(D)** $[-5, 5] \times [-10, 10]$

   (E) $[-10, 10] \times [-5, 5]$ **(F)** $[-0.5, 0.5] \times [-1, 1]$

   (G) $[-1, 1] \times [-1, 1]$ **(H)** $[-1, 1] \times [-10, 10]$

   Answer: **(H)**

5. Determine an appropriate viewing rectangle for the graph of the function $f(x) = 4x - |3x^2 - 10|$.

   (A) $[-5, 5] \times [-5, 2]$ **(B)** $[-50, 20] \times [-50, 10]$

   (C) $[-2, 5] \times [-1, 10]$ **(D)** $[-10, 10] \times [-500, 500]$

   (E) $[-10, 10] \times [-500, 5]$ **(F)** $[-2, 5] \times [-15, 10]$

   (G) $[-10, 5] \times [1, 10]$ **(H)** $[0, 10] \times [-2, 5]$

   Answer: **(F)**

6. Determine the number of real solutions of the equation $5x^4 - 3x^2 = 10x^5 + x^3 - 5$.

   (A) 0   **(B)** 1   **(C)** 2   **(D)** 3

   (E) 4   **(F)** 5   **(G)** 6   **(H)** 7

   Answer: **(B)**

7. Determine the number of solutions of the equation $8\sin 2x - 1 = 2x$.

   (A) 1   **(B)** 2   **(C)** 3   **(D)** 4

   (E) 5   **(F)** 6   **(G)** 7   **(H)** 8

   Answer: **(E)**

8. Find the difference between the largest and smallest solutions of the equation $-3x^2 - 9x = 2^x$, rounded to two decimal places.

(A) 0.02   (B) 0.23   (C) 0.80   (D) 1.05

(E) 2.06   (F) 2.88   (G) 3.09   (H) 3.92

Answer: (F)

9. Determine an appropriate viewing window for each of the following functions and use it to draw the graph.

(a) $f(x) = x^4 - 6x^2$ (b) $f(x) = \dfrac{1}{x^4 - 1}$

(c) $f(x) = \sin(x^2)$ (d) $f(x) = 80x - 5x^3$

(e) $f(x) = -3x^2 + 288x - 6862$ (f) $f(x) = -3x^2 + 288x + 6862$

Answer: (Possible answers — answers will vary.)

(a) $[-3, 3] \times [-10, 20]$ (b) $[-2, 2] \times [-10, 10]$

(c) $[-4, 4] \times [-2, 2]$ (d) $[-6, 6] \times [-140, 140]$

(e) $[40, 60] \times [-10, 60]$ (f) $[-30, 130] \times [-5000, 15,000]$

10. Consider the family of curves given by $y = x^2 + cx$. Graph the function for values of $c = -4, -2, 0, 2,$ and 4. What characteristics are shared by all of the graphs? How does changing the value of c affect the graph?

Answer:

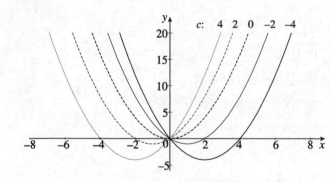

$f(x) = x^2 + cx = \left(x + \dfrac{c}{2}\right)^2 - \dfrac{c^2}{4}$. All of the graphs represent parabolas with vertex $\left(-\dfrac{c}{2}, -\dfrac{c^2}{4}\right)$. They have the same shape as $y = x^2$, and they all pass through $(0, 0)$. The value of c changes the coordinates of the vertex.

1.5 | Exponential Functions

1. The radioactive isotope Bismuth-210 has a half-life of 5 days. How many days does it take for 87.5% of a given amount to decay?

(A) 15   (B) 8   (C) 10   (D) 13

(E) 11   (F) 9   (G) 12   (H) 14

Answer: (A)

2. A bacteria culture starts with 200 bacteria and triples in size every ten minutes. After 1 hour, how many bacteria are there?

(A) 1800   (B) 3600   (C) 5400   (D) 16,200

(E) 48,600   (F) 145,800   (G) 437,400   (H) 1,312,200

Answer: (F)

3. A bacteria culture starts with 500 bacteria and doubles every 2 hours. How many bacteria are there after 6 hours?

(A) 1,000   (B) 1,500   (C) 2,000   (D) 2,500

(E) 3,000   (F) 4,000   (G) 5,000   (H) 10,000

Answer: (F)

4. For what value of x is $2^x = 8^{4-x}$?

(A) -2 (B) -1 (C) 0   (D) 1

(E) 2   (F) 3   (G) 4   (H) 5

Answer: (F)

5. Which of the following statements are true about the graph of the function $y = 3^x - 9$?

(i) It has no vertical asymptote.   (iii) It has a y-intercept at -2.

(ii) It has no horizontal asymptote.   (iv) It has an x-intercept at 2.

(A) (i) only   (B) (i), (iii), and (iv) only

(C) (ii), (iii), and (iv) only   (D) (iv) only

(E) (ii) and (iii) only   (F) (i) and (iv) only

(G) (ii) and (iv) only   (H) (i), (ii) and (iv) only

Answer: (F)

6. Make a rough sketch of the graph of $y = (1.1)^{-x}$. Do not use a calculator.

Answer:

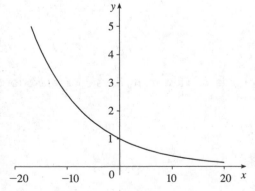

7. Make a rough sketch of the graph of $y = 2^{x+1}$. Do not use a calculator.

Answer:

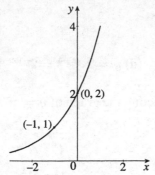

8. Make a rough sketch of the graph of $y = 3^{1-x}$. Do not use a calculator.

Answer:

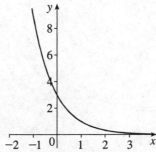

9. Make a rough sketch of the graph of $y = -2^{|x|}$. Do not use a calculator.

Answer:

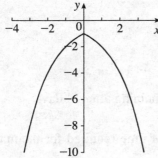

10. Make a rough sketch of the graph of $y = 3\left(4 - 2^x\right)$. Do not use a calculator.

Answer:

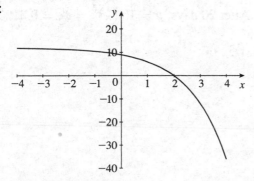

11. Given the graph of $y = 2^x$, find an equation of the graph that results from reflecting the given graph about

   (a) the line $x = 0$.

   (b) the line $y = 3$.

   (c) the line $y = -1$.

   (d) the line $x = 2$.

   Answer: (a) $y = 2^{-x}$ (b) $y = 6 - 2^x$ (c) $y = -2^x - 2$ (d) $y = 2^{-x+4} = 2^{-(x-4)}$

12. What single transformation of the graph of $y = e^x$ is the same as reflecting the graph of $y = e^x$ about the x-axis and then shifting the reflected graph 6 units upward?

   Answer: Reflecting the graph about the line $y = 3$.

13. For the exponential function $f(x) = c \cdot a^x + b$ whose graph is given below, determine the values of a, b, and c.

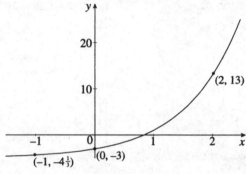

   Answer: $a = 3$, $b = -5$, $c = 2$

14. The half-life of a certain radioactive substance is 4 days. The initial size of a sample is 10 grams.

   (a) Find the amount of the substance remaining after 20 days.

   (b) Find the amount of the substance remaining after t days.

   (c) Use a graph to estimate, to the nearest 0.01 gram, the amount remaining after 14 days.

   (d) Use the graph to estimate, to the nearest 0.1 day, the amount of time required for the mass of the substance to be reduced to 0.1 gram.

   Answer:

   (a) The half-life is 4 days, so 20 days is 5 half-lives. After 20 days, $y = 10 \left(\frac{1}{2}\right)^5 = \frac{10}{32} = 0.3125$.

   (b) The half-life is 4 days, so after t days, $y = 10 e^{(\ln(1/2)/4)t}$.

   (c) When $t = 14$, $y \approx 0.884$ g.

   (d) When $y = 0.01$ gram, $t = \dfrac{\ln \frac{0.1}{10}}{\ln \frac{1/2}{4}} \approx 26.58$ days.

15. Match each set of function values in the table with the formula which best fits it. Assume that a, b, and c are constants.

	Function A			**Function B**			**Function C**	
	x	$f(x)$		x	$g(x)$		x	$h(x)$
	4	340		4	351		5	322
	5	367		5	365		6	354
	6	400		6	380		7	390
	7	428		7	395		8	429
	8	463		8	411		9	472

Formula 1	**Formula 2**	**Formula 3**
$y_1 = a(1.04)^x$	$y_2 = b(1.08)^x$	$y_3 = c(1.10)^x$

Answer: $f(x)$ generated by $250(1.08)^x$; $y_2 = f(x)$, $b \approx 250$

$g(x)$ generated by $300(1.04)^x$; $y_1 = g(x)$, $a \approx 300$

$h(x)$ generated by $200(1.10)^x$; $y_3 = h(x)$, $c \approx 200$

1.6 Inverse Functions and Logarithms

1. Find the inverse function for $f(x) = \dfrac{5 - 2x}{3}$.

(A) $\dfrac{5 - 3x}{2}$　　(B) $\dfrac{2x - 5}{3}$　　(C) $\dfrac{2 - 3x}{5}$　　(D) $\dfrac{3x - 2}{5}$

(E) $\dfrac{2x + 5}{3}$　　(F) $\dfrac{3}{5 - 2x}$　　(G) $\dfrac{2}{5 - 3x}$　　(H) $3x - 5$

Answer: (A)

2. Find the inverse function for $f(x) = \dfrac{x - 1}{x + 1}$.

(A) $\dfrac{x + 1}{x - 1}$　　(B) $\dfrac{x}{x + 1}$　　(C) $\dfrac{x + 1}{x}$　　(D) $\dfrac{1 + x}{1 - x}$

(E) $\dfrac{x + 1}{1 - x}$　　(F) $\dfrac{x}{x - 1}$　　(G) $\dfrac{x - 1}{x + 1}$　　(H) $\dfrac{x - 1}{x}$

Answer: (D)

3. Find the domain of the inverse for $f(x) = \sqrt{2x - 5}$.

(A) $\left(-\infty, -\frac{5}{2}\right]$　　(B) $(-\infty, 0]$　　(C) $\left[-\frac{5}{2}, \frac{5}{2}\right]$　　(D) $\left(-\infty, \frac{5}{2}\right]$

(E) $\left[-\frac{5}{2}, \infty\right)$　　(F) $[0, \infty)$　　(G) $\left[\frac{2}{5}, \infty\right)$　　(H) $\left[\frac{5}{2}, \infty\right)$

Answer: (F)

4. Find the range of the inverse for $f(x) = -\dfrac{3}{5 + 2x}$.

(A) $\left(-\infty, -\frac{5}{2}\right)$　　(B) $(-\infty, 0)$　　(C) $\left(-\frac{5}{2}, \frac{5}{2}\right)$　　(D) $\left(-\infty, \frac{5}{2}\right) \cup \left(\frac{5}{2}, \infty\right)$

(E) $\left(-\frac{5}{2}, \infty\right)$　　(F) $(0, \infty)$　　(G) $\left(\frac{5}{2}, \infty\right)$　　(H) $\left(-\infty, -\frac{5}{2}\right) \cup \left(-\frac{5}{2}, \infty\right)$

Answer: (H)

5. Given the function $\sin x$ with domain $\left[-\frac{\pi}{2}, \frac{\pi}{2}\right]$, find the domain of its inverse.

(A) $\left[-\frac{\sqrt{3}}{2}, \frac{\sqrt{3}}{2}\right]$ (B) $[0, \infty)$ (C) $[-\pi, \pi]$ (D) $[-1, 1]$

(E) $\left[-\frac{\pi}{2}, \frac{\pi}{2}\right]$ (F) $\left[-\frac{1}{2}, \frac{1}{2}\right]$ (G) $(-\infty, \infty)$ (H) $\left[-\frac{1}{\sqrt{2}}, \frac{1}{\sqrt{2}}\right]$

Answer: (D)

6. Find the value of $\log_{1/2} 1$.

(A) -1 (B) $-\frac{1}{2}$ (C) 0 (D) 10^2

(E) 1 (F) $\frac{1}{2}$ (G) 2 (H) -2

Answer: (C)

7. Find the value of $\log_2 \frac{1}{8}$.

(A) $\frac{1}{4}$ (B) $\frac{1}{3}$ (C) 0 (D) 1

(E) -1 (F) 2 (G) -2 (H) -3

Answer: (H)

8. Find the value of $\log_{16} 2$.

(A) $\frac{1}{2}$ (B) 2 (C) 4 (D) 1

(E) 3 (F) 0 (G) $\frac{1}{8}$ (H) $\frac{1}{4}$

Answer: (H)

9. Find the value of $\ln e^e$.

(A) -1 (B) $1/\sqrt{e}$ (C) e (D) 0

(E) $\sqrt{e}$ (F) $1/e$ (G) 1 (H) $-e$

Answer: (C)

10. Find the value of $\ln \sqrt{e^3}$.

(A) $\frac{2}{3}$ (B) $\sqrt{e}$ (C) $e^3/2$ (D) $\frac{3}{2}$

(E) e^3 (F) $e^3 - 2$ (G) $2e/3$ (H) $2/e^3$

Answer: (D)

11. Find the value of $e^{3\ln 2}$.

(A) $\frac{2}{3}$ (B) $\frac{3}{2}$ (C) 5 (D) 6

(E) 8 (F) 9 (G) 12 (H) 18

Answer: (E)

12. Find the value of $\log_2 e - \log_2 (e/16)$.

(A) -2 (B) e^{-2} (C) 4 (D) e^{16}

(E) -4 (F) e^2 (G) 2 (H) e^{-16}

Answer: (C)

13. Solve the equation $\log_2 (\ln x) = 1$.

(A) $x = 2^e$ (B) $x = 2e$ (C) $x = e/2$ (D) $x = 1$

(E) $x = \sqrt{e}$ (F) $x = 1/e$ (G) $x = 2/e$ (H) $x = e^2$

Answer: (H)

14. Solve the equation $e^{2x-2} = 4$.

   (A) $x = \ln 2$ (B) $x = 1 - \ln 2$ (C) $x = 1 + \ln 2$ (D) $x = 1 - 2\ln 2$

   (E) $x = 1 + 2\ln 2$ (F) $x = 2 + \ln 2$ (G) $x = 2 - \ln 2$ (H) $x = 2 - 2\ln 2$

   Answer: **(C)**

15. Solve the equation $e^{4-2x} = 16$.

   (A) $x = \ln 2$ (B) $x = -\ln 2$ (C) $x = 1 + \ln 2$ (D) $x = 1 - \ln 2$

   (E) $x = 1 + 2\ln 2$ (F) $x = 1 - 2\ln 2$ (G) $x = 2 + 2\ln 2$ (H) $x = 2 - 2\ln 2$

   Answer: **(H)**

16. Sketch the graph of f for $f(x) = \sqrt[3]{x}$ and determine if f^{-1} exists. If so, find a formula for $f^{-1}(x)$ and sketch its graph.

   Answer:

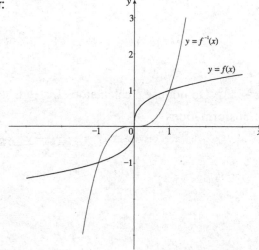

17. Determine whether or not the function $f(x) = x^2 - 2x + 5$ is one-to-one.

   Answer: f is not one-to-one. For example, $f(0) = f(2)$.

18. Determine whether or not the function $f(x) = \dfrac{3x}{x-1}$ is one-to-one.

   Answer: We see from its graph that the function passes the horizontal line test, so the function is one-to-one.
   Algebraically, let $f(x) = \dfrac{3x}{x-1}$. Suppose $f(a) = f(b)$. Then $\dfrac{3a}{a-1} = \dfrac{3b}{b-1}$ $\Rightarrow$ $3a(b-1) = 3b(a-1)$ $\Rightarrow$ $3ab - 3a = 3ab - 3b$ $\Rightarrow$ $-3a = -3b$ $\Rightarrow$ $a = b$. Since $a = b$ whenever $f(a) = f(b)$, f is a one-to-one function.

19. Find the inverse of $f(x) = \dfrac{x-2}{x+2}$.

   Answer: $f^{-1}(x) = \dfrac{2(1+x)}{1-x}$

20. Find the value of $\left(4\ln e^3 - e^{2\ln 3} + 5\ln 1\right)\left(\ln \sqrt[4]{e}\right)$.

   Answer: $\left(4\ln e^3 - e^{2\ln 3} + 5\ln 1\right)\left(\ln \sqrt[4]{e}\right) = (12 - 9 + 0)\frac{1}{4} = \frac{3}{4}$

21. Find the value of $4^{\log_2 3}$.

   Answer: $4^{\log_2 3} = 2^{2\log_2 3} = 2^{\log_2 9} = 9$

22. Suppose pH $= -\log\left[H^+\right]$. Suppose further that for vinegar, the hydrogen ion concentration in moles per liter is given by $\left[H^+\right] = 5.2\left(10^{-4}\right)$. Find the pH of the vinegar.

    Answer: pH $= 3.28$

23. Express $\log_2 x + 5\log_2(x+1) + \frac{1}{2}\log_2(x-1)$ as a single logarithm.

    Answer: $\log_2\left(x(x+1)^5\sqrt{x-1}\right)$

24. Make a rough sketch of the graph of $y = 2 + \log_3(x+1)$. Do not use a calculator. Instead, start with the graph of a simple function and apply any needed transformations.

    Answer:

    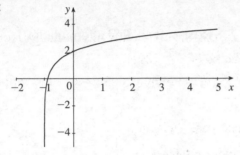

25. Make a rough sketch of the graph of $y = 2 + \log_2(x+1)$. Do not use a calculator. Instead, start with the graph of a simple function and apply any needed transformations.

    Answer:

    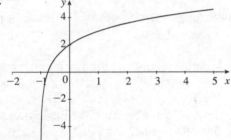

26. Solve for x: $e^{3\ln x} = \frac{27}{8}$.

    Answer: $e^{3\ln x} = \frac{27}{8}$ $\Rightarrow$ $e^{\ln x^3} = \frac{27}{8}$ $\Rightarrow$ $x^3 = \frac{27}{8}$ $\Rightarrow$ $x = \frac{3}{2}$

27. Solve for x: $\log_{10} x - 2 = \log_{10}(x-2)$.

    Answer: $\log_{10} x - 2 = \log_{10}(x-2)$ $\Rightarrow$ $\log_{10} x - \log_{10}(x-2) = 2$ $\Rightarrow$ $\dfrac{x}{x-2} = 100$ $\Rightarrow$ $x = \dfrac{200}{99}$

28. Find $f^{-1}(x)$ if $f(x) = \sqrt{e^x + 2}$.

    Answer: $f^{-1}(x) = \ln\left(x^2 - 2\right)$

29. Medical professionals sometimes use iodine-131, a radioactive substance, to diagnose certain conditions of the thyroid gland. The formula for the proportion P of iodine-131 remaining in a patient's system t days after receiving the substance is given by $P = e^{(\ln(1/2)/8)t}$.

    (a) Find the inverse of this function and explain its meaning.

    (b) How long does it take for the proportion to drop to 10% of the original dosage?

Answer:

(a) $t = \dfrac{8 \ln P}{\ln \frac{1}{2}} = -\dfrac{8 \ln P}{\ln 2}$. This expression gives the time necessary for the proportion of the original dosage to drop to P.

(b) $t(0.10) = -\dfrac{8 \ln (0.10)}{\ln 2} \approx 26.6$ days

30. Suppose that the number of bacteria in a culture at time t is given by $x = 5^4 e^{3t}$. Use natural logarithms to solve for t in terms of x.

Answer: $t = \dfrac{\ln x - 4 \ln 5}{3}$

31. Let $C(x)$ be the temperature (in degrees Celsius) when the column of mercury in a particular thermometer is x millimeters long. In practical terms what is the meaning of $C^{-1}(20)$?

Answer: The column of mercury in the thermometer is $C^{-1}(20)$ millimeters long when the temperature is $20°$ C.

32. Decide whether the given function has an inverse. Defend your decision.

(a) $P(x)$ is the cost, in cents, of mailing a letter that weighs x ounces.

(b) $C(t)$ is the total number of cars which have driven past a particular point along a highway during a specific day where t represents the time, in hours, since midnight.

(c) $F(d)$ is the amount of fuel, in gallons, in your car when you have traveled d miles on a particular tankful of gas.

(d) $S(t)$ is the number of shoppers entering the Mall of America where t is the number of minutes past midnight on one particular day.

(e) $T(t)$ is the temperature inside an oven where t is the time, in minutes, from the beginning to the end of the oven's self-cleaning cycle.

(f) $V(x)$ is the volume of a cube whose side has length x.

(g) $f(n)$ is the number of students enrolled in your calculus class on the nth day of the term.

Answer:

(a) $P(x)$ does not have an inverse. The price of mailing a 1.2 oz letter is the same as that of mailing a 1.3 oz letter.

(b) $C(t)$ does not have an inverse. The same number of cars have passed the point at different times.

(c) $F(d)$ has an inverse. The fuel level decreases as the distance increases.

(d) $S(t)$ does not have an inverse. The same number of shoppers have entered the mall at different times.

(e) $T(t)$ does not have an inverse. The temperature inside an oven increases at first, reaching a certain temperature, then cooling down.

(f) $V(x)$ has an inverse, namely the side length of a cube that has volume V.

(g) $f(n)$ does not have an inverse. The same number of students is enrolled in the class on many different days.

33. The following table defines the function $f(x)$. From this table, write a table for f^{-1}. Determine the domain for f^{-1}.

x	1	2	3	4	5	6	7
$f(x)$	-4	5	3	-2	6	-5	0

Answer:

x	-5	-4	-2	0	3	5	6
$f^{-1}(x)$	6	1	4	7	3	2	5

Domain of $f^{-1}(x)$ is $\{-5, -4, -2, 0, 3, 5, 6\}$

34. If a function f has an inverse and is an increasing function, can you determine if the inverse is increasing or decreasing? Explain.

Answer: $f^{-1}(x)$ is an increasing function since the graphs of $y = f(x)$ and $f^{-1}(x)$ are symmetric about $y = x$.

1.7 Parametric Curves

1. Eliminate the parameter in the equations $x = t^2$, $y = t^4$.

(A) $y = x^2$ for $x \geq 0$ (B) $y = \sqrt{x}$ for $x \geq 0$

(C) $y = 2x^2$ for $x \geq 0$ (D) $y = \sqrt{2x}$ for $x \geq 0$

(E) $y = 2\sqrt{x}$ for $x \geq 0$ (F) $y = x^2/2$ for $x \geq 0$

(G) $y = \sqrt{x}/2$ for $x \geq 0$ (H) $y = \sqrt{x/2}$ for $x \geq 0$

Answer: (A)

2. Eliminate the parameter in the equations $x = 2\tan t$, $y = 2\cos^2 t$, $0 \leq t \leq 2\pi$.

(A) $y = 2x^2$ (B) $y = x^2 + 4$

(C) $y = 8x^2 + 32$ (D) $y = \dfrac{x^2 + 4}{8}$

(E) $y = x^2 + 32$ (F) $y = 4x^2 + 8$

(G) $y = 8x^2 + 4$ (H) $y = \dfrac{8}{x^2 + 4}$

Answer: (H)

3. Describe the curve defined by $x = \sin t$, $y = \sin^2 t$.

(A) Circle   (B) Semicircle

(C) Quarter-circle   (D) Parabola

(E) Portion of a parabola   (F) Hyperbola

(G) Single branch of a hyperbola   (H) Portion of branch of hyperbola

Answer: (E)

4. At how many places does the curve $x = \cos 3t$, $y = \sin t$ cross the x-axis?

(A) 1   (B) 2   (C) 3   (D) 4

(E) 5   (F) 6   (G) 7   (H) 8

Answer: (B)

5. Describe the motion of a particle with position $x = 2 + \cos t$, $y = 3 + \sin t$ as t varies in the interval $[0, 2\pi]$.

Answer: The motion takes place on a unit circle centered at $(2, 3)$. As t goes from 0 to 2π, the particle makes one complete counterclockwise rotation around the circle, starting and ending at $(3, 3)$.

6. The position after t seconds of a projectile fired with initial velocity v_0 (measured in ft/s) at an angle α above the horizontal from an initial height of h_0 (measured in ft) is given by the parametric equations $x = (v_0 \cos \alpha)\, t$, $y = (v_0 \sin \alpha)\, t - 16t^2 + h_0$.

(a) Eliminate the parameter t to show that the trajectory of the projectile is a parabola.

(b) If the projectile is fired with an initial velocity of 300 ft/s from a height of 5 ft, what should be the angle of elevation in order to hit a target at the same height as the initial height, 900 ft downrange?

(c) If the projectile is fired with an angle of elevation of $40°$ and it strikes a target at the same height as the initial height, 600 ft downrange, what was the initial velocity of the projectile?

Answer:

(a) $y = -16 \left(\dfrac{x}{v_0 \cos \alpha} \right)^2 + v_0 \sin \alpha \cdot \dfrac{x}{v_0 \cos \alpha} + h_0 = k_1 x^2 + k_2 x + h_0$, which is an equation of a parabola.

(b) $900 = (300 \cos \alpha)\, t$ and $5 = (300 \sin \alpha)\, t - 16t^2 + 5$. Eliminating t, we get $-144 \tan^2 \alpha + 900 \tan \alpha - 144 = 0$. Solving for $\tan \alpha$, we get $\tan \alpha \approx 0.16432$ or $\tan \alpha \approx 6.0856$, which correspond to $\alpha \approx 9.3°$ or $\alpha \approx 80.7°$.

(c) $600 = (v_0 \cos 40°)\, t$ and $5 = (v_0 \sin 40°)\, t - 16t^2 + 5$. Eliminating t, we get $v_0^2 = \dfrac{16 \cdot 600^2}{600 \sin 40° \cos 40°}$, so $v_0 \approx 139.6$ ft/s.

7. A baseball slugger hits a knee-high pitch toward the outfield. Suppose that the position of the baseball after t seconds is given by

$$x = (v_0 \cos \alpha)\, t, \quad y = (v_0 \sin \alpha)\, t - 16t^2 + h_0$$

where v_0 is the velocity in feet per second at which the ball leaves the bat at an angle α to the horizontal and from a height h_0 above the ground.

(a) Suppose that the ball is struck 2 feet above the ground with an initial velocity of 120 ft/sec and at an angle of 35 degrees.

(i) When will the ball strike the ground?

(ii) How far will the ball travel (horizontally) before it touches the ground?

(iii) What is the maximum height reached by the ball?

(iv) Will the ball clear the 10 ft tall outfield fence, which is 410 feet away from the point where the ball is struck?

(b) If the ball is struck 2 feet above the ground at an initial velocity of 120 ft/sec and at an angle of 55 degrees:

(i) When will the ball strike the ground?

(ii) How far will the ball travel (horizontally) before it touches the ground?

(iii) What is the maximum height reached by the ball?

(iv) Will the ball clear the $10'$ tall outfield fence, which is 410 feet away from the point where the ball is struck?

Answer:

(a) (i) Find t when $y = 0$. $t = \dfrac{-120\sin 35° - \sqrt{(120\sin 35°)^2 - 4 \cdot (-16) \cdot 2}}{2 \cdot (-16)} \approx 4.33$ s

(ii) Find x when $t = 4.33$ s. $x = 120\cos 35° \cdot (4.33) \approx 425.6$ ft

(iii) Find y_{max}. $y_{max} = 16\left(\dfrac{120\sin 35°}{32}\right)^2 + 2 \approx 76.02$ ft

(iv) Determine if $y > 10$ when $x = 410$. When $x = 410$, $t = \dfrac{410}{120\cos 35°} \approx 4.17$ s, so $y = 120\sin 35° (4.17) - 16(4.17)^2 + 2 \approx 10.73$ ft. So the ball will clear the fence.

(b) (i) Find t when $y = 0$. $t = \dfrac{-120\sin 55° - \sqrt{(120\sin 55°)^2 - 4 \cdot (-16) \cdot 2}}{2 \cdot (-16)} \approx 6.16$ s.

(ii) Find x when $t = 6.16$ s. $x = 120\cos 55° \cdot (6.16) \approx 423.9$ ft

(iii) Find y_{max}. $y_{max} = 16\left(\dfrac{120\sin 55°}{32}\right)^2 + 2 \approx 152.98$ ft

(iv) Determine if $y > 10$ when $x = 410$. When $x = 410$, $t = \dfrac{410}{120\cos 55°} \approx 5.96$ s, so $y = 120\sin 55° (5.96) - 16(5.96)^2 + 2 \approx 19.8$ ft. So the ball will clear the fence.

8. (a) Sketch the curves represented by:

(i) $x = t/2, y = 1 - t$

(ii) $x = \frac{1}{2} - \frac{1}{2}t^2, y = t^2$

(iii) $x = \frac{1}{2}\cos^2 t, y = \sin^2 t$

(b) Describe the differences between the three curves in part (a).

(c) Produce Cartesian equations for the curves in parts (a)(i), (ii), and (iii) by eliminating the parameter. Compare your results.

Answer:

(a) (i) 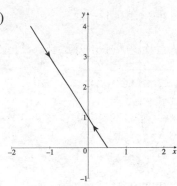 (ii) 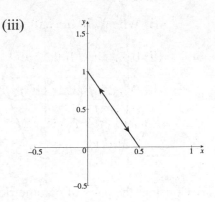 (iii)

(b) (i) This curve represents the entire line $y = -2x + 1$.

(ii) This curve represents the part of the line in (i) with $x \in \left(-\infty, \frac{1}{2}\right]$.

(iii) This curve represents the part of the line in (i) with $0 \le x \le \frac{1}{2}$.

(c) They have the same Cartesian equation, $y = -2x + 1$.

9. Sketch a possible parametric curve defined by the following table of values.

t	0	$\frac{\pi}{4}$	$\frac{\pi}{2}$	$\frac{3\pi}{4}$	π	$\frac{5\pi}{4}$	$\frac{3\pi}{2}$	$\frac{7\pi}{4}$	2π
x	0	0.18	0	-0.53	-1	-0.88	0	1.24	2
y	0	0.18	0.5	0.53	0	-0.88	-1.5	-1.24	0

Answer:

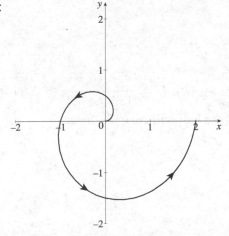

10. Sketch a possible parametric curve defined by the following table of values.

t	0	$\frac{\pi}{4}$	$\frac{\pi}{2}$	$\frac{3\pi}{4}$	π	$\frac{5\pi}{4}$	$\frac{3\pi}{2}$	$\frac{7\pi}{4}$	2π
x	2	$\sqrt{2}$	0	$-\sqrt{2}$	-2	$-\sqrt{2}$	0	$\sqrt{2}$	2
y	0	$\sqrt{2}$	-2	$\sqrt{2}$	0	$-\sqrt{2}$	2	$-\sqrt{2}$	0

Answer:

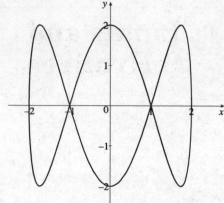

131. Consider the pairs of parametric equations

$$x = 2 - 3t, \, y = 7 - 6t \qquad \text{and} \qquad x = t - 1, \, y = 1 + 2t$$

(a) Show that these pairs of equations produce the same line.

(b) What are the slope and y-intercept of this line?

Answer: (a) $y = 2x + 3$ \hfill (b) Slope $= 2$, y-intercept $= 3$

2

Limits and Derivatives

2.1 | The Tangent and Velocity Problems

1. For the curve $f(x) = \sqrt{x+3}$, find the slope M_{PQ} of the secant line through the points $P = (1, f(1))$ and $Q = (6, f(6))$.

   (A) 2   (B) 1   (C) $\frac{2}{3}$ (D) $\frac{3}{2}$

   (E) 5   (F) $\frac{1}{5}$ (G) $\frac{1}{2}$ (H) 3

   Answer: (F)

2. The displacement in meters of a particle moving in a straight line is given by $s = t^3$, where t is measured in seconds. Find the average velocity in meters per second over the time period $[1, 2]$.

   (A) 5   (B) 3   (C) 8   (D) 1

   (E) 7   (F) 6   (G) 2   (H) 9

   Answer: (E)

3. Suppose you drive for 60 miles at 60 miles per hour, then for 60 miles at 30 miles per hour. In miles per hour, what is your average velocity?

   (A) 45   (B) 40   (C) 36   (D) 42

   (E) 52   (F) 55   (G) 50   (H) 48

   Answer: (B)

4. If a ball is thrown into the air with a velocity of 80 ft/s, its height in feet after t seconds is given by $s(t) = 80t - 16t^2$. It will be at maximum height when its instantaneous velocity is zero. Find its average velocity from the time it is thrown $(t = 0)$ to the time it reaches its maximum height.

   (A) 50   (B) 60   (C) 100   (D) 80

   (E) 40   (F) 30   (G) 48   (H) 32

   Answer: (E)

5. A weight is attached to a spring. Suppose the position (in meters) of the weight above the floor t seconds after it is released is given by $P(t) = 0.5 \sin\left(\pi t + \frac{\pi}{2}\right) + 1.2$. What is the average rate of change of the position of the weight (in m/s) over the time interval $[3, 5]$?

   (A) -1.7 (B) -1.0 (C) -0.5 (D) 0

   (E) 0.5   (F) 1.0   (G) 1.7   (H) Cannot be determined

   Answer: (D)

6. A car on a test track accelerates from 0 ft/s to 132 ft/s in 8 seconds. The car's velocity is given in the table below:

t (s)	0	1	2	3	4	5	6	7	8
$v(t)$ (ft/s)	0	14	30	48	69	89	107	120	132

On what time interval does the car have the greatest average acceleration?

(A) $[0, 1]$ **(B)** $[1, 2]$ **(C)** $[2, 3]$ **(D)** $[3, 4]$

(E) $[4, 5]$ **(F)** $[5, 6]$ **(G)** $[6, 7]$ **(H)** $[7, 8]$

Answer: **(D)**

7. A car on a test track accelerates from 0 ft/s to 132 ft/s in 8 seconds. The car's velocity is given in the table below:

t (s)	0	1	2	3	4	5	6	7	8
$v(t)$ (ft/s)	0	14	30	48	69	89	107	120	132

On what time interval does the car have the lowest average acceleration?

(A) $[0, 1]$ **(B)** $[1, 2]$ **(C)** $[2, 3]$ **(D)** $[3, 4]$

(E) $[4, 5]$ **(F)** $[5, 6]$ **(G)** $[6, 7]$ **(H)** $[7, 8]$

Answer: **(H)**

8. A car on a test track accelerates from 0 ft/s to 132 ft/s in 8 seconds. The car's velocity is given in the table below:

t (s)	0	1	2	3	4	5	6	7	8
$v(t)$ (ft/s)	0	14	30	48	69	89	107	120	132

On what time interval does the car's average acceleration most closely approximate the average acceleration for the entire 8-second run?

(A) $[0, 1]$ **(B)** $[1, 2]$ **(C)** $[2, 3]$ **(D)** $[3, 4]$

(E) $[4, 5]$ **(F)** $[5, 6]$ **(G)** $[6, 7]$ **(H)** $[7, 8]$

Answer: **(B)**

9. The point $P\left(1, \sqrt{3}\right)$ lies on the curve $y = \sqrt{4 - x^2}$. Let Q be the point $\left(x, \sqrt{4 - x^2}\right)$.

(a) What is the slope of the secant line PQ (correct to 6 decimal places) for the following values of x?

    (i) 2   (ii) 1.5   (iii) 1.1   (iv) 1.01   (v) 1.001

    (vi) 0   (vii) 0.5   (viii) 0.9   (ix) 0.99   (x) 0.999

(b) Use your results from part (a) to estimate the slope of the tangent line to the graph of $y = \sqrt{4 - x^2}$ at $x = 1$.

Answer:

  (a) (i) -1.732051 (ii) -0.818350 (iii) -0.617215 (iv) -0.581212 (v) -0.577735
     (vi) -0.267949 (vii) -0.408882 (viii) -0.540063 (ix) -0.573514 (x) -0.576965

  (b) The slope of the tangent line lies between -0.576965 and -0.577725, so it is approximately -0.577.

10. A car on a test track accelerates from 0 ft/s to 132 ft/s in 8 seconds. The car's velocity is given in the table below:

t (s)	0	1	2	3	4	5	6	7	8
v (ft/s)	0	14	30	48	69	89	107	120	132

(a) Find the car's average acceleration for the following time intervals:

    (i) $[4, 6]$ (ii) $[4, 5]$ (iii) $[3, 4]$

(b) Estimate the car's acceleration at $t = 4$.

Answer:

(a) (i) $\dfrac{107 - 69}{2} = 19$ ft/s   (ii) $\dfrac{89 - 69}{1} = 20$ ft/s   (iii) $\dfrac{48 - 69}{-1} = 21$ ft/s

(b) Answer may vary, about 20.5 ft/s

11. A projectile is launched vertically upward from the surface of Mars. The table below gives the height of the object at the indicated time following launch.

Time (seconds):	0	0.4	0.8	1.2	1.6	2.0	2.4	2.8	3.2	3.6
Height (feet):	0	18.2	34.4	48.4	60.4	70.4	78.3	84.2	88.1	90.0

Time (seconds):	4.0	4.4	4.8	5.2	5.6	6.0	6.4	6.8	7.2	7.6
Height (feet):	89.6	87.3	82.9	76.5	68.1	57.6	45.1	30.5	13.8	0

(a) Graph the data.

(b) Using the data, compute the average velocity of the projectile on the following time intervals:

    (i) $[0, 4.0]$ (iii) $[1.2, 2.8]$ (v) $[2.0, 2.4]$

    (ii) $[0.8, 3.2]$ (iv) $[1.6, 2.4]$ (vi) $[1.6, 2.0]$

(c) Estimate the velocity of the projectile when $t = 2.0$. Justify your results.

(d) Using your graph and the table of values, determine when the projectile reaches its maximum height. Justify your answer.

(e) Using the graph and table of values, estimate the velocity of the projectile throughout the interval $[0, 7.6]$ and sketch a graph of this velocity.

Answer:

(a)

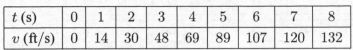

(b) (i) $v = \dfrac{89.6 - 0}{4 - 0} = 22.4$

     (ii) $v = \dfrac{88.1 - 34.4}{3.2 - 0.8} = \dfrac{53.7}{2.4} = 22.375$

     (iii) $v = \dfrac{84.2 - 48.4}{2.8 - 1.2} = \dfrac{35.8}{1.6} = 22.375$

     (iv) $v = \dfrac{78.3 - 60.4}{2.4 - 1.6} = \dfrac{17.9}{0.8} = 22.375$

     (v) $v = \dfrac{78.3 - 70.4}{2.4 - 2.0} = \dfrac{7.9}{0.4} = 19.75$

     (vi) $v = \dfrac{70.4 - 60.4}{2.0 - 1.6} = \dfrac{10}{0.4} = 25$

(c) Possible answer:

Time (seconds):	0.4	0.8	1.2	1.6	2.0	2.4	2.8	3.2	3.6	4
Velocity (feet/sec):	42.4	37.3	32.3	27.2	22.2	17.1	12.1	7.1	2.0	−3

Time(seconds):	4.4	4.8	5.2	5.6	6.0	6.4	6.8	7.2	7.6
Velocity (feet/sec):	−8.0	−13.1	−18.1	−23.2	−28.2	−33.2	−38.3	−43.3	−48.4

(d) The largest height given in the table is $t = 3.6$, but the actual maximum height appears to occur for a somewhat larger value – perhaps $t = 3.7$ or 3.8.

(e) The velocity is roughly
$y = -12.6x + 47.4.$

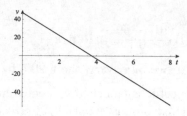

12. Suppose that the height of a projectile fired vertically upward from a height of 64 feet with an initial velocity of 48 feet per second is given by $h(t) = -16t^2 + 48t + 64$.

(a) Compute the height of the object for $t = 0, 1, 2, 3, 4$, and 5.

(b) What is the physical significance of $h(5)$? What does that suggest about the domain of h?

(c) What is the average velocity of the projectile for each of the following time intervals?

   (i) $[0, 3]$ (ii) $[0, 2]$ (iii) $[0, 1]$

(d) What is the physical significance of an average velocity of 0?

(e) When does the projectile reach its maximum height?

(f) For what value of t is $h(t) = 0$? Are all solutions to the equation valid? Explain.

Answer:

(a)

t	0	1	2	3	4	5
h	64	96	96	64	0	−96

(b) $h(5) = -96$ suggests that the object has already struck the ground. The domain of h should be $[0, 4]$.

(c) (i) $v = \dfrac{h(3) - h(0)}{3 - 0} = \dfrac{64 - 64}{3} = 0$ (ii) $v = \dfrac{h(2) - h(0)}{2 - 0} = \dfrac{96 - 64}{2} = \dfrac{32}{2} = 16$

   (iii) $v = \dfrac{h(1) - h(0)}{1 - 0} = \dfrac{96 - 64}{1} = \dfrac{32}{1} = 32$

(d) An average velocity of 0 indicates that the object has returned to its original height.

(e) The maximum height occurs when $t = 1.5$.

(f) $h(t) = 0$ when $t = 4$ and $t = -1$. The negative value indicates a time before the object is fired, and this solution is outside of the domain. Thus, the solution $t = -1$ is invalid.

13. A weight is attached to a spring. Suppose the position (in meters) of the weight above the floor t seconds after it is released is given by $P(t) = 0.5\sin\left(\pi t + \frac{\pi}{2}\right) + 1.2$.

   (a) What is the position of the weight when $t = 2$? When $t = 3$? When $t = 4$?

   (b) What is the average rate of change of the position of the weight (in m/s) over the time interval $[2, 4]$? Over the time interval $[2, 3]$?

   (c) The average rate of change of the position of the weight over the time period $[2, 6]$ is 0. Does this mean that the weight has come to a stop? Why or why not?

Answer:

   (a) 1.7 m, 0.7 m, 1.7 m

   (b) $\dfrac{1.7 - 1.7}{4 - 2} = 0; \dfrac{0.7 - 1.7}{3 - 2} = -1.0$

   (c) No, it simply means that the weight is in the same position at $t = 2$ and $t = 6$.

2.2 The Limit of a Function

Use the graph below for the following four questions:

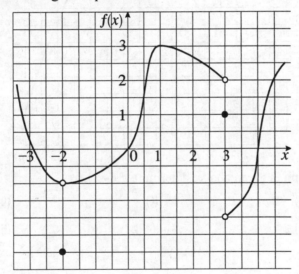

1. For the function whose graph is given above, determine $\lim\limits_{x \to 3^+} f(x)$.

   (A) −3   (B) −2   (C) −1   (D) 0

   (E) 1   (F) 2   (G) 3   (H) Does not exist

   Answer: (B)

2. For the function whose graph is given above, determine $\lim\limits_{x \to 3} f(x)$.

   (A) −3   (B) −2   (C) −1   (D) 0

   (E) 1   (F) 2   (G) 3   (H) Does not exist

   Answer: (H)

3. For the function whose graph is given above, determine $\lim\limits_{x \to -2^-} f(x)$.

(A) -3 (B) -2 (C) -1 (D) 0

(E) 1 (F) 2 (G) 3 (H) Does not exist

Answer: (C)

4. For the function whose graph is given above, determine $\lim\limits_{x \to -2} f(x)$.

(A) -3 (B) -2 (C) -1 (D) 0

(E) 1 (F) 2 (G) 3 (H) Does not exist

Answer: (C)

Use the graph below for the following four questions:

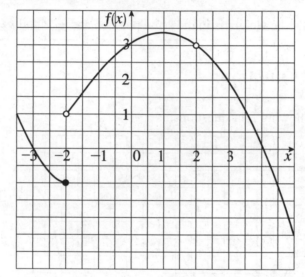

5. For the function whose graph is given above, determine $f(-2)$.

(A) -3 (B) -2 (C) -1 (D) 0

(E) 1 (F) 2 (G) 3 (H) Does not exist

Answer: (C)

6. For the function whose graph is given above, determine $\lim\limits_{x \to -2^-} f(x)$.

(A) -3 (B) -2 (C) -1 (D) 0

(E) 1 (F) 2 (G) 3 (H) Does not exist

Answer: (C)

7. For the function whose graph is given above, determine $\lim\limits_{x \to -2} f(x)$.

(A) -3 (B) -2 (C) -1 (D) 0

(E) 1 (F) 2 (G) 3 (H) Does not exist

Answer: (H)

8. For the function whose graph is given above, determine $\lim\limits_{x \to 2} f(x)$.

(A) -3 (B) -2 (C) -1 (D) 0

(E) 1   (F) 2   (G) 3   (H) Does not exist

Answer: (G)

9. Use the given graph to find the indicated quantities:

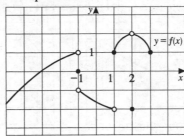

(a) $\lim\limits_{x \to -1^-} f(x)$ (b) $\lim\limits_{x \to -1^+} f(x)$ (c) $\lim\limits_{x \to -1} f(x)$ (d) $\lim\limits_{x \to 1^-} f(x)$ (e) $\lim\limits_{x \to 1^+} f(x)$

(f) $\lim\limits_{x \to 1} f(x)$ (g) $\lim\limits_{x \to 2^-} f(x)$ (h) $\lim\limits_{x \to 2^+} f(x)$ (i) $\lim\limits_{x \to 2} f(x)$ (j) $f(-1)$

(k) $f(0)$ (l) $f(1)$ (m) $f(2)$

Answer:

(a) $\lim\limits_{x \to -1^-} f(x) = 1$ (b) $\lim\limits_{x \to -1^+} f(x) = -1$ (c) $\lim\limits_{x \to -1} f(x)$ does not exist

(d) $\lim\limits_{x \to 1^-} f(x) = -2$ (e) $\lim\limits_{x \to 1^+} f(x) = 1$ (f) $\lim\limits_{x \to 1} f(x)$ does not exist

(g) $\lim\limits_{x \to 2^-} f(x) = 2$ (h) $\lim\limits_{x \to 2^+} f(x) = 2$ (i) $\lim\limits_{x \to 2} f(x) = 2$

(j) $f(-1) = 0$ (k) $f(0) \approx -1.7$ (l) $f(1) = 1$

(m) $f(2) = -1$

10. Use the graph of f below to determine the value of each of the following quantities, if it exists. If it does not exist, explain why.

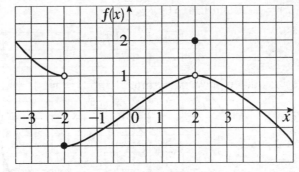

(a) $\lim\limits_{x \to -2} f(x)$ (b) $\lim\limits_{x \to 2} f(x)$ (c) $\lim\limits_{x \to -2^-} f(x)$ (d) $f(-2)$ (e) $f(2)$

Answer:

(a) The limit does not exist because the left- and right-hand limits are different.

(b) $\lim\limits_{x \to 2} f(x) = 1$ (c) $\lim\limits_{x \to -2^-} f(x) = 1$ (d) $f(-2) = -1$ (e) $f(2) = 2$

11. Use the given graph to find the indicated quantities:

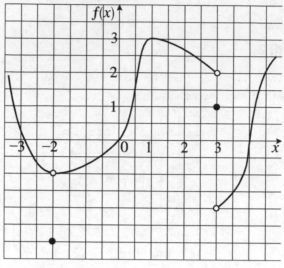

(a) $\lim\limits_{x \to 3^+} f(x)$ (b) $\lim\limits_{x \to 3} f(x)$ (c) $f(3)$

(d) $\lim\limits_{x \to -2^-} f(x)$ (e) $\lim\limits_{x \to -2} f(x)$ (f) $f(-2)$

Answer: (a) -2 (b) Does not exist   (c) 1   (d) -1 (e) -1 (f) Undefined

12. (a) Explain in your own words what is meant by $\lim\limits_{x \to -2} f(x) = 3$.

   (b) Is it possible for this statement to be true yet for $f(-2) = 5$? Explain.

   Answer:

   (a) (Answers will vary.) $\lim\limits_{x \to -2} f(x) = 3$ means that the values of f can be made as close as desired to 3 by taking values of x close enough to -2, but not equal to -2.

   (b) Yes, it is possible for $\lim\limits_{x \to -2} f(x) = 3$, but $f(-2) = 5$. The limit refers only to how the function behaves when x is close to -2. It does not tell us anything about the value of the function at $x = -2$.

13. Sketch the graph of a function f that satisfies all of the following conditions: $f(1) = 3$, $f(4) = -1$, $\lim\limits_{x \to 1^-} f(x) = 3$, $\lim\limits_{x \to 1^+} f(x) = -2$, and $\lim\limits_{x \to 4} f(x) = 3$.

   Answer: (Answers will vary)

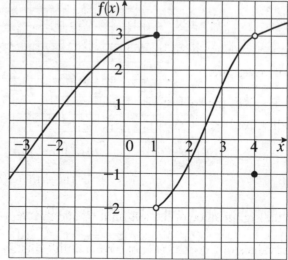

14. Consider the function $f(x) = \dfrac{x^2 - 5x + 6}{|x - 3|}$. Make an appropriate table of values in order to determine the indicated limits:

(a) $\lim\limits_{x \to 3^-} f(x)$

(b) $\lim\limits_{x \to 3^+} f(x)$

(c) Does $\lim\limits_{x \to 3} f(x)$ exist? If so, what is its value? If not, explain.

Answer:

One possible table:

x	$f(x)$
2	0
2.9	-0.9
2.99	-0.99
2.999	-0.999
2.9999	-0.9999
2.99999	-0.99999
2.999999	-0.999999
$\vdots$	$\vdots$

x	$f(x)$
$\vdots$	$\vdots$
3.000001	1.000001
3.00001	1.00001
3.0001	1.0001
3.001	1.001
3.01	1.01
3.1	1.1

Using the table values, the limits appear to be:

(a) $\lim\limits_{x \to 3^-} f(x) = -1$

(b) $\lim\limits_{x \to 3^+} f(x) = 1$

(c) Since the right-hand limit and the left-hand limit have different values, the limit does not exist at $x = 3$.

15. Use a table of values to estimate the value of each of the following limits, to 4 decimal places.

(a) $\lim\limits_{x \to 0} \dfrac{3^x - 1}{x}$

(b) $\lim\limits_{x \to 0} \dfrac{\sin 5x}{\sin 3x}$

(c) $\lim\limits_{x \to 0} (1 + x)^{1/x}$

Answer: (a) 1.0986   (b) 1.6667   (c) 2.7183

16. A cellular phone company has a roaming charge of 32 cents for every minute or fraction of a minute when you are out of your zone.

(a) Sketch a graph of the "out-of-your-zone" costs, C, of cellular phone usage as a function of the length of the call, t, for $0 \le t \le 5$.

(b) Evaluate:

(i) $\lim\limits_{t \to 2^-} C(t)$

(ii) $\lim\limits_{t \to 2^+} C(t)$

(c) Explain the significance of the left limit (i) and the right limit (ii) to the cell phone user.

(d) For what values of t does $C(t)$ not have a limit? Justify your answer.

Answer:

(a)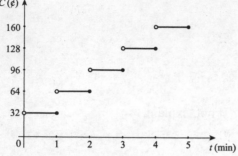

(b) (i) 64 cents

(ii) 96 cents

(c) The fact that $\lim_{t \to 2^-} C(t) \neq \lim_{t \to 2^+} C(t)$ shows that there is an abrupt change in the cost of cellular phone usage at $t = 2$.

(d) For $t_0 = 1, 2, 3,$ and 4, $\lim_{t \to t_0} C(t)$ does not exist, since $\lim_{t \to t_0^-} C(t) \neq \lim_{t \to t_0^+} C(t)$.

17. Using your graphing calculator, find a positive number δ such that whenever $0 < |x - 1| < \delta$ it will be the case that $\left| \sqrt{x + 3} - 2 \right| < 0.1$.

Answer: Answers will vary. Any δ such that $0 < \delta < 0.39$ is acceptable.

18. If $f(x) = 2^x$, how close to 3 does x have to be to ensure that $f(x)$ is within 0.1 of 8?

Answer: Answers will vary. One reasonable answer is that $f(x)$ is within 0.1 of 8 when x is within 0.017 of 3, that is, when $2.983 < x < 3.017$.

19. Determine $\lim_{x \to 1} \dfrac{x^{1000} - 1}{x - 1}$ by producing an appropriate table.

Answer:

x	$f(x)$
1.001	1716.92
1.0001	1052
1.00001	1005
1.000001	1000.5
1.0000001	1000.049

x	$\dfrac{x^{1000} - 1}{x - 1}$
0.99	99.9956828
0.999	632.304575
0.9999	951.671108
0.99999	995.021352
0.999999	999.499236
0.9999999	999.9500516637018

From the tables, it appears that $\lim_{x \to 1^+} \dfrac{x^{1000} - 1}{x - 1} = 1000$ and $\lim_{x \to 1^-} \dfrac{x^{1000} - 1}{x - 1} = 1000$, and therefore $\lim_{x \to 1} \dfrac{x^{1000} - 1}{x - 1} = 1000$.

2.3 Calculating Limits Using the Limit Laws

1. Find the value of the limit $\lim_{x \to 1} \left(x^{17} - x + 3 \right)$.

(A) -4 (B) 3   (C) -2 (D) 1

(E) -8 (F) 2   (G) 0   (H) -16

Answer: (B)

2. Find the value of the limit $\lim\limits_{x \to 3} \dfrac{x^2 - 9}{x^2 - 4x + 3}$.

(A) 8   (B) 4   (C) 12   (D) 2

(E) 6   (F) 1   (G) 0   (H) 3

Answer: (H)

3. Find the value of the limit $\lim\limits_{x \to 4^+} \dfrac{|x - 4|}{x - 4}$.

(A) 4   (B) -4 (C) $\frac{1}{2}$ (D) -2

(E) -1 (F) 2   (G) 1   (H) $-\frac{1}{2}$

Answer: (G)

4. Find the value of the limit $\lim\limits_{x \to 2^-} \dfrac{|x - 2|}{x - 2}$.

(A) 1   (B) -2 (C) $\frac{1}{2}$ (D) -4

(E) -1 (F) 4   (G) $-\frac{1}{2}$ (H) 2

Answer: (E)

5. Find the value of the limit $\lim\limits_{x \to 1} \dfrac{x - 1}{\sqrt{x} - 1}$.

(A) $\sqrt{2}$ (B) 1   (C) -1 (D) $-\sqrt{2}$

(E) 2   (F) -4 (G) 4   (H) -2

Answer: (E)

6. Find the value of the limit $\lim\limits_{x \to -2} \left(\dfrac{1}{x + 2} + \dfrac{4}{x^2 - 4} \right)$.

(A) -4 (B) -2 (C) $-\frac{1}{2}$ (D) $-\frac{1}{4}$

(E) $\frac{1}{4}$ (F) $\frac{1}{2}$ (G) 2   (H) 4

Answer: (D)

7. Find the value of the limit $\lim\limits_{x \to 3} \dfrac{1/x - 1/3}{x - 3}$.

(A) $\frac{1}{12}$ (B) $\frac{1}{6}$ (C) $-\frac{1}{6}$ (D) $\frac{1}{3}$

(E) $-\frac{1}{9}$ (F) $-\frac{1}{12}$ (G) $-\frac{1}{3}$ (H) $\frac{1}{9}$

Answer: (E)

8. Find the value of the limit $\lim\limits_{x \to 1} \dfrac{x - 1}{x^3 - 1}$.

(A) 0   (B) 2   (C) $\frac{1}{3}$ (D) 8

(E) $\frac{1}{4}$ (F) $\frac{1}{8}$ (G) $\frac{1}{32}$ (H) $\frac{1}{2}$

Answer: (C)

9. Find the value of the limit $\lim\limits_{x \to 9} \dfrac{\sqrt{x} - 3}{x - 9}$.

(A) -5 (B) -3 (C) -1 (D) 0

(E) 1 (F) 3 (G) 5 (H) $\frac{1}{6}$

Answer: (H)

10. Use the graphs of f and g below to evaluate each limit, if it exists. If it does not exist, explain why.

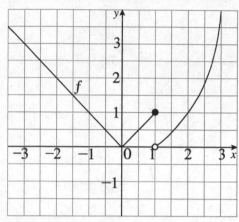 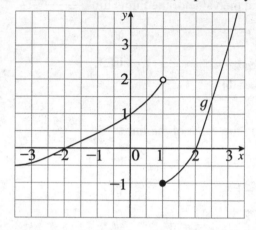

(a) $\lim\limits_{x \to -2} [f(x) + g(x)]$ (b) $\lim\limits_{x \to 2} \left[\dfrac{g(x)}{f(x)} \right]$ (c) $\lim\limits_{x \to 1} [f(x) \cdot g(x)]$ (d) $\lim\limits_{x \to 0} \left[(x-3)^2 \cdot g(x) \right]$

Answer:

(a) $\lim\limits_{x \to -2} [f(x) + g(x)] = 2 + 0 = 2$

(b) $\lim\limits_{x \to 2} \left[\dfrac{g(x)}{f(x)} \right] = \dfrac{0}{1} = 0$

(c) $\lim\limits_{x \to 1} [f(x) \cdot g(x)]$ does not exist because $\lim\limits_{x \to 1^-} [f(x) \cdot g(x)] = 2 \neq 0 = \lim\limits_{x \to 1^+} [f(x) \cdot g(x)]$.

(d) $\lim\limits_{x \to 0} \left[(x-3)^2 \cdot g(x) \right] = 9 \cdot 1 = 9$.

11. Given that $\lim\limits_{x \to 3} f(x) = 5$, $\lim\limits_{x \to 3} g(x) = 0$, and $\lim\limits_{x \to 3} h(x) = -8$, find the following limits, if they exist. If a limit does not exist, explain why.

(a) $\lim\limits_{x \to 3} (f(x) + h(x))$ (b) $\lim\limits_{x \to 3} x^2 f(x)$ (c) $\lim\limits_{x \to 3} f^2(x)$

(d) $\lim\limits_{x \to 3} \dfrac{f(x)}{2h(x)}$ (e) $\lim\limits_{x \to 3} \dfrac{g(x)}{f(x)}$ (f) $\lim\limits_{x \to 3} \dfrac{f(x)}{g(x)}$

(g) $\lim\limits_{x \to 3} \dfrac{2h(x)}{f(x) - h(x)}$ (h) $\lim\limits_{x \to 3} \sqrt[3]{h(x)}$

Answer: (a) -3 (b) 45 (c) 25 (d) $-\frac{5}{16}$ (e) 0

(f) Does not exist; the denominator is $\lim\limits_{x \to 3} g(x) = 0$, and the numerator is $\lim\limits_{x \to 3} f(x) = 5$.

(g) $-\frac{16}{13}$ (h) -2

12. Evaluate the limit, if it exists. If it does not exist, explain why.

(a) $\lim\limits_{x \to 2} \left(5x^3 - 3x^2 + 4\right)$

(b) $\lim\limits_{x \to 9} \dfrac{x - 9}{\sqrt{x} - 3}$

(c) $\lim\limits_{x \to -1} \dfrac{x^4 - 1}{x^2 - 1}$

(d) $\lim\limits_{x \to 3} \dfrac{\dfrac{2}{x} - \dfrac{2}{3}}{x - 3}$

(e) $\lim\limits_{x \to -3} \dfrac{|x + 3|}{2x + 6}$

(f) $\lim\limits_{x \to -3^-} \dfrac{|x + 3|}{2x + 6}$

Answer:

(a) $\lim\limits_{x \to 2} \left(5x^3 - 3x^2 + 4\right) = 5 \cdot 2^3 - 3 \cdot 2^2 + 4 = 32$

(b) $\lim\limits_{x \to 9} \dfrac{x - 9}{\sqrt{x} - 3} = 6$

(c) $\lim\limits_{x \to -1} \dfrac{x^4 - 1}{x^2 - 1} = \lim\limits_{x \to -1} \left(x^2 + 1\right) = 2$

(d) $\lim\limits_{x \to 3} \dfrac{\dfrac{2}{x} - \dfrac{2}{3}}{x - 3} = \lim\limits_{x \to 3} \dfrac{6 - 2x}{(x - 3) \cdot 3x} = \lim\limits_{x \to 3} \dfrac{-2(x - 3)}{(x - 3) \cdot 3x} = -\dfrac{2}{9}$

(e) $\lim\limits_{x \to -3} \dfrac{|x + 3|}{2x + 6}$ does not exist since the left- and right-hand limits are different.

(f) $\lim\limits_{x \to -3^-} \dfrac{|x + 3|}{2x + 6} = \lim\limits_{x \to -3^-} \dfrac{-(x + 3)}{2(x + 3)} = -\dfrac{1}{2}$

13. Given $f(x) = \begin{cases} x^3 + 2 & \text{if } x \leq -1 \\ x^2 + x + 1 & \text{if } -1 < x < 1 \\ x^4 + 2 & \text{if } x \geq 1 \end{cases}$ find the following limits. Justify your answers.

(a) $\lim\limits_{x \to -1^+} f(x)$

(b) $\lim\limits_{x \to -1^-} f(x)$

(c) $\lim\limits_{x \to -1} f(x)$

(d) $\lim\limits_{x \to 1^+} f(x)$

(e) $\lim\limits_{x \to 1^-} f(x)$

(f) $\lim\limits_{x \to 1} f(x)$

Answer:

(a) $\lim\limits_{x \to -1^+} f(x) = \lim\limits_{x \to -1^+} \left(x^2 + x + 1\right) = (-1)^2 + (-1) + 1 = 1 - 1 + 1 = 1$

(b) $\lim\limits_{x \to -1^-} f(x) = \lim\limits_{x \to -1^-} \left(x^3 + 2\right) = \lim\limits_{x \to -1^-} x^3 + \lim\limits_{x \to -1^-} 2 = (-1)^3 + 2 = 1$

(c) $\lim\limits_{x \to -1} f(x)$ exists since the left- and right-hand limits are equal.

(d) $\lim\limits_{x \to 1^+} f(x) = \lim\limits_{x \to 1^+} \left(x^4 + 2\right) = \lim\limits_{x \to 1^+} x^4 + \lim\limits_{x \to 1^+} 2 = 1^4 + 2 = 3$

(e) $\lim\limits_{x \to 1^-} f(x) = \lim\limits_{x \to 1^-} \left(x^2 + x + 1\right) = \lim\limits_{x \to 1^-} x^2 + \lim\limits_{x \to 1^-} x + \lim\limits_{x \to 1^-} 1 = 1^2 + 1 + 1 = 3$

(f) $\lim\limits_{x \to 1} f(x) = 3$ since the right- and left-hand limits are equal.

14. Explain why $\dfrac{(3x - 2)(x - 4)}{x - 4} \neq 3x - 2$, but $\lim\limits_{x \to 4} \dfrac{(3x - 2)(x - 4)}{x - 4} = \lim\limits_{x \to 4} (3x - 2)$.

Answer: $\dfrac{(3x - 2)(x - 4)}{x - 4} \neq 3x - 2$ because the expression on the left does not permit $x = 4$, while there is no similar restriction on the right.

However, since $\dfrac{(3x - 2)(x - 4)}{x - 4} = 3x - 2$ whenever $x \neq 4$, and neither $\lim\limits_{x \to 4} \dfrac{(3x - 2)(x - 4)}{x - 4}$ nor $\lim\limits_{x \to 4} (3x - 2)$ involve x ever being equal to 4, the second equation is true.

15. For each of the following problems, make an appropriate table to determine the limits.

(a) $\lim\limits_{x \to 1} \dfrac{|x| - x}{x - 1}$

(b) $\lim\limits_{x \to 0} \dfrac{\cos x - 1}{x}$

(c) $\lim\limits_{x \to 3} \dfrac{(1/x) - (1/3)}{x - 3}$

Answer:

(a)

x	$\dfrac{|x| - x}{x - 1}$
1.01	0
1.001	0
1.0001	0
1.0001	0

x	$\dfrac{|x| - x}{x - 1}$
0.99	0
0.999	0
0.9999	0

From the tables, it appears that

$$\lim_{x \to 1} \frac{|x| - x}{x - 1} = 0.$$

Algebraically: Note that as $x \to 1$, we can assume that $x > 0$ and therefore $|x| = x$, so

$$\lim_{x \to 1} \frac{|x| - x}{x - 1} = \lim_{x \to 1} \frac{x - x}{x - 1} = \lim_{x \to 1} 0 = 0.$$

(b)

x (radians)	$\dfrac{\cos x - 1}{x}$
0.01	-4.999958×10^{-3}
0.001	-5×10^{-4}
0.0002	-1×10^{-4}
0.00004	-2×10^{-5}

x (radians)	$\dfrac{\cos x - 1}{x}$
-0.01	4.999958×10^{-3}
-0.001	5×10^{-4}
-0.0002	1×10^{-4}
-0.00004	2×10^{-5}

From the tables, it appears that $\lim\limits_{x \to 0} \dfrac{\cos x - 1}{x} = 0$.

Algebraically:

$$\lim_{x \to 0} \frac{\cos x - 1}{x} = \lim_{x \to 0} \frac{(\cos x - 1)(\cos x + 1)}{x(\cos x + 1)} = \lim_{x \to 0} \frac{-\sin^2 x}{x(\cos x + 1)}$$

$$= \lim_{x \to 0} \frac{-\sin x \cdot \sin x}{x} \cdot \frac{1}{\cos x + 1}$$

$$= \lim_{x \to 0} -\sin x \cdot \lim_{x \to 0} \frac{\sin x}{x} \cdot \lim_{x \to 0} \frac{1}{\cos x + 1}$$

$$= 0 \cdot 1 \cdot \frac{1}{2} = 0$$

(c)

x	$\dfrac{\frac{1}{x} - \frac{1}{3}}{x - 3}$
2.9	-0.1149425
2.98	-0.1118568
2.999	-0.1111481
2.9999	-0.1111148

x	$\dfrac{\frac{1}{x} - \frac{1}{3}}{x - 3}$
3.01	-0.1107420
3.002	-0.111037
3.0005	-0.1110926
3.00001	-0.1111108

From the tables, it appears that $\lim\limits_{x \to 3^-} f(x) = -0.\overline{1} = -\frac{1}{9}$ and $\lim\limits_{x \to 3^+} f(x) = -0.\overline{1} = -\frac{1}{9}$, and so $\lim\limits_{x \to 3} f(x) = -\frac{1}{9}$.

Algebraically: $\lim\limits_{x \to 3} \dfrac{\frac{1}{x} - \frac{1}{3}}{x - 3} = \lim\limits_{x \to 3} \dfrac{3 - x}{3x} \cdot \dfrac{1}{(x - 3)} = \lim\limits_{x \to 3} \left(-\dfrac{1}{3x} \right) = -\dfrac{1}{9}$

16. Let $f(x) = \begin{cases} 2x - 1 & \text{if } x \text{ is rational} \\ 1 & \text{if } x \text{ is irrational} \end{cases}$

   (a) Determine whether or not the following limits exist. Justify your answers.

   (i) $\lim\limits_{x \to 0} f(x)$
           (ii) $\lim\limits_{x \to -1} f(x)$
           (iii) $\lim\limits_{x \to \sqrt{2}} f(x)$

   (b) Find a value b for which $\lim\limits_{x \to b} f(x)$ exists.

Answer:

   (a) (i) If we consider only rational values of x, then $\lim\limits_{x \to 0} f(x) = \lim\limits_{x \to 0} (2x - 1) = -1$. If we consider

   only irrational values of x, then $\lim\limits_{x \to 0} f(x) = \lim\limits_{x \to 0} 1 = 1$.

   Because these two values are different, $\lim\limits_{x \to 0} f(x)$ does not exist.

   (ii) If we consider only rational values of x, then $\lim\limits_{x \to -1} f(x) = \lim\limits_{x \to -1} (2x - 1) = -3$. If we consider

   only irrational values of x, then $\lim\limits_{x \to -1} f(x) = \lim\limits_{x \to -1} 1 = 1$. Because these two values are different,

   $\lim\limits_{x \to -1} f(x)$ does not exist.

   (iii) If we consider only rational values of x, then $\lim\limits_{x \to \sqrt{2}} f(x) = \lim\limits_{x \to \sqrt{2}} (2x - 1) = 2\sqrt{2} - 1$. If we

   consider only irrational values of x, then $\lim\limits_{x \to \sqrt{2}} f(x) = \lim\limits_{x \to \sqrt{2}} 1 = 1$. Because these two values

   are different, $\lim\limits_{x \to \sqrt{2}} f(x)$ does not exist.

   (b) If we consider only rational values of x, $\lim\limits_{x \to b} f(x) = \lim\limits_{x \to b} (2x - 1) = 2b - 1$.

   If we consider only irrational values of x, then $\lim\limits_{x \to b} f(x) = \lim\limits_{x \to b} 1 = 1$.

   In order for $\lim\limits_{x \to b} f(x)$ to exist (and equal, say, L), the one-sided limits must be equal, so we must have

   $L = 2b - 1 = 1 \implies b = 1$. So the limit exists only for $b = 1$.

17. Suppose we know that $4 - x^2 \leq g(x) \leq x^2 + 4$ for $x \in [-4, 4]$. Show that $\lim\limits_{x \to 0} g(x) = 4$.

Answer: Since $4 - x^2 \leq g(x) \leq x^2 + 4$ for $x \in [-4, 4]$ and $\lim\limits_{x \to 0} (4 - x^2) = 4 = \lim\limits_{x \to 0} (x^2 + 4)$, by the Squeeze Theorem, $\lim\limits_{x \to 0} g(x) = 4$.

2.4 Continuity

1. At what value of x does the function $\dfrac{(x+1)^2}{x^2 - 1}$ have a removable discontinuity?

(A) -3 (B) 3 (C) 2 (D) -1

(E) 1 (F) -4 (G) -2 (H) 4

Answer: (D)

2. At what value of x does the function $\dfrac{(x+1)^2}{x^2 - 1}$ have an infinite discontinuity?

(A) 3 (B) -4 (C) -2 (D) -3

(E) -1 (F) 1 (G) 2 (H) 4

Answer: (F)

3. Find the distance between the two values of x at which the function $\dfrac{1}{x^2 - 3x + 2}$ is discontinuous.

(A) 3 (B) 2 (C) 8 (D) 1

(E) 5 (F) 4 (G) 7 (H) 6

Answer: (D)

4. At what value or values of x is the function $f(x) = \begin{cases} x + 2 & \text{if } x \leq -1 \\ x^2 & \text{if } -1 < x < 1 \\ 3 - x & \text{if } x \geq 1 \end{cases}$ discontinuous?

(A) -1 (B) 0 (C) 1 (D) $-1, 0$

(E) $0, 1$ (F) $-1, 1$ (G) $-1, 0, 1$ (H) Continuous everywhere

Answer: (C)

5. Find the constant(s) c that make(s) the function $f(x) = \begin{cases} c^2 - x^2 & \text{if } x < 2 \\ 2(c - x) & \text{if } x \geq 2 \end{cases}$ continuous on $(-\infty, \infty)$.

(A) $-4, -2$ (B) $2, 0$ (C) 2 (D) 4

(E) $-2, 4$ (F) -2 (G) 0 (H) Does not exist

Answer: (B)

6. The definition of continuity of $f(x)$ at a point requires three things. List these three conditions, and in each case give an example (a graph or a formula) which illustrates how this condition can fail at $x = a$.

Answer:

The example below fails the requirement that a must lie in the domain of $f(x)$.

The example below fails the requirement that $\lim\limits_{x \to a} f(x)$ must exist.

The example below fails the requirement that $\lim\limits_{x \to a} f(x) = f(a)$.

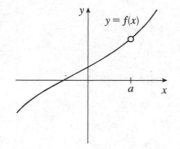
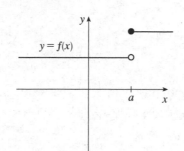
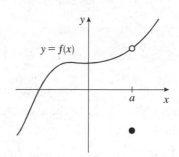

7. Given the graph of f below, state the intervals on which f is continuous.

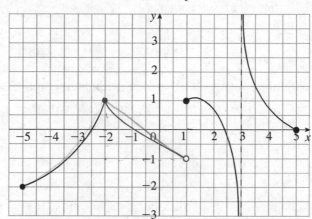

Answer: $[-5, 1)$, $(1, 3)$, and $(3, 5]$

8. At what value or values of x is the function $f(x) = \begin{cases} |x+1| - 1 & \text{if } x < 0 \\ x^2 + x & \text{if } 0 \leq x < 1 \\ 3 - x & \text{if } 1 \leq x \end{cases}$ discontinuous?

Answer: It is obvious that $f(x)$ is continuous on $(-\infty, 0)$, $(0, 1)$, and $(1, \infty)$. We need only examine $x = 0$ and $x = 1$.

$f(x)$ is continuous at $x = 0$, since $\lim\limits_{x \to 0^-} f(x) = \lim\limits_{x \to 0^-} |x+1| - 1 = 0 = \lim\limits_{x \to 0^+} f(x) = \lim\limits_{x \to 0^+} (x^2 + x)$ so $\lim\limits_{x \to 0} f(x) = 0 = f(0)$.

$f(x)$ is continuous at $x = 1$, since $\lim\limits_{x \to 1^-} f(x) = \lim\limits_{x \to 1^-} (x^2 + x) = 2 = \lim\limits_{x \to 1^+} (3 - x)$ so $\lim\limits_{x \to 1} f(x) = 2 = f(1)$. So f is continuous everywhere.

9. At what value or values of x is the function $f(x) = \begin{cases} x + 4 & \text{if } x \leq -1 \\ x^2 & \text{if } -1 < x < 1 \\ 2 - x & \text{if } x \geq 1 \end{cases}$ discontinuous?

Answer: We need only examine $x = -1$ and $x = 1$.

$f(x)$ is discontinuous at $x = -1$, since $\lim\limits_{x \to -1^-} f(x) = \lim\limits_{x \to -1^-} (x+4) = 3$, $\lim\limits_{x \to -1^+} f(x) = \lim\limits_{x \to -1^+} x^2 = 1$

so $\lim\limits_{x \to -1} f(x)$ does not exist.

$f(x)$ is continuous at $x = 1$, since $\lim\limits_{x \to 1^-} f(x) = \lim\limits_{x \to 1^-} x^2 = 1 = \lim\limits_{x \to 1^+} (2-x)$ so $\lim\limits_{x \to 1} f(x) = 1 = f(1)$.

So f is discontinuous at $x = -1$.

10. For $f(x) = \dfrac{x-3}{x^2-9}$, an infinite discontinuity occurs at what value of x?

Answer: We need only examine $x = \pm 3$.

$f(x)$ has a removable discontinuity at $x = 3$, since we can define $f(x) = \begin{cases} \dfrac{x-3}{x^2-9} & \text{if } x \neq 3 \\ \dfrac{1}{6} & \text{if } x = 3 \end{cases}$

$f(x)$ has an infinite discontinuity at $x = -3$, since $\lim\limits_{x \to -3^+} \dfrac{x-3}{x^2-9} = \infty$ and $\lim\limits_{x \to -3^-} \dfrac{x-3}{x^2-9} = -\infty$.

Thus, the only infinite discontinuity of f occurs at $x = -3$.

11. Consider $f(x) = \begin{cases} 3x - 5 & \text{if } x < 2 \\ (5 - 2x)^2 & \text{if } x > 2 \end{cases}$ The function f is not defined for $x = 2$. How should we

define $f(2)$ so that f is continuous at $x = 2$? Use the definition of continuity to verify your answer.

Answer: Since $\lim\limits_{x \to 2^-} f(x) = 1 = \lim\limits_{x \to 2^+} f(x)$, if we define $f(2) = 1$, then f is continuous at $x = 2$, by

definition.

12. Use the Intermediate Value Theorem to show that $x^3 - 5x - 7 = 0$ for some value of x in $(2, 3)$.

Answer: Answers will vary. One possible answer: Let $f(x) = x^3 - 5x - 7$. Since f is a polynomial, it is continuous on $\mathbb{R}$ and thus continuous on $[2, 3]$. Since $f(2) = -9 < 0 < 5 = f(3)$, by the Intermediate Value Theorem, there must be some number $c \in (2, 3)$ such that $f(c) = c^3 - 5c - 7 = 0$.

13. Suppose that $f(x)$ is defined on $[1, 3]$ and that $f(1) = 3$ and $f(3) = 5$. Sketch a possible graph of f that does not satisfy the conclusion of the Intermediate Value Theorem.

Answer: Answers will vary. One possible answer:

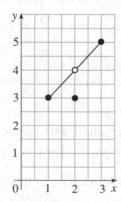

14. Let $f(x) = \dfrac{(x+1)^2}{x^2 - 1}$.

    (a) At what value(s), if any, does f have a removable discontinuity? Justify your answer.

    (b) At what value(s), if any, does f have an infinite discontinuity? Justify your answer.

Answer:

    (a) $f(x)$ has a removable discontinuity at $x = -1$. We redefine $f(x) = \begin{cases} \dfrac{x+1}{x-1} & \text{if } x \neq -1 \\ 0 & \text{if } x = -1 \end{cases}$

    (b) $f(x)$ has a infinite discontinuity at $x = 1$, since $\lim\limits_{x \to 1^+} f(x) = \infty$ and $\lim\limits_{x \to 1^-} f(x) = -\infty$.

15. A cellular phone company has a roaming charge of 32 cents for every minute or fraction of a minute when you are out of your zone.

    (a) Sketch a graph of the "out-of-your-zone" costs of cellular phone usage as a function of the length of the call.

    (b) Discuss the discontinuities of this function and their significance to the cell phone user.

Answer:

(a)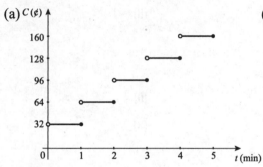

(b) We consider $t = 1$: $\lim\limits_{t \to 1^-} f(t) = 32$ cents and $\lim\limits_{t \to 1^+} f(t) = 64$ cents. These limits show that there is an abrupt change in the cost of cellular phone usage at $t = 1$. The left limit represents the cost of a call lasting less than one minute, and the right limit represents the cost of a call lasting more than one minute. A similar situation exists at each positive integer n. Thus, the cellular phone user should try to avoid calls which are slightly over n minutes long, and instead hang up just before an integral number of minutes has passed.

16. Determine whether each function is continuous or discontinuous. Explain your choice.

    (a) Postage charges to send a letter by first class mail.

    (b) The altitude of an airplane as a function of the time it has been in the air.

    (c) The temperature of an oven as it is run through its self cleaning cycle.

Answer:

    (a) The cost of sending a letter changes abruptly at certain weights. Therefore, this is not a continuous function.

    (b) The altitude of an airplane as a function of time is a continuous function, since a plane cannot jump from one altitude to another without passing through the intermediate altitudes.

    (c) The temperature of an oven changes gradually, so this is a continuous function.

2.5 Limits Involving Infinity

1. Find the value of the limit $\lim\limits_{x \to \infty} \dfrac{7 + 3x}{4 - x}$.

(A) $\frac{3}{4}$ (B) 3   (C) 7   (D) $-\frac{3}{4}$

(E) -3 (F) $-\frac{7}{4}$ (G) -7 (H) $\frac{7}{4}$

Answer: (E)

2. Find the value of the limit $\lim\limits_{x \to \infty} \dfrac{2x^2 - 1}{x^2 + 2x + 1}$.

(A) $-\frac{1}{2}$ (B) 1   (C) 2   (D) $\frac{1}{2}$

(E) -1 (F) $-\frac{1}{3}$ (G) -2 (H) $\frac{1}{3}$

Answer: (C)

3. Find the value of the limit $\lim\limits_{x \to \infty} \sqrt{\dfrac{x + 8x^2}{2x^2 - 1}}$.

(A) -2 (B) 1   (C) $-\frac{1}{2}$ (D) 4

(E) $\frac{1}{2}$ (F) 2   (G) 0   (H) -1

Answer: (F)

4. Find the value of the limit $\lim\limits_{x \to \infty} \left(\sqrt{x^2 + x} - x \right)$.

(A) $-\frac{1}{2}$ (B) $\sqrt{2}$ (C) $-\sqrt{2}$ (D) $\frac{1}{4}$

(E) ∞ (F) $-\frac{1}{4}$ (G) 0   (H) $\frac{1}{2}$

Answer: (H)

5. Find the value of the limit $\lim\limits_{x \to -\infty} \left(\sqrt{x^2 + 3x} - x \right)$.

(A) 3   (B) $\frac{3}{2}$ (C) 0   (D) 1

(E) 2   (F) ∞ (G) $-\infty$ (H) Does not exist

Answer: (F)

6. Find the value of the limit $\lim\limits_{x \to \infty} \dfrac{e^{2x}}{e^{2x} + 1}$.

(A) -2 (B) 1   (C) 2   (D) 4

(E) -1 (F) -3 (G) 0   (H) 3

Answer: (B)

7. Find the value of x at which the curve $y = \dfrac{2x + 1}{x + 3}$ has a vertical asymptote.

(A) -4 (B) -3 (C) -2 (D) -1

(E) 0   (F) 1   (G) 2   (H) 3

Answer: (H)

8. Find the value of x at which the curve $y = \dfrac{x^2 - 16}{x^2 - 5x + 4}$ has a vertical asymptote.

(A) -4 (B) -3 (C) -2 (D) -1

(E) 0 (F) 1 (G) 2 (H) 3

Answer: (F)

9. Given the following information about limits, select a graph which could be the graph of $y = f(x)$.

$$\lim_{x \to \infty} f(x) = \lim_{x \to -\infty} f(x) = -1 \qquad \lim_{x \to -1^+} f(x) = \lim_{x \to 1^-} f(x) = \infty$$

$$\lim_{x \to -1^-} f(x) = \lim_{x \to 1^+} f(x) = -\infty$$

(A) 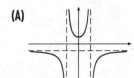   (B)   (C) 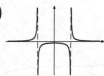   (D)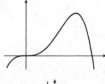

(E) 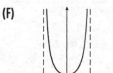   (F)   (G) 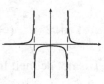   (H)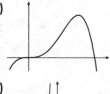

Answer: (A)

10. Given the following information about limits, select a graph which could be the graph of $y = f(x)$.

$$\lim_{x \to \infty} f(x) = \lim_{x \to -\infty} f(x) = 0 \qquad \lim_{x \to -1^-} f(x) = \lim_{x \to 1^+} f(x) = \infty$$

$$\lim_{x \to -1^+} f(x) = \lim_{x \to 1^-} f(x) = -\infty$$

(A) 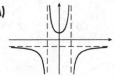 (B) (C) (D)

(E) (F) (G) (H)

Answer: (C)

11. Given the following information about limits, select a graph which could be the graph of $y = f(x)$.

$$\lim_{x \to \infty} f(x) = \lim_{x \to -\infty} f(x) = 0 \qquad \lim_{x \to -1^+} f(x) = \lim_{x \to 1^+} f(x) = \infty$$

$$\lim_{x \to -1^-} f(x) = \lim_{x \to 1^-} f(x) = -\infty$$

(A)

(B)

(C)

(D)

(E)

(F)

(G)

(H)

Answer: (B)

12. Using the graph below, determine the following:

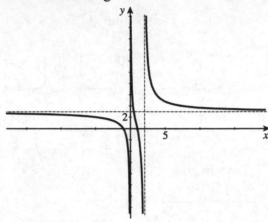

(a) $\displaystyle\lim_{x\to\infty} f(x)$

(b) $\displaystyle\lim_{x\to 2^+} f(x)$

(c) $\displaystyle\lim_{x\to 2^-} f(x)$

(d) $\displaystyle\lim_{x\to -\infty} f(x)$

(e) $\displaystyle\lim_{x\to 0^+} f(x)$

(f) $\displaystyle\lim_{x\to 0^-} f(x)$

(g) Find the horizontal asymptote(s) of the graph of $y = f(x)$.

(h) Find the vertical asymptote(s) of the graph of $y = f(x)$.

Answer:

(a) 3   (b) ∞ (c) $-\infty$ (d) 2   (e) ∞ (f) $-\infty$ (g) $y = 3$ (h) $x = 0, x = 2$

13. Suppose that $f(x) = \dfrac{x-3}{x^2-9}$. f is not defined for $x = \pm 3$.

(a) For which of these two values does f have an infinite discontinuity? Explain.

(b) For which of these two values does f have a removable discontinuity? Explain.

Answer:

(a) Since $\displaystyle\lim_{x\to -3^-} f(x) = \lim_{x\to -3^-} \dfrac{x-3}{x^2-9} = \lim_{x\to -3^-} \dfrac{x-3}{(x-3)(x+3)} = \lim_{x\to -3^-} \dfrac{1}{x+3} = \infty$, f has an infinite discontinuity at $x = -3$.

(a) Since $\displaystyle\lim_{x\to -3} f(x) = \lim_{x\to 3} \dfrac{x-3}{x^2-9} = \lim_{x\to 3} \dfrac{x-3}{(x-3)(x+3)} = \lim_{x\to 3} \dfrac{1}{x+3} = \dfrac{1}{6}$, f has a removable discontinuity at $x = 3$.

14. Given the following information about limits, sketch a graph which could be the graph of $y = f(x)$. Label all horizontal and vertical asymptotes.

$$\lim_{x \to \infty} f(x) = \lim_{x \to -\infty} f(x) = 1 \qquad \lim_{x \to -1^+} f(x) = \lim_{x \to 1^-} f(x) = -\infty$$

$$\lim_{x \to -1^-} f(x) = \lim_{x \to 1^+} f(x) = \infty \qquad f(0) = -1$$

Answer:

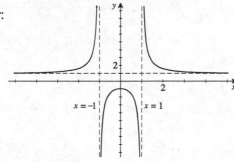

15. Given the following information about limits, sketch a graph which could be the graph of $y = f(x)$. Label all horizontal and vertical asymptotes.

$$\lim_{x \to \infty} f(x) = \lim_{x \to -\infty} f(x) = 0, \ \lim_{x \to 1} f(x) = \infty, \ \lim_{x \to -1} f(x) = -\infty, \text{ and } f(0) = 0$$

Answer:

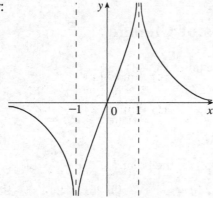

16. Given the following information about limits, sketch a graph which could be the graph of $y = f(x)$. Label all horizontal and vertical asymptotes.

$$\lim_{x \to \infty} f(x) = \lim_{x \to -\infty} f(x) = -1, \ \lim_{x \to 2^+} f(x) = \lim_{x \to -1^-} f(x) = -\infty,$$

$$\lim_{x \to -1^+} f(x) = \lim_{x \to 2^-} f(x) = \infty, \text{ and } f(0) = 1$$

Answer:

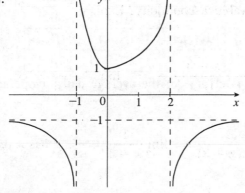

17. Find the limit.

    (a) $\lim\limits_{x \to 2^+} \dfrac{1}{x - 2}$ 　　(b) $\lim\limits_{x \to \infty} \dfrac{1 - 2x^2}{x^2 + x}$ 　　(c) $\lim\limits_{x \to \infty} \left(\sqrt{x^2 + 2x} - x \right)$

    Answer: (a) ∞ 　　(b) -2 　　(c) 1

18. Find the limit.

    (a) $\lim\limits_{x \to \infty} \sin x$ 　　(b) $\lim\limits_{x \to \infty} e^{-x}$ 　　(c) $\lim\limits_{t \to \infty} \dfrac{t^3 + 3t}{1 - t^4}$

    Answer: (a) Does not exist 　　(b) 0 　　(c) 0

19. Find the limit.

    (a) $\lim\limits_{x \to \infty} \dfrac{1}{x^2}$ 　　(b) $\lim\limits_{x \to \infty} \left(\sqrt{x^2 + x} - \sqrt{x^2 - x} \right)$ 　　(c) $\lim\limits_{x \to -\infty} \left(x - 3x^2 \right)$

    Answer: (a) 0 　　(b) 1 　　(c) $-\infty$

20. Find the vertical asymptote(s) of the curve $y = \dfrac{x^2 - 4}{9 - x^2}$.

    Answer: $\lim\limits_{x \to 3^+} \dfrac{x^2 - 4}{9 - x^2} = -\infty$ and $\lim\limits_{x \to 3^-} \dfrac{x^2 - 4}{9 - x^2} = \infty$, so $x = 3$ is a vertical asymptote. $\lim\limits_{x \to -3^+} \dfrac{x^2 - 4}{9 - x^2} = \infty$

    and $\lim\limits_{x \to -3^-} \dfrac{x^2 - 4}{9 - x^2} = -\infty$, so $x = -3$ is a vertical asymptote.

2.6 　Tangents, Velocities, and Other Rates of Change

1. Find an equation of the line tangent to $f(x) = x^2 - 4x$ at the point $(3, -3)$.

   (A) $2x - y = 9$ 　　(B) $x - 2y = 9$ 　　(C) $y - 2x = 9$ 　　(D) $2y - x = 9$

   (E) $x - y = 9$ 　　(F) $y - x = 9$ 　　(G) $2x - y = 4$ 　　(H) $x - 2y = 4$

   Answer: (A)

2. Find an equation of the line tangent to the curve $y = x + (1/x)$ at the point $\left(5, \frac{26}{25}\right)$.

   (A) $24x - 25y = 94$ 　　(B) $24x - 25y = -94$ 　　(C) $25x - 24y = 94$ 　　(D) $25x - 24y = -94$

   (E) $24x - 24y = 94$ 　　(F) $24x - 24y = -94$ 　　(G) $25x - 25y = 94$ 　　(H) $25x - 25y = -94$

   Answer: (B)

Items 3 and 4 refer to the following table:

Average Daily Temperatures in Moorhead, Minnesota						
Month	1 (Jan)	2 (Feb)	3 (Mar)	4 (Apr)	5 (May)	6 (Jun)
Temperature (°F)	6	14	26	43	57	66
Month	7 (Jul)	8 (Aug)	9 (Sep)	10 (Oct)	11 (Nov)	12 (Dec)
Temperature (°F)	71	70	58	46	27	13

3. During which of the following periods was the rate of change of the average daily temperature the greatest?

   (A) $[2, 3]$ 　　(B) $[3, 4]$ 　　(C) $[4, 5]$ 　　(D) $[5, 6]$

   (E) $[6, 7]$ 　　(F) $[2, 4]$ 　　(G) $[3, 5]$ 　　(H) $[3, 6]$

   Answer: (B)

4. During which of the following periods was the rate of change of the average daily temperature the smallest?

(A) $[2, 6]$ (B) $[4, 8]$ (C) $[4, 9]$ (D) $[6, 10]$

(E) $[8, 10]$ (F) $[9, 10]$ (G) $[10, 11]$ (H) $[11, 12]$

Answer: (G)

5. Below are the water levels for the Red River recorded in Fargo, North Dakota during the flood of 1997. Readings were made at 1:00 A.M. each day.

Date	04/01	04/02	04/03	04/04	04/05	04/06
Level (ft)	15.62	16.30	17.21	20.25	23.63	27.47

(a) Find the average rate of change of water level over the following periods.

(i) $[04/04, 04/06]$ (ii) $[04/04, 04/05]$ (iii) $[04/03, 04/04]$

(b) Estimate the rate of change of water level on April 4th.

Answer:

(a) (i) $\dfrac{27.47 - 20.25}{2} = 3.61$ ft/day   (ii) $\dfrac{23.63 - 20.25}{1} = 3.38$ ft/day   (iii) $\dfrac{20.25 - 17.21}{1} = 3.04$ ft/day

(b) About 3.21 ft/day (answers may vary).

6. The following table shows the relationship between pressure (in atmospheres) and volume (in liters) of hydrogen gas at $0\,^\circ$C.

Pressure (atm)	1	2	3	4	5	6
Volume (L)	22.4	11.2	7.5	5.6	4.5	3.7

(a) Find the average rate of change of volume with respect to pressure for the following pressure intervals:

(i) $[3, 5]$ (ii) $[3, 4]$ (iii) $[2, 3]$

(b) Estimate the rate of change of volume with respect to pressure if the pressure is 2 atmospheres.

Answer:

(a) (i) $\dfrac{4.5 - 7.5}{2} = -1.5 \dfrac{\text{liters}}{\text{atm}}$ (ii) $\dfrac{5.6 - 7.5}{1} = -1.9 \dfrac{\text{liters}}{\text{atm}}$ (iii) $\dfrac{11.2 - 7.5}{-1} = -3.7 \dfrac{\text{liters}}{\text{atm}}$

(b) About -2.8 liters/atm (answers may vary).

7. Below are the sunrise and sunset times for Moorhead, Minnesota on the 21st of each month.

Sunrise and Sunset in Moorhead, Minnesota on the 21st of each month			
Month	Sunrise	Sunset	Day Length (h)
1 (Jan)	08:03	17:14	9.18
2 (Feb)	07:21	18:01	10.67
3 (Mar)	06:28	18:41	12.22
4 (Apr)	05:29	19:24	13.92
5 (May)	04:45	20:02	15.28
6 (Jun)	04:32	20:25	15.88
7 (Jul)	04:54	20:12	15.30
8 (Aug)	05:32	19:27	13.92
9 (Sep)	06:12	18:27	12.25
10 (Oct)	06:53	17:29	10.60
11 (Nov)	07:39	16:47	9.13
12 (Dec)	08:09	16:41	8.53

(a) Find the rate of change of day length with respect to time in months

   (i) from March 21 through July 21.

   (ii) from March 21 through May 21.

   (iii) from March 21 through April 21.

(b) Estimate the instantaneous rate of change in day length per month on March 21.

(c) During which one-month period did the day length change at the greatest rate?

Answer:

(a) (i) 0.77 h/month   (ii) 1.53 h/month   (iii) 1.7 h/month

(b) Answers will vary. Using February through April, we get approximately 1.63 h/month.

(c) March 21–April 21, with a change of 1.7 h in one month.

8. The following table shows the concentration (in mol/l) of a certain chemical in terms of reaction time (in hours) during a decomposition reaction.

Time (hours)	0	5	10	20	30	50
Concentration (mol/L)	2.32	1.86	1.49	0.98	0.62	0.25

(a) Find the average rate of change of concentration with respect to time for the following time intervals:

   (i) $[0, 5]$ (ii) $[10, 20]$ (iii) $[30, 50]$

(b) Plot the points from the table and fit an appropriate exponential model to the data.

(c) From your model in part (b), determine the instantaneous rate of change of concentration with respect to time.

(d) Is the rate of change of concentration increasing or decreasing with respect to time? Justify your answer.

Answer:

(a) (i) -0.092 mol/L/h

  (ii) -0.051 mol/L/h

  (iii) -0.0185 mol/L/h

(b)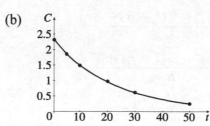

(c) $C(t) = 2.3357e^{-0.0445t}$ mol/L, $\dfrac{dC}{dt} = -0.1039e^{-0.0445t}$ mol/L/h

(d) Since $\dfrac{dC}{dt} < 0$, the rate of change of concentration is decreasing with respect to time.

9. (a) Find the slope of the tangent line to the curve $y = x - \dfrac{1}{x}$ at $(1,0)$

   (i) using Definition 1 from Section 2.6.

   (ii) using Definition 2 from Section 2.6.

   (b) Using your results from part (a), find an equation of the tangent line at $(1,0)$.

Answer:

(a) (i) $m = \lim\limits_{h \to 0} \dfrac{f(1+h) - f(1)}{h} = \lim\limits_{h \to 0} \dfrac{1 + h - \dfrac{1}{1+h} - 0}{h} = \lim\limits_{h \to 0} \dfrac{\left(1 + h - \dfrac{1}{1+h}\right)(1+h)}{h(1+h)}$

$\qquad = \lim\limits_{h \to 0} \dfrac{(1+h)^2 - 1}{h(1+h)} = \lim\limits_{h \to 0} \dfrac{(1 + 2h + h^2) - 1}{h(1+h)} = \lim\limits_{h \to 0} \dfrac{h(2+h)}{h(1+h)} = 2$

(ii) $m = \lim\limits_{x \to 1} \dfrac{f(x) - f(1)}{x - 1} = \lim\limits_{x \to 1} \dfrac{x - \dfrac{1}{x} - 0}{x - 1} = \lim\limits_{x \to 1} \dfrac{\left(x - \dfrac{1}{x}\right)x}{(x-1)x} = \lim\limits_{x \to 1} \dfrac{x^2 - 1}{(x-1)x}$

$\qquad = \lim\limits_{x \to 1} \dfrac{(x-1)(x+1)}{(x-1)x} = 2$

(b) $m = 2$; $y - 0 = 2(x - 1)$ or $y = 2x - 2$

2.7 Derivatives

1. If $f(x) = \sqrt{x}$, which of the following represents $f'(4)$?

(A) $\lim\limits_{x \to 4} \dfrac{\sqrt{x} - 4}{x - 4}$

(B) $\lim\limits_{x \to 4} \dfrac{\sqrt{x} - 2}{x - 4}$

(C) $\lim\limits_{x \to 4} \dfrac{\sqrt{x} - 4}{x - 2}$

(D) $\dfrac{\sqrt{x} - 2}{x - 4}$

(E) $\lim\limits_{x \to 4} \dfrac{\sqrt{x} - 4}{x}$

(F) $\lim\limits_{x \to 4} \dfrac{\sqrt{x} + 2}{x - 4}$

(G) Does not exist

(H) None of the above

Answer: (B)

2. If $f(x) = x^2 - 2x$, which of the following represents $f'(1)$?

(A) $\lim\limits_{h \to 0} \dfrac{(1+h)^2 - 2(1+h) - 1}{h}$

(B) $\lim\limits_{h \to 0} \dfrac{(1+h)^2 - 2 + h - 1}{h}$

(C) $\lim\limits_{h \to 0} \dfrac{(1+h)^2 - 2(1+h) + 1}{h}$

(D) $\dfrac{(1+h)^2 - 2(1+h) - 1}{h}$

(E) $\lim\limits_{h \to 0} \dfrac{h^2 + 1 - 2(1+h) + 1}{h}$

(F) $\lim\limits_{h \to 0} \dfrac{(1+h)^2 - 2 + 2h + 1}{h}$

(G) Does not exist

(H) None of the above

Answer: (C)

3. If $f(x) = \dfrac{x+1}{2x-1}$, which of the following represents $f'(0)$?

(A) $\lim\limits_{h \to 0} \dfrac{\frac{h+1}{h-1} + 1}{h}$

(B) $\lim\limits_{h \to 0} \dfrac{\frac{h+1}{2h-1} - 1}{h}$

(C) $\lim\limits_{h \to 0} \dfrac{\frac{h+1}{2h-1} + 1}{h}$

(D) $\lim\limits_{h \to 0} \dfrac{\frac{h+1}{2h-1} + 1}{h}$

(E) $\dfrac{\frac{h+1}{h-1} + 1}{h}$

(F) $\lim\limits_{h \to 0} \dfrac{\frac{h}{2h} + 1}{h}$

(G) Does not exist

(H) None of the above

Answer: (D)

4. If $f(x) = 5$, which of the following represents $f'(3)$?

(A) $\lim\limits_{\Delta x \to 0} \dfrac{5}{\Delta x}$

(B) 3

(C) $\lim\limits_{\Delta x \to 0} \dfrac{5 - 3}{\Delta x}$

(D) 5

(E) $\lim\limits_{\Delta x \to 0} \dfrac{5 - 5}{\Delta x}$

(F) $\lim\limits_{\Delta x \to 0} \dfrac{3}{\Delta x}$

(G) Does not exist

(H) None of the above

Answer: (E)

5. If $f(1) = 5$ and $f'(1) = -3$, find an equation of the tangent line at $x = 1$.

(A) $y = -3x + 5$

(B) $y = 5x - 3$

(C) $y = -3x + 8$

(D) $y = -3x - 8$

(E) $y = 3x + 8$

(F) $y = 3x - 8$

(G) Does not exist

(H) None of the above

Answer: (C)

6. If $f(-1) = 3$ and $f'(-1) = 2$, find an equation of the tangent line at $x = -1$.

(A) $y = -5 + 2x$ (B) $y = 1 + 2x$

(C) $y = -2x + 1$ (D) $y = 5 - 2x$

(E) $y = -1 + 2x$ (F) $y = 5 + 2x$

(G) Does not exist   (H) None of the above

Answer: **(F)**

7. The graph of f is given below. State, with reasons, the number(s) at which

(a) f is not differentiable.   (b) f is not continuous.

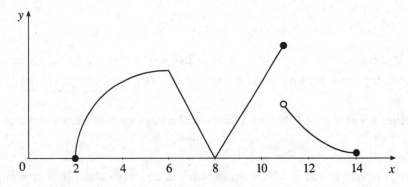

Answer:

(a) f is not differentiable at $x = 6$ or at $x = 8$, because the graph has a corner there; and at $x = 11$, because there is a discontinuity there.

(b) f is not continuous at $x = 11$ because $\lim\limits_{x \to 11} f(x)$ does not exist.

8. Consider the function $f(x) = |x - 2|$.

(a) What is the domain of f?

(b) At what number(s), if any, is f discontinuous? Explain your answer.

(c) At what number(s), if any, is f not differentiable? Explain your answer.

Answer:

(a) Domain is $(-\infty, \infty)$.

(b) f is continuous on $(-\infty, \infty)$.

(c) f is not differentiable at 2 because the graph of f has a corner there.

9. The graph of f is given below. State, with reasons, the number(s) at which

    (a) f is not differentiable.   (b) f is not continuous.

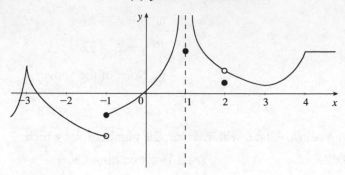

Answer:

    (a) f is not differentiable at $x = -3$ or at $x = 4$, because the graph has a corner there; at $x = -1$ or $x = 1$, because the limit does not exist there; and at $x = 2$, because $\lim\limits_{x \to 2} f(x) \neq f(2)$.

    (b) f is not continuous at $x = -1$ or $x = 1$ because the limit does not exist there; and at $x = 2$, because $\lim\limits_{x \to 2} f(x) \neq f(2)$.

10. For the function f whose graph is given, arrange the following values in increasing order and explain your reasoning.

$$f'(-3),\ f'(-2),\ f'(-1),\ f'(0),\ f'(1),\ f'(2),\ f'(3)$$

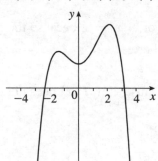

Answer: $f'(3) < f'(-1) < f'(0) < f'(2) < f'(1) < f'(-2) < f'(-3)$ by inspection of slopes.

11. Determine a function f and a number a where the given limit represents the derivative of f at a.

    (a) $\lim\limits_{h \to 0} \dfrac{\sqrt{(2+h)^2 + 5} - 3}{h}$ (b) $\lim\limits_{h \to 0} \dfrac{(6+h)^2 - 5(6+h) - 4 - 2}{h}$

    (c) $\lim\limits_{x \to 0} \dfrac{3e^x - 3}{x}$ (d) $\lim\limits_{x \to -4} \dfrac{x^3 + 64}{x + 4}$

Answer:

    (a) $f(x) = \sqrt{x^2 + 5},\ a = 2$ (b) $f(x) = x^2 - 5x - 4,\ a = 6$

    (c) $f(x) = e^x,\ a = 0$ (d) $f(x) = x^3,\ a = -4$

12. Water is flowing into a large cylindrical tank at a constant rate. Let $H(t)$ represent the height of the water level at time t.

    (a) Sketch a possible graph of $H(t)$.

    (b) Describe how the rate of change of H with respect to t varies as t increases.

    (c) Sketch a graph of $H'(t)$.

Answer:

(a)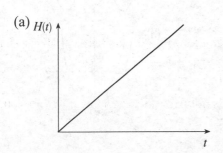

    (c) $H'(t)$

    (b) $H'(t)$ is constant.

13. A tank is in the shape of a large, inverted (point-down) cone. Water is flowing into the tank at a constant rate. Let $H(t)$ represent the height of the water level at time t.

    (a) Sketch a possible graph of $H(t)$.

    (b) Describe how the rate of change of H with respect to t varies as t increases.

    (c) Sketch a graph of $H'(t)$.

Answer:

(a)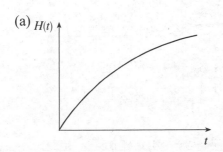

    (c) $H'(t)$

    (b) $H'(t)$ is always positive and decreasing.

2.8 | The Derivative as a Function

1. Given the graph of $y = f(x)$ below, select a graph which best represents the graph of $y = f'(x)$.

(A) 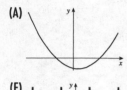 (B)  (C)  (D)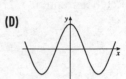

(E) 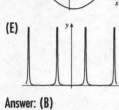 (F) 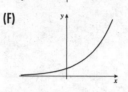 (G) 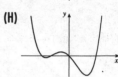 (H)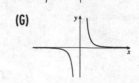

Answer: (B)

2. Given the graph of $y = f(x)$ below, select a graph which best represents the graph of $y = f'(x)$.

(A) 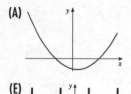 (B) 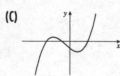 (C) 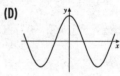 (D)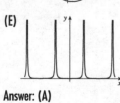

(E) 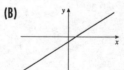 (F) 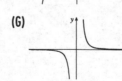 (G) 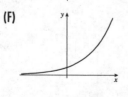 (H)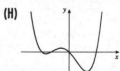

Answer: (A)

3. Given the graph of $y = f(x)$ below, select a graph which best represents the graph of $y = f'(x)$.

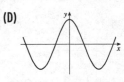

(A)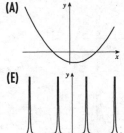

(B)

(C)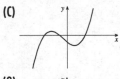

(D)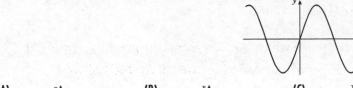

(E)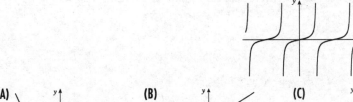

(F)

(G)

(H)

Answer: (D)

4. Given the graph of $y = f(x)$ below, select a graph which best represents the graph of $y = f'(x)$.

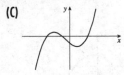

(A)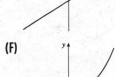

(B)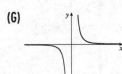

(C)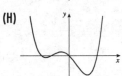

(D)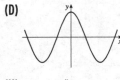

(E)

(F)

(G)

(H)

Answer: (E)

5. Given the graph of $y = f(x)$ below, select a graph which best represents the graph of $y = f'(x)$.

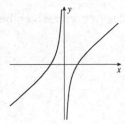

(A)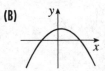

(B)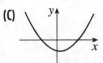

(C)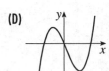

(D)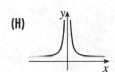

(E)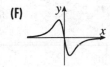

(F)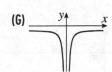

(G)

(H)

Answer: (H)

6. Given the graph of $y = f(x)$ below, select a graph which best represents the graph of $y = f'(x)$.

(A) 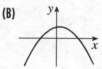   (B)   (C)   (D)

(E)   (F)   (G)   (H)

Answer: **(F)**

7. Given the graph of $y = f(x)$ below, select a graph which best represents the graph of $y = f'(x)$.

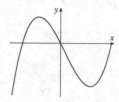

(A)   (B)   (C) 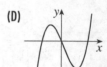   (D)

(E)   (F) 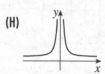   (G)   (H)

Answer: **(C)**

8. Given the graph of $y = f(x)$ below, select a graph which best represents the graph of $y = f'(x)$.

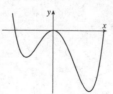

(A)   (B)   (C)   (D)

(E)   (F)   (G)   (H)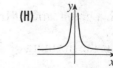

Answer: **(D)**

9. Given the graph of $y = f(x)$, sketch the graph of $y = f'(x)$.

(a)

(b)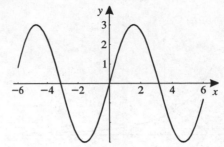

(c)

(d)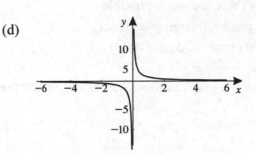

Answer:

(a)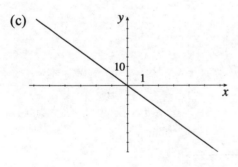

(b)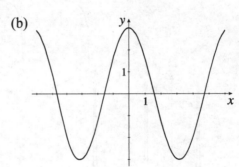

(c)

(d)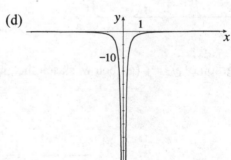

10. In order to determine an appropriate delivery schedule to a group of rural homes in North Dakota, a fuel oil distributor monitors fuel oil consumption and the daily outdoor temperature (in degrees Fahrenheit). A table was constructed for a function $F(T)$ of fuel oil consumption (in gallons per day) as a function of the temperature T.

   (a) Sketch a graph which you believe would approximate the graph of $y = F(T)$.

   (b) What is the meaning of $F'(T)$? What are its units?

   (c) Write a sentence that would explain to an intelligent layperson the meaning of $F'(0) = -0.4$.

Answer:

(a)

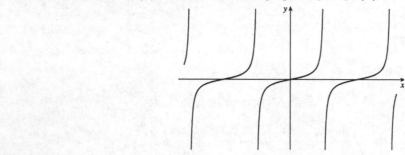

(There are many possible
graphs, though presumably
they are all decreasing!)

(b) $F'(T)$ represents the rate of change of fuel oil
consumption with respect to temperature. Its units are
(gallons/day) / (°F).

(c) $F'(0) = -0.4$ means that as the temperature increases
past 0 °F, the fuel consumption is decreasing by
0.4 (gallons/day) / (°F).

11. Given the graph of $y = f(x)$ below, sketch the graph of $y = f'(x)$.

Answer:

12. Given the graph of $y = f(x)$ below, sketch the graph of $y = f'(x)$.

Answer:

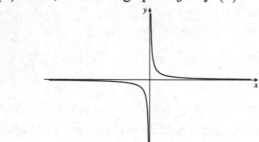

13. Given the graph of $y = f(x)$ below, sketch the graph of $y = f'(x)$.

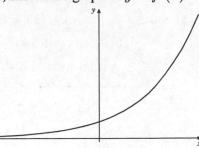

Answer:

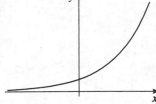

14. Given the graph of $y = f(x)$ below, sketch the graph of $y = f'(x)$.

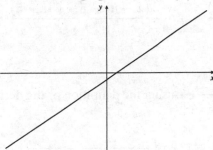

Answer:

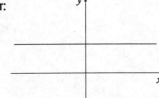

15. Below are the graphs of a function and its first and second derivatives. Identify which of the following graphs (a, b, and c) is $f(x)$, which is $f'(x)$, and which is $f''(x)$. Justify your choices.

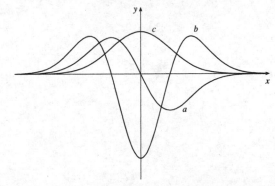

Answer: a must be the derivative of c since it is above the x-axis where c increases, below the x-axis where c decreases, and is 0 where c has a horizontal tangent line. Similarly, b must be the derivative of graph a. So $f(x) = c$, $f'(x) = a$, and $f''(x) = b$.

16. Given the graph of $y = f(x)$, find all values of x for which

   (a) $f'(x) > 0$ (b) $f'(x) < 0$ (c) $f'(x) = 0$ (d) $f''(x) > 0$

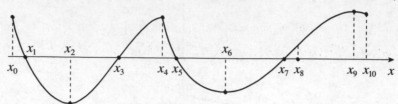

   (a) $f'(x) > 0$ on (x_2, x_4) and (x_6, x_9).

   (b) $f'(x) < 0$ on (x_0, x_2), (x_4, x_6), and (x_9, x_{10}).

   (c) $f'(x) = 0$ at x_2, x_6, and x_9.

   (d) $f''(x) > 0$ on (x_0, x_3) and (x_4, x_8).

17. Find the derivative of $f(x) = 3x - 5$ using the definition of the derivative.

   Answer:

   $$f'(x) = \lim_{h \to 0} \frac{f(x+h) - f(x)}{h} = \lim_{h \to 0} \frac{3(x+h) - 5 - (3x - 5)}{h} = \lim_{h \to 0} \frac{3x + 3h - 5 - 3x + 5}{h}$$

   $$= \lim_{h \to 0} \frac{3h}{h} = 3$$

18. Find the derivative of $f(x) = \dfrac{1}{2 - x}$ using the definition of the derivative.

   Answer:

   $$f'(x) = \lim_{h \to 0} \frac{f(x+h) - f(x)}{h} = \lim_{h \to 0} \frac{\left[\dfrac{1}{2 - (x+h)} - \dfrac{1}{2 - x}\right][2 - (x+h)](2 - x)}{h[2 - (x+h)](2 - x)}$$

   $$= \lim_{h \to 0} \frac{2 - x - (2 - x - h)}{h[2 - (x+h)](2 - x)} = \lim_{h \to 0} \frac{h}{h[2 - (x+h)](2 - x)}$$

   $$= \lim_{h \to 0} \frac{1}{[2 - (x+h)](2 - x)} = \frac{1}{(2 - x)^2}$$

2.9 | What Does f' Say About f?

1. Given the graph of $y = f'(x)$ below, select a graph which could be that of $y = f(x)$.

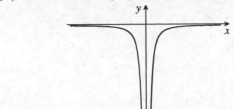

(A)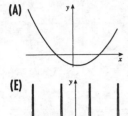

(B)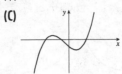

(C)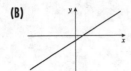

(D)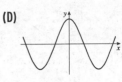

(E)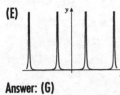

(F)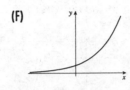

(G)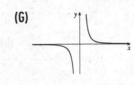

(H)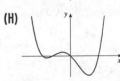

Answer: (G)

2. Given the graph of $y = f'(x)$ below, select a graph which could be that of $y = f(x)$.

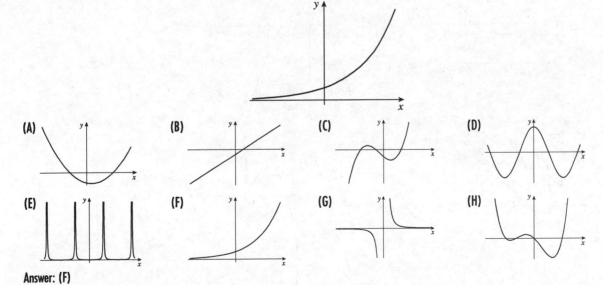

Answer: (F)

3. Given the graph of $y = f'(x)$ below, select a graph which could be that of $y = f(x)$.

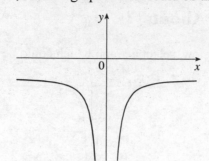

(A)

(B)

(C)

(D)

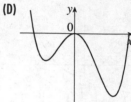

(E)

(F)

(G)

(H)

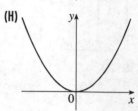

Answer: (E)

4. Given the graph of $y = f'(x)$ below, select a graph which could be that of $y = f(x)$.

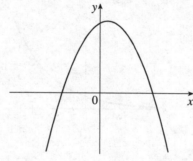

(A)

(B)

(C)

(D)

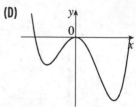

(E)

(F)

(G)

(H)

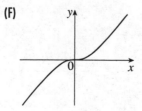

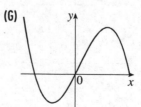

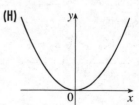

Answer: (G)

5. Given the graph of $y = f'(x)$ below, select a graph which could be that of $y = f(x)$.

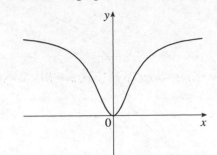

(A) 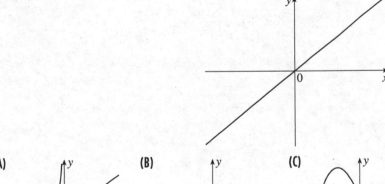 (B) (C) (D)

(E) (F) (G) (H)

Answer: (F)

6. Given the graph of $y = f'(x)$ below, select a graph which could be that of $y = f(x)$.

(A) (B) (C) 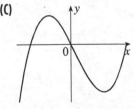 (D)

(E) (F) (G) 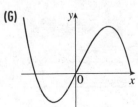 (H)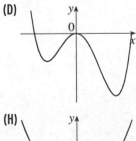

Answer: (H)

7. Given the graph of $y = f(x)$, answer the following questions.

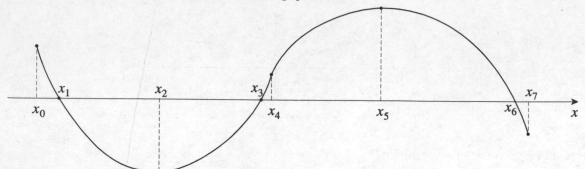

Find all values of x at which

(a) $f'(x) > 0$.

(b) $f'(x) < 0$.

(c) $f'(x) = 0$.

(d) f is increasing.

(e) f is decreasing.

(f) $f''(x) > 0$.

(g) $f''(x) < 0$.

(h) f has an inflection point.

(i) f' is increasing.

(j) f' is decreasing.

Answer:

(a) $f'(x) > 0$ on (x_2, x_5).

(b) $f'(x) < 0$ on (x_0, x_2) and (x_5, x_7).

(c) $f'(x) = 0$ at x_2 and $x = x_5$.

(d) f is increasing on (x_2, x_5).

(e) f is decreasing on (x_0, x_2) and (x_5, x_7).

(f) $f''(x) > 0$ on (x_0, x_4).

(g) $f''(x) < 0$ on (x_4, x_7).

(h) f has an inflection point at $x = x_4$.

(i) f' is increasing on (x_0, x_4).

(j) f' is decreasing on (x_4, x_7).

8. Given the graph of $y = f'(x)$, answer the questions that follow.

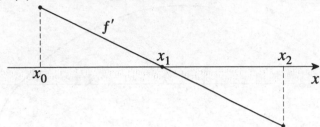

(a) Find all values of x at which

   (i) f is increasing.

   (ii) f is decreasing.

   (iii) $f''(x) > 0$.

   (iv) $f''(x) < 0$.

   (v) $f''(x) = 0$.

   (vi) f' is increasing.

   (vii) f' is decreasing.

   (viii) f has a local maximum.

   (ix) f has a local minimum.

(b) Sketch a graph which could represent $y = f(x)$.

Answer:

(a) (i) f is increasing on $[x_0, x_1]$.

   (ii) f is decreasing on $[x_1, x_2]$.

   (iii) $f''(x) > 0$ nowhere.

   (iv) $f''(x) < 0$ on (x_0, x_2).

   (v) $f''(x) = 0$ nowhere.

   (vi) f' is increasing nowhere.

   (vii) f' is decreasing on $[x_0, x_2]$.

   (viii) f has a local maximum at $x = x_1$.

   (ix) f has no local minimum.

(b)

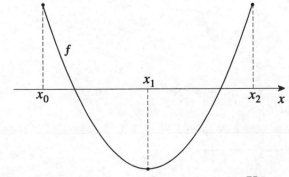

75

9. Given the graph of $y = f'(x)$, answer the questions that follow.

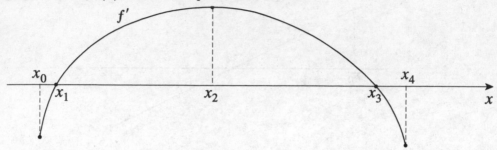

(a) Find all values of x at which

    (i) f is increasing.

    (ii) f is decreasing.

    (iii) $f''(x) > 0$.

    (iv) $f''(x) < 0$.

    (v) f has an inflection point.

    (vii) f' is decreasing.

    (viii) f has a local maximum.

(b) Sketch a graph which could represent $y = f(x)$.

Answer:

(a) (i) f is increasing on $[x_1, x_3]$.

    (ii) f is decreasing on $[x_0, x_1]$ and $[x_3, x_4]$.

    (iii) $f''(x) > 0$ on (x_0, x_2).

    (iv) $f''(x) < 0$ on (x_2, x_4).

    (v) f has an inflection point at $x = x_2$.

    (vi) f' is increasing on $[x_0, x_2]$.

    (vii) f' is decreasing on $[x_2, x_4]$.

    (viii) f has a local maximum at $x = x_3$.

    (ix) f has a local minimum at $x = x_2$.

(b)

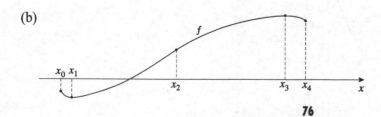

76

10. Given the graph of $y = f'(x)$, answer the questions that follow.

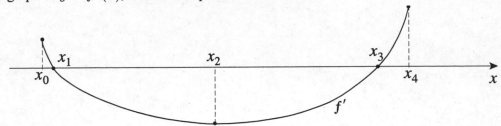

(a) Find all values of x at which

    (i) f is increasing.

    (ii) f is decreasing.

    (iii) $f''(x) > 0$.

    (iv) $f''(x) < 0$.

    (v) f has an inflection point.

    (vi) f' is increasing.

    (vii) f' is decreasing.

    (viii) f has a local maximum.

    (ix) f has a local minimum.

(b) Sketch a graph which could represent $y = f(x)$.

Answer:

(a)   (i) f is increasing on $[x_0, x_1]$ and $[x_3, x_4]$.

    (ii) f is decreasing on $[x_1, x_3]$.

    (iii) $f''(x) > 0$ on (x_2, x_4).

    (iv) $f''(x) < 0$ on (x_0, x_2).

    (v) f has an inflection point at $x = x_2$.

    (vi) f' is increasing on $[x_2, x_4]$.

    (vii) f' is decreasing on $[x_0, x_2]$.

    (viii) f has a local maximum at $x = x_1$.

    (ix) f has a local minimum at $x = x_3$.

(b)

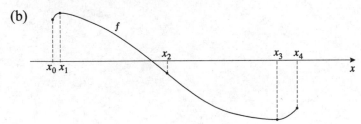

3 Differentiation Rules

3.1 Derivatives of Polynomials and Exponential Functions

1. If $f(x) = 3x - x^2$, find $f'(x)$.

   (A) $3 - 4x^2$ (B) $3x^2 - 4x^3$ (C) $3 - 4x$ (D) $6 - 4x^2$

   (E) $6 - 4x$ (F) $3 - x$ (G) $3x - x^2$ (H) $3 - 2x$

   Answer: (H)

2. Find the derivative of $f(x) = \sqrt{9x}$.

   (A) $\dfrac{3}{2\sqrt{x}}$ (B) $-\dfrac{3}{2\sqrt{x}}$ (C) $\dfrac{9}{2\sqrt{x}}$ (D) $-\dfrac{9}{2\sqrt{x}}$

   (E) $\dfrac{3}{\sqrt{x}}$ (F) $-3\sqrt{x}$ (G) $3\sqrt{x}$ (H) None of the above

   Answer: (A)

3. Find the derivative of $f(t) = \dfrac{t^3 + 3}{t}$.

   (A) $\dfrac{2t^2 + 3}{t^2}$ (B) $\dfrac{2t^2 - 3}{t^2}$ (C) $3t^2$ (D) $\dfrac{2t^3 - 3}{t^2}$

   (E) $3t^2 + 3$ (F) $\dfrac{2t^3 + 3}{t^2}$ (G) $\dfrac{2t^3 + 3}{t}$ (H) None of the above

   Answer: (D)

4. Find the derivative of $f(t) = t^2\sqrt{t} - \dfrac{1}{\sqrt[3]{t}}$.

   (A) $1 + \frac{1}{3}t^{-4/3}$ (B) $\frac{5}{2}t^{3/2} + \frac{1}{3}t^{-4/3}$ (C) $1 - \frac{1}{3}t^{-4/3}$ (D) $\frac{5}{2}t^{3/2} - \frac{1}{3}t^{-4/3}$

   (E) $1 + \frac{1}{3}t^{2/3}$ (F) $\frac{5}{2}t^{3/2} - \frac{1}{3}t^{2/3}$ (G) $1 - \frac{1}{3}t^{2/3}$ (H) None of the above

   Answer: (B)

5. If $f(x) = -\dfrac{1}{x^2}$, find $f'(1)$.

   (A) $-\frac{1}{3}$ (B) -2 (C) $\frac{1}{3}$ (D) $-\frac{1}{4}$

   (E) $\frac{1}{2}$ (F) $-\frac{1}{2}$ (G) 2 (H) $\frac{1}{4}$

   Answer: (G)

6. If $f(x) = \sqrt{3x}$, find $f'(3)$.

   (A) $-\dfrac{3}{2\sqrt{3}}$ (B) $\frac{1}{2}$ (C) $\dfrac{3}{2\sqrt{3}}$ (D) $-\frac{1}{4}$

   (E) $-\frac{1}{6}$ (F) $\frac{1}{4}$ (G) $-\frac{1}{2}$ (H) $\frac{1}{6}$

   Answer: (B)

7. If $f(x) = \sqrt[5]{x} + x^{-1.8}$, find $f'(1)$.

(A) $\frac{1}{5}$ (B) $\frac{2}{5}$ (C) $-\frac{8}{5}$ (D) $-\frac{2}{5}$

(E) $-\frac{1}{5}$ (F) $\frac{4}{5}$ (G) $\frac{8}{5}$ (H) $-\frac{4}{5}$

Answer: (C)

8. Find the slope of the tangent line to the curve $y = 3x^2 - 2x$ at the point $(1, 2)$.

(A) 10   (B) 8   (C) 6   (D) 4

(E) 3   (F) 5   (G) 1   (H) 2

Answer: (D)

9. Find the y-intercept of the tangent line to the curve $y = x^3$ at the point $(1, 1)$.

(A) -4 (B) 4   (C) -16 (D) 2

(E) -8 (F) 8   (G) -2 (H) 16

Answer: (G)

10. The curve $y = x^3 + x^2 - x$ has two horizontal tangents. Find the distance between these two horizontal lines.

(A) $\frac{11}{9}$ (B) $\frac{22}{27}$ (C) $\frac{32}{27}$ (D) $\frac{5}{3}$

(E) $\frac{14}{9}$ (F) $\frac{4}{3}$ (G) $\frac{13}{9}$ (H) $\frac{7}{3}$

Answer: (C)

11. Passing through the origin $(0, 0)$, there are two lines tangent to the curve $y = x^2 + 1$, one with negative slope, the other with positive slope. Find the value of the positive slope.

(A) $\frac{1}{8}$ (B) $\frac{1}{2}$ (C) $\frac{1}{4}$ (D) $\frac{1}{3}$

(E) 4   (F) 1   (G) 3   (H) 2

Answer: (H)

12. At how many different values of x does the curve $y = x^3 - 2x$ have a tangent line parallel to the line $y = x$?

(A) 0   (B) 1   (C) 2   (D) 3

(E) 4   (F) 5   (G) 6   (H) 7

Answer: (C)

13. Given $f(3) = 5$, $f'(3) = 1.1$, $g(3) = -4$ and $g'(3) = -1.3$, find the value of $(2f + g)'(3)$.

(A) 1.8   (B) 0.4   (C) -0.9 (D) -1.8

(E) 0.9   (F) -0.4 (G) 0.77   (H) -0.77

Answer: (E)

14. Given $f(3) = 5$, $f'(3) = 1.1$, $g(3) = -4$ and $g'(3) = 0.7$, find the value of $(f - 2g)'(3)$.

(A) 1.8   (B) 0.3   (C) -0.9 (D) -1.8

(E) 0.9   (F) -0.3 (G) 3.5   (H) -3.5

Answer: (F)

15. If $f(x) = 1/x^2$, find $f''(1)$.

   (A) 1   (B) 4   (C) 2   (D) 6

   (E) 3   (F) 0   (G) 5   (H) 8

   Answer: (D)

16. If $f(x) = x^3$, find $f''(1)$.

   (A) 8   (B) 4   (C) 2   (D) 3

   (E) 0   (F) 6   (G) 5   (H) 1

   Answer: (F)

17. If $f(x) = x^5$, find $f^{(5)}(3)$.

   (A) 90   (B) 360   (C) 30   (D) 60

   (E) 20   (F) 72   (G) 120   (H) 240

   Answer: (G)

18. If $f(x) = 2e^x - 3x^e + \sqrt{e}$, find $f'(x)$.

   (A) $2xe^{x-1} - 3xe^{e-1}$ (B) $2e^x - 3x^e + \sqrt{e}$

   (C) $2xe^{x-1} - 3x^{e-1} + \frac{1}{2}e^{-1/2}$ (D) $2e^x - 3ex^{e-1}$

   (E) $e^x - 3ex^{e-1}$ (F) $2e^x - 3x^{e-1}$

   (G) $2e^x - 3x^e$ (H) $2e^x - ex^{e-1}$

   Answer: (D)

19. Find $\dfrac{dy}{dx}$.

   (a) $y = 7^3 + x^3$ (c) $y = \left(x^3 - 3\sqrt[3]{x}\right)/x$

   (b) $y = x^{50} + 25x - 1$ (d) $y = 2e^x + x^e$

   Answer:

   (a) $\dfrac{dy}{dx} = 3x^2$ (b) $\dfrac{dy}{dx} = 50x^{49} + 25$ (c) $\dfrac{dy}{dx} = 2x + 2x^{-5/3}$ (d) $\dfrac{dy}{dx} = 2e^x + ex^{e-1}$

20. Differentiate the following functions:

   (a) $f(x) = \dfrac{3}{x^2} + x^2$ (c) $f(s) = e^\pi$

   (b) $f(t) = \dfrac{4\pi}{3}t^3$ (d) $f(r) = (4r - 3)^2$

   Answer:

   (a) $f'(x) = -\dfrac{6}{x^3} + 2x$ (b) $f'(t) = 4\pi t^2$ (c) $f'(s) = 0$ (d) $f'(r) = 32r - 24$

21. Differentiate the following functions:

   (a) $f(t) = 3e^t + 2$ (c) $f(s) = \dfrac{s^2 + 2s + 1}{s}$

   (b) $f(x) = \sqrt[3]{x}\,(x + 2)$ (d) $f(x) = (x + 1/x)(x - 1/x)$

   Answer:

   (a) $f'(t) = 3e^t$ (b) $f'(x) = \frac{4}{3}x^{1/3} + \frac{2}{3}x^{-2/3}$ (c) $f'(s) = 1 - 1/s^2$ (d) $f'(x) = 2x + 2/x^3$

22. Given $f(x) = e^x - x^3$, find $f'(x)$, $f''(x)$ and $f^{(3)}(x)$.

Answer: $f'(x) = e^x - 3x^2$, $f''(x) = e^x - 6x$, $f^{(3)}(x) = e^x - 6$

23. Find an equation of the tangent line to $y = \dfrac{1}{x}$ at $\left(4, \frac{1}{4}\right)$.

Answer: $\dfrac{dy}{dx} = \dfrac{-1}{x^2}$. At $\left(4, \dfrac{1}{4}\right)$, $\dfrac{dy}{dx} = -\dfrac{1}{16}$. The point-slope equation of the tangent line is $y - \frac{1}{4} = -\frac{1}{16}(x - 4)$, or $y = -\frac{1}{16}x + \frac{1}{2}$.

24. There are two tangent lines to the curve $y = 4x - x^2$ that pass through $(2, 5)$. Find an equation for each of the lines.

Answer: $\dfrac{dy}{dx} = 4 - 2x$. We seek points (x, y) on the curve $y = 4x - x^2$ where $\dfrac{dy}{dx} = \dfrac{y - 5}{x - 2}$. When

$$4 - 2x = \frac{y - 5}{x - 2} = \frac{4x - x^2 - 5}{x - 2}. \text{ So}$$

$$(4 - 2x)(x - 2) = 4x - x^2 - 5$$
$$\implies -2x^2 + 8x - 8 = -x^2 + 4x - 5$$
$$\implies 0 = x^2 - 4x + 3$$
$$\implies 0 = (x - 1)(x - 3)$$
$$\implies x = 1 \text{ or } x = 3$$

So the lines are $y - 5 = x - 2$ or $y = x + 3$, and $y - 5 = 3(x - 2)$ or $y = 3x - 1$.

25. There are two lines through the point $(2, -3)$ that are tangent to the parabola $y = x^2 + x$. Find the x-coordinates of the points where these lines touch the parabola.

Answer: -1 and 5

26. Given $f(x) = \dfrac{x - 4}{x - 1}$, find an equation of the line(s) tangent to the graph of $y = f(x)$ and parallel to $y - 3x + 7 = 0$.

Answer: $f(x) = \dfrac{x - 4}{x - 1}$, so $f'(x) = \dfrac{3}{(x - 1)^2}$. The tangent lines must have slope 3. Combining this information, $\dfrac{3}{(x - 1)^2} = 3 \implies (x - 1)^2 = 1 \implies x = 0$ or $x = 2$. The tangent lines are given by $y = 3x + 4$ and $y = 3x - 8$.

27. Given $f(x) = \sqrt{x}$:

(a) Find an equation of the tangent line to the graph of $y = f(x)$ at

(i) $x = 0$.

(ii) $x = 4$.

(iii) $x = 9$.

(b) Sketch a graph of $y = f(x)$ and the tangent lines you found in parts (i), (ii) and (iii) on one set of coordinate axes.

Answer:

(a) $f'(x) = \frac{1}{2}x^{-1/2}$

   (i) The slope of the tangent is undefined. The tangent line is the vertical line $y = 0$.

   (ii) The slope of the tangent is $\frac{1}{4}$. An equation of the tangent line is $(y - 2) = \frac{1}{4}(x - 4)$ or $y = \frac{1}{4}x + 1$.

   (iii) The slope of the tangent is $\frac{1}{6}$. An equation of the tangent line is $(y - 3) = \frac{1}{6}(x - 9)$ or $y = \frac{1}{6}x + \frac{3}{2}$.

(b)

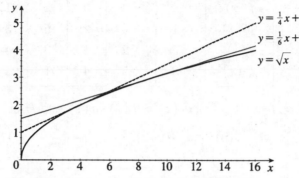

28. The position function for a particle is $s(t) = -16t^2 + 48t + 100$, where s is measured in feet and t is measured in seconds.

  (a) Find the velocity at $t = 2$.

  (b) When does the velocity equal zero?

Answer: (a) -16 ft/s   (b) 1.5 s

29. The velocity function for a particle is $v(t) = -8t^{3/2} + 48t + 100$, where v is measured in feet per second and t is measured in seconds. Find the acceleration at $t = 4$.

Answer: 24 ft/s^2

30. Show that the curve $y = x^5 + 2x^3 + 4x$ has no tangent line with slope 3.

Answer: $\dfrac{dy}{dx} = 5x^4 + 6x^2 + 4 \geq 4 > 3$

31. If $f(x) = e^x + x^e + e^\pi$, what are $f'(x)$ and $f''(x)$?

Answer: $f'(x) = e^x + ex^{e-1}$, $f''(x) = e^x + e(e-1)x^{e-2}$

32. Let $f(x) = \frac{4}{3}x^3 + 11x^2 + 10x + 4$. For what value of x is $f'(x) = 3$?

Answer: $f'(x) = 4x^2 + 22x + 10 = 3 \quad \Leftrightarrow \quad 4x^2 + 22x + 7 = 0 \quad \Rightarrow \quad x = \dfrac{-11 \pm \sqrt{93}}{4}$

33. Find an equation of the line tangent to the curve $y = \frac{4}{3}x^3 + 11x^2 + 10x + 4$ at $x = -3$.

Answer: $f'(x) = 4x^2 + 22x + 10$. $f'(-3) = -20$ and $f(-3) = 33$, so an equation is $y - 33 = -20[x - (-3)]$ or $y = -20x - 27$.

34. Suppose that $g(x)$ is a differentiable function. Find $f'(x)$ for each of the following, in terms of $g(x)$ and $g'(x)$.

  (a) $f(x) = x^2 g(x)$ (b) $f(x) = \dfrac{3g(x)}{e^x}$ (c) $f(x) = \sqrt{x} - e^x g(x)$

Answer:

(a) $f'(x) = 2xg(x) + x^2 g'(x)$

(b) $f'(x) = \dfrac{e^x \cdot 3g'(x) - 3g(x)e^x}{(e^x)^2} = 3e^{-x}[g'(x) - g(x)]$

(c) $f'(x) = \frac{1}{2}x^{-1/2} - [e^x g(x) + e^x g'(x)] = \dfrac{1}{2\sqrt{x}} - e^x[g(x) + g'(x)]$

35. Below is a table containing information about the differentiable fucntions f and g.

x	-2	-1	0	1	2
$f(x)$	4	3	5	2	1
$f'(x)$	1	4	2	5	3
$g(x)$	5	2	1	3	4
$g'(x)$	3	5	4	1	2

Suppose also that $F(x) = f(x) + g(x)$, $G(x) = f(x) \cdot g(x)$, and $H(x) = \dfrac{g(x)}{f(x)}$.

(a) Find $F'(0)$.　　　　　　(b) Find $G'(-2)$.　　　　　　(c) Find $H'(2)$.

Answer:

(a) $F'(0) = f'(0) + g'(0) = 2 + 4 = 6$

(b) $G'(-2) = f'(-2) \cdot g(-2) + g'(-2) \cdot f(-2) = 1 \cdot 5 + 3 \cdot 4 = 17$

(c) $H'(2) = \dfrac{f(2) \cdot g'(2) - g(2) \cdot f'(2)}{[f(2)]^2} = \dfrac{1 \cdot 2 - 4 \cdot 3}{1^2} = -10$

36. Given $f(x) = x^4 e^x$, find the value(s) of x where $f''(x) = 0$.

Answer: $f(x) = x^4 e^x \Rightarrow f'(x) = 4x^3 e^x + x^4 e^x \Rightarrow f''(x) = 12x^2 e^x + 8x^3 e^x + 4x^3 e^x + x^4 e^x = x^2 e^x (x^2 + 8x + 12) = x^2(x+2)(x+6)$. So $f''(x) = 0$ for $x = 0, -2$, or 6.

3.2　The Product and Quotient Rules

1. Find the derivative of $f(x) = e^x(x^2 + 2)$.

(A) $2xe^x$　　　　(B) $e^x(2x + 2)$　　　　(C) $2x^2 e^{x-1}$　　　　(D) $e^x(x^2 + 2x)$

(E) $x^2 e^{x-1}$　　　　(F) $e^x(x^2 + 2x + 2)$　　　(G) $e^x(2x + 2)$　　　(H) None of the above

Answer: (F)

2. Find the derivative of $f(x) = (x - \sqrt{x})(x + \sqrt{x})$.

(A) $\left(1 - \dfrac{1}{\sqrt{x}}\right)\left(1 + \dfrac{1}{\sqrt{x}}\right)$　　　　　　(B) $2x - 1$

(C) $\left(1 - \dfrac{1}{2\sqrt{x}}\right)\left(1 + \dfrac{1}{2\sqrt{x}}\right)$　　　　　　(D) $2x + 1$

(E) $\left(1 - \dfrac{1}{2\sqrt{x}}\right)\left(1 + \dfrac{1}{\sqrt{x}}\right)$　　　　　　(F) $x - 1$

(G) $\left(1 - \dfrac{1}{\sqrt{x}}\right)\left(1 + \dfrac{1}{2\sqrt{x}}\right)$　　　　　　(H) None of the above

Answer: (B)

3. Find the derivative of $f(x) = \dfrac{x}{x^2 + 3}$.

(A) $\dfrac{1}{2x + 3}$

(B) $\dfrac{-3 + x^2}{(x^2 + 3)^2}$

(C) $\dfrac{3 - x^2}{(x^2 + 3)^2}$

(D) $\dfrac{3 - x^2}{(x^2 + 3)}$

(E) $\dfrac{3}{(x^2 + 3)^2}$

(F) $\dfrac{1}{2x}$

(G) $\dfrac{3 - x}{(x^2 + 3)^2}$

(H) None of the above

Answer: (C)

4. Find the slope of the tangent line to the curve $y = \dfrac{1}{1 + 2x}$ at the point $\left(1, \frac{1}{3}\right)$.

(A) $-\frac{1}{4}$

(B) 2

(C) -1

(D) $\frac{1}{4}$

(E) $-\frac{2}{9}$

(F) -2

(G) 1

(H) $\frac{1}{2}$

Answer: (E)

5. If $f(x) = (x + 1)^2 (x + 2)$, find $f'(0)$.

(A) 6

(B) 9

(C) 4

(D) 12

(E) 8

(F) 16

(G) 5

(H) 20

Answer: (G)

6. If $f(x) = \dfrac{x^3}{(x + 2)^2}$, find $f'(-1)$.

(A) 8

(B) 5

(C) 10

(D) 4

(E) 20

(F) 9

(G) 12

(H) 16

Answer: (B)

7. If $f(x) = \dfrac{\sqrt{x} - 1}{\sqrt{x} + 1}$, find the value of $f'(4)$.

(A) $\frac{1}{9}$

(B) $\frac{1}{12}$

(C) $\frac{1}{15}$

(D) $\frac{1}{18}$

(E) $\frac{1}{21}$

(F) $\frac{1}{24}$

(G) $\frac{1}{27}$

(H) $\frac{1}{30}$

Answer: (D)

8. If $f(x) = 3xe^x$, find $f'(0)$.

(A) 0

(B) 1

(C) 2

(D) 3

(E) 4

(F) 5

(G) 6

(H) 7

Answer: (D)

9. If $f(x) = \dfrac{6x}{e^x + 1}$, find $f'(0)$.

(A) -3

(B) -2

(C) -1

(D) 0

(E) 1

(F) 2

(G) 3

(H) 4

Answer: (G)

10. Given $f(3) = 5$, $f'(3) = 1.1$, $g(3) = -4$ and $g'(3) = 0.7$, find the value of $(f \cdot g)'(3)$.

(A) 1.8

(B) 0.4

(C) -0.9

(D) -1.8

(E) 0.9

(F) -0.4

(G) 0.77

(H) -0.77

Answer: (C)

11. Given $f(3) = 5$, $f'(3) = 1.1$, $g(3) = -4$ and $g'(3) = 0.7$, find the value of $(f/g)'(3)$.

(A) 0.025 (B) 0.49375 (C) -0.49375 (D) -0.025

(E) 1.975 (F) -1.975 (G) 0.5625 (H) -0.5625

Answer: (C)

12. If $y = \tan x$, find $f''\left(\frac{\pi}{4}\right)$.

(A) -2 (B) 4 (C) $2\sqrt{3}$ (D) -6

(E) -8 (F) -4 (G) $\sqrt{2}$ (H) $2\sqrt{2}$

Answer: (B)

13. If $f(x) = \dfrac{e^x}{x}$, find $f''(x)$.

(A) $\dfrac{e^x(x+4)}{x^4}$ (B) $\dfrac{e^x(x^2-1)}{x^4}$ (C) $\dfrac{e^x(x^2+x)}{x^4}$ (D) $\dfrac{e^x(x^2+3)}{x^4}$

(E) $\dfrac{e^x(x-2)}{x^3}$ (F) $\dfrac{e^x(x^2+5x)}{x^3}$ (G) $\dfrac{e^x(x^2-2x+2)}{x^3}$ (H) $\dfrac{e^x(x^3-4x^2+3)}{x^3}$

Answer: (G)

14. If $f(x) = \dfrac{x}{x-1}$, find a formula for $f^{(n)}(x)$.

(A) $f^{(n)} = (-1)^n\, n!\, (x-1)^{-(n+1)}$ (B) $f^{(n)} = n!\, (x-1)^{-(n+1)}$

(C) $f^{(n)} = (-1)^n\, n!\, (x-1)^{-n}$ (D) $f^{(n)} = (-1)^n\, n!\, (x-1)^{-(n-1)}$

(E) $f^{(n)} = (-1)^{n+1}\, n!\, (x-1)^{-(n+1)}$ (F) $f^{(n)} = (-1)^n\, n!\, (x-1)^{n+1}$

(G) $f^{(n)} = n!\, (x-1)^{-n+1}$ (H) $f^{(n)} = (-1)^n\, n!\, (x+1)^{-(n+1)}$

Answer: (A)

15. Find an equation of the tangent line to the curve $y = \dfrac{1-x}{1+x}$ at $(-2,-3)$.

(A) $x + y + 5 = 0$ (B) $x + 2y + 8 = 0$

(C) $x + 3y + 11 = 0$ (D) $2x + y + 7 = 0$

(E) $3x + y + 9 = 0$ (F) $2x + 3y + 13 = 0$

(G) $2x - 3y - 5 = 0$ (H) $x - 3y - 7 = 0$

Answer: (D)

Items 16–22 refer to the following table:

x	$f(x)$	$f'(x)$	$g(x)$	$g'(x)$
-3	7	-7	-6	7
-2	1	-5	0	5
-1	-3	-3	4	3
0	-5	-1	6	1
1	-5	1	6	-1
2	-3	3	4	-3
3	1	5	0	5

16. Find $\dfrac{d}{dx}\left(f(x) \cdot g(x)\right)$ when $x = -1$.

   (A) -25 (B) -23 (C) -21 (D) -19

   (E) -17 (F) -15 (G) -13 (H) -11

   Answer: (C)

17. Find $\dfrac{d}{dx}\left(\dfrac{f(x)}{g(x)}\right)$ when $x = 0$.

   (A) $\frac{9}{36}$ (B) $\frac{7}{36}$ (C) $\frac{5}{36}$ (D) $\frac{3}{36}$

   (E) $\frac{1}{36}$ (F) $-\frac{1}{36}$ (G) $-\frac{3}{36}$ (H) $-\frac{5}{36}$

   Answer: (F)

18. Find $\dfrac{d}{dx}\left(\dfrac{g(x)}{f(x)}\right)$ when $x = -2$.

   (A) 0   (B) 1   (C) 2   (D) 3

   (E) 4   (F) 5   (G) 6   (H) 7

   Answer: (F)

19. Find $\dfrac{d}{dx}\left(f^3(x)\right)$ when $x = -2$.

   (A) -7 (B) -24 (C) -12 (D) 1

   (E) 7   (F) -15 (G) -1 (H) 20

   Answer: (F)

20. Find $\dfrac{d}{dx}\left(g^2(x)\right)$ when $x = 1$.

   (A) -7 (B) -24 (C) -12 (D) 1

   (E) 7   (F) -15 (G) -1 (H) 20

   Answer: (C)

21. Find $\dfrac{d}{dx}\left(x^2 f(x)\right)$ when $x = -2$.

   (A) -7 (B) -24 (C) -12 (D) 1

   (E) 7   (F) -15 (G) -1 (H) 20

   Answer: (B)

22. Find $\dfrac{d}{dx}\left(\dfrac{2 \cdot g(x)}{x^2+1}\right)$ when $x = 1$.

(A) -7 (B) -24 (C) -12 (D) 1

(E) 7 (F) -15 (G) -1 (H) 20

Answer: (A)

23. Each of the following is a derivative of a function obtained by using the Product Rule. Determine the original function:

(a) $f'(x) = 2xe^x + x^2 e^x$

(b) $g'(x) = -6x\left(5x^3 - 2x\right) + \left(1 - 3x^2\right)\left(15x^2 - 2\right)$

Answer:

(a) $f(x) = x^2 e^x + C$

(b) $g(x) = \left(1 - 3x^2\right)\left(5x^3 - 2x\right) + C$

24. Each of the following is a derivative of a function obtained by using the Quotient Rule. Determine the original function:

(a) $f'(x) = \dfrac{(x+3) - (x+1)}{(x+3)^2}$

(b) $g'(x) = \dfrac{3x^2 e^x - x^3 e^x}{e^{2x}}$

(c) $h'(x) = \dfrac{x^3 e^x - 3x^2 e^x}{x^6}$

Answer: (a) $f(x) = \dfrac{x+1}{x+3} + C$ (b) $g(x) = \dfrac{x^3}{e^x} + C$ (c) $h(x) = \dfrac{e^x}{x^3} + C$

25. Differentiate the following functions:

(a) $f(x) = x^3 e^x$

(b) $g(x) = \dfrac{x}{x+1}$

(c) $h(x) = \dfrac{e^x}{e^x + 1}$

(d) $\phi(x) = \left(1 - \dfrac{1}{x}\right)^2$

Answer:

(a) $f'(x) = e^x\left(3x^2 + x^3\right)$ (b) $g'(x) = \dfrac{1}{(x+1)^2}$ (c) $h'(x) = \dfrac{e^x}{(e^x + 1)^2}$ (d) $\phi'(x) = \dfrac{2}{x^2} - \dfrac{2}{x^3}$

26. Find the derivative of the following function:

(a) $f(x) = \dfrac{\sqrt[3]{x} + 2}{\sqrt[3]{x} - 2}$

(b) $f(x) = \dfrac{1}{x^2 + 1}$

(c) $f(r) = (1 + \sqrt{r})(1 - \sqrt{r})$

(d) $f(t) = \dfrac{te^t}{t^3 + t}$

Answer:

(a) $f'(x) = \left(\dfrac{-4}{3x^{2/3}\left(\sqrt[3]{x} - 2\right)^2}\right)$ (b) $f'(x) = \dfrac{-2x}{(x^2 + 1)^2}$ (c) $f'(r) = -1$ (d) $f'(t) = \dfrac{e^t (t - 1)^2}{(t^2 + 1)^2}$

27. The quantity q of Zeng Athletic Shoes which are sold depends on the selling price p. [That is, $q = f(p)$.]

    (a) If you know that $f(150) = 14{,}000$, what can you say about the sale of these shoes?

    (b) If you know that $f'(150) = -100$, what does that tell you about the sale of these shoes?

    (c) The total revenue, R, earned through the sale of Zeng shoes is given by $R = p \cdot q$. Find $\dfrac{dR}{dp}$ when $p = 150$.

    (d) Suppose that the shoes are currently priced at \$150. What effect will lowering the price likely have on the total revenue? Justify your answer.

Answer:

    (a) 14,000 pairs of shoes would be sold if the price of the shoes were \$150 per pair.

    (b) With the price at \$150 per pair, a dollar increase in price will decrease the number of pairs sold by 100.

    (c) $\dfrac{dR}{dp} = f(p) + pf'(p) = f(150) + 150f'(150) = -1{,}000$

    (d) Since $\dfrac{dR}{dp}$ is negative, lowering the price would increase the total revenue.

28. f and g are functions whose graphs are given below. Let $u(x) = f(x) \cdot g(x)$ and $v(x) = \dfrac{f(x)}{g(x)}$.

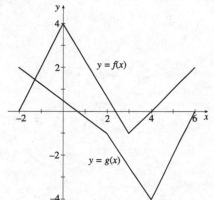

    (a) Find $u'(1)$.

    (b) Find $u'(-1)$.

    (c) Find $v'(-1)$.

Answer:

    (a) $u'(1) = f'(1)g(1) + f(1) \cdot g'(1) = \left(-\frac{5}{3}\right)\left(-\frac{1}{4}\right) + \left(\frac{7}{3}\right)\left(-\frac{3}{4}\right) = -\frac{4}{3}$

    (b) $u'(-1) = f'(-1)g(-1) + f(-1)g'(-1) = 2 \cdot \frac{5}{4} + 2 \cdot \left(-\frac{3}{4}\right) = 1$

    (c) $v'(-1) = \dfrac{f'(-1)g(-1) - f(-1) \cdot g'(-1)}{g(-1)^2} = \dfrac{2 \cdot \frac{5}{4} - 2 \cdot \left(-\frac{3}{4}\right)}{\left(\frac{5}{4}\right)^2} = \dfrac{64}{25}$

29. If $f(x) = e^x g(x)$, and if $g(0) = 3$ and $g'(0) = -2$, find $f'(0)$.

    Answer: $f'(x) = e^x g'(x) + e^x g(x)$, so $f'(0) = e^0 g'(0) + e^0 g(0) = 1(-2) + 1(3) = -2 + 3 = 1$.

30. Find an equation of the tangent line to the curve $y = e^x (x + 1)$ at $x = 0$.

    Answer: $y = 2x + 1$

31. Find an equation of the normal line to the curve $y = e^x (x + 1)$ at $x = 0$.

    Answer: $y = -\frac{1}{2}x + 1$

32. Find the point(s) where the tangent to the curve $y = \dfrac{x}{x^2 + 4}$ has zero slope.

    Answer: $\left(2, \frac{1}{4}\right)$, $\left(-2, -\frac{1}{4}\right)$

33. Find the x-coordinate(s) of the point(s) where the tangent to the curve $y = \left(9 - \dfrac{1}{x^2}\right)^2$ has zero slope.

    Answer: $x = \pm\frac{1}{3}$

34. (a) Differentiate e^{2x} by differentiating $e^x \cdot e^x$.

    (b) Differentiate e^{3x} by differentiating $e^x e^{2x}$ and using the result of part (a).

    (c) Continue as above to find $\dfrac{d}{dx} e^{4x}$ and $\dfrac{d}{dx} e^{5x}$ using the results from above.

    (d) Based upon your answers to parts (a)–(c), make a conjecture about $\dfrac{d}{dx} e^{nx}$.

    Answer:

    (a) $\dfrac{d}{dx} e^{2x} = e^x \cdot e^x + e^x \cdot e^x = 2e^{2x}$

    (b) $\dfrac{d}{dx} e^{3x} = e^x \cdot \dfrac{d}{dx} e^{2x} + e^x \cdot e^{2x} = e^x \cdot 2e^{2x} + e^x \cdot e^{2x} = 3e^{3x}$

    (c) $\dfrac{d}{dx} e^{4x} = e^x \cdot \dfrac{d}{dx} e^{3x} + e^x \cdot e^{3x} = e^x \cdot 3e^{3x} + e^x \cdot e^{3x} = 4e^{4x}$, $\dfrac{d}{dx} e^{5x} = e^x \cdot \dfrac{d}{dx} e^{4x} + e^x \cdot e^{4x} =$
    $e^x \cdot 4e^{4x} + e^x \cdot e^{4x} = 5e^{5x}$

    (d) $\dfrac{d}{dx} e^{nx} = ne^{nx}$

35. Given $f(x) = e^{2x}$:

    (a) Find $f'(x)$ by letting $f(x) = e^x \cdot e^x$.

    (b) Use the result from part (a) to find $f''(x)$.

    (c) Continue to find $f^{(3)}(x)$ and $f^{(4)}(x)$.

    (d) Based upon your answers to parts (a)–(c), make a conjecture for $f^{(n)}(x)$.

    Answer:

    (a) $f'(x) = e^x \cdot e^x + e^x \cdot e^x = 2e^{2x}$ (b) $f''(x) = \dfrac{d}{dx} 2e^{2x} = 2\dfrac{d}{dx} e^{2x} = 2 \cdot 2e^{2x} = 4e^{2x}$

    (c) $f^{(3)}(x) = \dfrac{d}{dx} 4e^{2x} = 8e^{2x}$, $f^{(4)}(x) = \dfrac{d}{dx} 8e^{2x} = 16e^{2x}$ (d) $f^{(n)}(x) = 2^n e^{2x}$

3.3 | Rates of Change in the Natural and Social Sciences

1. A stone is thrown into a pond, creating a circular wave whose radius increases at the rate of 1 foot per second. In square feet per second, how fast is the area of the circular ripple increasing 3 seconds after the stone hits the water?
   (A) π (B) 2π (C) $\frac{\pi}{3}$ (D) 6π
   (E) 3π (F) $\frac{\pi}{6}$ (G) $\frac{\pi}{12}$ (H) $\frac{\pi}{2}$
   Answer: (D)

2. The mass of a rod varies in such a way that the mass of a piece x meters long, measured from the left end, is x^2 kilograms. Find the density in kg/m at the point 2 meters from the left end.
   (A) 1   (B) 5   (C) 3   (D) 4
   (E) 7   (F) 6   (G) 2   (H) 8
   Answer: (D)

3. The population of a bacteria colony after t hours is $70 + 5t + 2t^2$. Find the growth rate when $t = 3$.
   (A) 18   (B) 9   (C) 7   (D) 19
   (E) 21   (F) 13   (G) 17   (H) 11
   Answer: (G)

4. A particle moves along a straight line with equation of motion $s = t^2 - 2t$. Find the instantaneous velocity of the particle at time $t = 1$.
   (A) 1   (B) 4   (C) 0   (D) 3
   (E) 8   (F) 6   (G) 5   (H) 2
   Answer: (C)

5. A particle moves along a straight line with equation of motion $s = t^2 - 3t + 2$. Find the value of t at which the particle reverses its direction.
   (A) $\frac{1}{2}$ (B) 0   (C) $\frac{3}{2}$ (D) $\frac{2}{3}$
   (E) 1   (F) 2   (G) $\frac{3}{4}$ (H) $\frac{4}{3}$
   Answer: (C)

6. A particle moves along a straight line with equation of motion $s = t^3 + 2t$. Find the smallest value of its velocity (for $t \geq 0$).
   (A) $\frac{1}{2}$ (B) -2 (C) $\frac{1}{3}$ (D) $-\frac{1}{2}$
   (E) -3 (F) 2   (G) 3   (H) $-\frac{1}{3}$
   Answer: (F)

7. A particle moves along a straight line with equation of motion $s = t^3 - t^2$. Find the value of t at which the acceleration is equal to zero.

(A) $-\frac{2}{3}$ (B) $-\frac{1}{3}$ (C) $\frac{2}{3}$ (D) $\frac{1}{3}$

(E) $-\frac{1}{2}$ (F) $\frac{1}{2}$ (G) $-\frac{3}{2}$ (H) $\frac{3}{2}$

Answer: (D)

8. The cost function of manufacturing x meters of a fabric is $C(x) = 25{,}000 + 3x - 0.002x^2 + 0.000001x^3$. Find $C'(5000)$.

(A) 58   (B) 580   (C) 5.8   (D) 5800

(E) 60   (F) 600   (G) 6   (H) 6000

Answer: (A)

9. Suppose that a baseball is tossed straight upward and that its height (in feet) as a function of time (in seconds) is given by the formula $h(t) = 128t - 16t^2$.

(a) Find the instantaneous velocity and acceleration of the baseball at time t.

(b) What is the maximum height attained by the ball?

(c) What is the average velocity of the ball during the time interval from $t = 1$ to $t = 4$?

(d) How long does it take before the ball lands?

(e) At what time is the height of the ball 112 feet?

Answer:

(a) $v(t) = h'(t) = 128 - 32t$ ft/s
$a(t) = v'(t) = -32$ ft/s/s

(b) The maximum height occurs when $v(t) = 0$ at $t = 4$. $h(4) = 256$ feet.

(c) Average velocity $= \dfrac{h(4) - h(1)}{4 - 1} = \dfrac{256 - 112}{3} = 48$ ft/s

(d) The ball lands when $t > 0$ and $h(t) = 0$. $h(t) = 0 \Leftrightarrow 128t - 16t^2 = 0 \Leftrightarrow t = 0$ or $t = 8$. The ball strikes the ground after 8 seconds.

(e) $h(t) = 112 \Leftrightarrow 128t - 16t^2 = 112 \Leftrightarrow 0 = 16t^2 - 128t + 112 \Leftrightarrow t = 1$ or $t = 7$. The ball is at a height of 112 feet at times 1 second and 7 seconds.

10. The position of a particle is given by the function $s(t) = 2t^3 - 9t^2 + 12t$, where t is measured in seconds and s in meters.

(a) Find the velocity at time t.

(b) When is the particle at rest?

(c) When is the particle moving in the positive direction?

(d) Draw a diagram to represent the motion of the particle.

(e) Find the total distance traveled by the particle during the time interval $[1, 3]$.

Answer:

(a) $v(t) = 6t^2 - 18t + 12$ (b) $t = 1, 2$ (c) $0 < t < 1$ or $t > 2$

(d)

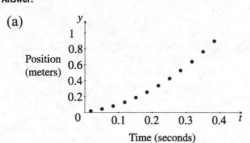

(e) 6 m

11. The cost function of manufacturing x meters of a fabric is $C(x) = 20{,}000 + 5x - 0.004x^2 + 0.000003x^3$.

    (a) Find the marginal cost function.

    (b) Find $C'(2000)$.

    Answer: (a) $C'(x) = 5 - 0.008x + 0.000009x^2$ (b) 25 dollars/m

12. A cost function is given by $C(x) = 15{,}000 + 100x + 2x^{3/2}$.

    (a) Find the marginal cost function.

    (b) Find $C'(100)$.

    Answer: (a) $C'(x) = 100 + 3\sqrt{x}$ (b) 130 dollars/unit

13. A physics experiment involving the acceleration of shuttle on a rail produced the following data:

Time (s)	0.017	0.05	0.083	0.117	0.15	0.183	0.217	0.25	0.283	0.317	0.35	0.383
Position (m)	0.020	0.046	0.081	0.129	0.187	0.256	0.337	0.427	0.529	0.640	0.765	0.899

    (a) Make a scatter plot of the data.

    (b) Fit a quadratic model to the data.

    (c) Based on your model, what was the initial position of the shuttle?

    (d) Using your model, estimate the velocity of the shuttle when $t = 0.1$ and when $t = 0.45$ seconds.

    (e) What is your estimated acceleration of the shuttle when $t = 0.1$ and when $t = 0.45$ seconds?

    Answer:

    (a)

    (b) $s(t) = 4.9001t^2 + 0.4374t + 0.0113$ m

    (c) $s(0) = 1.13$ cm

    (d) $v(0.1) = 1.41742$ m/s, $v(0.45) = 4.84749$ m/s

    (e) $a(0.1) = a(0.45) = 9.8002$ m/s/s

14. The equation of motion of a particle is $s = 2t^3 - t^2 + 1$, where s is in meters and t is in seconds. Find

    (a) the position of the particle at $t = 2$.

    (b) the velocity of the particle at $t = 2$.

    (c) the acceleration of the particle at $t = 2$.

    Answer: (a) 13 m   (b) 20 m/s   (c) 22 m/s^2

15. Suppose the amount of a drug left in the body t hours after administration is $\dfrac{20}{(t+1)}$ mg. In mg/h, find the rate of decrease of the drug 4 hours after administration.

    Answer: $\frac{4}{5}$ mg/h

93

16. When an electrical current passes through two resistors with resistances r_1 and r_2, which are connected in a parallel circuit, the combined resistance R can be calculated using the equation $\dfrac{1}{R} = \dfrac{1}{r_1} + \dfrac{1}{r_2}$. If we hold r_2 constant, express the rate at which the combined resistance R changes with respect to changes in r_1.

    Answer: $\dfrac{dR}{dr_1} = \dfrac{r_2^2}{(r_1 + r_2)^2}$

17. Show that the rate of change of the circumference of a circle, with respect to the radius of the circle, does not depend on the radius.

    Answer: $C = 2\pi r,\ \dfrac{dC}{dt} = 2\pi \dfrac{dr}{dt}$

18. Below is a table of the vapor pressure (in kilopascals) of water for various temperatures (in degrees Kelvin):

Pressure (kPa)	4.6	9.2	17.5	31.8	55.3	92.5	149.4	233.7	355.1	525.8	760
Temperature (°K)	273	283	293	303	313	323	333	343	353	363	373

(a) Estimate the rate of change of pressure with respect to temperature on the following intervals:

   (i) $[363, 373]$ (ii) $[333, 343]$ (iii) $[273, 283]$

(b) Plot the points from the table and fit an appropriate exponential model to these data.

(c) From the model in part (b), determine the instantaneous rate of change of pressure with respect to temperature.

(d) Is the rate of change of pressure increasing or decreasing with respect to temperature? Justify your answer.

Answer:

(a) (i) 23.42   (b)

(ii) 8.43

(iii) 0.46

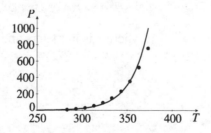

(c) $P = 6 \cdot 10^{-6} e^{0.0507T} \implies \dfrac{dP}{dT} = 3 \cdot 10^{-7} e^{0.0507T} \dfrac{\text{kPa}}{\text{K}}$

(d) Since $\dfrac{dP}{dT} > 0$, the rate of change of pressure is increasing with respect to temperature.

19. The following table shows the concentration (in mol/L) of a certain chemical in terms of reaction time (in hours) during a decomposition reaction.

Time (hours)	0	5	10	20	30	50
Concentration (mol/L)	2.32	1.86	1.49	0.98	0.62	0.25

(a) Find the average rate of change of concentration with respect to time for the following time intervals:

   (i) $[0, 5]$ (ii) $[10, 20]$ (iii) $[30, 50]$

(b) Plot the points from the table and fit an appropriate exponential model to the data.

(c) From your model in part (b), determine the instantaneous rate of change of concentration with respect to time.

(d) Is the rate of change of concentration increasing or decreasing with respect to time? Justify your answer.

Answer:

(a) (i) -0.092 mol/L/h   (b)

     (ii) -0.051 mol/L/h

     (iii) -0.0185 mol/L/h

(c) $C(t) = 2.3357e^{-0.0445t}$ mol/L $\Longrightarrow \dfrac{dC}{dt} = -0.1039e^{-0.0445t}$ mol/L/h

(d) Since $\dfrac{dC}{dt} < 0$, the rate of change of concentration is decreasing with respect to time.

20. The following table shows the relationship between pressure (in atmospheres) and volume (in liters) of hydrogen gas at $0\,^\circ$C.

Pressure (atm)	1	2	3	4	5	6
Volume (L)	22.4	11.2	7.5	5.6	4.5	3.7

(a) Find the average rate of change of volume with respect to pressure for the following pressure intervals:

   (i) $[1, 3]$ (ii) $[2, 3]$ (iii) $[4, 5]$

(b) Plot the data points and fit an appropriate power function to these data.

(c) Use the model from part (b) and determine the instantaneous rate of change of volume with respect to pressure.

(d) Compare the instantaneous rate at $P = 5$ with the average rate for $[4, 5]$. Which is larger? Why is this the case?

Answer:

(a) (i) -7.45 L/atm   (b)

     (ii) -3.7 L/atm

     (iii) -1.1 L/atm

(c) $v(P) = 22.444x^{-1.0018}$ L $\Longrightarrow \dfrac{dv}{dP} = -22.48x^{-2.0018}$ L/atm

(d) $v'(5) = -0.90$ L/atm > -1.1 L/atm of (iii). The slope of the tangent line at $P = 5$ is -0.90, and the slope of the secant line between $(4, 5.6)$ and $(5, 4.5)$ is -1.1.

3.4 Derivatives of Trigonometric Functions

1. Find the value of the limit $\displaystyle\lim_{x \to 0} \frac{\cos x - 1}{2x}$.

(A) 3   (B) 0   (C) $\frac{1}{3}$ (D) 4

(E) $\frac{1}{4}$ (F) 2   (G) $\frac{1}{2}$ (H) 1

Answer: (B)

2. Find the value of the limit $\displaystyle\lim_{x \to 0} \frac{\sin x}{2x}$.

(A) $\frac{1}{3}$ (B) 3   (C) 0   (D) 1

(E) $\frac{1}{2}$ (F) $\frac{1}{4}$ (G) 4   (H) 2

Answer: (E)

3. Find the value of the limit $\displaystyle\lim_{x \to 0} \frac{\tan 2x}{x}$.

(A) 4   (B) 1   (C) $\frac{1}{4}$ (D) 2

(E) $\frac{1}{2}$ (F) 0   (G) $\frac{1}{3}$ (H) 3

Answer: (D)

4. Find the value of the limit $\displaystyle\lim_{t \to 0} \frac{\sin 6t}{\sin 4t}$.

(A) 0   (B) 0.5   (C) 1   (D) 1.5

(E) 2   (F) 2.5   (G) 3   (H) Does not exist

Answer: (D)

5. Find the derivative of $f(x) = \sin^2 x$.

(A) $2\cos x$ (B) $\cos(x^2)$ (C) $2\sin x$ (D) $\cos^2 x$

(E) $2\cos^2 x$ (F) $2\cos(x^2)$ (G) $2\sin x \cos x$ (H) $-2\sin x \cos x$

Answer: (G)

6. Find the derivative of $f(x) = x^2 \cos x$.

(A) $2x\cos x$ (B) $2x\cos x - x^2 \sin x$

(C) $-2x\sin x$ (D) $2x\cos x + x^2 \sin x$

(E) $2x\sin x$ (F) $3x^2 \cos(x^3)$

(G) $-x^2 \sin x$ (H) None of the above

Answer: (B)

7. Find the derivative of $f(x) = \dfrac{\cos x}{x^3}$.

(A) $-\dfrac{\sin x}{3x^2}$

(B) $\dfrac{3\cos x - x\sin x}{x^4}$

(C) $\dfrac{\sin x}{3x^2}$

(D) $\dfrac{x\sin x + 3\cos x}{x^4}$

(E) $\dfrac{\cos x}{3x^2}$

(F) $-\dfrac{x\sin x + 3\cos x}{x^4}$

(G) $-\dfrac{\sin x}{x^3}$

(H) None of the above

Answer: (F)

8. Find the derivative of $f(x) = \dfrac{\tan x}{x^3}$.

(A) $\dfrac{\sec x}{3x^2}$

(B) $\dfrac{x\sec^2 x - 3\tan x}{x^4}$

(C) $\dfrac{\sec^2 x}{3x^2}$

(D) $\dfrac{x\sec^2 x + 3\tan x}{x^4}$

(E) $\dfrac{\tan x}{3x^2}$

(F) $\dfrac{x\sec x - 3\tan x}{x^4}$

(G) $\dfrac{\sec^2 x}{x^3}$

(H) None of the above

Answer: (B)

9. If $f(x) = x^2 \cos x$, find $f'(0)$.

(A) $\frac{1}{2}$ (B) 2   (C) 0   (D) 1

(E) $\frac{1}{3}$ (F) 4   (G) $\frac{1}{4}$ (H) 3

Answer: (C)

10. If $f(x) = x\tan x$, find $f'\left(\frac{\pi}{4}\right)$.

(A) $1 + \frac{\pi}{4}$ (B) $\frac{\pi}{4}$ (C) $\frac{\pi}{4} - 1$ (D) $1 - \frac{\pi}{4}$

(E) $\frac{\pi}{2} - 1$ (F) $1 - \frac{\pi}{2}$ (G) $1 + \frac{\pi}{2}$ (H) $\frac{\pi}{2}$

Answer: (G)

11. If $f(x) = \sin^2 x$, find $f'\left(\frac{\pi}{4}\right)$.

(A) $\sqrt{2}$ (B) $\frac{\sqrt{2}}{3}$ (C) 2   (D) 1

(E) $\frac{1}{2}$ (F) 0   (G) $\frac{\sqrt{3}}{4}$ (H) $\frac{\sqrt{2}}{2}$

Answer: (D)

12. If $f(x) = \dfrac{x}{\sin x}$, find $f'\left(\frac{\pi}{4}\right)$.

(A) $1 + \frac{\pi}{4}$ (B) $1 + \frac{\pi}{2}$ (C) $\sqrt{2}\left(\left(1 + \frac{\pi}{2}\right)\right)$ (D) $1 - \frac{\pi}{2}$

(E) $1 - \frac{\pi}{4}$ (F) $\sqrt{2}\left(1 + \frac{\pi}{4}\right)$ (G) $\sqrt{2}\left(1 - \frac{\pi}{2}\right)$ (H) $\sqrt{2}\left(1 - \frac{\pi}{4}\right)$

Answer: (H)

13. Find an equation of the tangent to the curve $y = 2\sin^2 x$ at $x = \frac{\pi}{4}$.

Answer: $y = 2x + 1 - \frac{\pi}{2}$

14. Find the x-coordinate(s) of the point(s) where the tangent to the curve $y = x + 2\cos x$, $0 \leq x \leq 2\pi$ has zero slope.

Answer: $x = \frac{\pi}{6}, \frac{5\pi}{6}$

15. Find the x-coordinate(s) of the point(s) where the tangent to the curve $y = x + \cos x$, $0 \leq x \leq 2\pi$ has zero slope.

Answer: $x = \frac{\pi}{2}$

16. Show that the curve $y = x^3 + 2x + \cos x$ has no tangent line with slope 0.

Answer: $\dfrac{dy}{dx} = 3x^2 + 2 - \sin x \geq 3x^2 + 2 - 1 = 3x^2 + 1 \geq 1 > 0$

17. Differentiate each of the following functions:

(a) $f(x) = \sin x - 2\tan x$

(c) $h(x) = x \cdot \tan x \cdot e^x$

(b) $g(x) = e^x \cos x$

(d) $\phi(x) = \dfrac{\sin x}{x}$

Answer:

(a) $f'(x) = \cos x - 2\sec^2 x$

(b) $g'(x) = e^x (\cos x - \sin x)$

(c) $h'(x) = e^x \left(\tan x + x\sec^2 x + x\tan x\right)$

(d) $\phi'(x) = \dfrac{x\cos x - \sin x}{x^2}$

18. Differentiate the following functions:

(a) $f(x) = \cos x + \sec x$

(c) $h(x) = \dfrac{\tan x}{e^x + 1}$

(b) $g(x) = x^2 \sin x$

(d) $\phi(x) = \dfrac{e^x \cos x}{x^2 + 1}$

Answer:

(a) $f'(x) = -\sin x + \sec x \tan x$

(b) $g'(x) = 2x\sin x + x^2 \cos x$

(c) $h'(x) = \dfrac{\sec^2 x\,(e^x + 1) - e^x \tan x}{(e^x + 1)^2}$

(d) $\phi'(x) = \dfrac{e^x (\cos x - \sin x)\,(x^2 + 1) - 2xe^x \cos x}{(x^2 + 1)^2}$

19. Consider the function $f(x) = x^2 \cdot \sin x$ on the interval $[-2\pi, 2\pi]$.

(a) Find $f'(x)$.

(b) Find equations of the lines tangent to the graph of $y = f(x)$ at $x = \pi$ and at $x = -\pi$. What do you notice about these two lines? Draw a sketch of this graph along with the two tangent lines, to illustrate what you found.

(c) On what interval(s) is f increasing?

(d) Find $f''(x)$.

(e) On what interval(s) is f concave downward?

Answer:

(a) $f'(x) = 2x\sin x + x^2 \cos x$

(b) $y = -\pi^2 (x - \pi)$ and $y = -\pi^2 (x + \pi)$. The two tangent lines are parallel.

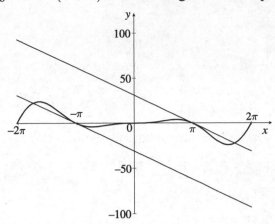

(c) f is increasing on $(-2\pi, -5.087)$, $(-2.289, 2.289)$, and $(5.087, 2\pi)$.

(d) $f'' (x) = \left(2 - x^2\right) \sin x + 4x \cos x$

3.5 The Chain Rule

1. Find the derivative of $f (x) = \dfrac{1}{\left(1 - 2x\right)^3}$.

(A) $\dfrac{6}{\left(1 - 2x\right)^4}$

(B) $-\dfrac{6}{\left(1 - 2x\right)^4}$

(C) $\dfrac{3}{\left(1 - 2x\right)^4}$

(D) $-\dfrac{1}{6 \left(1 - 2x\right)^2}$

(E) $-\dfrac{3}{\left(1 - 2x\right)^4}$

(F) $\dfrac{1}{3 \left(1 - 2x\right)^2}$

(G) $-\dfrac{2}{\left(1 - 2x\right)^4}$

(H) None of the above

Answer: (A)

2. Find the derivative of $f (x) = \sin^3 x$.

(A) $3 \cos^2 x$

(B) $\cos \left(3x^2\right)$

(C) $3 \sin^2 x$

(D) $3 \sin^2 x \cos x$

(E) $3x^2 \sin x$

(F) $3x^2 \cos \left(x^3\right)$

(G) $3x^2 \cos x$

(H) None of the above

Answer: (D)

3. Find the derivative of $f (x) = \sin \left(x^3\right)$.

(A) $3 \cos^2 x$

(B) $\cos \left(3x^2\right)$

(C) $3 \sin^2 x$

(D) $3 \sin^2 x \cos x$

(E) $3x^2 \sin x$

(F) $3x^2 \cos \left(x^3\right)$

(G) $3x^2 \cos x$

(H) None of the above

Answer: (F)

4. If $f (x) = \left(x^2 + 1\right)^4$, find $f' (0)$.

(A) 0

(B) 28

(C) 4

(D) 32

(E) 16

(F) 24

(G) 12

(H) 8

Answer: (A)

5. If $f(x) = \sqrt[3]{x^2 - 1}$, find $f''(3)$.

   (A) $\frac{1}{4}$ (B) $\frac{1}{12}$ (C) $-\frac{1}{12}$ (D) $\frac{3}{4}$

   (E) $\frac{1}{3}$ (F) $\frac{4}{3}$ (G) $-\frac{4}{3}$ (H) None of the above

   Answer: (C)

6. If $f(x) = \left(\frac{x+1}{x-1}\right)^3$, find $f'(3)$.

   (A) 4 (B) $-\frac{2}{3}$ (C) 12 (D) 3

   (E) -6 (F) -3 (G) 6 (H) None of the above

   Answer: (E)

7. If $f(x) = \sqrt{x + \sqrt{x}}$, find $f'(1)$.

   (A) $\frac{3\sqrt{2}}{8}$ (B) $\frac{\sqrt{2}}{4}$ (C) $\frac{1}{4}$ (D) $\frac{1}{8}$

   (E) $\frac{\sqrt{2}}{2}$ (F) $\frac{1}{2}$ (G) $\sqrt{2}$ (H) 1

   Answer: (A)

8. Let $f(x) = e^{-1/x}$. Find the value of $f'(1)$.

   (A) $2e$ (B) e (C) $2e^{-1}$ (D) $-2e$

   (E) e^{-1} (F) $-e$ (G) $-2e^{-1}$ (H) $-e^{-1}$

   Answer: (E)

9. Let $f(x) = e^{-x^2}$. Find the value of $f'(1)$.

   (A) $2e^{-1}$ (B) $2e$ (C) $-2e$ (D) $-e$

   (E) e (F) $-2e^{-1}$ (G) e^{-1} (H) $-e^{-1}$

   Answer: (F)

10. Let $F(x) = \sin(g(x))$, where g is differentiable. Find $F'(x)$.

    (A) $g(x)\cos x$ (B) $-g(x)\sin x$ (C) $-g'(x)\sin x$ (D) $g'(x)\cos x$

    (E) $g'(x)\cos(g(x))$ (F) $g'(x)\sin(g(x))$ (G) $\cos(g(x))$ (H) $\cos(g'(x))$

    Answer: (E)

11. Suppose that $h(x) = f(g(x))$ and $g(3) = 6$, $g'(3) = 4$, $f'(3) = 2$, $f'(6) = 7$. Find the value of $h'(3)$.

    (A) 4 (B) 8 (C) 12 (D) 16

    (E) 20 (F) 24 (G) 28 (H) 32

    Answer: (G)

12. Suppose that $F(x) = f(g(x))$ and $g(3) = 5$, $g'(3) = 3$, $f'(3) = 1$, $f'(5) = 4$. Find the value of $F'(3)$.

    (A) 3 (B) 4 (C) 7 (D) 9

    (E) 12 (F) 15 (G) 17 (H) 20

    Answer: (E)

13. Suppose that $w = u \circ v$ and $u(0) = 1$, $v(0) = 2$, $u'(0) = 3$, $u'(2) = 4$, $v'(0) = 5$ and $v'(2) = 6$. Find $w'(0)$.

   (A) 5   (B) 10   (C) 15   (D) 20

   (E) 25   (F) 30   (G) 35   (H) 40

   Answer: (D)

14. If $f(x) = (1 + 3x)^2$, find $f'(1)$.

   (A) 4   (B) 12   (C) 8   (D) 32

   (E) 6   (F) 16   (G) 24   (H) 2

   Answer: (G)

15. If $f(x) = (x + 1)^2 (x + 2)^3$, find $f'(0)$.

   (A) 4   (B) 24   (C) 28   (D) 12

   (E) 16   (F) 8   (G) 32   (H) 6

   Answer: (C)

16. If $f(x) = \cos^2(2x)$, find $f'\left(\frac{\pi}{3}\right)$.

   (A) $\sqrt{3}$ (B) $\frac{\sqrt{3}}{4}$ (C) 1   (D) -1

   (E) $-\sqrt{3}$ (F) $-\frac{\sqrt{3}}{2}$ (G) $\frac{\sqrt{3}}{2}$ (H) $-\frac{\sqrt{3}}{4}$

   Answer: (A)

17. If $f(x) = \cos 2x$, find the value of $f^{(8)}(0)$.

   (A) 1   (B) -1 (C) 2   (D) 0

   (E) 256   (F) -256 (G) 128   (H) -128

   Answer: (E)

18. If $g(x) = \sin 2x$, find the value of $g^{(6)}(0)$.

   (A) 0   (B) 2   (C) -2 (D) 8

   (E) -8 (F) 64   (G) -64 (H) 128

   Answer: (A)

19. If $f(x) = \dfrac{1}{x^2 + 1}$, find $f''(1)$.

   (A) $-\frac{1}{4}$ (B) $-\frac{1}{3}$ (C) $-\frac{1}{2}$ (D) 0

   (E) $\frac{1}{4}$ (F) $\frac{1}{3}$ (G) $\frac{1}{2}$ (H) None of the above

   Answer: (G)

20. Find the y-intercept of the tangent line to the curve $y = \sqrt{x + 3}$ at the point $(1, 2)$.

   (A) $\frac{3}{4}$ (B) $\frac{7}{4}$ (C) $\frac{1}{4}$ (D) 2

   (E) $\frac{1}{2}$ (F) 1   (G) $\frac{3}{2}$ (H) $\frac{5}{4}$

   Answer: (B)

21. Find the slope of the tangent to the curve $x = \sin t$, $y = \cos t$ when $t = \frac{\pi}{3}$.

(A) $-\frac{1}{\sqrt{3}}$ (B) $\frac{1}{\sqrt{2}}$ (C) $\frac{1}{\sqrt{3}}$ (D) 1

(E) -1 (F) $-\sqrt{3}$ (G) $\sqrt{3}$ (H) $-\frac{1}{\sqrt{2}}$

Answer: (F)

22. Find the slope of the tangent to the curve $x = t^3$, $y = t^4$ when $t = 3$.

(A) $\frac{9}{4}$ (B) $\frac{3}{16}$ (C) $\frac{4}{9}$ (D) $\frac{4}{3}$

(E) 3   (F) $\frac{3}{4}$ (G) $\frac{16}{3}$ (H) 4

Answer: (H)

23. At what value of t does the curve $x = t^2 - t$, $y = t^2 + t$ have a vertical tangent?

(A) $-\frac{1}{3}$ (B) $\frac{1}{2}$ (C) -2 (D) 1

(E) $-\frac{1}{2}$ (F) -3 (G) -1 (H) 2

Answer: (B)

24. At what value of t does the curve $x = t^2 - t$, $y = t^2 + t$ have a horizontal tangent?

(A) $-\frac{1}{2}$ (B) -2 (C) $\frac{1}{2}$ (D) 2

(E) $-\frac{1}{3}$ (F) 1   (G) -3 (H) -1

Answer: (A)

25. Given $x = e^t$, $y = \sin t$, find the value of $\frac{d^2y}{dx^2}$ when $t = 0$.

(A) $\frac{-1}{\sqrt{2}}$ (B) -2 (C) $\frac{1}{\sqrt{2}}$ (D) $\frac{1}{2}$

(E) -1 (F) 2   (G) 1   (H) $-\frac{1}{2}$

Answer: (E)

26. Find the slope of the tangent to the curve with parametric equations $x = t + t^2$, $y = t + e^t$ at the point $(0, 1)$.

(A) -3 (B) -2 (C) -1 (D) 0

(E) 1   (F) 2   (G) 3   (H) 4

Answer: (F)

27. Find $\frac{dy}{dx}$.

(a) $y = \sqrt{2x - x^2}$ (c) $y = \sin\left(\frac{1}{x}\right)$

(b) $y = \left(x^2 + 1\right)^{50}$ (d) $y = \tan(3x)$

Answer:

(a) $\dfrac{dy}{dx} = \dfrac{1 - x}{\sqrt{2x - x^2}}$ (b) $\dfrac{dy}{dx} = 100x\left(x^2 + 1\right)^{49}$ (c) $\dfrac{dy}{dx} = -\dfrac{1}{x^2}\cos\left(\dfrac{1}{x}\right)$ (d) $\dfrac{dy}{dx} = 3\sec^2(3x)$

28. Find $\dfrac{dy}{dx}$.

(a) $y = \left(x^2 + 3x + 2\right)^4$

(c) $y = xe^{1/x}$

(b) $y = \sqrt[3]{1 + x^3}$

(d) $y = \dfrac{1}{\left(x^2 + 4x + 1\right)^3}$

Answer:

(a) $\dfrac{dy}{dx} = 4\left(x^2 + 3x + 2\right)^3 (2x + 3)$

(b) $\dfrac{dy}{dx} = \dfrac{x^2}{\sqrt[3]{\left(1 + x^3\right)^2}}$

(c) $\dfrac{dy}{dx} = e^{1/x}\left(1 - \dfrac{1}{x}\right)$

(d) $\dfrac{dy}{dx} = \dfrac{-3\,(2x + 4)}{\left(x^2 + 4x + 1\right)^4}$

29. Find $\dfrac{dy}{dx}$.

(a) $y = (\sin \pi + 1)^4$

(c) $y = \cos x^3$

(b) $y = \cos^3 x$

(d) $y = \left(1 + \tan\left(e^x\right)\right)^3$

Answer:

(a) $\dfrac{dy}{dx} = 0$ (b) $\dfrac{dy}{dx} = -3\cos^2 x \sin x$ (c) $\dfrac{dy}{dx} = -3x^2 \sin\left(x^3\right)$ (d) $\dfrac{dy}{dx} = 3\left(1 + \tan e^x\right)^2 \sec^2\left(e^x\right)e^x$

30. Find $\dfrac{dy}{dx}$.

(a) $y = \sqrt{x^2 - 5x}$

(c) $y = x^2 \cdot e^{\sqrt{x}}$

(b) $y = \dfrac{\sin\left(xe^x\right)}{x^3 + x}$

(d) $y = e^{\sqrt{x^3 + 1}}$

Answer:

(a) $\dfrac{dy}{dx} = \dfrac{2x - 5}{2\sqrt{x^2 - 5x}}$

(b) $\dfrac{dy}{dx} = \dfrac{\cos\left(xe^x\right)\left(e^x + xe^x\right)\left(x^3 + x\right) - \left(3x^2 + 1\right)\sin\left(xe^x\right)}{\left(x^3 + x\right)^2}$

(c) $\dfrac{dy}{dx} = e^{\sqrt{x}}\left(2x + \tfrac{1}{2}x^{3/2}\right)$

(d) $\dfrac{dy}{dx} = \dfrac{3x^2 e^{\sqrt{x^3 + 1}}}{2\sqrt{x^3 + 1}}$

31. Find $\dfrac{dy}{dx}$.

(a) $y = \left(\dfrac{x + 1}{x - 3}\right)^4$

(c) $y = xe^{x^2 + 7}$

(b) $y = e^{2x} + e^{99}$

(d) $y = \tan\left(\sin x^2\right)$

Answer:

(a) $\dfrac{dy}{dx} = -\dfrac{16\,(x + 1)^3}{(x - 3)^5}$ (b) $\dfrac{dy}{dx} = 2e^{2x}$ (c) $\dfrac{dy}{dx} = e^{x^2 + 7}\left(1 + 2x^2\right)$ (d) $\dfrac{dy}{dx} = 2x\sec^2\left(\sin x^2\right)\cos\left(x^2\right)$

32. Suppose that u and v are differentiable functions and that $w = u \circ v$ and $u\,(0) = 1$, $v\,(0) = 2$, $u'\,(0) = 3$, $u'\,(2) = 4$, $v'\,(0) = 5$, $v'\,(2) = 6$. Find $w'\,(0)$.

Answer: $w'\,(0) = u'\,(v\,(0)) \cdot v'\,(0) = u'\,(2) \cdot 5 = 4 \cdot 5 = 20$

33. f and g are functions whose graphs are shown below. Let $u(x) = f(g(x))$, $v(x) = g(f(x))$ and $w(x) = f(f(x))$. Find each derivative, if it exists. If it does not exist, explain.

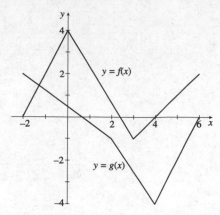

(a) $u'(-1)$ (b) $v'(-1)$ (c) $w'(-1)$

(d) $u'(2)$ (e) $v'(2)$ (f) $u'(4)$

(g) $w'(2)$ (h) $v'(4)$ (i) $w'(4)$

Answer:

(a) $u'(-1) = f'(g(-1)) \cdot g'(-1) = f'\left(\frac{5}{4}\right) \cdot \left(-\frac{3}{4}\right) = \left(-\frac{5}{3}\right) \cdot \left(-\frac{3}{4}\right) = \frac{5}{4}$

(b) $v'(-1)$ does not exist, because $v'(-1) = g'(f(-1)) \cdot f'(-1) = g'(2) \cdot 2$, but $g(x)$ is not differentiable at 2.

$$\lim_{h \to 0^+} \frac{g(2+h) - g(2)}{h} = -\frac{3}{2} \neq -\frac{3}{4} = \lim_{h \to 0^-} \frac{g(2+h) - g(2)}{h}$$

(c) $w'(-1) = f'(f(-1)) \cdot f'(-1) = f'(2) \cdot 2 = -\frac{5}{3} \cdot 2 = -\frac{10}{3}$

(d) $u'(2)$ does not exist, because $u'(2) = f'(g(2)) \cdot g'(2)$, but $g(x)$ is not differentiable at 2.

(e) $v'(2) = g'(f(2)) \cdot f'(2) = g'(-1) \cdot \left(-\frac{5}{3}\right) = \left(-\frac{3}{4}\right)\left(-\frac{5}{3}\right) = \frac{5}{4}$

(f) $u'(4)$ does not exist, because $u'(4) = f'(g(4)) \cdot g'(4)$, but $g(x)$ is not differentiable at 4.

$$\lim_{h \to 0^+} \frac{g(4+h) - g(4)}{h} = 2 \neq -\frac{3}{2} = \lim_{h \to 0^-} \frac{g(4+h) - g(4)}{h}$$

(g) $w'(2) = f'(f(2)) \cdot f'(2) = f'(-1) \cdot f'(2) = 2 \cdot \left(-\frac{5}{3}\right) = -\frac{10}{3}$

(h) $v'(4) = g'(f(4)) \cdot f'(4) = g'(0) \cdot 1 = \left(-\frac{3}{4}\right) \cdot 1 = -\frac{3}{4}$

(i) $w'(4)$ does not exist, because $w'(4) = f'(f(4)) \cdot f'(4) = f'(0) \cdot f'(4)$, but $f(x)$ is not differentiable at 0.

$$\lim_{h \to 0^+} \frac{f(h) - f(0)}{h} = -\frac{5}{3} \neq 2 = \lim_{h \to 0^-} \frac{f(h) - f(0)}{h}$$

34. Suppose that $h(x) = f(g(x))$ and that we are given the following information:

x	0.1	0.2	0.3	0.4	0.5	0.6	0.7
$f(x)$	2.2	2.4	2.7	3.0	3.3	3.6	4.0
$g(x)$	0.85	0.60	0.50	0.40	0.25	0.10	0.00

Use the table to estimate the value of $h'(0.3)$. Justify your estimation.

Answer: $h'(0.3) = f'(g(0.3)) \cdot g'(0.3) = f'(0.5) \cdot g'(0.3) = 3 \cdot (-1) = -3$

35. Find an equation of the tangent line to the curve $y = (x^2 + 1)^3$ at the point $(1, 8)$.

Answer: The slope is 24, so an equation of the tangent line is $y = 24x - 16$.

36. Find an equation of the tangent to the curve $y = \sqrt{2x + 5}$ at $x = 2$.

Answer: $y = \frac{1}{3}x + \frac{7}{3}$

37. Find the point where the tangent to the curve $y = x\sqrt{3 - x}$ has zero slope.

Answer: $(2, 2)$

38. Find the y-intercept of the tangent line to the curve $y = x\sin(2x)$ at the point $\left(\frac{\pi}{2}, 0\right)$.

Answer: $\left(0, \frac{\pi^2}{2}\right)$

39. A particle moves along a straight line. Its position is given by $y = \sqrt{t^2 + 7}$, where y is measured in feet and t is measured in seconds. Find the acceleration of the particle when $t = 3$.

Answer: $\frac{7}{64}$ ft/s^2

40. The position of a particle moving along the x-axis is given by $x = 0.08\sin(12t + 0.3)$ meters, where t is measured in seconds.

   (a) Determine the position, velocity, and acceleration of the particle when $t = 0.65$.

   (b) Show that the acceleration of the particle is proportional to its position, but in the opposite direction.

   Answer:

   (a) $x(0.65) \approx 0.07759$ m; $v(0.65) = x'(0.65) = -0.2338$ m/s; $a(0.65) = x''(0.65) = -11.173$ m/s^2

   (b) $a(t) = -11.52\sin(12t + 0.3) = -11.52x(t)$

41. The angular displacement θ of a simple pendulum is given by $\theta = \theta_0 \sin(\omega t + \phi)$, where θ_0 is the angular amplitude, ω the angular frequency and ϕ a phase constant depending on initial conditions. If we are given that $\omega = 10$ and $\phi = \frac{\pi}{2}$, find the angular velocity $\frac{d\theta}{dt}$ when $\theta = \frac{\theta_0}{2}$.

   Answer: $\theta = \theta_0 \sin\left(10t + \frac{\pi}{2}\right)$; when $\theta = \frac{\theta_0}{2}$, $\sin\left(10t + \frac{\pi}{2}\right) = \frac{1}{2}$ so $\cos\left(10t + \frac{\pi}{2}\right) = \frac{\sqrt{3}}{2}$. So $\theta'\left(\frac{\theta_0}{2}\right) = 10\theta_0 \frac{\sqrt{3}}{2} = 5\sqrt{3}\theta_0$.

42. The displacement of a particle is given by $x = 0.03\sin\left(20\pi t + \frac{\pi}{2}\right)$ meters. Find all times $t > 0$ where

   (a) The displacement attains its maximum value.

   (b) The velocity attains its maximum value.

   (c) The acceleration attains its maximum value.

Answer:

$$(a)\, t = \frac{k}{10},\, k = 1, 2, 3, \dots \qquad (b)\, t = \frac{3}{40} + \frac{k}{10},\, k = 1, 2, 3, \dots \qquad (c)\, t = \frac{1}{20} + \frac{k}{10},\, k = 1, 2, 3, \dots$$

43. Let $x(t) = 200\left(1 - e^{-\frac{3}{200}t}\right)$ be the amount of salt (in kg) in a tank after time t minutes. Find:

   (a) How much salt is in the tank after 1 hour?

   (b) Find the rate of change of salt after 1 hour?

   Answer: (a) $200\left(1 - e^{-9/10}\right) kg \approx 118.69$ kg   (b) $3e^{-0.9} \approx 1.22$ kg/min

44. Let $p(t) = \dfrac{20,000}{1 + 1999e^{-0.1t}}$ be the population of a bacteria colony at time t hours. Find the growth rate of the bacteria after 10 hours.

   Answer: About 2.7/h

45. Let $p(t) = \dfrac{1,000\left(e^{0.1t} + 3\right)}{e^{0.1t} + 9}$ be the population of a bacteria colony at time t hours. Find the growth rate of the bacteria after 10 hours.

   Answer: $\dfrac{600e}{(e+9)^2} \approx 11.9$/h

46. Consider the two functions $f(x) = e^{\sin x}$ and $g(x) = \sin(e^x)$.

   (a) Which, if either, of these functions is periodic? Justify your answer.

   (b) For each function, consider the limit as x increases without bound. Does either function also increase without bound like an exponential function? Explain.

   (c) Where, if anywhere, does each function have an x-intercept? Justify your answer.

   (d) Where, if anywhere, does each function have a horizontal tangent line? Justify your answer.

   (e) Where, if anywhere, does each function attain its maximum value? its minimum value? Justify your answers.

Answer:

   (a) Since $f(x + 2\pi) = e^{\sin(x+2\pi)} = e^{\sin x} = f(x)$, $f(x)$ is periodic.

   (b) No, $e^{-1} \le e^{\sin x} < e$ and $-1 \le \sin(e^x) \le 1$. Both functions are bounded.

   (c) $g(x) = \sin(e^x) = 0 \Longrightarrow e^x = \pi k \quad k = 1, 2, 3, \dots \Longrightarrow x = \ln(\pi k)$ are x-intercepts of $g(x)$. $e^{\sin x} > 0$ for all x, so f has no x-intercepts.

   (d) $f(x)$ has horizontal tangent lines where $f'(x) = e^{\sin x} \cos x = 0 \Longrightarrow \cos x = 0 \Longrightarrow x = \frac{\pi}{2} + \pi k$, $k = 0, \pm 1, \pm 2, \dots$.
   $g(x)$ has horizontal tangent lines where $g'(x) = \cos(e^x) \cdot e^x = 0 \Longrightarrow \cos(e^x) = 0 \Longrightarrow e^x = \frac{\pi}{2} + \pi k$, $k = 0, 1, 2, 3, \dots \Longrightarrow x = \ln\left(\frac{\pi}{2} + \pi k\right)$

   (e) $f(x) = e^{\sin x}$ is maximized when $\sin x = 1$, that is, when $x = \frac{\pi}{2} \pm 2k\pi$, $k = 0, 1, 2, \dots$.
   $g(x) = \sin e^x$ is maximized when $e^x = \frac{\pi}{2} \pm 2k\pi$, that is, when $x = \ln\left(\frac{\pi}{2} \pm 2k\pi\right)$, $k = 0, 1, 2, \dots$.
   $f(x) = e^{\sin x}$ is minimized when $\sin x = -1$, that is, when $x = \frac{3\pi}{2} \pm 2k\pi$, $k = 0, 1, 2, \dots$.
   $g(x) = \sin e^x$ is minimized when $e^x = \frac{3\pi}{2} \pm 2k\pi$, that is, when $x = \ln\left(\frac{3\pi}{2} \pm 2k\pi\right)$, $k = 0, 1, 2, \dots$.

47. The function f is graphed below.

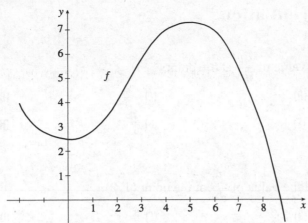

Let $g(x) = f(f(x))$, $h(x) = f(x^3)$ and $k(x) = [f(x)]^3$. Use the graph to estimate each of the following.

(a) $g'(2)$ (b) $h'(2)$ (c) $k'(2)$

Answer:

(a) $g'(2) = f'(f(2)) \cdot f'(2) = f'(4) \cdot 2 = 1 \cdot 2 = 2$

(b) $h'(2) = \left[f'(x^3) \cdot 3x^2 \right]_{x=2} = f'(8) \cdot 12 = (-2)(12) = -24$

(c) $k'(x) = 3(f(x))^2 \cdot f'(x)$. So $k'(2) = 3(f(2))^2 \cdot f'(2) = 3 \cdot 16 \cdot 2 = 96$

48. Find the derivative $\dfrac{dp}{dt}$ if $p = \dfrac{mv}{\sqrt{1 - (v^2/c^2)}}$, where m and c are constants, v is velocity function.

Answer: $\dfrac{dp}{dt} = \dfrac{m}{\left(1 - (v^2/c^2)\right)^{3/2}} \dfrac{dv}{dt}$

49. Consider the curve given by $x = t^2 + 3$, $y = 2t^3 - t$. Find $\dfrac{dy}{dx}$ at the point corresponding to $t = 2$.

Answer: $\dfrac{dy}{dx}\bigg|_{t=2} = \dfrac{23}{4}$

50. Consider the curve given by $x = t^2 + 3$, $y = 2t^3 - t$. Find $\dfrac{d^2y}{dx^2}$ at the point corresponding to $t = 2$.

Answer: $\dfrac{d^2y}{dx^2}\bigg|_{t=2} = \dfrac{25}{32}$

51. Find an equation in x and y for the tangent line to the curve $x = e^t$, $y = e^{-t}$ at the point $\left(\frac{1}{3}, 3 \right)$.

Answer: $y = -9x + 6$

52. Find $\dfrac{dy}{dx}$ for the parametric curve given by $x = t^4 - t^2 + t$, $y = \sqrt[3]{t}$.

Answer: $\dfrac{dy}{dx} = \dfrac{1}{3t^{2/3}\left(4t^3 - 2t + 1\right)}$

53. Find $\dfrac{d^2y}{dx^2}$ for the parametric curve given by $x = t^4 - t^2 + t$, $y = \sqrt[3]{t}$.

Answer: $\dfrac{d^2y}{dx^2} = \dfrac{-44t^3 + 10t - 2}{9t^{5/3}\left(4t^3 - 2t + 1\right)^3}$

3.6 Implicit Differentiation

1. If $x^2 + y^2 = 25$, find the value of $\dfrac{dy}{dx}$ at the point $(3, 4)$.

(A) $\frac{3}{5}$

(B) $-\frac{3}{5}$

(C) $-\frac{4}{5}$

(D) $\frac{3}{4}$

(E) 0

(F) 1

(G) $\frac{4}{5}$

(H) $-\frac{3}{4}$

Answer: (H)

2. If $x^2 + xy + y^2 = 7$, find the value of $\dfrac{dy}{dx}$ at the point $(1, 2)$.

(A) $-\frac{3}{5}$

(B) $-\frac{3}{4}$

(C) $\frac{3}{5}$

(D) $\frac{4}{5}$

(E) $-\frac{4}{5}$

(F) $\frac{3}{4}$

(G) 1

(H) 0

Answer: (E)

3. If $\sqrt{x} + \sqrt{y} = 3$, find the value of $\dfrac{dx}{dy}$ at the point $(4, 1)$.

(A) -3

(B) 0

(C) 2

(D) -1

(E) 1

(F) 3

(G) -2

(H) 4

Answer: (G)

4. Find the y-intercept of the tangent to the ellipse $x^2 + 3y^2 = 1$ at the point $\left(\frac{1}{2}, \frac{1}{2}\right)$.

(A) 3

(B) $\frac{-1}{\sqrt{3}}$

(C) $\frac{1}{3}$

(D) $-\frac{1}{3}$

(E) -1

(F) -3

(G) $\frac{1}{\sqrt{3}}$

(H) $\frac{2}{3}$

Answer: (H)

5. Find the slope of the tangent to the curve $xy^2 + x^2y = 2$ at the point $(1, 1)$.

(A) 5

(B) -1

(C) -3

(D) 1

(E) -5

(F) 0

(G) 3

(H) 4

Answer: (B)

6. Let $y = f(x)$. If $xy^3 + xy = 6$ and $f(3) = 1$, find $f'(3)$.

(A) 0

(B) 1

(C) 2

(D) $\frac{1}{3}$

(E) -4

(F) $\frac{1}{5}$

(G) $-\frac{1}{6}$

(H) 8

Answer: (G)

7. Find the slope of the tangent line to the curve $x^3 + y^3 = 6xy$ at the point $(3, 3)$.

(A) -3

(B) -2

(C) -1

(D) 0

(E) 1

(F) 2

(G) 3

(H) 4

Answer: (C)

8. Find the equation of the line normal to the curve defined by the equation $x^3y^4 - 5 = x^3 - x^2 + y$ at the point $(2, -1)$.

(A) $33x + 4y - 62 = 0$ (B) $33x - 4y - 62 = 0$

(C) $33x + 4y + 62 = 0$ (D) $33x - 4y + 62 = 0$

(E) $4x - 33y - 41 = 0$ (F) $4x + 33y - 41 = 0$

(G) $4x - 33y + 41 = 0$ (H) $4x + 33y + 41 = 0$

Answer: (A)

9. What is the slope of the tangent line to the curve $xy^3 + y - 1 = 0$ at the point $(0, 1)$?

(A) -3 (B) -2 (C) -1 (D) 0

(E) 1 (F) 2 (G) 3 (H) 4

Answer: (C)

10. If $x^2 + y^2 = 1$, find an expression for y''.

(A) $\dfrac{-2x}{y^5}$ (B) $\dfrac{x}{y^3}$ (C) $\dfrac{-3x}{y^4}$ (D) $\dfrac{x^3 - y^3}{y^6}$

(E) $\dfrac{x^3 + y^3}{y^6}$ (F) $\dfrac{-1}{y^3}$ (G) $\dfrac{6x^2}{y^5}$ (H) $\dfrac{-3x^3}{y^4}$

Answer: (F)

11. If $x^4 + y^4 = 1$, find an expression for $\dfrac{d^2y}{dx^2}$.

(A) $\dfrac{y^2}{x^5}$ (B) $\dfrac{-x^2}{y^2}$ (C) $\dfrac{-2x^4}{y^4}$ (D) $\dfrac{-2x^2}{y^5}$

(E) $\dfrac{-3x^2}{y^7}$ (F) $\dfrac{-5x^4}{y^9}$ (G) $\dfrac{-6x^4}{y^5}$ (H) $\dfrac{6x^4}{y^7}$

Answer: (E)

12. If $x^3 + y^3 = 1$, find an expression for y''.

(A) $\dfrac{-2x}{y^5}$ (B) $\dfrac{x}{y^3}$ (C) $\dfrac{-3x}{y^4}$ (D) $\dfrac{x^3 - y^3}{y^6}$

(E) $\dfrac{x^3 + y^3}{y^6}$ (F) $\dfrac{-x^2}{y^3}$ (G) $\dfrac{6x^2}{y^5}$ (H) $\dfrac{-3x^3}{y^4}$

Answer: (A)

13. Let $f(x) = \tan^{-1} x$. Find the value of $f'(1)$.

(A) $-\frac{1}{2}$ (B) $\frac{1}{2}$ (C) $-\frac{1}{3}$ (D) 1

(E) $\frac{1}{3}$ (F) $-\frac{1}{4}$ (G) $\frac{1}{4}$ (H) -1

Answer: (B)

14. Let $f(x) = \sin^{-1}(2x)$. Find the value of $f'(0)$.

(A) $-\frac{1}{2}$ (B) 2 (C) -2 (D) 1

(E) $\frac{1}{2}$ (F) -1 (G) 0 (H) $-\dfrac{1}{\sqrt{2}}$

Answer: (B)

15. Let $f(x) = \tan^{-1}(x^2 + 1)$. Find the value of $f'(1)$.

(A) 0 (B) 0.1 (C) 0.2 (D) 0.3

(E) 0.4 (F) 0.5 (G) 0.6 (H) 0.8

Answer: (E)

16. Find the domain of the function $f(x) = \sin^{-1}(3 - 2x)$.

(A) $[0, 1]$ (B) $[1, 2]$ (C) $[0, 2]$ (D) $[0, 3]$

(E) $[1, 3]$ (F) $[2, 3]$ (G) $[-3, -1]$ (H) $[-3, -2]$

Answer: (B)

17. Let $f(x) = \sin^{-1}\left(\dfrac{4}{x}\right)$. Find the value of $f'(8)$.

(A) $-\dfrac{1}{8\sqrt{3}}$ (B) $-\dfrac{1}{4\sqrt{3}}$ (C) $-\dfrac{1}{2\sqrt{3}}$ (D) $-\dfrac{1}{\sqrt{3}}$

(E) $\dfrac{\pi}{8}$ (F) $\dfrac{\pi}{4}$ (G) $\dfrac{\pi}{2}$ (H) π

Answer: (A)

18. Find $\dfrac{dy}{dx}$ if $x^2 - 2xy^2 = y^4$.

Answer: $\dfrac{dy}{dx} = \dfrac{x - y^2}{2y^3 + 2xy}$

19. Find $\dfrac{dy}{dx}$ if $x \sin y + \cos 2y + xe^{x^4} = 4$.

Answer: $\dfrac{dy}{dx} = \dfrac{\sin y + e^{x^4}(1 + 4x^4)}{2\sin(2y) - x\cos y}$

20. Find $\dfrac{dy}{dx}$ if $xy + e^{3x} = \sin(x + y)$.

Answer: $\dfrac{dy}{dx} = \dfrac{y + 3e^{3x} - \cos(x + y)}{\cos(x + y) - x}$

21. Find an equation of the tangent line to the curve $x^2y^4 + xy = 2$ at $(1, 1)$.

Answer: $3x + 5y - 8 = 0$

22. Find an equation of the tangent line to the curve $y^2 - 3xy + 2x^2 = 4$ at $(3, 2)$.

Answer: $6x - 5y - 8 = 0$

23. The curve $y^2 - x^2y - 6 = 0$ has two tangents at $x = 1$. What are their equations?

Answer: $6x - 5y + 9 = 0, 4x - 5y - 14 = 0$

24. There are two lines passing through the point $(1, 0)$ tangent to the parabola $y^2 + 4x = 0$. Find their equations.

Answer: $y = -x + 1, y = x - 1$

25. Find the point(s) where the curve $2x^2 - 2xy + y^2 = 4$ has a horizontal tangent.

Answer: $(\sqrt{2}, 2\sqrt{2})$, $(-\sqrt{2}, -2\sqrt{2})$

26. If $\sqrt{x + y} + \sqrt{x - y} = 4$, find the value of $\dfrac{dy}{dx}$ at the point $(5, 4)$.

Answer: $\dfrac{dy}{dx}\bigg|_{(5,4)} = 2$

27. If $\sin y = x$, find the value of $\dfrac{dy}{dx}$ at the point $\left(\frac{1}{2}, \frac{\pi}{6}\right)$.

Answer: $\dfrac{dy}{dx}\bigg|_{\left(\frac{1}{2}, \frac{\pi}{6}\right)} = \dfrac{2\sqrt{3}}{3}$

28. Find an equation of the tangent line to the curve $2x^3 + 2y^3 - 9xy = 0$ at the point $(1, 2)$.

Answer: The slope is $\frac{4}{5}$, so an equation of the line is $y = \frac{4}{5}x + \frac{6}{5}$.

29. If $x \cos y + y \cos x = 1$, find an expression for $\dfrac{dy}{dx}$.

Answer: $\dfrac{dy}{dx} = \dfrac{y \sin x - \cos y}{\cos x - x \sin y}$

30. Use implicit differentiation to find y'' if $2xy = y^2$.

Answer: $y'' = \dfrac{y^2 - 2xy}{(y - x)^3}$

31. Differentiate the following functions:

(a) $f(t) = \tan^{-1} \sqrt{1 - t}$

(b) $f(x) = \sin^{-1}\left(\sqrt{2x + 1}\right)$

(c) $g(x) = \sqrt{\tan^{-1}(3x)}$

Answer:

(a) $f'(t) = \dfrac{1}{2(2 - t)\sqrt{1 - t}}$ (b) $f'(x) = \dfrac{1}{\sqrt{(-2x)(2x + 1)}}$ (c) $g'(x) = \dfrac{3}{2(1 + 9x^2)\sqrt{\tan^{-1} 3x}}$

32. Find the critical numbers for $f(x) = \tan^{-1}\left(\dfrac{x}{a}\right) - \tan^{-1}\left(\dfrac{x}{b}\right)$, $a > b$ and identify each as a relative maximum, relative minimum, or neither.

Answer: $f'(x) = \dfrac{1}{\left(1 + \dfrac{x^2}{a^2}\right) a} - \dfrac{1}{\left(1 + \dfrac{y^2}{b^2}\right) b} = \dfrac{(a - b)\left(x^2 - ab\right)}{(a^2 + x^2)(b^2 + x^2)}$

If $a \cdot b < 0$, $f(x)$ does not have critical numbers. If $a \cdot b > 0$, then $x = \pm\sqrt{ab}$ are critical numbers of $f(x)$.

$f\left(\sqrt{ab}\right) = \tan^{-1}\left(\dfrac{\sqrt{b}}{\sqrt{a}}\right) - \tan^{-1}\left(\dfrac{\sqrt{a}}{\sqrt{b}}\right)$ is a relative minimum value.

$f\left(-\sqrt{ab}\right) = -\tan^{-1}\left(\dfrac{\sqrt{b}}{\sqrt{a}}\right) + \tan^{-1}\left(\dfrac{\sqrt{a}}{\sqrt{b}}\right)$ is a relative maximum value.

33. Show that the curves $3x^2 + 2x - 3y^2 = 1$ and $6xy + 2y = 0$ are orthogonal.

Answer: $3x^2 + 2x - 3y^2 = 1 \Longrightarrow m_1 = \dfrac{dy}{dx} = \dfrac{6x + 2}{6y}$, $6xy + 2y = 0 \Longrightarrow m_2 = \dfrac{dy}{dx} = \dfrac{-6y}{6x + 2}$,

$m_1 \cdot m_2 = \dfrac{6x + 2}{6y} \cdot \dfrac{-6y}{6x + 2} = -1$

34. Show that the curves $x^3 - 3xy^2 + y = 0$ and $3x^2y - y^3 - x = 4$ are orthogonal.

Answer: $x^3 - 3xy^2 + y = 0 \Longrightarrow m_1 = \dfrac{dy}{dx} = \dfrac{3y^2 - 3x^2}{1 - 6xy}$, $3x^2y - y^3 - x = 4 \Longrightarrow m_2 = \dfrac{dy}{dx} = \dfrac{1 - 6xy}{3x^2 - 3y^2}$,

$m_1 \cdot m_2 = -1$

35. Contour lines on a map of a hilly region are curves that join points with the same elevation. The path of steepest ascent is orthogonal to the contour lines. Given the contour map below, sketch the path of steepest ascent from starting positions A and B to the highest point C.

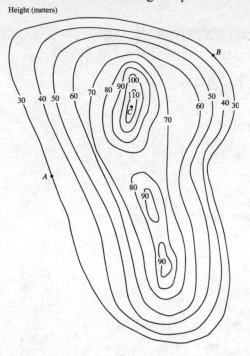

Answer:

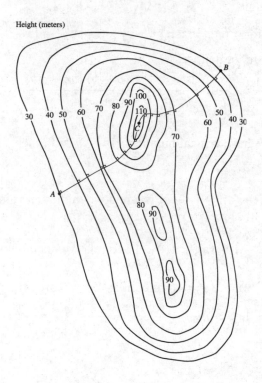

36. Lake bottoms are frequently mapped using contour lines, which are curves joining points of the same depth. The path of steepest descent is orthogonal to the contour lines. Given the contour map below, sketch the path of steepest descent from starting positions A and B to the deepest point C.

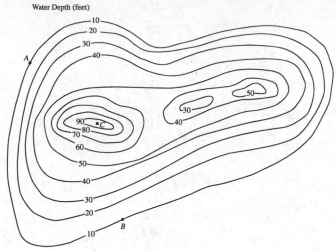

Answer:

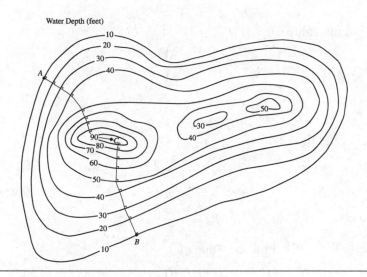

3.7	**Derivatives of Logarithmic Functions**

1. Let $f(x) = \log_2 x$. Find the value of $f'(1)$.

   (A) 2
   (B) e^2
   (C) $\ln\left(\frac{1}{2}\right)$
   (D) $e^{-1/2}$

   (E) 2^e
   (F) $\frac{1}{2}$
   (G) $\dfrac{1}{\ln 2}$
   (H) $e^{1/2}$

   Answer: (G)

2. Let $f(x) = \log_3 x^2$. Find the value of $f'(2)$.

   (A) 3^e
   (B) $\ln 3$
   (C) $\ln\left(\frac{1}{3}\right)$
   (D) 1

   (E) $\frac{1}{\sqrt{3}}$
   (F) $\dfrac{1}{\ln 3}$
   (G) $\frac{1}{3}$
   (H) $\sqrt{3}$

   Answer: (F)

3. Let $f(x) = \ln(\ln(x))$. Find the value of $f'(e)$.

(A) $\dfrac{1}{e^2}$ (B) e^2 (C) $1 + e$ (D) $\dfrac{1}{e}$

(E) $\ln 2$ (F) 1 (G) e (H) 0

Answer: (D)

4. Let $f(x) = \log_2(3x)$. Find the value of $f'(1)$.

(A) $\ln\left(\frac{1}{2}\right)$ (B) $e^{-1/3}$ (C) e^3 (D) 3

(E) $e^{1/3}$ (F) 3^e (G) $\frac{1}{3}$ (H) $\dfrac{1}{\ln 2}$

Answer: (H)

5. Let $f(x) = x\ln\left(x^2 - 3\right)$. Find the value of $f'(2)$.

(A) 0 (B) 2 (C) 4 (D) 6

(E) 8 (F) 10 (G) 12 (H) 14

Answer: (E)

6. Let $f(x) = x^{2x}$. Find the value of $f'(1)$.

(A) 2 (B) $e - 1$ (C) $e^e - 1$ (D) $e + 1$

(E) e (F) e^{e+1} (G) e^{e-1} (H) e^2

Answer: (A)

7. Let $f(x) = (\sin x)^x$. Find the value of $f'\left(\frac{\pi}{2}\right)$.

(A) 0 (B) 1 (C) 2 (D) $e^{\pi/2}$

(E) e^π (F) $\frac{\pi}{2}$ (G) π (H) 2π

Answer: (A)

8. Let $f(x) = \ln\left(3x^2 + 1 + e^{-x}\right)$. Find the value of $f'(0)$.

(A) -1 (B) 0 (C) $\frac{1}{2}$ (D) $-\frac{1}{2}$

(E) e^{-1} (F) $\sqrt{e}$ (G) $1 + \ln 2$ (H) $3\ln 2$

Answer: (D)

9. Let $f(x) = x^{1/x}$. Find the value of $f'(e)$.

(A) 0 (B) 1 (C) 2 (D) 3

(E) 4 (F) 5 (G) 6 (H) 7

Answer: (A)

10. Let $f(x) = 5^{\tan x}$. Find the value of $f'\left(\frac{\pi}{4}\right)$.

(A) 1 (B) 2 (C) 5 (D) 10

(E) $\ln 5$ (F) $2\ln 5$ (G) $5\ln 5$ (H) $10\ln 5$

Answer: (H)

11. Let $f(x) = x^{\sqrt{x}}$. Find the value of $f'(4)$.

    (A) 2   (B) 4   (C) 8   (D) 16

    (E) $2 + \ln 4$ (F) $4 + \ln 2$ (G) $8 + 4\ln 4$ (H) $16 + 4\ln 2$

    Answer: (G)

12. Let $f(x) = 2x + \ln x$ and let g be the inverse function of f. Find the value of $g'(2)$.

    (A) 1   (B) $\frac{1}{2}$ (C) $\frac{1}{3}$ (D) $\frac{1}{4}$

    (E) $\dfrac{1}{\ln 2}$ (F) $\dfrac{1}{2\ln 2}$ (G) $\dfrac{1}{e}$ (H) $\dfrac{1}{e^2}$

    Answer: (C)

13. Let $f(x) = \sqrt{x}\ln x$. Find the interval on which f is increasing.

    (A) $(0, \infty)$ (B) $(0, 1]$ (C) $[1, \infty)$ (D) $(0, e^{-1}]$

    (E) $[e^{-1}, \infty)$ (F) $(0, e^{-2}]$ (G) $[e^{-2}, \infty)$ (H) $(0, \sqrt{e})$

    Answer: (G)

14. Let $f(x) = \sqrt{x}\ln x$. Find the interval on which f is concave upward.

    (A) $(0, \infty)$ (B) $(0, 1]$ (C) $[1, \infty)$ (D) $(0, e^{-1}]$

    (E) $[e^{-1}, \infty)$ (F) $(0, e^{-2}]$ (G) $[e^{-2}, \infty)$ (H) $(0, \sqrt{e})$

    Answer: (B)

15. Find the interval on which the graph of $f(x) = \ln(x^2 + 1)$ is concave upward.

    (A) $(-1, 1)$ (B) $(-1, 2)$ (C) $(-2, 1)$ (D) $(-2, 2)$

    (E) $(-1, 3)$ (F) $(-3, 2)$ (G) $(-3, 3)$ (H) $(-\infty, \infty)$

    Answer: (A)

16. Find an equation of the tangent line to the graph of $y = x\ln x$ at the point $(1, 0)$.

    Answer: $y = x - 1$

17. Find the x-coordinate of the point at which the graph of $y = x\ln x$ has a horizontal tangent.

    Answer: $x = 1/e$

18. Find an equation of the tangent line to the graph of $y = \dfrac{\ln x}{x}$ at the point $\left(e^2, \dfrac{2}{e^2}\right)$.

    Answer: $y = -\dfrac{1}{e^4}x + \dfrac{3}{e^2}$

19. Find the x-coordinate of the point at which the graph of $y = \dfrac{\ln x}{x}$ has a horizontal tangent.

    Answer: $x = e$

20. Differentiate the following functions:

    (a) $f(x) = (\ln x)^3$

    (b) $f(x) = \sqrt{x}\ln x$

    (c) $f(x) = \ln\left(\dfrac{\tan x}{x^2 + 1}\right)$

Answer:

(a) $f'(x) = \dfrac{3(\ln x)^2}{x}$　　　　(b) $f'(x) = \dfrac{2 + \ln x}{2\sqrt{x}}$　　　　(c) $f'(x) = \dfrac{1}{\sin x \cos x} - \dfrac{2x}{x^2 + 1}$

21. Find $\dfrac{dy}{dx}$.

(a) $y = \ln(\sec x + \tan x)$

(b) $y = \ln \ln x$

(c) $y = x^{\sin x}$

Answer:

(a) $\dfrac{dy}{dx} = \sec x$　　　　(b) $\dfrac{dy}{dx} = \dfrac{1}{x \ln x}$　　　　(c) $\dfrac{dy}{dx} = x^{\sin x}\left(\cos x \ln x + \dfrac{\sin x}{x}\right)$

22. Find $\dfrac{dy}{dx}$.

(a) $y = \ln \sqrt{\dfrac{4x - 7}{x^2 + 2x}}$

(b) $y = (\ln(\sec x))^4$

(c) $y = \left(1 + \dfrac{1}{x}\right)^{2x}$

Answer:

(a) $\dfrac{dy}{dx} = \dfrac{2}{4x - 7} - \dfrac{x + 1}{x^2 + 2x}$　　　　(b) $\dfrac{dy}{dx} = 4(\ln(\sec x))^3 \tan x$

(c) $\dfrac{dy}{dx} = 2\left(1 + \dfrac{1}{x}\right)^{2x}\left(\ln\left(1 + \dfrac{1}{x}\right) - \dfrac{1}{x + 1}\right)$

23. If $y = \dfrac{(x + 3)\left(x^2 + 1\right)^3 (x + 1)^2}{\left(x^2 + 10\right)^{1/2}}$, find y' by logarithmic differentiation.

Answer: $y' = \left(\dfrac{1}{x + 3} + \dfrac{6x}{x^2 + 1} + \dfrac{2}{x + 1} - \dfrac{x}{x^2 + 10}\right) \cdot \dfrac{(x + 3)\left(x^2 + 1\right)^3 (x + 1)^2}{\left(x^2 + 10\right)^{1/2}}$

3.8 Linear Approximations and Differentials

1. Find the linear approximation to $f(x) = \dfrac{1}{(2 + x)^3}$ at $a = 0$.

(A) $\frac{1}{8} - \frac{1}{8}x$　　　　(B) $\frac{1}{8} + \frac{1}{8}x$　　　　(C) $\frac{1}{8} + \frac{3}{16}x$　　　　(D) $\frac{1}{8} + \frac{1}{16}x$

(E) $\frac{1}{8} - \frac{3}{16}x$　　　　(F) $\frac{1}{8} - \frac{3}{4}x$　　　　(G) $\frac{1}{8} - \frac{1}{16}x$　　　　(H) $\frac{1}{8} + \frac{3}{4}x$

Answer: (E)

2. Find the linear approximation to $f(x) = e^{-3x}$ at $a = 0$.

(A) $1 + x$　　　　(B) $1 + 3x$　　　　(C) $1 - x$　　　　(D) $1 - 3x$

(E) $3 + 3x$　　　　(F) $-3x$　　　　(G) $3 - 3x$　　　　(H) None of the above

Answer: (D)

3. Find the linear approximation to $f(x) = \sqrt[3]{x^2 - 1}$ at $a = 3$.

(A) $-1 + x$ (B) $2 + x$ (C) $1 + x$ (D) $2 + \frac{1}{2}x$

(E) $\frac{1}{2} - \frac{1}{2}x$ (F) $-\frac{1}{2} + \frac{1}{2}x$ (G) $\frac{1}{2} + \frac{1}{2}x$ (H) None of the above

Answer: (G)

4. Let $y = x^2$, $x = 2$, and $\Delta x = 1$. Find the value of the differential dy.

(A) 2   (B) $\frac{1}{2}$ (C) $\frac{1}{3}$ (D) 4

(E) $\frac{1}{4}$ (F) $\frac{1}{8}$ (G) 3   (H) 1

Answer: (D)

5. Let $y = x^2$, $x = 3$, and $\Delta x = 1$. Find the value of the corresponding change Δy.

(A) 4   (B) 8   (C) 7   (D) 2

(E) 3   (F) 6   (G) 1   (H) 5

Answer: (C)

6. Use differentials to approximate $\sqrt{26}$.

(A) 5.1   (B) 5.2   (C) 5.15   (D) 5.3

(E) 5.4   (F) 5.25   (G) 5.35   (H) 5.05

Answer: (A)

7. Use differentials to obtain an approximation for $\sqrt{16.2}$.

(A) 4.026   (B) 4.03   (C) 4.025   (D) 4.05

(E) 4.015   (F) 0.02498   (G) 4.0185   (H) 4.0245

Answer: (C)

8. Let $y = x^4 + x^2 + 1$, $x = 1$, and $dx = 1$. Find the value of the differential dy.

(A) 2   (B) 4   (C) 6   (D) 8

(E) 10   (F) 0.12   (G) 0   (H) $\frac{1}{2}$

Answer: (C)

9. Find the linear approximation of the function $f(x) = \sqrt{x + 3}$ at $x_1 = 1$ and use it to approximate $\sqrt{3.98}$.

(A) 2.005   (B) 2.000   (C) 1.995   (D) 1.990

(E) 1.985   (F) 1.980   (G) 1.975   (H) 1.970

Answer: (C)

10. Find the linear approximation of the function $f(x) = \sqrt{x + 3}$ at $x_1 = 1$ and use it to approximate $\sqrt{4.05}$.

(A) 2.0125   (B) 2.0120   (C) 2.0115   (D) 2.0110

(E) 2.0105   (F) 2.0100   (G) 2.0130   (H) 2.0135

Answer: (A)

11. Let $f(x) = x^{2/3}$.

  (a) Find a linear approximation of f at $x = 8$.

  (b) Use this linear approximation to estimate the value of the function at 7, 9, 7.99, and 8.01.

  (c) Make a table comparing your estimates with the actual function values. Discuss what this tells you about the linear approximation.

  (d) Graph the original function and its linear approximation over the interval $[7, 9]$. What does the graph tell you about the size of the difference between the function values and the linear approximation values?

Answer:

  (a) $y = \frac{1}{3}x + \frac{4}{3}$

(b), (c)

x	$x^{2/3}$	$\frac{1}{3}x + \frac{4}{3}$
7	3.65930	$3.\bar{6}$
9	4.32674	$4.\bar{3}$
7.99	3.99666	3.99666
8.01	4.00333	4.00333

The linear approximation $\frac{1}{3}x + \frac{4}{3}$ is a good approximation to $x^{2/3}$ when x is near 8.

(d)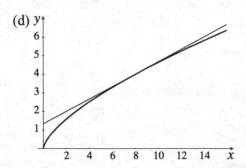

12. Use differentials to approximate the change in the function $f(x) = x^2 + x - 2$ when x varies from 1 to 1.01.

Answer: $\Delta y \approx dy = f'(1)\,\Delta x = (2x + 1) \cdot (1.01 - 1) = 3 \cdot 0.01 = 0.03$

13. (a) Find the linearization of the function $f(x) = \sin x$ when $x = 0$.

  (b) Use these results to approximate $\sin(0.05)$ and $\sin(-0.005)$.

Answer: (a) $l(x) = x$ (b) $\sin(0.05) \approx 0.05$; $\sin(-0.005) \approx -0.005$

14. The diameter of a sphere is measured to be 6 inches with a possible error of 0.05 inches. Use differentials to estimate the maximum error in the calculated surface area.

Answer: 0.6π in^2

15. The diameter of a sphere is measured to be 6 inches with a possible error of 0.05 inches. Use differentials to estimate the maximum error in the calculated volume.

Answer: 0.9π in^3

16. A side of a square field is measured to be 144 feet with a possible error of 1 inch.

  (a) Use differentials to estimate the maximum error in the calculated area of the field.

  (b) What is the relative error?

Answer: (a) 24 ft^2 (b) $\dfrac{24}{144^2} \approx 0.0012$

17. The period of a pendulum is given by the formula $T = 2\pi\sqrt{\dfrac{L}{g}}$, where L is the length of the pendulum in feet, $g = 32$ ft/s^2 is the acceleration due to gravity, and T is the length of one period in seconds. If the length of the pendulum is measured to be three feet long to within $\pm\frac{1}{8}$ inch, what is the approximate percentage error in the calculated period, T?

Answer: $T = \dfrac{2\pi}{\sqrt{g}}\sqrt{L} \Longrightarrow dT = \dfrac{2\pi}{\sqrt{g}}\dfrac{1}{2\sqrt{L}}\Delta L = \dfrac{\pi}{\sqrt{g}\sqrt{L}}\Delta L.\ \dfrac{\Delta T}{T} \approx \dfrac{dT}{T} = \dfrac{\pi\Delta L}{\sqrt{g}\sqrt{L}}\cdot\dfrac{\sqrt{g}}{2\pi\sqrt{L}} = \dfrac{\Delta L}{2L} = $

$\dfrac{\pm\frac{1}{8}}{2\cdot 3} = \pm\dfrac{1}{48}$

18. Show that for sufficiently small values of h, $\sqrt{4+h} \approx 2 + \dfrac{h}{4}$.

Answer: $L(x) = f(4) + f'(4)(x-4).\ f(x) = \sqrt{x}$ so $f(4) = 2$, and $f'(x) = \dfrac{1}{2\sqrt{x}}$ so $f'(4) = \frac{1}{4}$. Thus, $L(x) = 2 + \frac{1}{4}(x-4) = 2 + \frac{1}{4}h \approx \sqrt{4+h}$.

19. The linear approximation of a function is useful only if the change in x is small. Illustrate this fact by approximating $\sqrt{18}$ by regarding 18 to be "near" 36 instead of 16.

Answer: $L(x) = f(36) + f'(36)(x-36).\ f(x) = \sqrt{x} \Longrightarrow f(36) = 6$ and $f'(x) = \dfrac{1}{2\sqrt{x}} \Longrightarrow$ $f'(36) = \frac{1}{12}$, so $L(x) = 6 + \frac{1}{12}(x-36)$, and $L(18) = 6 + \frac{1}{12}(-18) = 4.5$. From a calculator, $\sqrt{18} = 4.2426407$.

For comparison, if we choose to regard 18 as being near 16, we have $L(x) = f(16) + f'(16)(x-16) = 4 + \frac{1}{8}(x-16)$ and $L(18) = 4 + \frac{1}{8}\cdot 2 = 4.25$

20. During the flood of 1997 in Fargo, North Dakota, the Red River of the North rose menacingly during the month of April. Suppose that the official river level at noon on day t is given by the function $R(t)$. We know that $R(\text{April } 9) = 35.5$ feet and $R'(\text{April } 9) = 1$.

(a) What are the units of $R'(t)$?

(b) Construct a linear function to estimate the water level of the Red River for dates near April 9.

(c) Use this model from part (b) to estimate $R(\text{April } 7)$ and $R(\text{April } 11)$.

(d) The Red River crested on April 17 at 39.79 feet. What is $R'(\text{April } 17)$?

(e) If the Red River level on April 22, $R(\text{April } 22)$, was 39 feet and $R'(\text{April } 22)$ was -0.3, use a linear model to estimate $R(\text{April } 26)$.

Answer:

(a) Its units are feet per day.

(b) Let $T = 0$ represent April 9. Then $L(t) = R(0) + R'(0)t = 35.5 + t$.

(c) $R(\text{April } 7) \approx L(-2) = 35.5 - 2 = 33.5$ ft, $R(\text{April } 11) \approx L(2) = 35.5 + 2 = 37.5$ ft

(d) $R'(\text{April } 17) = 0$.

(e) Let $t = 0$ be April 22. Then $L(t) = 39 - 0.3t$, so $R(\text{April } 26) \approx L(4) = 39 - 0.3\cdot 4 = 37.8$ ft.

21. Let $f(x) = x^3 - 4x^2$.

   (a) Find a linear approximation of f at $x = 1$.

   (b) Use this linear approximation to predict the value of the function at $-1, 0, 0.9, 1.1, 2,$ and 3.

   (c) Make a table comparing your estimates with the actual function values. Discuss what this tells you about the linear approximation.

   (d) Graph the original function and its linear approximation over the interval $[-1, 3]$. What does the graph tell you about the size of the difference between the function values and the linear approximation values?

Answer:

   (a) $y = -5x + 2$

(b), (c)

x	$x^3 - 4x^2$	$-5x + 2$
-1	-5	7
0	0	2
0.9	-2.511	-2.5
1.1	-3.509	-3.5
2	-8	-8
3	-9	-13

(d)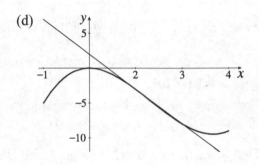

The linear approximation $-5x + 2$ is a good approximation to $x^3 - 4x^2$ when x is near 1, but it is not a good approximation for x far away from 1, $(2, -8)$ is the intersection point of $y = x^3 - 4x^2$ and $y = -5x + 2$.

22. Let $f(x) = \cos^2 x$.

   (a) Find a linear approximation of f at $x = \frac{\pi}{3}$.

   (b) Use this linear approximation to predict the value of the function at $\frac{\pi}{3} - 1, \frac{\pi}{3} - 0.1, \frac{\pi}{3} + 1,$ and $\frac{\pi}{3} + 0.1$.

   (c) Make a table comparing your estimates with the actual function values. Discuss what this tells you about the linear approximation.

   (d) Graph the original function and its linear approximation over the interval $\left[\frac{\pi}{3} - 1, \frac{\pi}{3} + 1\right]$. What does the graph tell you about the size of the difference between the function values and the linear approximation values?

Answer:

(a) $-\frac{\sqrt{3}}{2}x + \frac{\sqrt{3}\pi}{6} + \frac{1}{4}$

(b), (c)

x	$\cos^2 x$	$-\frac{\sqrt{3}}{2}x + \frac{\sqrt{3}\pi}{6} + \frac{1}{4}$
$\frac{\pi}{3} - 1$	0.997773	1.11602
$\frac{\pi}{3} - 0.1$	0.341009	0.336602
$\frac{\pi}{3} + 1$	0.210299	−0.616025
$\frac{\pi}{3} + 0.1$	0.168957	0.163397

The linear approximation $-\frac{\sqrt{3}}{2}x + \frac{\sqrt{3}\pi}{6} + \frac{1}{4}$ is a good approximation to $\cos^2 x$ when x is near $\frac{\pi}{3}$.

(d)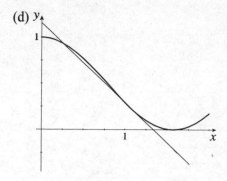

4 Applications of Differentiation

4.1 Related Rates

1. The length of a rectangle is increasing at the rate of 2 feet per second, while the width is increasing at the rate of 1 foot per second. When the length is 5 feet and the width is 3 feet, how fast is the area increasing?

(A) 5 ft^2/s   (B) 11 ft^2/s   (C) 6 ft^2/s   (D) 10 ft^2/s

(E) 15 ft^2/s   (F) 20 ft^2/s   (G) 8 ft^2/s   (H) 12 ft^2/s

Answer: (B)

2. The length of a rectangle is increasing at the rate of 2 feet per second, while the width is increasing at the rate of 1 foot per second. When the length is 4 feet and the width is 3 feet, how fast is the length of the diagonal of the rectangle increasing?

(A) 1 ft/s   (B) 1.5 ft/s   (C) 2.5 ft/s   (D) 1.2 ft/s

(E) 2 ft/s   (F) 2.3 ft/s   (G) 2.2 ft/s   (H) 3 ft/s

Answer: (G)

3. The length of a rectangle is decreasing at the rate of 1 foot per second, but the area remains constant. How fast is the rectangle's width increasing when its length is 10 feet and its width is 5 feet?

(A) $\frac{1}{2}$ ft/s   (B) 4 ft/s   (C) $\frac{1}{10}$ ft/s   (D) 2 ft/s

(E) 5 ft/s   (F) $\frac{1}{4}$ ft/s   (G) 10 ft/s   (H) $\frac{1}{5}$ ft/s

Answer: (A)

4. A ladder 10 feet long is leaning against a wall. If the foot of the ladder is being pulled away from the wall at 3 feet per second, how fast is the top of the ladder sliding down the wall when the foot of the ladder is 8 feet away from the wall?

(A) 6 ft/s   (B) 1 ft/s   (C) 3 ft/s   (D) 10 ft/s

(E) 5 ft/s   (F) 8 ft/s   (G) 2 ft/s   (H) 4 ft/s

Answer: (H)

5. A ladder 10 feet long is leaning against a wall. If the top of the ladder is sliding down the wall at 4 feet per second, how fast is the foot of the ladder being pulled away from the wall when the foot of the ladder is 8 feet away from the wall?

(A) 6 ft/s   (B) 1 ft/s   (C) 3 ft/s   (D) 10 ft/s

(E) 5 ft/s   (F) 8 ft/s   (G) 2 ft/s   (H) 4 ft/s

Answer: (C)

6. A ladder 10 feet long is leaning against a wall. If the top of the ladder is sliding down the wall at 4 feet per second, how fast is the angle between the top of the ladder and the wall changing when the foot of the ladder is 8 feet away from the wall?

(A) 4 rad/s   (B) 5 rad/s   (C) $\frac{2}{3}$ rad/s   (D) $\frac{3}{2}$ rad/s

(E) 3 rad/s   (F) $\frac{1}{2}$ rad/s   (G) 2 rad/s   (H) $\frac{3}{10}$ rad/s

Answer: (F)

7. Two cars are each 100 miles away from the town of Tucumcari, one directly to the north and the other directly to the east. The car to the north is heading toward the town at 60 miles per hour, while the one to the east is heading toward the town at 30 miles per hour. How fast are the cars approaching each other?

(A) $200\sqrt{2}$ mi/h   (B) 100 mi/h   (C) $100\sqrt{2}$ mi/h   (D) 200 mi/h

(E) $50\sqrt{2}$ mi/h   (F) $45\sqrt{2}$ mi/h   (G) 45 mi/h   (H) 50 mi/h

Answer: (F)

8. A plane flying horizontally at an altitude of 1 km and a speed of 500 km/h passes directly over a radar station. Find the rate at which the distance from the plane to the station is increasing when it is 2 km away from the station.

(A) $125\sqrt{3}$ km/h   (B) $175\sqrt{3}$ km/h   (C) $250\sqrt{3}$ km/h   (D) $275\sqrt{3}$ km/h

(E) $125\sqrt{2}$ km/h   (F) $175\sqrt{2}$ km/h   (G) $250\sqrt{2}$ km/h   (H) $275\sqrt{2}$ km/h

Answer: (C)

9. A lighthouse is on a small island 3 km away from the nearest point P on a straight shoreline, and its light makes 4 revolutions per minute. At what rate is the beam of light moving along the shoreline when it is 1 km away from P?

(A) 20π km/min   (B) $\frac{70\pi}{3}$ km/min   (C) $\frac{80\pi}{3}$ km/min   (D) $\frac{100\pi}{3}$ km/min

(E) $\frac{110\pi}{3}$ km/min   (F) 40π km/min   (G) $\frac{130\pi}{3}$ km/min   (H) $\frac{140\pi}{3}$ km/min

Answer: (C)

10. A rectangular swimming pool with a horizontal bottom is being drained. If its length and width are 25 ft and 20 ft, and the water level is falling at the rate of $\frac{1}{2}$ ft/min, how fast is the water draining?

Answer: 250 ft^3/min

11. Let V be the volume of a cylinder having height h and radius r, and assume that h and r vary with time. When the height is 5 in. and is increasing at 0.2 in./s, the radius is 3 in. and is decreasing at 0.1 in./s. How fast is the volume changing at that instant? Is the volume increasing or decreasing at that instant?

Answer: $\frac{dV}{dt} = -1.2\pi$ in^3/s. It is decreasing.

12. A kite is flying 100 feet above the ground at the end of a string 125 feet long. The girl flying the kite lets out the string at a rate of 1 foot per second. If the kite remains 100 feet above the ground, how fast is its horizontal distance from the girl increasing?

Answer: $\frac{5}{3}$

124

13. A student 5 feet tall is 10 feet away from a lamppost 15 feet tall. She is walking away from the lamppost at 2 feet per second. How fast is the tip of her shadow moving away from the foot of the lamppost?

    Answer: 3

14. A frugal young man has decided to extract one of his teeth by tying a stout rubber band from his tooth to the chain on a garage door opener which runs on a horizontal track 3 feet above his mouth. If the garage door opener moves the chain at $\frac{1}{4}$ ft/s, how fast is the rubber band expanding when it is stretched to a length of 5 feet?

    Answer: $\frac{1}{5}$ ft/s

15. Two straight roads intersect at right angles in Newtonville. Car A is on one road moving toward the intersection at a speed of 50 miles/h. Car B is on the other road moving away from the intersection at a speed of 30 miles/h. When car A is 2 miles from the intersection and car B is 4 miles from the intersection, how fast is the distance between the cars changing?

    Answer: $\sqrt{20}$ mi/h

16. A particle starts at the origin and moves along the parabola $y = x^2$ such that its distance from the origin increases at 4 units per second. How fast is its x-coordinate changing as it passes through the point $(1, 1)$?

    Answer: $4\sqrt{2}/3$ units/s

17. A particle moves along a path described by $y = 4 - x^2$. At what point along the curve are x and y changing at the same rate?

    Answer: $\left(-\frac{1}{2}, \frac{15}{4}\right)$

18. Mr. Wilson is standing near the top of a ladder 24 feet long which is leaning against a vertical wall of his house. Dennis, the little boy next door, ties a rope from his tricycle to the bottom of the ladder and starts to pull the foot of the ladder away from the house wall. The bottom end of the ladder begins to slide away from the wall at the rate of 1 foot per second.

    (a) How fast is the top of the ladder sliding down the wall when the foot of the ladder is 8 feet from the wall?

    (b) How fast is the top of the ladder sliding down the wall when the top of the ladder is 16 feet from the ground?

    (c) How fast is the angle between the top of the ladder and the wall changing when the foot of the ladder is 8 feet from the wall?

    Answer: (a) $-\frac{\sqrt{2}}{4}$ ft/s   (b) $-\frac{\sqrt{5}}{2}$ ft/s   (c) $\frac{\sqrt{2}}{32}$

19. A boat floating several feet away from a dock is pulled toward the dock by a rope wound by a winch at the rate of 20 feet per minute. If the winch is 10 feet above the level of the boat, how fast is the boat moving through the water when there is 100 feet of rope between the boat and the winch?

    Answer: $\frac{200\sqrt{11}}{33}$ ft/min

20. A stone dropped into a still pond sends out a circular ripple whose radius increases at a constant rate of 3 feet per second. Does the area also increase at a constant rate? Explain your answer.

Answer: No, since $\dfrac{dA}{dt} = 2\pi r \dfrac{dr}{dt} = 6\pi r$ ft^2/s. The rate of change of the area of the circle depends on the radius of the ripple.

21. The pressure P (in kilopascals), volume V (in liters), and temperature T (in degrees Kelvin), of a mole of an ideal gas are related by the equation $PV = 8.31\,T$. Find the rate at which the pressure in a container of gas is changing when the temperature is $300\,^\circ$K and increasing at a rate of $0.1\,^\circ$K/s and the volume is 100 liters and increasing at a rate of 0.2 L/s.

Answer: -0.04155 kilopascals/s

22. A man who is 6 feet tall walks away from a 24 foot tall lamppost at a constant rate of w feet per second. Does the tip of the man's shadow also move at a constant rate? Explain your answer.

Answer: Yes, since the tip of the man's shadow moves at the rate of $\frac{4}{3}w$ ft/s.

23. If a diagonal of a square increases at the rate of 1 inch/s, how fast is the area changing when the side of the square is 13 inches?

Answer: $13\sqrt{2}$ in^2/s

24. A water tank has the shape of an inverted circular cone with base radius 6 feet and height of 12 feet. The tank is full of water. If the water level is falling at the rate of 2 inches/m, how fast is the tank losing water when the water is 8 feet deep?

Answer: -32π ft^3/m

25. A hot air balloon is rising vertically. An observer on the ground is 2000 meters from the point where the balloon took off. The angle between the ground and the observer's line of sight increases at a rate of $\frac{1}{2000}$ radian/s when the balloon reaches a height of 3000 meters. How fast is the balloon rising at that moment?

Answer: 3.25 m/s

26. Two cars start moving from the same point. One travels south at v miles per hour and the other travels west at w miles per hour. Show that the rate of the distance between two cars is changing at a constant rate of $\sqrt{v^2 + w^2}$ miles per hour.

Answer: $\dfrac{dx}{dt} = v$ and $\dfrac{dy}{dt} = w$, so $x = vt$, $y = wt$, and $D = \sqrt{(vt)^2 + (wt)^2}$. $D^2 = x^2 + y^2 \;\Rightarrow\;$

$2D\dfrac{dD}{dt} = 2x\dfrac{dx}{dt} + 2\dfrac{dy}{dt} \;\Rightarrow\; \dfrac{dD}{dt} = \dfrac{xv + yw}{D} = \dfrac{v^2 t + w^2 t}{\sqrt{(vt)^2 + (wt)^2}} = \sqrt{v^2 + w^2}.$

4.2 | Maximum and Minimum Values

1. Find all critical numbers for the function $f(x) = x^3 - 12x^2$.

(A) 0 (B) 0, 8 (C) 0, 4 (D) No critical number

(E) 8 (F) 1, −1 (G) 4 (H) None of the above

Answer: (B)

2. Find all critical numbers for the function $f(x) = \dfrac{x-1}{x+1}$.

   (A) 1   (B) 1, 2   (C) -1 (D) No critical number

   (E) 2   (F) 1, -1 (G) $-1, 2$ (H) None of the above

Answer: (D)

3. Find all critical numbers for the function $f(x) = \sqrt[3]{9 - x^2}$.

   (A) 0   (B) -3 (C) $0, -3$ (D) No critical number

   (E) 3   (F) 3, -3 (G) $0, 3, -3$ (H) None of the above

Answer: (G)

4. Find all critical numbers for the function $f(x) = \dfrac{1}{x^2 - 9}$.

   (A) 0   (B) -3 (C) $0, -3$ (D) No critical number

   (E) 3   (F) 3, -3 (G) $0, 3, -3$ (H) None of the above

Answer: (A)

5. Find all critical numbers for the function $f(x) = \left| x^2 - 9 \right|$.

   (A) 0   (B) -3 (C) $0, -3$ (D) No critical number

   (E) 3   (F) 3, -3 (G) $0, 3, -3$ (H) None of the above

Answer: (G)

6. Find the minimum value of the function $f(x) = x^2 - 2x + 2$.

   (A) -1 (B) $\frac{3}{4}$ (C) $\frac{1}{2}$ (D) 1

   (E) $-\frac{1}{2}$ (F) 0   (G) $-\frac{1}{4}$ (H) $\frac{1}{4}$

Answer: (D)

7. Find the value x at which the minimum of the function $f(x) = x^2 - 2x + 2$ occurs.

   (A) 1   (B) $-\frac{1}{4}$ (C) $-\frac{1}{2}$ (D) $\frac{3}{4}$

   (E) 0   (F) $\frac{1}{4}$ (G) -1 (H) $\frac{1}{2}$

Answer: (A)

8. Find the distance between the two critical numbers of the function $f(x) = x^3 - 3x + 27$.

   (A) 4   (B) 1   (C) 8   (D) 3

   (E) 2   (F) 9   (G) 6   (H) 5

Answer: (E)

9. Find the difference between the local maximum and the local minimum values of the function $f(x) = x^3 - 3x + 27$.

   (A) 4   (B) 1   (C) 9   (D) 2

   (E) 6   (F) 5   (G) 8   (H) 3

Answer: (A)

10. Find the absolute maximum of the function $f(x) = x^3 - x^2 - x$ on the interval $-10 \le x \le 2$.

    (A) $\frac{1}{9}$ (B) $\frac{1}{5}$ (C) 0 (D) $\frac{1}{7}$

    (E) 1 (F) $\frac{1}{4}$ (G) $\frac{1}{3}$ (H) 2

    Answer: **(H)**

11. Find the absolute minimum and maximum values of the function $f(x) = 4x^3 - 15x^2 + 12x + 7$ on the closed interval $[0, 3]$.

    (A) $0, 3$ (B) $0, 5$ (C) $3, 5$ (D) $3, 9.75$

    (E) $3, 16$ (F) $5, 7$ (G) $7, 16$ (H) $5, 10.25$

    Answer: **(E)**

12. Find the minimum and maximum values of $y = x^3 - 9x + 8$ on the interval $[-3, 1]$.

    (A) $8, 8 + 6\sqrt{3}$ (B) $0, 8 + 6\sqrt{3}$

    (C) $0, 8$ (D) $8, 8 + \sqrt{3}$

    (E) $0, 8 + \sqrt{3}$ (F) $8 + \sqrt{3}, 8 + 6\sqrt{3}$

    (G) $\sqrt{3}, 8$ (H) $\sqrt{3}, 8 + 6\sqrt{3}$

    Answer: **(B)**

13. Given that $f(x) = x^3 + ax^2 + bx$ has critical numbers at $x = 1$ and $x = 3$, find a and b.

    (A) $-9, 6$ (B) $-8, 7$ (C) $-7, 8$ (D) $-6, 9$

    (E) $-9, 3$ (F) $-8, 4$ (G) $-7, 5$ (H) $-6, 6$

    Answer: **(D)**

14. Find the absolute maximum of the function $f(x) = \dfrac{e^{-x}}{1 + x^2}$.

    (A) $\frac{4}{3}$ (B) 1 (C) e^{-1} (D) $e^{-1/2}$

    (E) 2 (F) $\frac{1}{2}$ (G) $\frac{3}{2}$ (H) No absolute maximum

    Answer: **(H)**

15. Find the maximum and minimum values of $f(x) = x - \ln x^{100}$ where $1 \le x \le 100$.

    Answer: Maximum value 1; minimum value $100(1 - 2\ln 10)$

16. Find the maximum and minimum values of $f(x) = |9 - x^2|$ where $-2 \le x \le 4$.

    Answer: Maximum value 9; minimum value 0

17. Use the graph to state the absolute and local maximum and minimum values of the function:

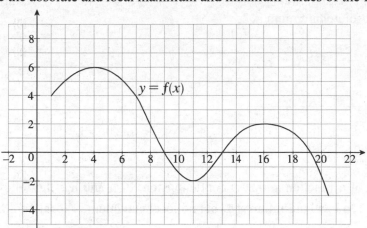

Answer: $f(x)$ has an absolute maximum value of 6 and an absolute minimum value of -3. $f(x)$ has local maximum values of 2 and 6, and a local minimum value of -2.

18. The graph of the derivative of $f(x)$ is given. Find the critical numbers of f and determine whether f has a local maximum or minimum at each critical number.

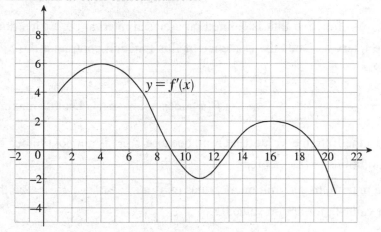

Answer: Critical numbers 9, 13, and approximately 19.25; local maxima at 9 and 19.25; local minimum at 13

19. Sketch the graph of a function f that is continuous on $[0, 4]$ and has the following properties: Absolute minimum at 0, absolute maximum at 4, local maximum at 2, and local minimum at 3.

Answer:

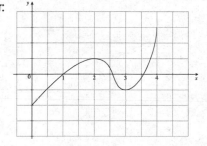

20. Sketch the graph of a function f that is continuous on $[0, 4]$ and has the following properties: Absolute maximum at 1, absolute minimum at 3.

Answer:

21. Sketch the graph of a function f that is continuous on $[0, 4]$ and has the following properties: Critical numbers at 1 and 3, a local minimum at 1, but no local maximum or local minimum at 3.

Answer:

22. Give an example of a function that is defined on a closed interval but which does not have an absolute maximum on the interval. Does the existence of this function contradict the Extreme Value Theorem? Why or why not?

Answer: Let $f(x) = \begin{cases} 1/x & \text{if } 0 < x \le 4 \\ 1 & \text{if } x = 0 \end{cases}$ $f(x)$ does not have an absolute maximum on $[0, 4]$. It is not a counterexample to the Extreme Value Theorem, because $f(x)$ is not continuous over $[0, 4]$ and thus does not satisfy the conditions of the theorem.

23. Find the absolute maximum and minimum values of $f(x) = 2x^3 + 3x^2 + 4$ on the interval $[-2, 1]$.

Answer: Maximum value 9, minimum value 0

24. Find the absolute maximum and minimum values of $f(x) = \dfrac{x}{x^2 + 1} + 1$ on the interval $[0, 2\pi]$.

Answer: Maximum value 1.5, minimum value 1

25. Find the range of the function $f(x) = e^{\cos x}$.

Answer: $\dfrac{1}{e} \le f(x) \le e$

26. Let $f(x) = \dfrac{\ln x}{x}$. Find the maximum value of f.

Answer: $1/e$

27. Find the minimum value of the function $f(x) = x \ln x$.

Answer: $-1/e$

28. Find the absolute maximum of the function $f(x) = \dfrac{e^{-x}}{1 + x^2}$.

Answer: No absolute maximum

29. Find the minimum value of $f(x) = \dfrac{e^x}{x}$ on $(0, \infty)$.

Answer: e

30. Find the maximum and minimum values of $f(x) = x\sqrt{2-x}$ and sketch its graph.

Answer: Maximum value $\frac{4\sqrt{6}}{9}$, no minimum value

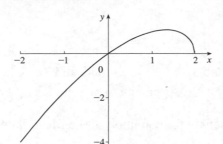

31. A ball is thrown straight upward from the top of a tower. After t seconds its height in feet above the ground is given by $h(t) = 48 + 32t - 16t^2$. What is the greatest height that the ball will attain?

Answer: 64 ft

32. A manufacturer estimates that the profit in dollars from producing x yards of a certain fabric will be $P(x) = 40x - 0.01x^2 - 600$. How many yards should she produce to yield a maximum profit?

Answer: 2000 yd

33. A rancher intends to fence off three sides of a rectangular region along a straight stretch of river (no fence along the river). The enclosed area is to be 1800 square meters. The total length of fencing material, F, needed is given by $F = 2x + \dfrac{1800}{x}$, where x represents the lengths of the sides that are perpendicular to the river. What is the least amount of fencing material that is needed?

Answer: 120 m

34. The quantity of charge Q, in Coulombs, that has passed through a point in a wire up to time t (in seconds) is given by $Q(t) = t^3 - t^2 + 6t + 1$. At what time is the current the lowest?

Answer: 0

4.3 Derivatives and the Shapes of Curves

1. Consider the function $f(x) = x^2$ on the interval $\left[0, \frac{1}{2}\right]$. According to the Mean Value Theorem, there must be a number c in $\left(0, \frac{1}{2}\right)$ such that $f'(c)$ is equal to a particular value d. What is d?

(A) $\frac{3}{2}$ (B) 1   (C) $\frac{1}{2}$ (D) 2

(E) $\frac{2}{3}$ (F) $\frac{3}{4}$ (G) $\frac{1}{4}$ (H) 3

Answer: (C)

2. Which of the statements below are true?

    1 If $f'(c) = 0$, then $f(x)$ has a maximum or minimum value at $x = c$.

    2 If $f'(x) = g'(x)$ for all x in an interval I, then $f(x) = g(x)$ on I.

    3 If $f(x)$ is differentiable on the open interval (a, b), and c is a point of local maximum for f in (a, b), then $f'(c) = 0$.

(A) None	(B) 1	(C) 2	(D) 3
(E) 1 and 2	(F) 1 and 3	(G) 2 and 3	(H) All

Answer: (D)

3. Find all value(s) (if any) that satisfy the condition of the Mean Value Theorem for the function $f(x) = 10 - \dfrac{16}{x}$ on the interval $[2, 8]$.

Answer: 4

4. Find all value(s) of c (if any) that satisfy the conclusion of the Mean Value Theorem for the function $f(x) = \dfrac{1}{1 + x}$ on the interval $[0, 1]$.

(A) $\frac{1}{2}$	(B) $\frac{1}{\sqrt{2}}$	(C) $\frac{1}{4}$	(D) $-\frac{1}{4}$
(E) $\sqrt{2} - 1$	(F) $2 - \sqrt{2}$	(G) 0	(H) No value

Answer: (E)

5. At what value of x does the function $f(x) = \dfrac{1}{1 + x^2}$ change from increasing to decreasing?

(A) 1	(B) -1	(C) $-\frac{1}{2}$	(D) 2
(E) $\frac{1}{2}$	(F) -2	(G) 0	(H) $-\frac{3}{2}$

Answer: (G)

6. At what value of x does the function $f(x) = 3x - \sqrt[3]{x}$ change from decreasing to increasing?

(A) $\frac{1}{8}$	(B) $\frac{1}{2}$	(C) $\frac{1}{3}$	(D) $\frac{1}{27}$
(E) $\frac{1}{9}$	(F) $\frac{\sqrt{3}}{4}$	(G) $\frac{\sqrt{3}}{3}$	(H) $\frac{1}{32}$

Answer: (D)

7. At what value of x does the function $f(x) = x^3 - 3x^2 - 9x$ change from decreasing to increasing?

(A) 3	(B) 1	(C) 4	(D) -3
(E) 2	(F) 0	(G) -2	(H) -1

Answer: (A)

8. What is the length of the largest interval on which the function $f(x) = x^3 - 3x^2 - 9x$ is decreasing?

(A) $3\sqrt{2}$	(B) 1	(C) 4	(D) $2\sqrt{2}$
(E) 3	(F) $2\sqrt{3}$	(G) $\sqrt{3}$	(H) 2

Answer: (C)

9. What is the length of the largest interval on which the function $f(x) = \dfrac{x}{x^2+1}$ is increasing?

(A) 3   (B) $2\sqrt{3}$ (C) $2\sqrt{2}$ (D) 1

(E) 4   (F) $\sqrt{3}$ (G) 2   (H) $3\sqrt{2}$

Answer: (G)

10. The function $f(x) = x + 1/x$, $x \neq 0$, is

(A) Increasing on $(-1, 0)$.   (B) Decreasing on $(0, 1)$.

(C) Increasing on $(0, 1)$.   (D) Decreasing on $(1, \infty)$.

(E) Increasing on $(0, \infty)$.   (F) Decreasing on $(0, \infty)$.

(G) Increasing on $(-\infty, 0)$.   (H) Decreasing on $(-\infty, 0)$.

Answer: (B)

11. On what interval is the function $f(x) = \dfrac{x}{x^2+1}$ increasing?

(A) $[-1, 1]$ (B) $[-1, 2]$ (C) $[-2, 1]$ (D) $[-2, 2]$

(E) $(-\infty, 1]$ (F) $(-\infty, 2)$ (G) $[-2, \infty)$ (H) $(-\infty, \infty)$

Answer: (A)

12. Find the interval on which $f(x) = x - 2\sin x$, $0 \leq x \leq 2\pi$ is increasing.

(A) $\left[\frac{\pi}{3}, \frac{5\pi}{3}\right]$ (B) $\left[0, \frac{\pi}{3}\right]$ (C) $\left[\frac{5\pi}{3}, 2\pi\right]$ (D) $\left[0, \frac{\pi}{2}\right]$

(E) $\left[\frac{\pi}{2}, \frac{3\pi}{2}\right]$ (F) $\left[\frac{3\pi}{2}, 2\pi\right]$ (G) $[0, \pi]$ (H) $[\pi, 2\pi]$

Answer: (A)

13. Find the interval on which $f(x) = x + \cos x$, $0 \leq x \leq 2\pi$ is increasing.

(A) $\left[\frac{\pi}{3}, \frac{5\pi}{3}\right]$ (B) $\left[0, \frac{\pi}{3}\right]$ (C) $\left[\frac{5\pi}{3}, 2\pi\right]$ (D) $\left[0, \frac{\pi}{2}\right]$

(E) $\left[\frac{\pi}{2}, \frac{3\pi}{2}\right]$ (F) $\left[\frac{3\pi}{2}, 2\pi\right]$ (G) $[0, \pi]$ (H) $[0, 2\pi]$

Answer: (H)

14. Find the interval on which $f(x) = xe^{-x}$ is increasing.

(A) $(-\infty, 1]$ (B) $(-\infty, 2]$ (C) $(-\infty, 3]$ (D) $[1, 2]$

(E) $[1, e]$ (F) $(-\infty, e]$ (G) $(-\infty, \infty)$ (H) $(-\infty, 1/e]$

Answer: (A)

15. Find the x-coordinate of the point of inflection of the function $f(x) = x^3 - x^2 - x + 1$.

(A) $-\frac{3}{4}$ (B) $-\frac{3}{2}$ (C) $\frac{3}{4}$ (D) $-\frac{1}{3}$

(E) $\frac{3}{2}$ (F) $\frac{1}{3}$ (G) $-\frac{2}{3}$ (H) $\frac{2}{3}$

Answer: (F)

16. Find the y-coordinate of the point of inflection of the function $f(x) = x^3 - 3x^2$.

(A) 2   (B) -2 (C) 0   (D) 2

(E) -1 (F) 1   (G) $-\frac{2}{3}$ (H) $\frac{2}{3}$

Answer: (B)

133

17. How many points of inflection does the function $f(x) = 3x^5 - 10x^3 + 5$ have?

(A) 5   (B) 0   (C) 2   (D) 7

(E) 6   (F) 1   (G) 3   (H) 4

Answer: (G)

18. How many points of inflection does the function $f(x) = x^8 - x^2$ have?

(A) 1   (B) 0   (C) 4   (D) 5

(E) 6   (F) 3   (G) 2   (H) 7

Answer: (G)

19. How many points of inflection does the function $f(x) = x^4 - 4x^3 + 6x^2$ have?

(A) 7   (B) 3   (C) 2   (D) 6

(E) 0   (F) 1   (G) 5   (H) 4

Answer: (E)

20. How many points of inflection does $f(x) = x^3 e^{-x}$ have?

(A) 0   (B) 1   (C) 2   (D) 3

(E) 4   (F) 5   (G) 6   (H) Infinitely many

Answer: (D)

21. On what interval is the graph of $f(x) = (1 - 1/x)^2$ concave downward?

(A) $(-\infty, 0)$ (B) $\left(\frac{3}{2}, \infty\right)$ (C) $(0, \infty)$ (D) $(1, \infty)$

(E) $(-\infty, -1)$ (F) $\left(1, \frac{3}{2}\right)$ (G) $\left(-\frac{3}{2}, -1\right)$ (H) $(0, 1)$

Answer: (B)

22. Determine the largest interval on which the function $f(x) = x + 1/x$ is concave upward.

(A) $(-1, 0)$ (B) $(-\infty, -1)$ (C) $(-\infty, 0)$ (D) $(0, \infty)$

(E) $(1, \infty)$ (F) $(0, 1)$ (G) $\left(0, \frac{1}{2}\right)$ (H) $\left(-\frac{1}{2}, 0\right)$

Answer: (D)

23. Find the interval on which the graph of $f(x) = \ln\left(x^2 + 1\right)$ is concave upward.

(A) $(-1, 1)$ (B) $(-1, 2)$ (C) $(-2, 1)$ (D) $(-2, 2)$

(E) $(-1, 3)$ (F) $(-3, 2)$ (G) $(-3, 3)$ (H) $(-\infty, \infty)$

Answer: (A)

24. Find the minimum value of the function $f(x) = x \ln x$.

(A) $-e$ (B) -1 (C) $-1/e$ (D) 0

(E) e (F) $e^{1/e}$ (G) e^e (H) e^{-e}

Answer: (C)

25. On the domain $(0, \infty)$, find the minimum value of $f(x) = e^x/x$.

(A) 0 (B) $1/e^2$ (C) $1/e$ (D) 1

(E) $e - 1$ (F) e (G) $e^2 - 1$ (H) e^2

Answer: (F)

26. Use the graph of f to estimate the values of c that satisfy the Mean Value Theorem for the interval $[0, 8]$.

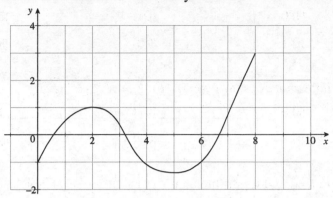

Answer: 1.4 or 5.5

27. Use the graph of f to estimate the values of c that satisfy the Mean Value Theorem for the interval $[0, 8]$.

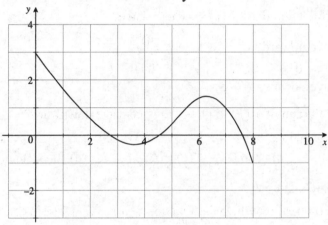

Answer: 3 or 6.5

28. If f is continuous over $[1, 3]$ and differentiable over $(1, 3)$, suppose that $2 \leq f'(x) \leq 5$ for all x in $[1, 3]$, and $f(1) = 4$. What is the maximum possible value that $f(3)$ can be? What is the minimum possible value that $f(3)$ can be?

Answer: The maximum possible value of $f(3)$ is 14, the minimum possible value of $f(3)$ is 8

29. If $f(x)$ is continuous over the closed interval $[1, 4]$ and differentiable on the open interval $(1, 4)$, and that $f'(x) \leq 5$ for all x in $[1, 4]$. If $f(1) = 2$, what is the maximum possible value that $f(4)$ can be?

Answer: The maximum possible value of $f(4)$ is 17.

30. While driving through a certain state, a tourist passed through a turnpike toll booth and got a ticket punched for 2:10 p.m. Down the road 74 miles, the tourist exited the turnpike and handed in his ticket which was punched at 3:05 p.m. In addition to the toll amount, he was handed a speeding ticket for driving in excess of 80 miles per hour in a 65 mph zone. Is the speeding ticket justifiable? Explain.

Answer: Yes, since his average velocity is about 80.72 mi/h.

31. The graph of f is given below.

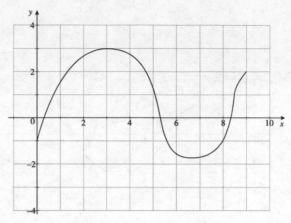

    (a) Where is f increasing?

    (b) Where is f decreasing?

    (c) Where is f concave upward?

    (d) Where is f concave downward?

Answer:

    (a) $(0, 3)$ and $(6.6, 9)$ (b) $(3, 6.6)$ (c) $(5.2, 8.5)$ (d) $(0, 5.2)$ and $(8.5, 9)$

32. The graph of f is given below.

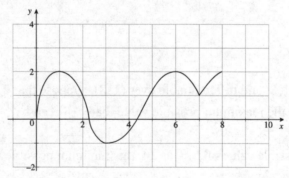

    (a) Where is f increasing?

    (b) Where is f decreasing?

    (c) Where is f concave upward?

    (d) Where is f concave downward?

Answer:

    (a) $(0, 1)$, $(3, 6)$, and $(7, 8)$ (b) $(1, 3)$ and $(6, 7)$ (c) $(2.2, 4.5)$ (d) $(0, 2.2)$, $(4.5, 7)$, and $(7, 8)$

33. The graph of f is given below.

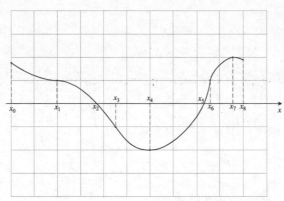

(a) Where is f increasing?

(b) Where is f decreasing?

(c) Where is f concave upward?

(d) Where is f concave downward?

Answer:

(a) (x_4, x_7) (b) (x_0, x_4) and (x_7, x_8) (c) (x_0, x_1) and (x_3, x_6) (d) (x_1, x_3) and (x_6, x_8)

34. The graph of the first derivative f' of a function f is given below.

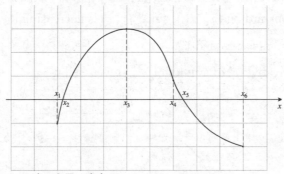

(a) On what intervals is f increasing? Explain.

(b) At what values of x does f have a local maximum or local minimum? Explain.

(c) On what intervals is f concave up? concave down? Explain.

(d) What are the coordinates of the inflection points of f? Explain.

Answer:

(a) (x_2, x_5), where $f'(x) > 0$

(b) $f(x)$ has a local minimum at x_2, $f(x)$ has a local maximum at x_5

(c) $f(x)$ is concave upward on (x_1, x_3), since $f'(x)$ is increasing there, that is, $f''(x) > 0$
$\quad$ $f(x)$ is concave downward on (x_3, x_6), since $f'(x)$ is decreasing there, that is, $f''(x) < 0$

(d) $f(x)$ has an inflection point at x_3

35. The graph of the first derivative f' of a function f is given below.

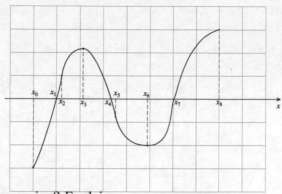

(a) On what intervals is f increasing? Explain.

(b) At what values of x does f have a local maximum or local minimum? Explain.

(c) On what intervals is f concave up? concave down? Explain.

(d) What are the coordinates of the inflection points of f? Explain.

Answer:

(a) (x_1, x_5) and (x_7, x_8), where $f'(x) > 0$

(b) $f(x)$ has local minima at x_1 and x, and a local maximum at x_4.

(c) $f(x)$ is concave up on (x_0, x_3) and (x_6, x_8), since $f'(x)$ is increasing there, that is, $f''(x) > 0$.
  $f(x)$ is concave downward on (x_3, x_6), since $f'(x)$ is decreasing there, that is, $f''(x) < 0$.

(d) $f(x)$ has inflection points at x_3 and x_6.

36. The graph of the first derivative f' of a function f is given below.

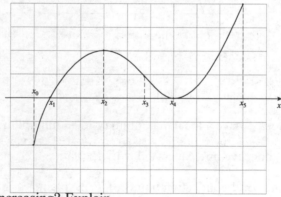

(a) On what intervals is f increasing? Explain.

(b) At what values of x does f have a local maximum or local minimum? Explain.

(c) On what intervals is f concave up? concave down? Explain.

(d) What are the coordinates of the inflection points of f? Explain.

Answer:

(a) (x_1, x_4) and (x_4, x_5), where $f'(x) > 0$

(b) $f(x)$ has a local minimum at x_1.

(c) $f(x)$ is concave upward on (x_0, x_2) and (x_4, x_5), since $f'(x)$ is increasing there, that is, $f''(x) > 0$. $f(x)$ is concave downward on (x_2, x_4), since $f'(x)$ is decreasing there, that is, $f''(x) < 0$.

(d) $f(x)$ has inflection points at x_2 and x_4.

37. Let $f(x) = x^6 + 192x + 17$. Find the intervals on which f is decreasing.
Answer: $(-\infty, -2)$

38. Find the intervals on which $f(x) = 2 \sin x + \sin^2 x$ is increasing.
Answer: $\left(-\frac{\pi}{2} + 2n\pi, \frac{\pi}{2} + 2n\pi\right)$ n any integer

39. Find the critical number(s) (if any) and test them to determine if $f(x) = x^4 - 8x^2 + 16$ has a local maximum or local minimum or neither at each critical number.
Answer: $f(x)$ has critical numbers $x = 0, \pm 2$. $f(x)$ has local minimum values of 0 at $x = \pm 2$ and a local maximum value of 16 at $x = 0$.

40. Find the critical number(s) (if any) and test them to determine if $f(x) = \dfrac{x}{1-x^2}$ has a local maximum or local minimum or neither at each critical number.
Answer: $f(x)$ has no critical number, and therefore has neither a local minimum nor a local maximum.

41. Find the critical number(s) (if any) and test them to determine if $f(x) = 3x^4 - 8x^3 + 9$ has a local maximum or local minimum or neither at each critical number.
Answer: $f(x)$ has critical numbers $x = 0, 2$. $f(x)$ has a local minimum value of -7 at $x = 2$. f has neither a local maximum nor a local minimum at $x = 0$.

42. Find the critical number(s) (if any) and test them to determine if $f(x) = |4 - x^2|$ has a local maximum or local minimum or neither at each critical number.
Answer: $f(x)$ has critical numbers $x = 0, \pm 2$. $f(x)$ has local minimum values of 0 at $x = \pm 2$ and a local maximum value of 4 at $x = 0$.

43. Find the largest interval on which the function $f(x) = \dfrac{x}{x^2 + 1}$ is concave upward.
Answer: $\left(\sqrt{3}, \infty\right)$

44. Find the x-coordinates of the points of inflection of $f(\theta) = \theta + \sin \theta$.
Answer: $n\pi$, n an integer

45. Find the intervals on which $f(\theta) = \cos^2 \theta$ is concave upward.
Answer: $\left(n\pi + \frac{\pi}{4}, n\pi + \frac{3\pi}{4}\right)$, n an integer

46. Find the interval on which $f(x) = xe^{-x}$ is concave upward.
Answer: $(2, \infty)$

47. Suppose that f is a continuous function and $f(0) = 0$, $f(2) = f(-2) = 1$, $f'(0) = 0$, $f'(x) > 0$ for $x > 0$, $f'(x) < 0$ for $x < 0$, $f''(x) > 0$ for $|x| < 2$, $f''(x) < 0$ for $|x| > 2$, and $\lim_{x \to \infty} f(x) = \lim_{x \to -\infty} f(x) = 2$. Sketch the graph of $y = f(x)$.

Answer:

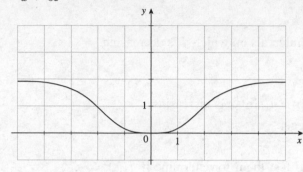

48. The graph of the derivative $f'(x)$ of a function $f(x)$ is given below.

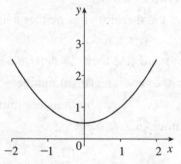

Sketch a possible graph of $y = f(x)$ on the interval $[-2, 2]$ such that $f(-2) = 0$. On your graph, label the critical point(s) and inflection point(s).

Answer:

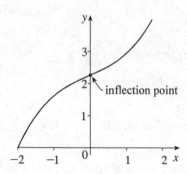

inflection point

49. The graph of the derivative $f'(x)$ of a function $f(x)$ is given below.

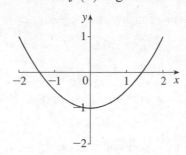

Sketch a possible graph of $y = f(x)$ on the interval $[-2, 2]$ such that $f(-2) = 0$. On your graph, label the critical point(s) and inflection point(s).

Answer:

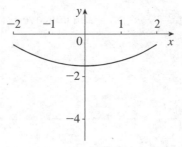

50. The graph of the derivative $f'(x)$ of a function $f(x)$ is given below.

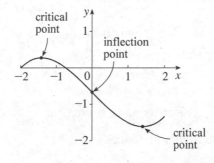

Sketch a possible graph of $y = f(x)$ on the interval $[-2, 2]$ such that $f(-2) = 0$. On your graph, label the critical point(s) and inflection point(s).

Answer:

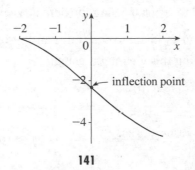

51. Consider $f(x) = x^4 - 6x^2$.

    (a) Find the intervals on which f is increasing or decreasing.

    (b) Find the local maximum and minimum values of f.

    (c) Find the intervals of concavity and the inflection points.

    (d) Using the information in (a), (b) and (c) to sketch a graph of f.

    Answer:

    (a) f is increasing on $(-\sqrt{3}, 0) \cup (\sqrt{3}, \infty)$ and decreasing on $(-\infty, -\sqrt{3}) \cup (0, \sqrt{3})$.

    (b) Local maximum value 0 at $x = 0$; local minimum value -9 at $x = \pm\sqrt{3}$.

    (c) f is concave up on $(-\infty, -1) \cup (1, \infty)$ and concave down on $(-1, 1)$. Inflection points $x = \pm 1$

    (d)

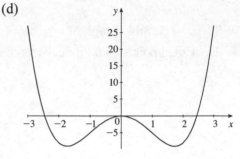

52. Consider $f(x) = e^{-x^3}$.

    (a) Find the intervals on which f is increasing or decreasing.

    (b) Find the local maximum and minimum values of f.

    (c) Find the intervals of concavity and the inflection points.

    (d) Using the information in (a), (b) and (c) to sketch a graph of f.

    Answer:

    (a) $f(x)$ is decreasing on $(-\infty, \infty)$

    (b) $f(x)$ has no local maximum and no local minimum.

    (c) f is concave up on $(-\infty, 0)$ and $\left(\frac{\sqrt[3]{18}}{3}, \infty\right)$, and concave down on $\left(0, \frac{\sqrt[3]{18}}{3}\right)$.

    (d)

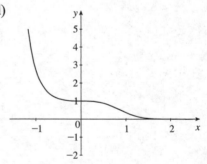

4.4 Graphing with Calculus *and* Calculators

1. Let $f(x) = 0.01x^3 - x^2 + 5$.

    (a) Use your graphing calculator to graph f using the default viewing rectangle.

    (b) Find the critical points of f and use them to determine an appropriate viewing rectangle (or rectangles) for f. Then graph f again using this viewing rectangle.

    (c) Compare the graphs in parts (a) and (b).

    Answer:

    (b) Critical points are $(0, 5)$ and $\left(\frac{200}{3}, -\frac{39,865}{27} \approx -1476.48\right) \approx (66.67, -1476.48)$.

(c) Possible viewing rectangles are $[-5, 5] \times [-10, 10]$ and $[-40, 120] \times [-1600, 800]$.

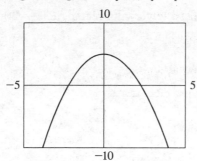 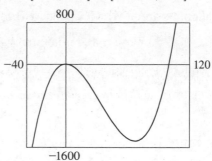

2. Let $f(x) = x^4 - 4x^3$.

(a) Use your graphing calculator to graph f using the default viewing rectangle.

(b) Find the critical points of f and use them to determine an appropriate viewing rectangle (or rectangles) for f. Then graph f again using this viewing rectangle.

(c) Compare the graphs in parts (a) and (b).

Answer:

(b) Critical points are $(0, 0)$ and $(3, -27)$.

(c) A possible viewing rectangle is $[-2, 5] \times [-30, 20]$.

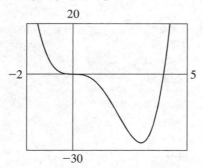

3. Let $f(x) = \dfrac{x}{x^2 + 25}$.

(a) Use your graphing calculator to graph f using the default viewing rectangle.

(b) Find the critical points of f and use them to determine an appropriate viewing rectangle (or rectangles) for f. Then graph f again using this viewing rectangle.

(c) Compare the graphs in parts (a) and (b).

Answer:

(b) Critical points are $(-5, -0.1)$ and $(5, 0.1)$. A possible viewing rectangle is $[-20, 20] \times [-0.15, 0.15]$.

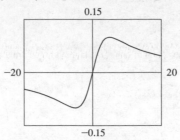

4. Let $f(x) = \dfrac{2x^2 + 3x + 6}{x + 2}$. Use the graphs of f and f' to estimate, to two decimal places,

   (a) the interval(s) where f is decreasing.

   (b) the interval(s) where f is concave upward.

   (c) the critical numbers of f.

   Answer: (a) $(-4, -2)$ and $(-2, 0)$ (b) $(-2, \infty)$ (c) $-4, 0$

5. Let $g(x) = x\sqrt{1 - x}$. Use the graphs of g and g' to estimate, to two decimal places,

   (a) the critical numbers of g.

   (b) the interval(s) where g is increasing.

   (c) the interval(s) where g is decreasing.

   Answer:

   (a) Critical numbers are $x = 0.67$ and $x = 1$.

   (b) f is increasing on $(-\infty, 0.67)$.

   (c) f is decreasing on $(0.67, 1)$.

6. Let $f(x) = x^4 - 2x^2 + 1$. Use the graphs of f, f', and f'' to estimate, to two decimal places,

   (a) the critical numbers of f.

   (b) the interval(s) where f is decreasing.

   (c) the interval(s) where f is concave upward.

   Answer:

   (a) Critical numbers are -1, 0, and 1.

   (b) f is decreasing on $(-\infty, -1]$ and $[0, 1]$.

   (c) f is concave upward on $(-\infty, -0.58)$ and $(0.58, \infty)$.

7. Let $f(x) = 2x^4 - 3x^3 - 10x^2 + 20$. Use the graphs of f, f', and f'' to estimate, to two decimal places, each of the following:

   (a) The critical numbers of f.

   (b) The intervals where f is increasing.

   (c) The x values where f has inflection points.

   (d) The intervals where f is concave downward.

Answer:

(a) The critical numbers are approximately $x = -1.12$, $x = 0$, and $x = 2.24$.

(b) f is increasing on $[-1.12, 0]$ and $[2.24, \infty]$.

(c) $f'(x) = 8x^3 - 9x^2 - 20x$, $f''(x) = 24x^2 - 18x - 20$, $f''(x) = 0 \Longrightarrow 24x^2 - 18x - 20 = 0$, $f''(x) = 0 \Longrightarrow 12x^2 - 9x - 10 = 0$

(d) f is concave downward on $(-0.61, 1.36)$.

4.5 Indeterminate Forms and L'Hospital's Rule

1. Find the value of the limit $\lim\limits_{x \to 0^+} \dfrac{\cos x - 1}{x^2}$.

(A) $\frac{1}{4}$ (B) -2 (C) ∞ (D) $-\frac{1}{2}$

(E) 2 (F) 0 (G) $\frac{1}{2}$ (H) 4

Answer: (D)

2. Find the value of the limit $\lim\limits_{x \to 0^+} \dfrac{x}{\sin x + \tan x}$.

(A) -2 (B) 0 (C) $-\frac{1}{2}$ (D) $\frac{1}{4}$

(E) 2 (F) ∞ (G) $\frac{1}{2}$ (H) 4

Answer: (G)

3. Find the value of the limit $\lim\limits_{x \to \infty} x \sin\left(\dfrac{1}{x}\right)$.

(A) 0 (B) 4 (C) $-\frac{1}{2}$ (D) $\frac{1}{4}$

(E) 1 (F) $\frac{1}{2}$ (G) 2 (H) -2

Answer: (E)

4. Find the value of the limit $\lim\limits_{x \to 0^+} \dfrac{e^{x^2} - 1}{x}$.

(A) 4 (B) $\frac{1}{4}$ (C) -2 (D) ∞

(E) 2 (F) 0 (G) $\frac{1}{2}$ (H) $-\frac{1}{2}$

Answer: (F)

5. Find the value of the limit $\lim\limits_{x \to \infty} x^{2/x}$.

(A) 2 (B) e (C) $\ln 2$ (D) 0

(E) 1 (F) ∞ (G) $\frac{1}{2}$ (H) $\sqrt{2}$

Answer: (E)

6. Find the value of the limit $\lim\limits_{x \to \infty} \dfrac{(\ln x)^2}{x}$.

(A) $-\infty$ (B) -1 (C) 0 (D) $\dfrac{1}{e}$

(E) 1 (F) e (G) $e^{1/e}$ (H) ∞

Answer: (C)

7. Let $a > 1$ and $b > 1$. Find the value of the limit $\lim\limits_{x \to 0} \dfrac{a^x - b^x}{x}$.

   (A) 0   (B) 1   (C) $a - b$ (D) $b - a$

   (E) $\ln (a - b)$ (F) $\ln (b - a)$ (G) $\ln \left(\dfrac{a}{b}\right)$ (H) $\ln \left(\dfrac{b}{a}\right)$

   Answer: **(G)**

8. Find the value of the limit $\lim\limits_{x \to 1} \left(\dfrac{1}{x - 1} - \dfrac{1}{\ln x} \right)$.

   (A) -1 (B) $-\frac{1}{2}$ (C) 0   (D) $\frac{1}{2}$

   (E) 1   (F) ∞ (G) $-\infty$ (H) Does not exist

   Answer: **(B)**

9. Find the value of the limit $\lim\limits_{k \to \infty} \left(1 + \dfrac{1}{10^k} \right)^{10^k}$.

   (A) 0   (B) 1   (C) 2   (D) e

   (E) 3   (F) π (G) 4   (H) ∞

   Answer: **(D)**

10. Find the value of the limit $\lim\limits_{x \to 2} \left(\dfrac{1}{x - 2} - \dfrac{4}{x^2 - 4} \right)$. Use l'Hospital's Rule, if applicable.

    Answer: $\frac{1}{4}$

11. Find the value of the limit $\lim\limits_{x \to 0} (1 + x)^{1/x}$. Use l'Hospital's Rule, if applicable.

    Answer: e

12. Find the value of the limit $\lim\limits_{x \to 0} (1 - x)^{1/x}$. Use l'Hospital's Rule, if applicable.

    Answer: $1/e$

13. Find the value of the limit $\lim\limits_{x \to 0^+} (1 + x)^{1/x^2}$. Use l'Hospital's Rule, if applicable.

    Answer: The limit does not exist.

14. Find the value of the limit $\lim\limits_{x \to 0} \left(1 + x^2 \right)^{1/x}$. Use l'Hospital's Rule, if applicable.

    Answer: 1

15. Find the value of the limit $\lim\limits_{x \to \infty} \dfrac{\sqrt{1 + x^2}}{x}$. Use l'Hospital's Rule, if applicable.

    Answer: 1. L'Hospital's Rule does not apply.

16. Find the value of the limit $\lim\limits_{x \to \infty} \dfrac{2x + \cos x}{x}$. Use l'Hospital's Rule, if applicable.

    Answer: 2. L'Hospital's Rule does not apply.

17. Find the value of the limit $\lim\limits_{x \to \infty} \sqrt{x^2 + 20x} - x$. Use l'Hospital's Rule, if applicable.

    Answer: 10

18. Find each of the following limits or explain why it does not exist.

    (a) $\lim\limits_{x \to 1} \dfrac{x^3 - 3x + 2}{1 - x}$ (b) $\lim\limits_{x \to 0^+} \dfrac{\cos x - 1}{x^2}$ (c) $\lim\limits_{x \to 0^+} x^2 (\ln x)$

    Answer: (a) 0   (b) $-\frac{1}{2}$ (c) 0

19. Find each of the following limits or explain why it does not exist.

    (a) $\lim\limits_{x \to 0} \dfrac{x - \sin x}{x^3}$
    (b) $\lim\limits_{x \to \infty} e^{-x} x^2$
    (c) $\lim\limits_{x \to 0^+} x^{2/x}$

    Answer: (a) $\frac{1}{6}$ (b) 0   (c) 1

20. Find each of the following limits or explain why it does not exist.

    (a) $\lim\limits_{x \to 1^+} \dfrac{\ln (2x)}{\ln x}$
    (b) $\lim\limits_{x \to 0} \dfrac{e^{-2x} - 1}{x^2 - x}$
    (c) $\lim\limits_{x \to \pi/2} (\sec x - \tan x)$

    Answer: (a) 1   (b) 2   (c) 0

21. Find each of the following limits or explain why it does not exist.

    (a) $\lim\limits_{x \to \infty} \dfrac{\ln (a + be^{cx})}{x}$
    (b) $\lim\limits_{x \to \infty} x \sin \left(\dfrac{1}{x} \right)$
    (c) $\lim\limits_{x \to 0^+} \left(\dfrac{x}{1 + x} \right)^x$

    Answer: (a) c (b) 1   (c) 1

4.6   Optimization Problems

1. A farmer has 20 feet of fence, and he wishes to make from it a rectangular pen for his pig Wilbur, using a barn as one of the sides. In square feet, what is the maximum area possible for this pen?

   (A) 64   (B) 75   (C) 60   (D) 32

   (E) 56   (F) 25   (G) 40   (H) 50

   Answer: (H)

2. A farmer intends to fence off a rectangular pen for his pig Wilbur, using the barn as one of the sides. If the enclosed area is to be 50 square feet, what is smallest amount of fence needed, in feet?

   (A) 30   (B) 40   (C) 20   (D) 10

   (E) 50   (F) 8   (G) $20\sqrt{2}$ (H) 45

   Answer: (C)

3. A rancher wishes to fence in a rectangular corral enclosing 1300 square yards and must divide it in half with a fence down the middle. If the perimeter fence costs \$5 per yard and the fence down the middle costs \$3 per yard, determine the dimensions of the corral so that the fencing cost will be as small as possible.

   (A) $10\sqrt{10} \times 13\sqrt{10}$ (B) $13\sqrt{10} \times 13\sqrt{10}$ (C) $10\sqrt{13} \times 13\sqrt{13}$ (D) 10×10

   (E) $10\sqrt{10} \times 10\sqrt{10}$ (F) $10\sqrt{10} \times 13\sqrt{10}$ (G) $10\sqrt{13} \times 10\sqrt{13}$ (H) 13×13

   Answer: (A)

4. Find the point on the line $y = 2x - 3$ that is nearest to the origin.

   (A) $(0.5, -2)$ (B) $(7.5, -1.5)$ (C) $(0.875, -1.25)$ (D) $(1, -0.5)$

   (E) $(1.1, -0.8)$ (F) $(1.2, -0.6)$ (G) $(1.25, -0.5)$ (H) $(1.5, 0)$

   Answer: (F)

5. Find the shortest distance from the point $(4,0)$ to a point on the parabola $y^2 = 2x$.

   (A) 1   (B) $\sqrt{2}$ (C) $\sqrt{3}$ (D) 2

   (E) $\sqrt{5}$ (F) $\sqrt{6}$ (G) $\sqrt{7}$ (H) $2\sqrt{2}$

   Answer: (G)

6. Farmer Brown wants to fence in a rectangular plot in a large field, using a rock wall which is already there as the north boundary. The fencing for the east and west sides of the plot will cost \$3/yard, but she needs to use special fencing which will cost \$5/yard on the south side of the plot. If the area of the plot is to be 600 square yards, find the dimensions for the plot which will minimize the cost of the fencing. Dimensions below are listed east by south.

   (A) $10\sqrt{5}$ by $12\sqrt{5}$ yards   (B) $12\sqrt{5}$ by $10\sqrt{5}$ yards

   (C) 10 by 60 yards   (D) 60 by 10 yards

   (E) $8\sqrt{5}$ by $15\sqrt{5}$ yards   (F) $15\sqrt{5}$ by $8\sqrt{5}$ yards

   (G) 15 by 40 yards   (H) 40 by 15 yards

   Answer: (A)

7. A plastic right cylinder with closed ends is to hold V cubic feet. If there is no waste in construction, find the ratio between the height and diameter that results in the minimum use of materials.

   (A) $1{:}\pi$ (B) $1{:}\frac{\pi}{2}$ (C) $1{:}2\pi$ (D) $1{:}2$

   (E) $2{:}\pi$ (F) $2{:}\frac{\pi}{3}$ (G) $1{:}\frac{\pi}{3}$ (H) $1{:}3$

   Answer: (A)

8. A square is to be cut from each corner of a piece of paper which is 8 cm by 10 cm, and the sides are to be folded up to create an open box. What should the side of the square be for maximum volume? (State your answer correct to two decimal places.)

   (A) 1.35 cm   (B) 1.39 cm   (C) 1.41 cm   (D) 1.47 cm

   (E) 1.52 cm   (F) 1.55 cm   (G) 1.60 cm   (H) 1.62 cm

   Answer: (D)

9. Two positive numbers have product 200. Find the minimum value of the sum of one number plus twice the other.

   Answer: 40

10. An open box is made from a 16 inch $\times$ 16 inch piece of cardboard by cutting equal squares from each corner and folding up the sides. For maximum volume, what size squares should be cut out?

    Answer: $\frac{8}{3} \times \frac{8}{3}$ in. squares

11. A poster is to have a total area of 486 square inches with 3-inch margins at the bottom and top and a 2-inch margin at each side. What dimensions of a poster will give the largest printed area?

    Answer: 27×18 inches

12. A rectangle with base on the x-axis has its upper vertices on the curve $y = 12 - x^2$. Find the maximum area of such a rectangle.

    Answer: 32

13. A rectangle with base on the x-axis has its upper vertices on the curve $y = 4 - \frac{1}{2}x^2$. Find the maximum perimeter of such a rectangle.

    Answer: 12

14. It is desired to make a rectangular pen with diameter equal to 40 feet. It is not necessary, however, to achieve maximum area. In fact, any area that is greater than or equal to 75% of the maximum area will be satisfactory. Under these conditions, find the maximum acceptable length of the longer side.

    Answer: 15

15. A lakefront runs east-west. A man in a rowboat is 5 miles due north of point A on the shore. He wishes to get to B, 5 miles due east of A, in the least time. He is able to row 3 miles per hour and walk 5 miles per hour. What is the minimum time, in minutes?

    Answer: 140

16. A drinking cup is made in the shape of a right circular cylinder. For a fixed volume, we wish to make the total material used (the circular bottom and the cylindrical side) as small as possible. Under this condition, what is the ratio of the height to the diameter?

    Answer: $\frac{1}{2}$

17. A gas pipeline is to be constructed from a storage tank, which is right on a road, to a house which is 600 feet down the road and 300 feet back from the road. Pipe laid along the road costs $8.00 per foot, while pipe laid off the road costs $10.00 per foot. What is the minimum cost for which this pipeline can be built?

    Answer: $6600

18. A rectangular region with area 3200 square feet is to be enclosed within a fence. The two sides which run north-south will use fencing materials costing $1.00 per foot, while the other two sides require fencing materials which cost $2.00 per foot. Find the dimensions of the region which gives the smallest material cost.

    Answer: 80 ft (north-south fence) by 40 ft (east-west fence)

19. What is the smallest slope for a tangent line to the graph of $y = 2x^3 - 2x^2 + 5x + 1$?

    Answer: $\frac{13}{3}$

20. A large, closed shipping container with a square base is to be made from 1000 square feet of fiberboard. Find the dimensions of the container with the greatest volume.

    Answer: $\frac{10\sqrt{15}}{3}$ ft by $\frac{10\sqrt{15}}{3}$ ft by $\frac{10\sqrt{15}}{3}$ ft

21. A hog weighs 250 pounds. A high-yield diet allows the animal to gain 6 pounds a day at a cost of $0.56 a day. The market price for hogs is currently $0.75 per pound, but it is falling at a rate of $0.01 per day, and that price decline is expected to remain steady for the foreseeable future. When should the hog be sold in order to provide the farmer with the highest financial gain?

    Answer: 12 days

22. A 400-meter-long running track is to be constructed with two parallel straightaways of length s joining two semi-circular curves of radius r. What are the dimensions of the track that will enclose the largest infield area?

    Answer: The track must be a circle with radius $\frac{200}{\pi}$ m.

4.7 Applications To Economics

1. A company has cost function $C(x) = 1000 - 10x + x^2$. Find the average cost of producing 100 units.

   (A) 150   (B) 200   (C) 210   (D) 120

   (E) 250   (F) 90   (G) 180   (H) 100

   Answer: (H)

2. The cost to produce x units of a certain product is given by $C(x) = 10{,}000 + 8x + \frac{1}{16}x^2$. Find the value of x that gives the minimum average cost.

   (A) 400   (B) 25   (C) 160,000   (D) 4000

   (E) 500   (F) 64   (G) 40,000   (H) Does not exist

   Answer: (A)

3. A revenue function is given by $R(x) = 6000x - 0.4x^3$ where x is the number of units sold. Find the marginal revenue when $x = 50$.

   (A) 4000   (B) 300   (C) 250,000   (D) 5000

   (E) 500   (F) 3000   (G) 40,000   (H) Does not exist

   Answer: (F)

4. A revenue function is given by $R(x) = 6000x - 0.2x^3$, where x is the number of units sold. Find the number of units x that produces maximum revenue.

   (A) 200   (B) 300   (C) 1000   (D) 100

   (E) 500   (F) 3000   (G) 400   (H) Does not exist

   Answer: (D)

5. A company has cost function $C(x) = 1000 - 10x + x^2$. Find the marginal cost of producing 100 units.

   (A) 210   (B) 120   (C) 190   (D) 150

   (E) 250   (F) 200   (G) 100   (H) 180

   Answer: (C)

6. A company has cost function $C(x) = 200 - 50x + x^2$ and demand function $p(x) = 50 - x$. How many units should it make to maximize its profit?

   (A) 15   (B) 25   (C) 8   (D) 5

   (E) 30   (F) 10   (G) 20   (H) 35

   Answer: (B)

7. Suppose that $C(x)$ is the number of dollars in the total cost of producing x tables $(x > 6)$ and $C(x) = 25 + 4x + 18x^{-1}$. Find the marginal cost when $x = 15$.

   (A) $3.72   (B) $3.75   (C) $3.79   (D) $3.82

   (E) $3.89   (F) $3.92   (G) $3.97   (H) $4.00

   Answer: (F)

8. A rental estate management company manages an apartment complex with 20 units. The manager estimates that all 20 units can be rented if the rent is $150 per unit per month, and that for each increase in rent of $25, one apartment will be vacated. What rent should the manager charge to maximize revenue?

Answer: $325

9. A company estimates that the initial cost of producing a commodity would be $680. The additional cost of manufacturing each item can be modeled by the function $m(x) = 3x + 0.01x^2$, where x is the number of items produced and m is the manufacturing cost, in dollars. A market survey indicates the demand function can be estimated by $p(x) = 12 - 0.002x$.

   (a) Find the production level that maximizes profit. What is the maximum profit?

   (b) What should the selling price be to maximize the profit?

   Answer: (a) $x = 375$, maximum profit is $1007.50.   (b) $11.25 per unit

10. A school band decides to raise with a car wash. Labor and material are donated, so pure profit is realized from the sale of the tickets. They know that if they charge $5 per ticket, they will sell 1000, while if they charge $4 per ticket, they will sell 1500. Assuming the demand function is linear, what should they charge to maximize their profit?

    Answer: $3.50

11. The cost of operating a bus between Moose Jaw and Saskatoon is $100 + 5x$, where x is the number of passengers. If a ticket costs $20, there will be 10 passengers, while if a ticket costs $15, there will be 20 passengers. Assuming the demand function is linear, what is the maximum profit?

    Answer: $100

12. If the cost of manufacturing x units per day of a certain commodity is $c = 600 + 0.04x + 0.002x^2$, and if each unit sells for $10.00, what daily production will maximize the profit?

    Answer: 2490 units

13. Suppose that the cost function (in dollars) for producing Fuzzy Widgets® is given by $C(x) = 0.004x^3 - 0.02x^2 + 6x + 1000$. Determine the minimum marginal cost.

    Answer: $\frac{179}{30} \approx 5.97 per unit

14. A company has cost function $C(x) = 10,000 + 20x + x^2$. Find:

    (a) The average cost function.

    (b) The marginal cost function.

    (c) The production level x that will minimize the average cost.

    (d) The minimum average cost.

    Answer:

    (a) $C(x) = \dfrac{10,000}{x} + 20 + x$

    (b) $C'(t) = 20 + 2x$

    (c) 100

    (d) $220

15. A certain company has cost function $C(x) = 1000 + 2x + 0.01x^2$ and demand function $P(x) = 74 - 0.02x$. Find the production level x that will yield a maximum profit.

    Answer: 1200

16. In its report to stockholders, a certain manufacturing company reported its total cost and revenue functions using the graphs given below:

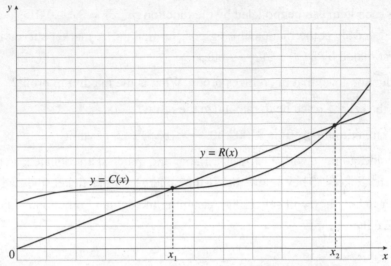

    (a) Using the graph, sketch each of the following as a function of the quantity produced, x.

       (i) Marginal cost

       (ii) Marginal revenue

       (iii) Profit

    (b) What is the significance of x_1? x_2?

    (c) What is the meaning of $C'(0)$?

    (d) Describe in words how the marginal cost changes as the quantity produced increases.

    (e) Explain the economic significance, in terms of marginal cost, of the point where the concavity of the cost function changes.

    Answer:

    (a) (i) 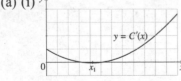 (ii)  (iii)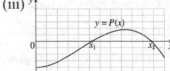

    (b) $C(x_1) = R(x_1)$ and $C(x_2) = R(x_2)$. x_1 and x_2 are called break-even points.

    (c) $C'(0)$ is the rate of change of cost when there is no production.

    (d) If the production level is less than x_1, then the marginal cost is decreasing.

       If the production level is greater than x_1, then the marginal cost is increasing.

    (e) x_1 is the inflection point; see part (d).

17. One model of a company's costs is given by the short-run Cobb-Douglas cost curve $C(x) = Kx^{1/a} + F$, where a is a positive constant, F is the fixed cost, and K measures the available technology.

(a) What is the marginal cost function?

(b) For what values of a will C be concave downward?

Answer: (a) $\dfrac{K}{a} x^{1/a-1}$ (b) $a > 1$

18. One model of a company's costs is given by the short-run Cobb-Douglas cost curve $C(x) = Kx^{1/a} + F$, where a is a positive constant, F, is the fixed cost, and K measures the available technology. The average cost of manufacturing a quantity x of a good is defined to be $A(x) = \dfrac{C(x)}{x}$.

(a) What is the average cost function for the Cobb-Douglas model?

(b) If average cost is minimized when it is equal to the marginal cost, find the quantity x which yields the minimum average cost.

Answer:

(a) $Kx^{1/a-1} + \dfrac{F}{x}$

(b) If $a \geq 1$, there is no value of x that gives the minimum average cost. If $a < 1$, $x = \left(\dfrac{aF}{K(1-a)}\right)^a$ gives the minimum average cost.

19. Using the language of calculus to explain the following economic principles for output price decisions.

(a) Maximum profit requires the firm to choose the level of output at which marginal revenue is equal to marginal cost.

(b) A change in fixed cost will not change the profit maximizing level of output.

(c) It may pay a firm to expand its output if it is selling at a price greater than marginal cost, even if that price happens to be below average cost.

Answer: Let $P(x)$ be the profit function, $R(x)$ the revenue function, and $C(x)$ the cost function.

(a) $P(x) = R(x) - C(x)$. Maximum profit occurs at $P'(x) = 0$, and $P'(x) = R'(x) - C'(x) = 0$ $\Rightarrow$ $R'(x) = C'(x)$

(b) Let C_0 be the fixed change in cost. $P(x) = R(x) - (C(x) + C_0)$. Since $(C_0)' = 0$, $P'(x) = R'(x) - C'(x) = 0$.

(c) Let $R(x) = ax$, where a is the price. $P(x) = ax - C(x)$ $\Rightarrow$ $P'(x) = a - C'(x) > 0$ if $a > C'(x)$ $\Rightarrow$ $P(x)$ is increasing.

4.8 Newton's Method

1. Use Newton's method with the initial approximation $x_1 = 2$ to find x_2, the second approximation to a root of the equation $x^5 - 34 = 0$.

(A) $\dfrac{79}{40}$ (B) $\dfrac{81}{40}$ (C) $\dfrac{77}{40}$ (D) $\dfrac{161}{80}$

(E) $\dfrac{83}{40}$ (F) $\dfrac{157}{80}$ (G) $\dfrac{163}{80}$ (H) $\dfrac{159}{80}$

Answer: (B)

2. If Newton's method is used to solve $2x^3 + 2x + 1 = 0$ with first approximation $x_1 = -1$, what is the second approximation, x_2?

(A) -0.500 (B) -0.525 (C) -0.550 (D) -0.575

(E) -0.600 (F) -0.625 (G) -0.650 (H) -0.675

Answer: (F)

3. Use Newton's method to find the root of $6x^3 - x^2 - 19x + 6 = 0$ that lies between 0 and 1.

(A) 0.316 (B) 0.333 (C) 0.158 (D) 0.167

(E) 0.474 (F) 0.500 (G) 0.079 (H) 0.084

Answer: (B)

4. Use Newton's method to approximate a solution to the following equation: $x^3 + 2x = 3.1$.

(A) 1.00 (B) 1.01 (C) 1.02 (D) 1.03

(E) 1.04 (F) 1.05 (G) 1.06 (H) 1.07

Answer: (C)

5. If Newton's method is used to find the cube root of a number a with first approximation x_1, find an expression for x_2.

Answer: $x_2 = x_1 - \dfrac{x_1^3 - a}{3x_1^2}$

6. Sketch the graph of $f(x) = x^4 + x - 3$ on the interval $[-3, 3]$. Suppose that Newton's method is used to approximate the positive root of f with initial approximation $x_1 = 2$.

(a) On your sketch, draw the tangent lines that you would use to find x_2 and x_3, and estimate the numerical values of x_2 and x_3.

(b) To approximate the negative root of f, use $x_1 = -2$ as the starting approximation. As before, draw the tangent lines that you would use to find x_2 and x_3, and estimate the numerical values of x_2 and x_3.

(c) Suppose that you had used $x_1 = 0$ as the starting point for approximating the negative root. Discuss what would happen.

Answer:

(a)

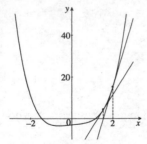

$x_2 \approx 1.55$; $x_3 \approx 1.27$

(b)

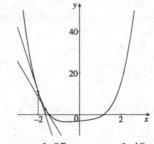

$x_2 \approx -1.65$; $x_3 \approx -1.49$

(c)

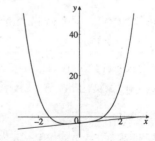

Newton's Method would fail to find the negative root if $x_1 = 0$ were chosen. (It would converge slowly to the positive root.)

7. Graph the function $f(x) = 2x^3 + 5x^2 + x - 1$ on $[-3, 3]$. For each initial approximation given below, determine graphically what happens if Newton's Method is used to approximate the roots of $f(x) = 0$.

(a) $x_1 = -2$

(b) $x_1 = -1$

(c) $x_1 = 0$

(d) $x_1 = 1$

(e) $x_1 = -1.56$

Answer:

(a)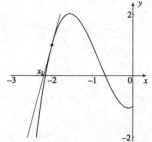

(b)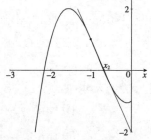

(c)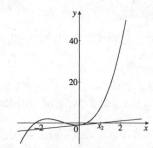

Using $x_1 = -2$, Newton's Method will approximate the root between -3 and -2.

Using $x_1 = -1$, Newton's Method will approximate the root between -1 and 0.

Using $x_1 = 0$, Newton's Method will approximate the root between 0 and 1.

(d)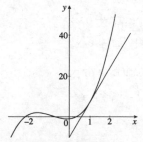

(e)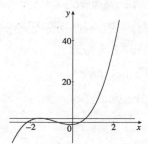

Using $x_1 = 1$, Newton's Method will approximate the root between 0 and 1.

Using $x_1 = -1.56$, Newton's Method will converge very slowly to the root between -3 and -2, because $f'(1.56)$ is close to 0.

8. Use Newton's Method to find $\sqrt{89}$ correct to four decimal places.

Answer: 9.43398

9. Find, correct to six decimal places, the root of $\sin x + x - 1 = 0$.

Answer: 0.5109734

10. Sketch the graph of $y = x^{1/3}$. Clearly the only x-intercept is zero. However, Newton's method fails to converge here. Explain this failure.

Answer: $f'(x) = \dfrac{1}{3\sqrt[3]{x^2}}$, $\displaystyle\lim_{x \to 0} \dfrac{1}{3\sqrt[3]{x^2}} = \infty$

11. Use Newton's Method to approximate all real roots of $x^4 + x^3 - 3x^2 + 4x - 28 = 0$.

Answer: -3.192258 or 2.19258

12. (a) Explain why Newton's Method is unable to find a root for $x^3 - 3x + 4 = 0$ if $x_1 = 1$ or $x_1 = -1$.

   (b) Using $x_1 = -2$, use Newton's Method to approximate a root of this equation to four decimal places.

   Answer: (a) Since $f'(x) = 3x^2 - 3$, $f'(\pm 1) = 0$.   (b) -2.19582

4.9 Antiderivatives

1. Find the most general antiderivative of the function $f(x) = 9x^2$.

  (A) $3x^3 + C$ (B) $2x + C$ (C) $\dfrac{x}{2} + C$ (D) $2x^2 + C$

  (E) $\dfrac{x^3}{3} + C$ (F) $3x + C$ (G) $\dfrac{x}{3} + C$ (H) $3x^2 + C$

  Answer: (A)

2. Find the most general antiderivative of $\sec^2 x + \sin x$.

  (A) $\frac{1}{3}\sec^3 x + \sin x + C$ (B) $\tan^2 x - \sin x + C$

  (C) $\tan x + \cos x + C$ (D) $\tan x - \cos x + C$

  (E) $\tan^2 x + \sin x + C$ (F) $\frac{1}{3}\sec^3 x + \frac{1}{2}\sin^2 x + C$

  (G) $\frac{1}{3}\sec^3 x - \sin x + C$ (H) $\frac{1}{3}\sec^3 x - \frac{1}{2}\sin^2 x + C$

  Answer: (D)

3. Find the most general antiderivative of the function $f(x) = 2x^3 - x^2 + 5$.

  (A) $x^4 - \frac{1}{3}x^3 + 5x + C$ (B) $\frac{1}{2}x^4 - x^3 + 5x + C$

  (C) $2x^4 - \frac{1}{3}x^3 + 5x + C$ (D) $\frac{1}{2}x^4 - \frac{1}{3}x^3 + C$

  (E) $\frac{1}{2}x^4 - \frac{1}{3}x^3 + 5x + C$ (F) $\frac{1}{4}x^4 - \frac{1}{3}x^3 + 5x + C$

  (G) $\frac{1}{2}x^4 - \frac{1}{3}x^2 + 5x + C$ (H) $6x^2 - 2x + C$

  Answer: (E)

4. Find the most general antiderivative of the function $f(x) = \dfrac{2}{x^3}$.

  (A) $\dfrac{2}{3x^2} + C$ (B) $\dfrac{1}{x^4} + C$ (C) $-\dfrac{1}{x^2} + C$ (D) $\dfrac{2}{x^4} + C$

  (E) $\dfrac{1}{x^2} + C$ (F) $-\dfrac{2}{x^4} + C$ (G) $-\dfrac{2}{x^2} + C$ (H) $2x^4 + C$

  Answer: (C)

5. Find the most general antiderivative of the function $f(x) = \dfrac{2 + x^3}{x^3}$.

  (A) $\dfrac{2 + 3x^2}{3x^2} + C$ (B) $\dfrac{2x + \frac{1}{4}x^4}{x^4} + C$ (C) $-\dfrac{1}{x^2} + 1 + C$ (D) $-\dfrac{1}{x^2} + C$

  (E) $\dfrac{1}{x^2} + x + C$ (F) $\dfrac{1}{x^2} + 1 + C$ (G) $-\dfrac{1}{x^2} + x + C$ (H) $\dfrac{2}{x^2} + C$

  Answer: (G)

6. Find the most general antiderivative of the function $f(x) = \dfrac{1+3x}{\sqrt{x}}$.

(A) $2\sqrt{x} + 2\sqrt[3]{x^2} + C$

(B) $2\sqrt{x} + 3\sqrt{x^3} + C$

(C) $\sqrt{x} + 2\sqrt{x^3} + C$

(D) $-\frac{1}{2}x^{-3/2} + \frac{3}{2}x^{-1/2} + C$

(E) $2\sqrt{x} + \sqrt{x^3} + C$

(F) $2\sqrt{x} + 2\sqrt{x^3} + C$

(G) $2\sqrt{x} + \sqrt[3]{x^2} + C$

(H) $\sqrt{x} + 2\sqrt[3]{x^2} + C$

Answer: (F)

7. Find the most general antiderivative of the function $f(x) = \dfrac{1+3x}{x\sqrt{x}}$.

(A) $x^{-1/2} + 6x^{1/2} + C$

(B) $-2x^{-1/2} - 6x^{1/2} + C$

(C) $-2x^{-1/2} + x^{1/2} + C$

(D) $-2x^{-1/2} + 3x^{1/2} + C$

(E) $-2x^{-1/2} + 6x^{1/2} + C$

(F) $3\sqrt{x} + C$

(G) $2x^{-1/2} + 6x^{1/2} + C$

(H) $x + 6\sqrt{x} + C$

Answer: (E)

8. Find the most general antiderivative of the function $f(x) = \dfrac{2e^x - e^{2x}}{e^x}$.

(A) $2x + e^x + C$

(B) $2x - e^x + C$

(C) $2 - e^x + C$

(D) $\dfrac{2e^x - e^{2x}}{e^x} + C$

(E) $2x - 2e^x + C$

(F) $\dfrac{2e^x - \frac{1}{2}e^{2x}}{e^x} + C$

(G) $2 + xe^{x-1} + C$

(H) $2x + \dfrac{1}{1+x}e^{x+1} + C$

Answer: (B)

9. Given $f'(x) = \dfrac{1}{2\sqrt{x}}$ and $f(1) = 2$, find $f\left(\frac{1}{4}\right)$.

(A) $\frac{1}{3}$

(B) 2

(C) $\frac{3}{2}$

(D) -2

(E) $\frac{2}{3}$

(F) $\frac{1}{2}$

(G) $-\frac{1}{2}$

(H) 3

Answer: (C)

10. Given $f''(x) = 2$, $f'(0) = 1$, and $f(0) = \frac{3}{2}$, find $f(1)$.

(A) $\frac{10}{3}$

(B) $\frac{17}{3}$

(C) $\frac{7}{2}$

(D) $\frac{3}{10}$

(E) $\frac{17}{2}$

(F) $\frac{13}{3}$

(G) $\frac{23}{3}$

(H) $\frac{21}{2}$

Answer: (C)

11. A chocolate cream pie is thrown vertically up from the ground with velocity 72 ft/s. Find the amount of time in seconds until it hits the ground.

(A) 6.5

(B) 4.5

(C) 6

(D) 7.5

(E) 5.5

(F) 7

(G) 5

(H) 4

Answer: (B)

157

12. If $f''(x) = 12x^2 - 2$, $f(-1) = -4$, and $f(0) = 2$, find $f(1)$.

    (A) 1   (B) 2   (C) 3   (D) 4

    (E) 5   (F) 6   (G) 7   (H) 8

    Answer: (H)

13. Find the most general antiderivative of the function.

    (a) $f(x) = 12x^2 + 6x - 5$

    (b) $f(x) = \left(1 - \frac{1}{\sqrt{x}}\right)\left(1 + \frac{1}{\sqrt{x}}\right)$

    (c) $f(x) = \frac{1}{x^2} - \frac{2}{x^3}$

    (d) $f(t) = \frac{t^3 + 2t^2}{\sqrt{t}}$

    Answer:

    (a) $4x^3 + 3x^2 - 5x + C$ (b) $x - \ln|x| + C$ (c) $\frac{1}{x^2} - \frac{1}{x} + C$ (d) $\frac{2}{7}t^{7/2} + \frac{4}{5}t^{5/2} + C$

14. Find the most general antiderivative of the function.

    (a) $f(x) = \pi^3$

    (b) $f(t) = \sec^2 t + t^2$

    (c) $f(\theta) = \left(e^{\theta/2} + e^{-\theta/2}\right)^2$

    (d) $f(x) = \frac{x^4 + x^3 + 1}{x^4}$

    Answer:

    (a) $\pi^3 x + C$ (b) $\tan t + \frac{1}{3}t^3 + C$ (c) $e^\theta - e^{-\theta} + 2\theta + C$ (d) $x + \ln|x| + \frac{1}{3x^3} + C$

15. Find the most general antiderivative of the function.

    (a) $f(t) = 3\cos t - 4\sin t$

    (b) $f(x) = \frac{4}{\sqrt{1 - x^2}} + 1$

    (c) $f(x) = \left(x - \frac{1}{x}\right)\left(x + \frac{1}{x}\right)$

    (d) $f(x) = e^x + \sec x \tan x$

    Answer:

    (a) $3\sin t + 4\cos t + C$ (b) $4\sin^{-1} x + x + C$ (c) $\frac{1}{3}x^3 + \frac{1}{x} + C$ (d) $e^x + \sec x + C$

16. A direction field for a function f is given below. Use this to sketch the antiderivative F that satisfies $F(0) = 2$.

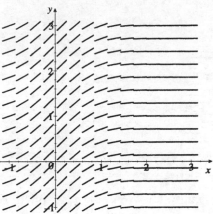

Answer:

17. The direction field for a function f is given below. Use it to draw the antiderivative F that satisfies $F(0) = 1$.

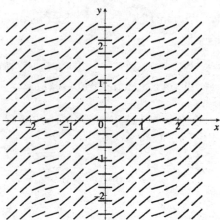

Answer:

18. Draw a direction field for the function $f(x) = \dfrac{1 - \cos x}{x^2}$, $0 < x < 2\pi$. Use this direction field to sketch several members of the family of antiderivatives.

Answer:

19. (a) Draw a direction field for the function $f(x) = \sin x$. Use this direction field to sketch several members of the family of antiderivatives.

(b) Compute the general antiderivative for $f(x) = \sin x$ explicitly and sketch several specific antiderivatives. Compare these results with your sketches from part (a).

Answer:

(a)

(b) $\int \sin x\, dx = -\cos x + c$

20. (a) Draw a direction field for the function $f(x) = 9x^2$. Use this direction field to sketch several members of the family of antiderivatives.

(b) Compute the general antiderivative for $f(x) = 9x^2$ explicitly and sketch several specific antiderivatives. Compare these results with your sketches from part (a).

Answer:

(a)

(b) $\int 9x^2\, dx = 3x^3 + c$

21. If $f''(x) = -4\sin 2x$, $f(0) = 0$, $f'(0) = 2$, find the value of $f\left(\frac{\pi}{4}\right)$.

Answer: 1

22. If $f''(x) = 12x^2 - 6x + 2$, $f(0) = 1$, $f(2) = 11$, find $f(x)$.

    Answer: $f(x) = x^4 - x^3 + x^2 - x + 1$

23. If $f''(x) = 2e^x + 4\cos x$, $f(0) = 1$, $f'(0) = 2$, find $f(x)$.

    Answer: $f(x) = 2e^x - 4\cos x + 3$

24. Find the position function $s(t)$ given acceleration $a(t) = 3t$ if $v(2) = 0$ and $s(2) = 1$.

    Answer: $s(t) = \left(\dfrac{t^3}{2}\right) - 6t + 9$

25. A cyclist traveling at 40 ft/s decelerates at a constant 4 ft/s². How many feet does she travel before coming to a complete stop?

    Answer: 200

26. A custard pie is thrown vertically up from the ground with velocity 48 ft/s. Find the greatest height that it attains.

    Answer: 36

27. An astronaut stands on a platform 3 meters above the moon's surface and throws a rock directly upward with an initial velocity of 32 m/s. Given that the acceleration due to gravity on the moon's surface is 1.6 m/s², how high above the surface of the moon will the rock travel?

    Answer: 323 m

28. A ball is thrown directly upward at a speed of 64 feet per second from a cliff 80 feet above the ground.

    (a) Find expressions for the velocity and height of the ball t seconds after it was released.

    (b) At what time does the ball reach its highest point? How high above the ground at the base of the cliff does it reach?

    (c) When does the ball strike the ground at the base of the cliff? What is its velocity at that instant?

    Answer:

    (a) $v(t) = -32t + 64$ ft/s; $h(t) = -16t^2 + 64t + 80$ ft

    (b) 2 s; 169 ft   (c) 5 s; −96 ft/s

29. On the surface of the moon, a ball is thrown directly upward at a speed of 64 feet per second from a cliff 80 feet above the ground. The acceleration due to lunar gravity is 5.2 ft/s².

    (a) Find expressions for the velocity and height of the ball t seconds after it was released.

    (b) At what time does the ball reach its highest point? How high above the ground at the base of the cliff does it reach?

    (c) When does the ball strike the ground at the base of the cliff? What is its velocity at that instant?

    Answer:

    (a) $v(t) = -5.2t + 64$ ft/s; $h(t) = -2.6t^2 + 64t + 80$ ft

    (b) 12.31 s; 473.85 ft   (c) 25.81 s; −70.21 ft/s

30. Is it possible for the velocity of an object to be zero at the same time that its acceleration is not zero? Explain.

    Answer: It is possible. For example, if $v(t) = -32t + 64$, then $v(2) = 0$ and $a(2) = -32$.

31. A ball is dropped from a tower. When it strikes the ground it is traveling downward at a rate of 60 feet per second. How tall is the tower?

Answer: 56.25 ft

5 Integrals

5.1 Areas and Distances

1. Suppose we wish to estimate the area under the curve $y = x$ between $x = 1$ and $x = 2$ using 2 subintervals of equal length. What is the largest value the approximation could have?

(A) $\frac{5}{16}$ (B) 0   (C) $\frac{1}{4}$ (D) $\frac{3}{8}$

(E) $\frac{5}{4}$ (F) $\frac{7}{4}$ (G) $\frac{1}{2}$ (H) $\frac{3}{16}$

Answer: (F)

2. Suppose we wish to estimate the area under the graph of $f(x) = x^2$ for $0 \le x \le 2$. What is the value of the estimate using four approximating rectangles and taking sample points to be right-hand endpoints?

(A) $\frac{1}{2}$ (B) $\frac{7}{4}$ (C) $\frac{21}{8}$ (D) 3

(E) $\frac{15}{4}$ (F) $\frac{29}{8}$ (G) $\frac{9}{2}$ (H) 5

Answer: (E)

3. Suppose we wish to estimate the area under the graph of $f(x) = x^2$ for $0 \le x \le 2$. What is the value of the estimate using four approximating rectangles and taking sample points to be left-hand endpoints?

(A) $\frac{1}{2}$ (B) $\frac{7}{4}$ (C) $\frac{21}{8}$ (D) 3

(E) $\frac{15}{4}$ (F) $\frac{29}{8}$ (G) $\frac{9}{2}$ (H) 5

Answer: (B)

4. Suppose we wish to estimate the area under the graph of $f(x) = x^2$ for $0 \le x \le 2$. What is the value of the estimate using four approximating rectangles and taking sample points to be midpoints?

(A) $\frac{1}{2}$ (B) $\frac{7}{4}$ (C) $\frac{21}{8}$ (D) 3

(E) $\frac{15}{4}$ (F) $\frac{29}{8}$ (G) $\frac{9}{2}$ (H) 5

Answer: (C)

5. Let $f(x) = \dfrac{1}{x}$ on the interval $[1, 2]$. Let the interval be divided into four equal subintervals. Find the value of the Riemann sum $\sum_{i=1}^{n} f(x_i^*) \Delta x_i$ if each x_i^* is the left endpoint of its subinterval.

(A) $\frac{319}{105}$ (B) $\frac{319}{420}$ (C) $\frac{533}{210}$ (D) $\frac{533}{840}$

(E) $\frac{11}{2}$ (F) $\frac{11}{8}$ (G) $\frac{13}{2}$ (H) $\frac{13}{8}$

Answer: (B)

6. Let $f(x) = \dfrac{1}{x}$ on the interval $[1, 2]$. Let the interval be divided into four equal subintervals. Find the value of the Riemann sum $\displaystyle\sum_{i=1}^{n} f(x_i^*) \Delta x_i$ if each x_i^* is the right endpoint of its subinterval.

(A) $\frac{319}{105}$ (B) $\frac{319}{420}$ (C) $\frac{533}{210}$ (D) $\frac{533}{840}$

(E) $\frac{11}{2}$ (F) $\frac{11}{8}$ (G) $\frac{13}{2}$ (H) $\frac{13}{8}$

Answer: (D)

7. Let $f(x) = \dfrac{1}{x}$ on the interval $[1, 2]$. Let the interval be divided into two equal subintervals. Find the value of the Riemann sum $\displaystyle\sum_{i=1}^{n} f(x_i^*) \Delta x_i$ if each x_i^* is the midpoint of its subinterval.

(A) $\frac{3}{4}$ (B) 3 (C) $\frac{48}{35}$ (D) $\frac{12}{35}$

(E) $\frac{3}{2}$ (F) $\frac{7}{8}$ G) $\frac{24}{35}$ (H) $\frac{6}{35}$

Answer: (G)

8. Let $f(x) = x^3$ on the interval $[0, 2]$. Let the interval be divided into two equal subintervals. Find the value of the Riemann sum $\displaystyle\sum_{i=1}^{n} f(x_i^*) \Delta x_i$ if each x_i^* is the midpoint of its subinterval.

(A) $\frac{5}{6}$ (B) $\frac{7}{6}$ (C) $\frac{7}{8}$ (D) $\frac{7}{4}$

(E) $\frac{5}{2}$ (F) $\frac{5}{3}$ (G) $\frac{5}{4}$ (H) $\frac{7}{2}$

Answer: (H)

9. Estimate the area under the graph of $f(x) = 16 - x^2$ from $x = 0$ to $x = 4$ using four rectangles and right endpoints.

(A) 20   (B) 22   (C) 24   (D) 26

(E) 28   (F) 30   (G) 32   (H) 34

Answer: (H)

10. Use the Midpoint Rule with $n = 5$ to approximate $\displaystyle\int_1^2 \frac{1}{x}\, dx$.

(A) 0.6909   (B) 0.6913   (C) 0.6919   (D) 0.6925

(E) 0.6928   (F) 0.6932   (G) 0.6937   (H) 0.6945

Answer: (C)

11. Use left endpoints with $n = 4$ to approximate $\int_1^3 \ln x\, dx$.

(A) 2.015   (B) 0.5037   (C) 1.5568   (D) 0.3317

(E) 1.0075   (F) 3.1135   (G) 0.7784   (H) 0.3844

Answer: (E)

12. Given the graph below, use 5 rectangles to find an estimate for the area under the graph from $x = 0$ to $x = 10$. Find lower and upper estimates for the area.

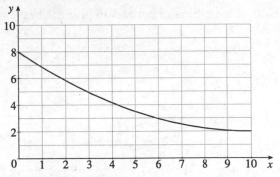

Answer: Lower estimate ≈ 34.4; upper estimate ≈ 46.4

13. Given the graph below, use 3 rectangles to find an estimate for the area under the graph from $x = 0$ to $x = 9$. Find lower and upper estimates for the area.

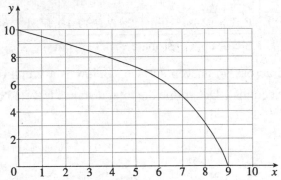

Answer: Lower estimate ≈ 43.2; upper estimate ≈ 73.2

14. Given the graph below, use 5 rectangles to estimate the area under the graph from $x = 0$ to $x = 5$. Compute L_5 (sample points are left endpoints), R_5 (sample points are right endpoints) and M_5 (sample points are midpoints). Which of the estimates appears to give the best estimate? Justify your answer.

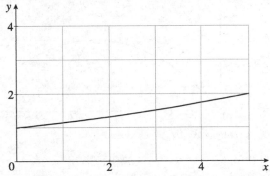

Answer: $L_5 \approx 6.6$; $R_5 \approx 7.6$; $M_5 \approx 7.1$; midpoints appear to give the best estimate since $f(x)$ is monotonic.

15. Given the graph below, use 5 rectangles to estimate the area under the graph from $x = 0$ to $x = 5$. Compute L_5 (sample points are left endpoints), R_5 (sample points are right endpoints) and M_5 (sample points are midpoints). Which of the estimates appears to give the best estimate? Justify your answer.

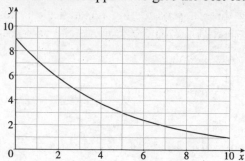

Answer: $L_5 \approx 44.8$, $R_5 \approx 28.8$, $M_5 \approx 36.2$. Since the graph of the function is decreasing, using midpoints appears to give the best approximation.

16. The velocity v (in cm/s) of a rolling ball at time t (in seconds) is recorded below. Find an upper and lower estimate for the distance the ball has traveled during the ten-second interval.

t	0	1	2	3	4	5	6	7	8	9	10
v	1	2.9	6.6	12.1	19.4	28.5	39.4	52.1	66.6	82.9	101

Answer: Lower estimate ≈ 311.5 cm; upper estimate ≈ 411.5 cm

17. A dry ice puck is pushed across an uneven surface. Below is a graph of the velocity v (in cm/s) as a function of the time t (in seconds). Determine the total distance traveled by the puck for $0 \le t \le 9$.

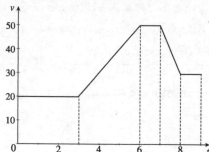

Answer: 285 cm

18. The graph of a function f is given below. Estimate $\int_0^8 f(x)\, dx$ using 4 subintervals with sample points:

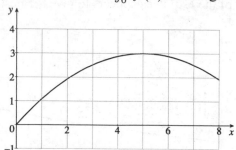

   (a) right endpoints.   (b) left endpoints.   (c) midpoints.

Answer: (a) $R_4 \approx 19.2$ (b) $L_4 \approx 15.4$ (c) $M_4 \approx 18.2$

19. Use the Midpoint Rule with $n = 6$ to approximate $\int_2^8 \frac{1}{1+x^2} \, dx$.

Answer: About 0.33305

20. Estimate $\int_2^5 1 + x^2 \, dx$ using three approximating rectangles and taking the sample points to be left endpoints. Use a picture to explain why your estimation is an overestimate or an underestimate.

Answer: $\int_2^5 1 + x^2 dx \approx 32$, an underestimate

21. Use right endpoints with $n = 4$ to approximate $\int_1^2 \ln 2x \, dx$.

Answer: $\frac{1}{4} \ln 105$

22. Use Definition 2 to show that the area under the curve $y = 1 - x$, $0 \le x \le 1$ is $\frac{1}{2}$.

23. Use Definition 2 to show that the area under the curve $y = x^3$, $0 \le x \le 1$ is $\frac{1}{4}$. Recall that
$$\sum_{k=1}^n k^3 = \frac{n^2 (n+1)^2}{4}.$$

24. Suppose $f(x)$ is a decreasing function on the interval $1 \le x \le 4$. If you estimate $\int_1^4 f(x) \, dx$ using right endpoints, explain why the estimate is an overestimate or an underestimate.

Answer: The estimate using right endpoints is an underestimate. Since $f(x)$ is decreasing, $f(x)$ has a minimum value at right endpoints over each subinterval.

25. Suppose $f(x)$ is an increasing function on the interval $1 \le x \le 4$. If you estimate $\int_1^4 f(x) \, dx$ using right endpoints, explain why the estimate is an overestimate or an underestimate.

Answer: The estimate using right endpoints is an overestimate. Since $f(x)$ is increasing, $f(x)$ has a maximum value at right endpoints over each subinterval.

26. Express $\lim\limits_{n \to \infty} \left\{ \sum\limits_{i=1}^n \left[5 + \left(\frac{3i}{n} \right)^2 \right] \frac{3}{n} \right\}$ as a definite integral.

Answer: $\int_0^3 5 + x^2 \, dx$

27. Express $\lim\limits_{n \to \infty} \left\{ \sum\limits_{i=1}^n \left[\frac{3}{16 - \left(4 + \frac{5i}{n} \right)^2} \right] \frac{5}{n} \right\}$ as a definite integral.

Answer: $\int_4^9 \frac{3}{16 - x^2} \, dx$

28. Express $\lim\limits_{n \to \infty} \left[\sum\limits_{i=1}^n \left(\cos \frac{\pi \cdot i}{n} \right) \frac{\pi}{n} \right]$ as a definite integral.

Answer: $\int_0^\pi \cos x \, dx$

29. Express $\lim\limits_{n \to \infty} \left[\sum\limits_{i=1}^n 2^{(1+5i/n)} \left(\frac{5}{n} \right) \right]$ as a definite integral.

Answer: $\int_1^6 2^x \, dx$

5.2 The Definite Integral

1. Let $f(x) = x^2 - 2$ on the interval $[0, 2]$. Let the interval be divided into four equal subintervals. Find the value of the Riemann sum $\sum_{i=1}^{4} f(x_i^*) \Delta x_i$ if x_i^* is the left endpoint of the subinterval.

(A) $-\frac{11}{4}$ (B) $-\frac{1}{4}$ (C) $-\frac{9}{4}$ (D) $\frac{9}{2}$

(E) $-\frac{1}{2}$ (F) $-\frac{11}{8}$ (G) $-\frac{9}{2}$ (H) $\frac{7}{2}$

Answer: (C)

2. Let $f(x) = x^2 - 2$ on the interval $[0, 2]$. Let the interval be divided into four equal subintervals. Find the value of the Riemann sum $\sum_{i=1}^{4} f(x_i^*) \Delta x_i$ if x_i^* is the right endpoint of the subinterval.

(A) $-\frac{11}{4}$ (B) $-\frac{1}{4}$ (C) $-\frac{9}{4}$ (D) $\frac{9}{2}$

(E) $-\frac{1}{2}$ (F) $-\frac{11}{8}$ (G) $-\frac{9}{2}$ (H) $\frac{7}{2}$

Answer: (B)

3. Let $f(x) = x^2 - 2$ on the interval $[0, 2]$. Let the interval be divided into four equal subintervals. Find the value of the Riemann sum $\sum_{i=1}^{4} f(x_i^*) \Delta x_i$ if x_i^* is the midpoint of the subinterval.

(A) $-\frac{11}{4}$ (B) $-\frac{1}{4}$ (C) $-\frac{9}{4}$ (D) $\frac{9}{2}$

(E) $-\frac{1}{2}$ (F) $-\frac{11}{8}$ (G) $-\frac{9}{2}$ (H) $\frac{7}{2}$

Answer: (F)

4. Let $f(x) = \ln\left(\frac{1}{2}x + 1\right)$ on the interval $[-1, 1]$. Let the interval be divided into four equal subintervals. Find the value of the Riemann sum $\sum_{i=1}^{4} f(x_i^*) \Delta x_i$ if x_i^* is the left endpoint of the subinterval.

(A) -0.7577 (B) 0.1705 (C) -0.1673 (D) 0.2

(E) -0.3788 (F) 0.3409 (G) -0.0836 (H) -0.2

Answer: (E)

5. Let $f(x) = \ln\left(\frac{1}{2}x + 1\right)$ on the interval $[-1, 1]$. Let the interval be divided into four equal subintervals. Find the value of the Riemann sum $\sum_{i=1}^{4} f(x_i^*) \Delta x_i$ if x_i^* is the right endpoint of the subinterval.

(A) -0.7577 (B) 0.1705 (C) -0.1673 (D) 0.2

(E) -0.3788 (F) 0.3409 (G) -0.0836 (H) -0.2

Answer: (B)

6. Let $f(x) = \ln\left(\frac{1}{2}x + 1\right)$ on the interval $[-1, 1]$. Let the interval be divided into four equal subintervals.

Find the value of the Riemann sum $\sum_{i=1}^{4} f(x_i^*)\Delta x_i$ if x_i^* is the midpoint of the subinterval.

(A) -0.7577 (B) 0.1705 (C) -0.1673 (D) 0.2

(E) -0.3788 (F) 0.3409 (G) -0.0836 (H) -0.2

Answer: (G)

7. If $\int_0^1 f(x)\,dx = 7$ and $\int_0^3 f(x)\,dx = 4$, find the value of $\int_1^3 f(x)\,dx$.

(A) 1 (B) 3 (C) 0 (D) -3

(E) -1 (F) -2 (G) 2 (H) Cannot be determined

Answer: (D)

8. If $\int_0^4 f(x)\,dx = 5$ and $\int_0^4 g(x)\,dx = 2$, find the value of $\int_0^4 f(x)\,g(x)\,dx$.

(A) 10 (B) 6 (C) 1 (D) 8

(E) 4 (F) 3 (G) 2 (H) Cannot be determined

Answer: (H)

9. If $\int_0^3 f(x)\,dx = 4$, $\int_3^6 f(x)\,dx = 4$, and $\int_2^6 f(x)\,dx = 5$, find the value of $\int_0^2 f(x)\,dx$.

(A) -3 (B) 3 (C) 2 (D) -1

(E) 0 (F) 1 (G) -2 (H) Cannot be determined

Answer: (B)

10. If $\int_0^3 f(x)\,dx = 12$ and $\int_0^6 f(x)\,dx = 42$, find the value of $\int_3^6 (2f(x) - 3)\,dx$.

(A) 50 (B) 51 (C) 52 (D) 56

(E) 53 (F) 54 (G) 55 (H) Cannot be determined

Answer: (B)

11. The graph of a function f is given below. Estimate $\int_0^8 f(x)\,dx$ using 4 subintervals with sample points:

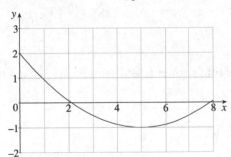

    (a) right endpoints.   (b) left endpoints.   (c) midpoints.

Answer: (a) $R_4 \approx -3.2$ (b) $L_4 \approx 0.6$ (c) $M_4 \approx -2.2$

12. Use the definition of the definite integral to evaluate $\int_0^2 (1 - 2x)\,dx$.

Answer: -2

13. Use the definition of the definite integral to evaluate $\int_0^1 (1 - 2x)\,dx$.

Answer: 0

14. Use the definition of the definite integral to evaluate $\int_2^5 \left(x^2 - 3x + 1\right) dx$.

Answer: 10.5

15. Use the definition of the definite integral to evaluate $\int_0^4 \left(2x - x^2\right) dx$.

Answer: $-\frac{16}{3}$

16. Express $\displaystyle\int_1^4 \left(2x - \frac{1}{x^2}\right) dx$ as the limit of a sum.

Answer: $\displaystyle\lim_{n\to\infty} \sum_{i=1}^{n} \left[2\left(1 + \frac{3i}{n}\right) - \frac{1}{\left(1 + \frac{3i}{n}\right)^2}\right]\frac{3}{n}$

17. Express $\int_4^{64} \left[\sin\left(\pi x\right)\right] dx$ as the limit of a sum.

Answer: $\displaystyle\lim_{n\to\infty} \sum_{i=1}^{n} \sin\left[\pi\left(4 + \frac{60i}{n}\right)\right]\frac{60}{n}$

18. Express $\int_1^4 \left(3^x\right) dx$ as the limit of a sum.

Answer: $\displaystyle\lim_{n\to\infty} \sum_{i=1}^{n} \left[3^{1+(3i/n)}\right]\frac{3}{n}$

19. The graph of f below consists of line segments and semicircles. Use it to evaluate the following integrals.

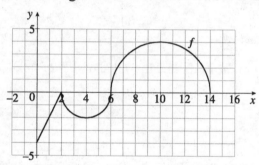

(a) $\int_0^{14} f\left(x\right) dx$
(b) $\int_2^{10} f\left(x\right) dx$

Answer: (a) $6\pi - 4$ (b) 2π

20. The graph of f below consists of line segments and semicircles. Use it to evaluate the following integrals.

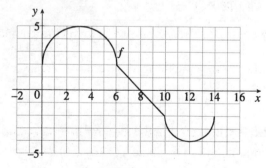

(a) $\int_0^{14} f\left(x\right) dx$
(b) $\int_0^{10} f\left(x\right) dx$
(c) $\int_3^{12} f\left(x\right) dx$

Answer: (a) $4 + \frac{5\pi}{2}$ (b) $12 + \frac{9\pi}{2}$ (c) $2 + \frac{5\pi}{4}$

21. Given functions f and g, use the facts that $\int_0^4 f(x)\,dx = 4$, $\int_4^6 f(x)\,dx = 3$, $\int_0^6 g(x)\,dx = -5$, and $\int_2^6 g(x)\,dx = -4$ to evaluate the following integrals:

   (a) $\int_0^4 (3 \cdot f(x) + 1)\,dx$ (b) $\int_0^6 f(x)\,dx$ (c) $\int_0^6 [f(x) - 4 \cdot g(x)]\,dx$ (d) $\int_0^2 g(x)\,dx$

   Answer: (a) 16   (b) 7   (c) 27   (d) −1

22. The graph of a function f is given below. List the following quantities from smallest to largest.

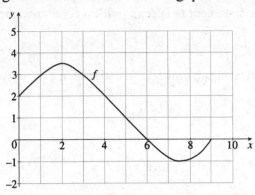

   (a) $\int_0^9 f(x)\,dx$ (b) $\int_6^9 f(x)\,dx$ (c) $\int_0^5 f(x)\,dx$ (d) $\int_0^6 f(x)\,dx$ (e) $f'(5)$

   Answer: (b) < (e) < (a) < (c) < (d)

23. Given the graph of $y = h(x)$ below:

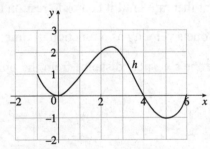

   (a) Find c in $[0, 6]$ which will maximize $\int_0^c h(x)\,dx$.

   (b) Show that $\int_{-1}^3 h(x)\,dx$ is between 4 and 7.

   Answer: (a) 4   (b) By simply adding areas, we can see that this integral has a value between 4 and 7.

24. Evaluate $\int_{-1}^2 (2 - |x|)\,dx$ by interpreting the integral in terms of area.

   Answer: $\frac{7}{2}$

25. Evaluate $\int_{-1}^1 \left(2 - \sqrt{1 - x^2}\right)\,dx$ by interpreting the integral in terms of area.

   Answer: $4 - \frac{\pi}{2}$

26. Use the Comparison Properties of Integrals to show that for any $b \geq 0$, $\int_0^b 2^t\,dt \geq b$.

   Answer: Since $2^t \geq 1$ for $t \geq 0$, $\int_0^b 2^t\,dt \geq \int_0^b 1\,dt = b$.

27. Use the Comparison Properties of Integrals to show that $\dfrac{2}{9} \le \displaystyle\int_0^2 \dfrac{1}{1+x^3}\,dx \le 2$.

Answer: $\dfrac{1}{1+2^3} < \dfrac{1}{1+x^3} < \dfrac{1}{1+0^3}$, since $f = \dfrac{1}{1+x^3}$ is decreasing over $[0,2]$. $\dfrac{2}{9} = \displaystyle\int_0^2 \dfrac{1}{9}\,dx <$

$\displaystyle\int_0^2 \dfrac{1}{1+x^3}\,dx < \displaystyle\int_0^2 1\,dx = 2$

28. Determine whether each of the following statements is true or false. If the statement is true, provide an appropriate justification. If the statement is false, provide a counterexample.

(a) If $f(x) \neq 0$ on $[a,b]$ then $\int_a^b f(x)\,dx \neq 0$.

(b) If f is continuous on an interval containing a, b, and c, then $\int_a^b f(x)\,dx = \int_a^c f(x)\,dx - \int_b^c f(x)\,dx$.

(c) If $\int_a^b f(x)\,dx \ge 0$, then $f(x) \ge 0$ on $[a,b]$.

Answer:

(a) False. $\sin x \neq 0$ on $\left[-\dfrac{\pi}{2}, \dfrac{\pi}{2}\right]$, but $\int_{-\pi/2}^{\pi/2} \sin x = 0$

(b) True

(c) False. $\int_{-1}^2 x\,dx = \dfrac{3}{2} > 0$, but $f(x) = x < 0$ on $(-1, 0)$

29. A stone is dropped off a bridge into a still pond. The stone has initial velocity of zero and falls increasingly faster under the pull of gravity. When it enters the water it slows down at a constant rate, coming to a terminal velocity then continuing at that rate until it comes to rest on the bottom of the pond.

(a) Sketch a rough graph of the stone's velocity as a function of time.

(b) Sketch a rough graph of the stone's vertical distance from the point from which it was dropped as a function of time.

Answer: (a) 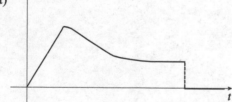   (b)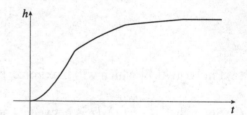

30. The graph of a function f is given below. List the following quantities from smallest to largest.

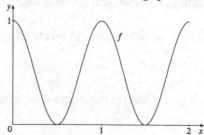

(a) $\int_0^2 f(x)\,dx$ (b) $\int_0^2 \sqrt{f(x)}\,dx$ (c) $\int_0^2 f^2(x)\,dx$ (d) $\int_0^2 f'(x)\,dx$ (e) $\int_0^1 f^2(x)\,dx$

Answer: (d) < (e) < (c) < (a) < (b)

172

5.3 | Evaluating Definite Integrals

1. Find the value of the integral $\int_4^6 2x\,dx$.

(A) 16   (B) 18   (C) 15   (D) 20

(E) 4   (F) 8   (G) 10   (H) 12

Answer: (D)

2. Find the value of the integral $\int_0^1 (x+1)^2\,dx$.

(A) $\frac{7}{3}$ (B) 0   (C) 1   (D) $\frac{5}{3}$

(E) 2   (F) $\frac{1}{3}$ (G) $\frac{4}{3}$ (H) $\frac{2}{3}$

Answer: (A)

3. Find the value of the integral $\int_1^3 \frac{1}{x^2}\,dx$.

(A) $\frac{2}{3}$ (B) $\frac{1}{2}$ (C) $-\frac{1}{2}$ (D) $-\frac{1}{3}$

(E) $-\frac{2}{3}$ (F) 1   (G) $\frac{1}{3}$ (H) -1

Answer: (A)

4. Find the value of the integral $\int_{-1}^8 \sqrt[3]{x}\,dx$.

(A) $\frac{49}{4}$ (B) $\frac{41}{4}$ (C) $\frac{45}{4}$ (D) $\frac{35}{4}$

(E) $\frac{39}{4}$ (F) $\frac{37}{4}$ (G) $\frac{47}{4}$ (H) $\frac{43}{4}$

Answer: (C)

5. Find the value of the integral $\int_{-3}^3 \sqrt[3]{2x^3 - 5x}\,dx$

(A) 19   (B) 16   (C) 11   (D) 0

(E) 9   (F) 17   (G) 13   (H) 12

Answer: (D)

6. Find the value of the integral $\int_{-2}^0 |x+1|\,dx$.

(A) $\frac{1}{2}$ (B) $\frac{1}{4}$ (C) $\frac{3}{4}$ (D) $\frac{3}{2}$

(E) $\frac{5}{4}$ (F) $\frac{5}{2}$ (G) 1   (H) 0

Answer: (G)

7. If $\int_3^b 3x^2\,dx = 37$, find the value of b.

(A) 4   (B) 5   (C) 6   (D) 7

(E) 8   (F) 9   (G) 10   (H) 11

Answer: (A)

8. Find the value of the integral $\int_1^2 \frac{x^2 - 1}{x}\, dx$.

(A) $\frac{1}{2}$ (B) 1   (C) $\frac{3}{2}$ (D) 2

(E) $\frac{1}{2}\ln 2$ (F) $1 + \ln 2$ (G) $\frac{3}{2} - \ln 2$ (H) $2 + \ln 2$

Answer: (G)

9. The velocity of a particle moving along a line is $1 - 2t$ meters per second. Find the displacement in meters of the particle during the time interval $0 \le t \le 1$.

(A) 0   (B) 1   (C) $\frac{1}{8}$ (D) $\frac{1}{2}$

(E) 4   (F) 3   (G) 2   (H) $\frac{1}{4}$

Answer: (A)

10. The velocity of a particle moving along a line is $1 - 2t$ meters per second. Find the distance traveled in meters during the time interval $0 \le t \le 1$.

(A) 0   (B) 1   (C) $\frac{1}{8}$ (D) $\frac{1}{2}$

(E) 4   (F) 3   (G) 2   (H) $\frac{1}{4}$

Answer: (D)

11. The velocity of a particle moving along a line is $t^3 - t$ meters per second. Find the displacement in meters of the particle during the time interval $0 \le t \le 2$.

(A) 0   (B) 1   (C) $\frac{5}{2}$ (D) $\frac{3}{2}$

(E) 4   (F) 2   (G) 3   (H) $\frac{7}{4}$

Answer: (F)

12. The velocity of a particle moving along a line is $t^3 - t$ meters per second. Find the distance traveled in meters during the time interval $0 \le t \le 2$.

(A) $\frac{7}{4}$ (B) $\frac{4}{3}$ (C) $\frac{2}{3}$ (D) $\frac{3}{4}$

(E) $\frac{3}{2}$ (F) $\frac{2}{5}$ (G) $\frac{5}{2}$ (H) $\frac{9}{4}$

Answer: (G)

13. Find the value of the integral $\int_1^2 \frac{4}{x^3}\, dx$.

(A) 0   (B) 3   (C) $\frac{5}{2}$ (D) $\frac{3}{2}$

(E) 4   (F) -3 (G) $-\frac{3}{2}$ (H) $\frac{5}{2}$

Answer: (D)

14. Find the value of the integral $\int_{-e^2}^{-e} \frac{3}{x}\, dx$.

(A) -3 (B) $-e$ (C) e^3 (D) $\frac{1}{3}$

(E) $\ln 2$ (F) $-\ln 3$ (G) $e - \ln 3$ (H) $e^2 - \ln 3$

Answer: (A)

15. Find the value of the integral $\int_0^1 \frac{1}{1+x^2}\,dx$.

(A) $\frac{\pi}{6}$ (B) $\frac{1}{2}\ln 2$ (C) $\frac{\pi}{4}$ (D) 1

(E) $\frac{\pi}{2}$ (F) $\frac{\pi}{8}$ (G) -1 (H) $-\frac{1}{2}\ln 2$

Answer: (C)

16. Evaluate the following integrals:

(a) $\int_2^3 2x - 6x^2\,dx$

(c) $\int_1^3 \frac{x^2 - 4x}{x^2}\,dx$

(b) $\int_1^3 5^x\,dx$

(d) $\int_1^7 \frac{1}{\sqrt[3]{t}}\,dt$

Answer: (a) -33 (b) $\frac{120}{\ln 5}$ (c) $-4\ln 3 + 2$ (d) $\frac{3\sqrt[3]{49}}{2} - \frac{3}{2}$

17. Evaluate the following integrals:

(a) $\int x(5 + \sqrt{x})\,dx$

(c) $\int_0^{\pi/6} 1 + \cos\theta\,d\theta$

(b) $\int_0^1 \frac{5}{1+x^2}\,dx$

(d) $\int_{\pi/4}^{\pi/3} \sec^2\theta\,d\theta$

Answer: (a) $\frac{2}{5}x^{5/2} + \frac{5}{2}x^2 + c$ (b) $\frac{5\pi}{4}$ (c) $\frac{\pi}{6} + \frac{1}{2}$ (d) $\sqrt{3} - 1$

18. Evaluate the following integrals:

(a) $\int \frac{2}{x^2} + \frac{1}{x}\,dx$

(c) $\int \sec\theta \cdot \tan\theta\,d\theta$

(b) $\int e^x + \frac{5}{\sqrt[3]{x^2}}\,dx$

(d) $\int 5^2\,dt$

Answer: (a) $-\frac{2}{x} + \ln|x| + c$ (b) $e^x + 15x^{1/3} + c$ (c) $\sec\theta + c$ (d) $25t + c$

19. Evaluate the following integrals:

(a) $\int \left(2 + \frac{1}{\sqrt{t}}\right)\left(2 - \frac{1}{\sqrt{t}}\right)\,dt$

(c) $\int_0^{1/2} \frac{1}{\sqrt{1-t^2}}\,dt$

(b) $\int_0^3 |2 - x|\,dx$

(d) $\int_{\ln 2}^{\ln 3} e^{2x}\,dx$

Answer: (a) $4t - \ln|t| + c$ (b) $\frac{5}{2}$ (c) $\frac{\pi}{6}$ (d) $\frac{5}{2}$

20. A particle travels along a line. Its velocity in meters per second is given by $v(t) = 3t^2 - 12t$. Find

(a) the displacement from $t = 0$ to $t = 8$.

(b) the distance traveled by the particle from $t = 0$ to $t = 8$.

Answer: (a) 128 m   (b) 192 m

21. Prove that $\frac{-x^3}{3}\cos x$ is not an antiderivative of $x^2\sin x$.

Answer: $\left(-\frac{x^3}{3}\cos x\right)' = -x^2\cos x + \frac{x^3}{3}\sin x \neq x^2\sin x$

22. (a) Find $g(t)$ so that $\int g(t)\,dt = \frac{t}{2}\sqrt{4 - t^2} + 2 \cdot \sin^{-1}\frac{t}{2}$.

   (b) Evaluate $\int_0^2 g(t)\,dt$ using the Evaluation Theorem.

   (c) Evaluate $\int_0^2 g(t)\,dt$ by the area interpretation of the integral. Compare your answer with part (b) above.

   (d) Evaluate $\int_0^{\sqrt{3}} g(t)\,dt$.

   Answer: (a) $\sqrt{4 - t^2}$ (b) π (c) π (d) $\frac{2\pi}{3} + \frac{\sqrt{3}}{2}$

23. (a) If $f(x)$ is measured in pounds and x is measured in feet, what are the units of measurement for $\int_a^b f(x)\,dx$?

   (b) Give a physical interpretation of $f(x)$ and $\int_a^b f(x)\,dx$.

   Answer: (a) ft-lb   (b) $f(x)$ measures force, $\int_a^b f(x)\,dx$ measures work

24. If $p(x)$ is measured in grams per centimeter and x is measured in centimeters, what does $\int_a^b p(x)\,dx$ represent?

   Answer: $\int_a^b p(x)\,dx$ is measured in grams. It represents mass.

25. (a) If x represents the number of units produced for a certain commodity and $C'(x)$ is the rate of change of cost with respect to x, what are the units of $C'(x)$?

   (b) What does $\int_a^b C'(x)\,dx$ represent?

   Answer: (a) dollars per unit   (b) cost in dollars

26. Given $\int_0^4 f(x)\,dx = -5$ and $\int_0^6 f(x)\,dx = 3$, use the properties of definite integrals to find $\int_6^4 f(x)\,dx$.
   Answer: -8

27. A car's velocity $v(t)$ at time t is given by the graph below:

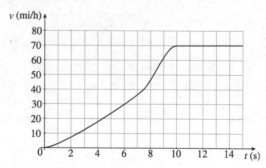

   Use the graph to estimate how far the car travels

   (a) during the first 10 seconds.

   (b) on the interval from 10 to 15 seconds.

   (c) on the interval from 0 to 15 seconds.

   Answer: (a) About 0.08 mph (answer may vary)   (b) $\frac{7}{72}$ mph   (c) ≈ 0.18 mph

5.4 The Fundamental Theorem of Calculus

1. Let $f(x) = \frac{1}{2} \int_0^x t^3 dt$. Find the value of $f'(2)$.

   (A) -24 (B) -12 (C) 8 (D) 24

   (E) 4 (F) -4 (G) 12 (H) -8

   Answer: (E)

2. Let $f(x) = \int_x^{10} t^3 dt$. Find the value of $f'(2)$.

   (A) 8 (B) 4 (C) -24 (D) 12

   (E) -4 (F) -8 (G) 24 (H) -12

   Answer: (F)

3. Let $f(x) = \int_0^{x^2} t^2 dt$. Find the value of $f'(1)$.

   (A) 4 (B) 6 (C) 8 (D) 0

   (E) 2 (F) 1 (G) 3 (H) 5

   Answer: (E)

4. If $F(x) = \int_2^{3x} e^{t^4} dt$, find the value of $F'(0)$.

   (A) 1 (B) 2 (C) 3 (D) 4

   (E) 6 (F) 8 (G) e^8 (H) e^{16}

   Answer: (C)

5. Let $f(x) = \int_0^{x^2} t^4 dt$. Find $f'(x)$.

   (A) 0 (B) x^4 (C) $2x^5$ (D) $2x^6$

   (E) $2x^7$ (F) x^8 (G) $2x^8$ (H) $2x^9$

   Answer: (H)

6. Let $f(x) = \int_0^{x^2} t^4 dt$. Find $f''(x)$.

   (A) 0 (B) $2x^7$ (C) $18x^8$ (D) $14x^6$

   (E) x^2 (F) x^8 (G) $12x^5$ (H) $2x^9$

   Answer: (C)

7. Let $f(x) = \int_0^5 t^4 dt$. Find $f'(x)$.

   (A) 0 (B) $2x^6$ (C) $18x^8$ (D) x^6

   (E) $2x^2$ (F) x^4 (G) $12x^5$ (H) $2x^9$

   Answer: (A)

8. Let $f(x) = \int_0^x \frac{\sin t}{t^2} dt$, where $t > 0$. Find $f'(x)$.

   (A) $\dfrac{\sin t}{t^2}$ (B) $-\dfrac{\sin t}{t^2}$ (C) $\dfrac{\cos x}{x^2}$ (D) $-\dfrac{\sin x}{x^2}$

   (E) $\dfrac{\sin x}{x^2}$ (F) $-\dfrac{\cos x}{x^2}$ (G) $\dfrac{\cos x}{2x}$ (H) $-\dfrac{\cos x}{2x}$

   Answer: (E)

9. Let $f(x) = \int_x^2 \frac{\sin t}{t^2}\, dt$, where $t > 0$. Find $f'(x)$.

(A) $\dfrac{\sin t}{t^2}$ (B) $-\dfrac{\sin t}{t^2}$ (C) $\dfrac{\cos x}{x^2}$ (D) $-\dfrac{\sin x}{x^2}$

(E) $\dfrac{\sin x}{x^2}$ (F) $-\dfrac{\cos x}{x^2}$ (G) $\dfrac{\cos x}{2x}$ (H) $-\dfrac{\cos x}{2x}$

Answer: **(D)**

10. Let $f(x) = \int_{3x}^2 \frac{\sin t}{t^2}\, dt$, where $t > 0$. Find $f'(x)$.

(A) $\dfrac{\sin 3x}{3x^2}$ (B) $-\dfrac{\sin 3x}{3x^2}$ (C) $\dfrac{\cos x}{x^2}$ (D) $-\dfrac{\sin 3x}{9x^2}$

(E) $\dfrac{\sin 3x}{9x^2}$ (F) $-\dfrac{\cos 3x}{9x^2}$ (G) $\dfrac{\cos x}{2x}$ (H) $-\dfrac{\cos x}{2x}$

Answer: **(B)**

11. If $f(x) = \int_x^{x^2} t^2\, dt$, find $f'(x)$.

Answer: $2x^5 - x^2$

12. Compute $\dfrac{d}{dx} \int_x^4 \sin\left(t^3\right) dt$.

Answer: $-\sin\left(x^3\right)$

13. Compute $\dfrac{d}{dx} \int_2^{e^{x^2}} \ln(t)\, dt$.

Answer: $2x^3 e^{x^2}$

14. Compute $\dfrac{d}{dx} \int_{\cos x}^{x^3} e^{-t^2}\, dt$.

Answer: $3x^2 e^{-x^6} + \sin x\, e^{-\cos^2 x}$

15. Compute $\dfrac{d}{dx} \int_{2x}^{3x} e^{\sin t}\, dt$.

Answer: $3e^{\sin 3x} - 2e^{\sin 2x}$

16. Let $f(x) = \int_{-3}^x g(t)\, dt$ where g is the function whose graph is shown below:

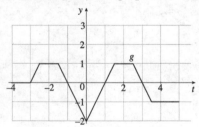

    (a) Evaluate $f(-3)$, $f(-1)$, $f(0)$, $f(1)$, $f(3)$ and $f(5)$.

    (b) On what interval(s) is f increasing?

    (c) What are the maximum and minimum values of f over $[-3, 5]$?

Answer:

    (a) $f(-3) = 0$, $f(-1) = \frac{3}{2}$, $f(0) = \frac{1}{2}$, $f(1) = -\frac{1}{2}$, $f(3) = 1$, $f(5) = -\frac{3}{4}$

    (b) $(-3, -1)$ and $(1, 3)$

    (c) $f(x)$ has a maximum value of $\frac{3}{2}$ and a minimum value of $-\frac{3}{4}$

17. Let $g(x) = \int_{-2}^{x} h(t)\, dt$, where h is the function whose graph is shown below:

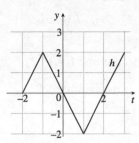

(a) Evaluate $g(-2)$, $g(2)$, $g(0)$, and $g(3)$.

(b) On what interval(s) is g increasing?

(c) What are the maximum and minimum values of g over $[-2, 3]$?

Answer:

(a) $g(-2) = 0$, $g(2) = 0$, $g(0) = 2$, $g(3) = 1$

(b) $(-2, 0)$ and $(2, 3)$

(c) $g(x)$ has a maximum value of 2 and a minimum value of 0

18. Let $g(x) = \int_{0}^{x} f(t)\, dt$, where f is the function whose graph is shown below:

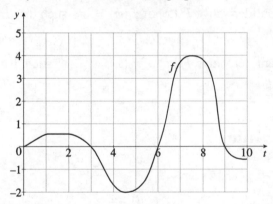

(a) Use the Comparison Properties of Integrals to estimate the value of the following integrals:

(i) $\int_{0}^{3} f(t)\, dt$ (iii) $\int_{6}^{9} f(t)\, dt$

(ii) $\int_{3}^{6} f(t)\, dt$ (iv) $\int_{9}^{10} f(t)\, dt$

(b) At what values of x does g have a local maximum or minimum?

(c) At what values of x does g attain its absolute maximum or minimum?

Answer:

(a) (i) $0 < \int_{0}^{3} f(t)\, dt < \frac{3}{2}$ (ii) $-6 < \int_{3}^{6} f(t)\, dt < 0$ (iii) $0 < \int_{6}^{9} f(t)\, dt < 12$ (iv) $-1 <$ $\int_{9}^{10} f(t)\, dt < 0$

(b) $g(x)$ has a local maximum at 3 and 9, $g(x)$ has a local minimum at 6

(c) $g(x)$ attains its absolute maximum at 9 and its absolute minimum at 6

19. Let $f(x) = \begin{cases} 0 & \text{if } x < 0 \\ 2x & \text{if } 0 \le x \le 1 \\ 2 & \text{if } 1 < x \end{cases}$ and $g(x) = \int_0^x f(t)\,dt$.

(a) Find an expression for $g(x)$ similar to the one for $f(x)$.

(b) Where is f differentiable? Where is g differentiable?

Answer:

(a) $g(x) = \begin{cases} 0 & \text{if } x < 0 \\ x^2 & \text{if } 0 \le x \le 1 \\ 2x - 1 & \text{if } 1 < x \end{cases}$

(b) $f(x)$ is differentiable on $(-\infty, 0)$, $(0, 1)$, and $(1, \infty)$. $g(x)$ is differentiable on $(-\infty, \infty)$.

20. If $\int_0^{x^2} f(t)\,dt = x \ln x$, where f is a continuous function, find $f(1)$.

Answer: $\frac{1}{2}$

21. If $\int_1^{2x} f(t)\,dt = x \sin^{-1} x$, where f is a continuous function, find $f(1)$.

Answer: $\frac{\pi}{12} + \frac{\sqrt{3}}{6}$

22. Use FTC1 to write down an antiderivative $F(x)$ of $f(x) = e^{x^2}$ such that $F(0) = 2$.

Answer: $F(x) = \int_0^x e^{t^2}\,dt + 2$

23. Use FTC1 to write down an antiderivative $F(x)$ of $f(x) = \sqrt{x}e^x$ such that $F(1) = 4$.

Answer: $F(x) = 4 + \int_1^x \sqrt{t}e^t\,dt$

5.5 The Substitution Rule

1. Find the value of the integral $\int_0^{\pi/4} \cos 2x\,dx$.

(A) 0   (B) 1   (C) $\frac{\sqrt{3}}{2}$ (D) $\frac{\pi}{2}$

(E) $\frac{\sqrt{2}}{4}$ (F) 2   (G) $\frac{\sqrt{2}}{2}$ (H) $\frac{1}{2}$

Answer: (H)

2. Find the value of the integral $\int_0^1 \left(x^2 + 1\right)^5 2x\,dx$.

(A) $\frac{17}{4}$ (B) $\frac{17}{2}$ (C) $\frac{21}{8}$ (D) $\frac{21}{2}$

(E) $\frac{17}{8}$ (F) $\frac{21}{4}$ (G) $\frac{25}{17}$ (H) $\frac{28}{3}$

Answer: (D)

3. Find the value of the integral $\int_0^1 \frac{x^2}{\left(x^3 + 1\right)^2}\,dx$.

(A) $\frac{3}{4}$ (B) 2   (C) $\frac{3}{7}$ (D) $\frac{7}{3}$

(E) $\frac{1}{6}$ (F) $\frac{3}{2}$ (G) $\frac{2}{3}$ (H) 1

Answer: (E)

4. Find the value of the integral $\int_0^{\pi/4} \sin^2 x \cos x \, dx$.

(A) $\frac{\sqrt{2}}{18}$ (B) $\frac{\pi}{4}$ (C) $\frac{3\pi}{2}$ (D) $\frac{\sqrt{2}}{12}$

(E) $\frac{\sqrt{2}}{6}$ (F) $\frac{\sqrt{2}}{9}$ (G) $\frac{2\pi}{3}$ (H) $\frac{\pi}{2}$

Answer: (D)

5. Find the value of the integral $\int_0^{\pi/3} \sec x \tan x \, (1 + \sec x) \, dx$.

(A) 4 (B) $\frac{5}{2}$ (C) 3 (D) $\frac{11}{2}$

(E) $\frac{9}{2}$ (F) 2 (G) $\frac{7}{2}$ (H) 5

Answer: (B)

6. Find the value of the integral $\displaystyle\int_1^4 \frac{1}{\left(1 + \sqrt{x}\right)^2} \frac{1}{\sqrt{x}} \, dx$.

(A) $\frac{6}{5}$ (B) $\frac{1}{3}$ (C) $\frac{2}{3}$ (D) $\frac{5}{2}$

(E) $\frac{4}{9}$ (F) $\frac{3}{2}$ (G) $\frac{5}{6}$ (H) $\frac{1}{6}$

Answer: (B)

7. Find the value of the integral $\int_0^{\pi/2} \cos x \sin(\sin x) \, dx$.

(A) $\frac{\pi}{2}$ (B) $1 - \frac{\pi}{4}$ (C) $\sin 1$ (D) $1 - \cos 1$

(E) $\frac{\pi}{2} - \sin 1$ (F) $\frac{\pi}{4} + \cos 1$ (G) $1 + \frac{3\pi}{4}$ (H) $1 + \tan 1$

Answer: (D)

8. Find the value of the integral $\displaystyle\int_{-3}^3 \frac{x}{\sqrt{1 + 3x^2}} \, dx$.

(A) $\frac{2}{3}\left(\sqrt{7} - 1\right)$ (B) $\sqrt{7} - 1$ (C) 0 (D) $\frac{1}{3}$

(E) $\frac{2}{3}$ (F) $\frac{1}{\sqrt{7}}$ (G) $\sqrt{7}$ (H) Does not exist

Answer: (C)

9. Find the value of $\displaystyle\int_e^{e^2} \frac{(\ln x)^2}{x} \, dx$.

(A) $\ln 2$ (B) $\frac{1}{2} \ln 2$ (C) $\frac{1}{2}$ (D) $\frac{3}{2}$

(E) 1 (F) $1/(\ln 2)$ (G) 0 (H) $\frac{7}{3}$

Answer: (H)

10. Find the value of $\displaystyle\int_e^{e^4} \frac{dx}{x\sqrt{\ln x}}$.

(A) 0 (B) 1 (C) 2 (D) 3

(E) 4 (F) 5 (G) 6 (H) 7

Answer: (C)

11. Find the value of the integral $\int_0^1 x^2 e^{-x^3}\, dx$.

(A) $\dfrac{-e}{2}$ (B) $\dfrac{e}{2}$ (C) $\dfrac{1-e^{-1}}{2}$ (D) e

(E) $-e$ (F) $\dfrac{1-e^{-1}}{3}$ (G) $\dfrac{e^{-1}}{2}$ (H) e^{-1}

Answer: (F)

12. Find the value of the integral $\displaystyle\int_0^1 \dfrac{e^x}{e^x + 1}\, dx$.

(A) $e + 1$ (B) $\ln(e-1)$ (C) $\dfrac{e-1}{2}$ (D) $\ln\dfrac{e+1}{2}$

(E) $\frac{1}{2}\ln(e-1)$ (F) $\dfrac{e+1}{2}$ (G) $\frac{1}{2}\ln(e+1)$ (H) $e-1$

Answer: (D)

13. Find the value of $\int_0^{\ln 3} e^{4x}\, dx$.

(A) $\frac{45}{4}$ (B) 11 (C) 80 (D) $\frac{21}{2}$

(E) $\frac{41}{4}$ (F) 10 (G) 20 (H) $\frac{19}{2}$

Answer: (G)

14. Find the value of the integral $\displaystyle\int_0^{1/2} \dfrac{\sin^{-1} x}{\sqrt{1-x^2}}\, dx$.

(A) $\dfrac{\pi^2}{36}$ (B) $\dfrac{\pi}{36}$ (C) $\dfrac{1}{36}$ (D) $\dfrac{\pi}{6}$

(E) $\dfrac{\pi^2}{72}$ (F) $\dfrac{\pi}{72}$ (G) $\dfrac{1}{72}$ (H) $\dfrac{\pi}{2}$

Answer: (E)

15. Evaluate the following integrals:

(a) $\int xe^{x^2}\, dx$ (c) $\displaystyle\int \dfrac{\sec^2 x}{\tan x}\, dx$

(b) $\displaystyle\int \dfrac{\cos(\ln x)}{x}\, dx$ (d) $\displaystyle\int \dfrac{3x^2}{1+x^6}\, dx$

Answer:

     (a) $\frac{1}{2}e^{x^2} + C$ (b) $\sin(\ln x) + C$ (c) $\ln|\tan x| + C$ (d) $\tan^{-1}(x^3) + C$

16. Evaluate the following integrals:

(a) $\int_0^{\pi/4} \sin 2x \sin x\, dx$ (c) $\displaystyle\int_{-1}^2 \dfrac{x}{\sqrt{x+2}}\, dx$

(b) $\int e^x \sin(e^x)\, dx$ (d) $\int \tan x\, dx$

Answer:

     (a) $\frac{\sqrt{2}}{6}$ (b) $-\cos e^x + C$ (c) $\frac{2}{3}$ (d) $\ln|\sec x| + C$

17. Evaluate the following integrals:

(a) $\int \dfrac{x}{(x^2+1)^4}\, dx$

(c) $\int \dfrac{e^{1/x}}{x^2}\, dx$

(b) $\int_e^{e^2} \dfrac{1}{x\,(\ln x)^2}\, dx$

(d) $\int_0^1 \dfrac{x}{x+1}\, dx$

Answer:

(a) $\dfrac{-1}{6\,(x^2+1)^3}+C$ (b) $\frac{1}{2}$ (c) $-e^{1/x}+C$ (d) $1-\ln 2$

18. Evaluate the following integrals:

(a) $\int (e^x + e^{-x})^2\, dx$

(c) $\int \dfrac{x+3}{x^2+6x}\, dx$

(b) $\int \dfrac{x+3}{(x^2+6x)^2}\, dx$

(d) $\int_{-\pi/2}^{\pi/2} \dfrac{x\cos x}{1+x^4}\, dx$

Answer:

(a) $\frac{1}{2}e^{2x}-\frac{1}{2}e^{-2x}+2x+C$ (b) $-\dfrac{1}{2\,(x^2+6x)}+C$ (c) $\frac{1}{2}\ln\left|x^2+6x\right|+C$ (d) 0

19. Evaluate the following integrals:

(a) $\int \dfrac{\sqrt{u}+\sqrt[3]{u}}{u}\, du$

(c) $\int_0^1 \sqrt[3]{t^3+1}\cdot t^5\, dt$

(b) $\int_{-2}^1 |2x+1|\, dx$

(d) $\int_{-4}^4 \sqrt{16-x^2}\, dx$

Answer:

(a) $2\sqrt{u}+3\sqrt[3]{u}+C$ (b) $\frac{9}{2}$ (c) $\frac{\sqrt[3]{2}}{14}+\frac{3}{28}$ (d) 8π

20. Evaluate the following integrals:

(a) $\int_0^{\pi/2} \sin x\cos^2 x\, dx$

(c) $\int_{-4}^4 \dfrac{\sin x\cdot\sqrt{16-x^2}}{4+x^2}\, dx$

(b) $\int_0^{\pi/2} \dfrac{\cos x}{\sqrt{1-\sin x}}\, dx$

(d) $\int_{-2}^2 \left(x^3+2\sqrt{4-x^2}\right) dx$

Answer:

(a) $\frac{1}{3}$ (b) 2 (c) 0 (d) 4π

5.6 | Integration by Parts

1. Find the value of the integral $\int_0^1 xe^x\, dx$.

(A) 2

(B) $e^2 - e$

(C) 1

(D) e^2

(E) e

(F) $e - 1$

(G) $e - 2$

(H) $\dfrac{e-1}{2}$

Answer: (C)

2. Find the value of the integral $\int_1^e \ln x \, dx$.

(A) e^2 (B) e (C) 2 (D) $e^2 - e$

(E) $e - 2$ (F) 1 (G) $e - 1$ (H) $\dfrac{e - 1}{2}$

Answer: (F)

3. Find the value of the integral $\int_0^\pi x \cos x \, dx$.

(A) -2 (B) $2\pi - 2$ (C) $\frac{\pi}{2}$ (D) 4

(E) 2 (F) π (G) 2π (H) -4

Answer: (A)

4. Find the value of the integral $\int_0^{\pi/2} e^x \cos x \, dx$.

(A) $\dfrac{e^{\pi/4} + 1}{2}$ (B) $\dfrac{e^{\pi/2} + 1}{2}$ (C) $\dfrac{e^{\pi/4} + 1}{4}$ (D) $\dfrac{e^{\pi/2} - 1}{4}$

(E) $\dfrac{e^{\pi/4} - 1}{4}$ (F) $\dfrac{e^{\pi/4} - 1}{2}$ (G) $\dfrac{e^{\pi/2} + 1}{4}$ (H) $\dfrac{e^{\pi/2} - 1}{2}$

Answer: (H)

5. Find the value of the integral $\int_1^4 \dfrac{\ln x}{x^2} \, dx$.

(A) e (B) $2e - 1$ (C) $\dfrac{3}{2} - \ln 2$ (D) $\dfrac{1}{2} - \dfrac{\ln 2}{2}$

(E) $e - 2$ (F) $e - 1$ (G) $\dfrac{3}{4} - \dfrac{\ln 2}{2}$ (H) $1 - \ln 2$

Answer: (G)

6. Find the value of the integral $\int_0^1 x \tan^{-1} x \, dx$.

(A) $\frac{\pi}{4}$ (B) $\pi - 2$ (C) $\frac{\pi}{2}$ (D) $\frac{\pi - 2}{2}$

(E) $\frac{\pi - 2}{4}$ (F) $\pi - 1$ (G) $\frac{\pi - 1}{2}$ (H) $\frac{\pi - 1}{4}$

Answer: (E)

7. Find the value of the integral $\int_0^\pi x^2 \cos x \, dx$.

(A) π (B) 2π (C) 2 (D) 0

(E) -2 (F) -2π (G) $-\pi$ (H) $\frac{\pi}{2}$

Answer: (F)

8. Find the value of the integral $\int_0^1 x e^{2x} \, dx$.

(A) $1 - e^2$ (B) $e + e^2$ (C) $\dfrac{1 - e}{2}$ (D) $\dfrac{e^2 + 3}{2}$

(E) $\dfrac{2 - e^2}{3}$ (F) $\dfrac{e^2 + 1}{4}$ (G) $\dfrac{e^2 - 3}{4}$ (H) $\dfrac{1 - e^2}{8}$

Answer: (F)

9. Find the value of the integral $\int_0^1 x^7 e^{-x^4} \, dx$.

(A) $\frac{1}{4}(2 + 1/e)$ (B) $\frac{1}{2}(2 + 2/e)$ (C) $\frac{1}{2}(2 - 1/e)$ (D) $\frac{1}{4}(1 + 1/e)$

(E) $\frac{1}{4}(2 - 1/e)$ (F) $\frac{1}{4}(1 - 2/e)$ (G) $\frac{1}{2}(2 + 1/e)$ (H) $\frac{1}{2}(2 - 2/e)$

Answer: (F)

10. Find the value of the integral $\int_0^1 \ln\left(1 + x^2\right) dx$.

(A) $\ln 2$ (B) $\frac{\pi}{8}$ (C) $\frac{\pi}{2} - 2 + \ln 2$ (D) $2 - \ln 2$

(E) $\frac{\pi}{4} + \ln 2$ (F) $\pi - 4$ (G) $\pi - 2$ (H) $\pi - \ln 2$

Answer: (C)

11. Evaluate the integral $\displaystyle\int \frac{1 + \ln x}{x \ln x} \, dx$.

(A) $\ln x + C$ (B) $\ln \ln x + C$

(C) $x + \ln x + C$ (D) $\ln x + \ln \ln x + C$

(E) $\dfrac{x}{\ln x} + C$ (F) $\dfrac{\ln x}{(x + \ln x)} + C$

(G) $x \ln x + C$ (H) $x \ln \ln x + C$

Answer: (D)

12. Evaluate the integral $\int \cos \sqrt{x} \, dx$.

(A) $2 \sin \sqrt{x} + C$ (B) $2\sqrt{x} \cos \sqrt{x} + C$

(C) $\sqrt{x} \left(\cos \sqrt{x} + \sin \sqrt{x}\right) + C$ (D) $\dfrac{\cos \sqrt{x} + \sin \sqrt{x}}{\sqrt{x}} + C$

(E) $2 \left(\sqrt{x} \sin \sqrt{x} + \cos \sqrt{x}\right) + C$ (F) $2 \left(\sqrt{x} \cos \sqrt{x} + \sin \sqrt{x}\right) + C$

(G) $\sqrt{x} \cos \sqrt{x} + \dfrac{\sin \sqrt{x}}{\sqrt{x}} + C$ (H) $\sqrt{x} \sin \sqrt{x} + \dfrac{\cos \sqrt{x}}{\sqrt{x}} + C$

Answer: (E)

13. Evaluate $\displaystyle\int \cos\left(\ln x\right) dx$.

(A) $\sin\left(\ln x\right) + C$ (B) $\dfrac{x^2}{2} \left[\cos\left(\ln x\right) + \sin\left(\ln x\right)\right] + C$

(C) $\cos\left(\dfrac{1}{x}\right) + C$ (D) $\dfrac{x}{4} \left[\cos\left(\ln x\right) + \sin\left(\ln x\right)\right] + C$

(E) $\dfrac{\sin x}{x} + C$ (F) $x \left[\cos\left(\ln x\right) + \sin\left(\ln x\right)\right] + C$

(G) $-\sin\left(\dfrac{1}{x}\right) + C$ (H) $\dfrac{x}{2} \left[\cos\left(\ln x\right) + \sin\left(\ln x\right)\right] + C$

Answer: (H)

14. Evaluate the following integrals:

(a) $\int x \sin x \, dx$ (b) $\int x \sin\left(x^2\right) dx$

(c) $\int \sin^{-1} x \, dx$ (d) $\int x e^{3x} \, dx$

Answer:

(a) $-x \cos x + \sin x + C$ (b) $\dfrac{-\cos\left(x^2\right)}{2} + C$ (c) $x \sin^{-1} x + \sqrt{1 - x^2} + C$ (d) $\dfrac{x e^{3x}}{3} - \dfrac{e^{3x}}{9} + C$

15. Evaluate the following integrals:

(a) $\int x \sec^2 x \, dx$

(b) $\int (3x^2 + 1) \ln (x^2 + 1) \, dx$

(c) $\int \dfrac{e^{\sqrt{x}}}{\sqrt{x}} \, dx$

(d) $\int e^{\sqrt{x}} \, dx$

Answer:

(a) $\ln |\cos x| + x \tan x + C$

(b) $(x^3 + x) \ln (x^2 + 1) - \dfrac{2x^3}{3} + C$

(c) $2e^{\sqrt{x}} + C$

(d) $2e^{\sqrt{x}} (\sqrt{x} - 1) + C$

16. Evaluate the following integrals:

(a) $\int x \cot^{-1} x \, dx$

(b) $\int_1^e (\ln x)^2 \, dx$

(c) $\int x^2 \cos x \, dx$

(d) $\int \cos (\ln x) \, dx$

Answer:

(a) $\dfrac{x^2}{2} \cot^{-1} x + \dfrac{x}{2} - \frac{1}{2} \tan^{-1} x + C$

(b) $e - 2$

(c) $2x \cos x + x^2 \sin x - 2 \sin x + C$

(d) $\dfrac{x}{2} (\cos (\ln x) + \sin (\ln x)) + C$

17. Determine a reduction formula for $\int_1^e x (\ln x)^n \, dx$.

Answer: $I_n = \dfrac{e^2}{2} - \dfrac{n}{2} I_{n-1}$, where $I_{n-1} = \int_1^e x (\ln x)^{n-1} \, dx$

18. (a) Use integration by parts to prove the reduction formula:

$$\int x^n \cos x \, dx = x^n \sin x - n \int x^{n-1} \sin x \, dx$$

(b) Demonstrate your understanding of this formula by using it to evaluate $\int x^4 \cos x \, dx$.

Answer:

(a) $u = x^n, \ dv = \cos x \, dx$

(b) $(4x^3 - 24x) \cos x + (x^4 - 12x^2 + 24) \sin x + C$

19. Let f be a twice differentiable function such that $f(0) = 5$, $f(3) = 1$, and $f'(3) = -2$. Determine the value of $\int_0^3 x \cdot f''(x) \, dx$.

Answer: -2

5.7 Additional Techniques of Integration

1. Find the value of the integral $\int_0^1 \sqrt{1 - u^2} \, du$.

(A) 2

(B) 1

(C) $\frac{\pi}{4}$

(D) $\frac{1}{4}$

(E) $\frac{1}{2}$

(F) π

(G) $\frac{\pi}{2}$

(H) 2π

Answer: (C)

2. Find the value of the integral $\int_{-1}^1 1 - \sqrt{1 - u^2} \, du$.

(A) $2 - \frac{\pi}{2}$

(B) $2 + \frac{\pi}{4}$

(C) $1 - \frac{\pi}{4}$

(D) $1 + \frac{\pi}{4}$

(E) $\frac{\pi}{2} - 1$

(F) $2 - \frac{\pi}{4}$

(G) $1 + \frac{\pi}{2}$

(H) $2 + \frac{\pi}{2}$

Answer: (A)

3. Find the value of the integral $\int_{\pi/4}^{\pi/2} \csc u \, du$.

(A) $-\frac{1}{2}\ln\left(\sqrt{2}-1\right)$ (B) $\ln\left(2-\sqrt{2}\right)$ (C) $\frac{1}{2}\ln\left(\sqrt{2}-1\right)$ (D) $-\ln\left(2-\sqrt{2}\right)$

(E) $\ln\left(\sqrt{2}-1\right)$ (F) $-\frac{1}{2}\ln 2 - \sqrt{2}$ (G) $\frac{1}{2}\ln 2 - \sqrt{2}$ (H) $-\ln\left(\sqrt{2}-1\right)$

Answer: (H)

4. Find the value of the integral $\int_{1}^{2} \sqrt{u^2 - 1} \, du$.

(A) $\sqrt{3}+\frac{1}{2}\ln\left(4-\sqrt{3}\right)$

(B) $\sqrt{3}-\frac{1}{2}\ln\left(2+\sqrt{3}\right)$

(C) $\sqrt{3}-\frac{1}{2}\ln\left(4+\sqrt{3}\right)$

(D) $\sqrt{3}+\frac{1}{2}\ln\left(2-\sqrt{3}\right)$

(E) $\sqrt{3}-\frac{1}{2}\ln\left(4-\sqrt{3}\right)$

(F) $\sqrt{3}+\frac{1}{2}\ln\left(4+\sqrt{3}\right)$

(G) $\sqrt{3}+\frac{1}{2}\ln\left(2+\sqrt{3}\right)$

(H) $\sqrt{3}-\frac{1}{2}\ln\left(2-\sqrt{3}\right)$

Answer: (B)

5. Find the value of the integral $\int_{0}^{1} \tan^{-1} u \, du$.

(A) $\frac{\pi}{4} - \ln 2$ (B) $\frac{\pi}{2} + \frac{1}{2}\ln 2$ (C) $\frac{\pi}{2} - \ln 2$ (D) $\frac{\pi}{2} + \ln 2$

(E) $\frac{\pi}{4} + \ln 2$ (F) $\frac{\pi}{2} - \frac{1}{2}\ln 2$ (G) $\frac{\pi}{4} - \frac{1}{2}\ln 2$ (H) $\frac{\pi}{4} + \frac{1}{2}\ln 2$

Answer: (G)

6. Find the value of the integral $\int_{0}^{\pi/12} \sin^2 u \, du$.

(A) $\dfrac{\pi - 3}{18}$ (B) $\dfrac{\pi - 3}{16}$ (C) $\dfrac{\pi - 3}{24}$ (D) $\dfrac{\pi - 3}{72}$

(E) $\dfrac{\pi - 3}{36}$ (F) $\dfrac{\pi - 3}{12}$ (G) $\dfrac{\pi - 3}{48}$ (H) $\dfrac{\pi - 3}{60}$

Answer: (C)

7. Find the value of the integral $\int_{1}^{e} u^{10} \ln u \, du$.

(A) $\dfrac{10e^{10} + 1}{121}$ (B) $\dfrac{10e^{10} - 1}{121}$ (C) $\dfrac{11e^{10} + 1}{121}$ (D) $\dfrac{11e^{10} - 1}{121}$

(E) $\dfrac{10e^{11} + 1}{121}$ (F) $\dfrac{11e^{11} + 1}{121}$ (G) $\dfrac{11e^{11} - 1}{121}$ (H) $\dfrac{10e^{11} - 1}{121}$

Answer: (E)

8. Evaluate $\displaystyle\int \frac{\cos x}{4 + \sin^2 x} \, dx$.

(A) $\tan^{-1}\left(\dfrac{\sin x}{2}\right) + C$

(B) $\frac{1}{2}\tan^{-1}\left(\dfrac{\sin x}{2}\right) + C$

(C) $\frac{1}{2}\tan^{-1}\left(\sin x\right) + C$

(D) $\frac{1}{2}\tan^{-1}\left(\dfrac{\cos x}{2}\right) + C$

(E) $\frac{1}{4}\tan^{-1}\left(\dfrac{\sin x}{2}\right) + C$

(F) $\ln\left(\dfrac{\sin x}{2}\right) + C$

(G) $2\tan^{-1}\left(\dfrac{\sin x}{2}\right) + C$

(H) $\frac{1}{2}\ln\left(\dfrac{\sin x}{2}\right) + C$

Answer: (B)

9. Evaluate $\int \dfrac{3x+2}{x-1}\, dx$.

(A) $5\ln|x-1| + 3x + C$

(B) $5\ln|x-1| + C$

(C) $3\ln|x-1| + 3x + C$

(D) $3x + C$

(E) $3\ln|x-1| + 5x + C$

(F) $5x + C$

(G) $2\ln|x-1| + 3x + C$

(H) $2\ln|x| + C$

Answer: (A)

10. Evaluate $\int \dfrac{\cos\sqrt{x}}{\sqrt{x}}\, dx$.

(A) $-2\sin\sqrt{x} + C$

(B) $-\sqrt{x}\sin\sqrt{x} + C$

(C) $2\sin\sqrt{x} + C$

(D) $-\cos\sqrt{x} + C$

(E) $\frac{1}{2}\sin\sqrt{x} + C$

(F) $-2\cos\sqrt{x} + C$

(G) $\sin(2\sqrt{x}) + C$

(H) $-\sqrt{x}\cos\sqrt{x} + C$

Answer: (C)

11. Evaluate $\int \dfrac{x}{\sqrt{x-1}}\, dx$.

(A) $(x+2)\sqrt{x-1} + C$

(B) $5\ln|x-1| + C$

(C) $\sqrt{(x-1)(x+2)} + C$

(D) $x\sqrt{x-1} + C$

(E) $x + \sqrt{x-1} + C$

(F) $\frac{2}{3}(x+2)\sqrt{x-1} + C$

(G) $2 + \sqrt{x-1} + C$

(H) $\frac{3}{2}(x+2)\sqrt{x-1} + C$

Answer: (F)

12. Evaluate $\int \dfrac{1}{x^2 e^{3/x}}\, dx$.

(A) $-e^{-3/x} + C$

(B) $-\frac{1}{3}e^{-3/x} + C$

(C) $3e^{-3/x} + C$

(D) $-3e^{-3/x} + C$

(E) $xe^{-3/x} + C$

(F) $\frac{1}{3}xe^{-3/x} + C$

(G) $\frac{1}{3}e^{-3/x} + C$

(H) $-\frac{1}{3}xe^{-3/x} + C$

Answer: (G)

13. Evaluate $\int \dfrac{1}{x^2-4}\, dx$.

(A) $\frac{1}{4}\ln\left|\dfrac{x+2}{x-2}\right| + C$

(B) $\ln|x^2-4| + C$

(C) $4\ln\left|\dfrac{x+2}{x-2}\right| + C$

(D) $\frac{1}{4}\ln\left|\dfrac{x-2}{x+2}\right| + C$

(E) $\frac{1}{2}\ln\left|\dfrac{x+2}{x-2}\right| + C$

(F) $\frac{1}{4}\ln|x^2-4| + C$

(G) $\frac{1}{2}\ln\left|\dfrac{x-2}{x+2}\right| + C$

(H) $-\dfrac{1}{x} - 4x + C$

Answer: (D)

188

14. Evaluate the following integrals:

(a) $\displaystyle\int \frac{\ln x}{x^2}\, dx$

(b) $\displaystyle\int \frac{x^2 + x + 1}{x^2 - 1}\, dx$

(c) $\displaystyle\int \frac{\cos x}{4 + \sin^2 x}\, dx$

(d) $\int x^3 \sqrt{4 - x^2}\, dx$

Answer:

(a) $-\dfrac{\ln x}{x} - \dfrac{1}{x} + C$

(b) $x + \frac{1}{2}\ln\left(\dfrac{|x-1|^3}{|x+1|}\right) + C$

(c) $\frac{1}{2}\tan^{-1}\left(\dfrac{\sin x}{2}\right) + C$

(d) $-\frac{1}{15}\left(3x^2 + 8\right)\left(4 - x^2\right)^{3/2} + C$

15. Evaluate the following integrals:

(a) $\int (x + \sin x)^2\, dx$

(b) $\int x e^{x^2 + 1}\, dx$

(c) $\int_0^{\pi/2} \cos x \sin^3 x\, dx$

(d) $\displaystyle\int \frac{7x - 23}{x^2 - 7x + 12}\, dx$

Answer:

(a) $-\frac{1}{4}\sin 2x - 2x\cos x + 2\sin x + \dfrac{x^3}{3} + \dfrac{x}{2} + C$

(b) $\frac{1}{2}e^{x^2 + 1} + C$

(c) $\frac{1}{4}$

(d) $\ln\left((x - 3)^2 |x - 4|^5\right) + C$

16. Evaluate the following integrals:

(a) $\int x\sqrt{x^2 - 4}\, dx$

(b) $\int \sqrt{x^2 - 4}\, dx$

(c) $\displaystyle\int \frac{1}{x^2 + 2x + 2}\, dx$

(d) $\displaystyle\int \frac{x^3}{1 + x^2}\, dx$

Answer:

(a) $\frac{1}{3}\left(x^2 - 4\right)^{3/2} + C$

(b) $-2\ln\left(\sqrt{x^2 - 4} + x\right) + \dfrac{x\sqrt{x^2 - 4}}{2} + C$

(c) $\tan^{-1}(x + 1) + C$

(d) $\frac{1}{2}\left[x^2 - \ln\left(x^2 + 1\right)\right] + C$

17. Evaluate the following integrals:

(a) $\int \left(x^2 + 1\right) e^{x^3 + 3x}\, dx$

(b) $\int \sin\sqrt{x}\, dx$

(c) $\displaystyle\int \frac{x^2 + x + 1}{\sqrt{x}}\, dx$

(d) $\int \sqrt{4 + x^2}\, dx$

Answer:

(a) $\frac{1}{3}e^{(x^3 + 3x)} + C$

(b) $-2\sqrt{x}\cos\sqrt{x} + 2\sin\sqrt{x} + C$

(c) $\frac{2}{5}x^{5/2} + \frac{2}{3}x^{3/2} + 2\sqrt{x} + C$

(d) $2\ln\left|\sqrt{x^2 + 4} + x\right| + \dfrac{x\sqrt{x^2 + 4}}{2} + C$

18. Evaluate the following integrals:

(a) $\displaystyle\int_0^{1/2} \frac{x}{\sqrt{1-x^2}}\, dx$

(b) $\int e^{x+e^x}\, dx$

(c) $\displaystyle\int \frac{3x+2}{x-1}\, dx$

(d) $\int \ln\left(1+x^2\right)\, dx$

Answer:

(a) $1 - \frac{\sqrt{3}}{2}$

(b) $e^{e^x} + C$

(c) $5\ln|x-1| + 3x + C$

(d) $x\ln\left(x^2+1\right) + 2\tan^{-1}x - 2x + C$

5.8 Integration Using Tables And Computer Algebra Systems

1. Use the Table of Integrals in your textbook to evaluate each of the following:

(a) $\int e^{3x}\cos 2x\, dx$

(b) $\int \sqrt{4x - x^2}\, dx$

(c) $\int \sqrt{4x - 25x^2}\, dx$

(d) $\int u^3 \sin u\, du$

(e) $\int \cos^4(2t)\, dt$

(f) $\displaystyle\int \frac{1}{x^2 + 2x + 2}\, dx$

(g) $\int \sqrt{9 + 4u^2}\, du$

(h) $\int \sqrt{9 - 4u^2}\, du$

(i) $\int \sqrt{4u^2 - 9}\, du$

(j) $\int \sin^2 t \cos t\, e^{\sin t}\, dt$

Answer:

(a) $e^{3x}\left(\dfrac{3\cos 2x}{13} + \dfrac{2\sin 2x}{13}\right) + C$ (Formula 99)

(b) $\dfrac{x-2}{2}\sqrt{4x - x^2} + 2\cos^{-1}\left(\dfrac{2-x}{2}\right) + C$ (Formula 113)

(c) $\left(\dfrac{x}{2} - \dfrac{1}{25}\right)\sqrt{4x - 25x^2} + \dfrac{2}{125}\cos^{-1}\left(\dfrac{2 - 25x}{2}\right) + C$ (Formula 113)

(d) $-u^3\cos u + 3u^2\sin u + 6u\cos u - 6\sin u + C$ (Formulas 84 and 85)

(e) $\frac{1}{8}\cos^3(2t)\sin(2t) + \frac{3}{8}t + \frac{3}{32}\sin(4t) + C$ (Formula 74)

(f) $\tan^{-1}(x+1) + C$ (Formula 17)

(g) $u\sqrt{\frac{9}{4} + u^2} + \frac{9}{4}\ln\left|u + \sqrt{\frac{9}{4} + u^2}\right| + C$ (Formula 21)

(h) $u\sqrt{\frac{9}{4} - u^2} + \frac{9}{4}\sin^{-1}\left(\dfrac{2u}{3}\right) + C$ (Formula 30)

(i) $u\sqrt{u^2 - \frac{9}{4}} - \frac{9}{4}\ln\left|u + \sqrt{\frac{9}{4} + u^2}\right| + C$ (Formula 39)

(j) $\sin^2 t\, e^{\sin t} - 2\sin t\, e^{\sin t} + 2e^{\sin t} + C$ (Formula 97)

2. Use the Table of Integrals in the back of your textbook to evaluate each of the following:

(a) $\int e^x \sec e^x \, dx$

(f) $\int_0^2 \dfrac{x^2}{\sqrt{16 - x^2}} \, dx$

(b) $\int \sin^4 x \cos^2 x \, dx$

(g) $\int_2^4 \dfrac{dx}{\sqrt{6x - x^2 - 5}}$

(c) $\int \dfrac{1}{\cos^3 x} \, dx$

(h) $\int_0^{\pi/2} \dfrac{\sin t}{1 + \cos^2 t} \, dt$

(d) $\int x^3 \sin x^2 \, dx$

(i) $\int_2^5 \dfrac{\sqrt{4 + x^2}}{x^4} \, dx$

(e) $\int \dfrac{1}{\sqrt{4 - 9x^2}} \, dx$

(j) $\int_0^{\pi/2} e^{-x} \sin x \, dx$

Answer:

(a) $\ln \left| \sec e^x + \tan e^x \right| + C$ (Formula 14)

(b) $\frac{1}{6} \sin^5 x \cos x - \frac{1}{24} \sin^3 x \cos x - \frac{1}{32} \sin 2x + \frac{1}{16} x + C$ (Formula 73)

(c) $\frac{1}{2} \sec x \tan x + \frac{1}{2} \ln \left| \sec x + \tan x \right| + C$ (Formula 71)

(d) $\frac{1}{2} \sin \left(x^2 \right) - \dfrac{x^2}{2} \cos \left(x^2 \right) + C$ (Formula 82)

(e) $\frac{1}{3} \sin^{-1} \left(\dfrac{3x}{2} \right) + C$ (Formula 16)

(f) $\frac{4\pi}{3} - 2\sqrt{3}$

(g) $\frac{\pi}{3}$

(h) $\frac{\pi}{4}$

(i) $\frac{\sqrt{2}}{6} - \dfrac{29\sqrt{29}}{1500}$

(j) $\frac{1}{2} - \frac{1}{2} e^{-\pi/2}$

5.9 | Approximate Integration

1. Use the Trapezoidal Rule with $n = 1$ to approximate the integral $\int_0^1 \left(\sqrt{x} + 2 \right) dx$.

(A) $\frac{1}{2}$ (B) $\frac{9}{16}$ (C) $\frac{7}{16}$ (D) $\frac{1}{4}$

(E) $\frac{3}{8}$ (F) $\frac{2}{3}$ (G) $\frac{5}{2}$ (H) $\frac{5}{8}$

Answer: (G)

2. Use Simpson's Rule with $n = 2$ to approximate the integral $\int_0^1 x^3 \, dx$.

(A) $\frac{5}{8}$ (B) $\frac{1}{3}$ (C) $\frac{3}{8}$ (D) $\frac{2}{3}$

(E) $\frac{7}{16}$ (F) $\frac{1}{4}$ (G) $\frac{9}{16}$ (H) $\frac{1}{2}$

Answer: (F)

3. Use the Trapezoidal Rule with $n = 2$ to approximate the integral $\int_0^1 x^3 \, dx$.

(A) $\frac{5}{16}$ (B) $\frac{1}{4}$ (C) $\frac{1}{2}$ (D) $\frac{5}{8}$

(E) $\frac{1}{3}$ (F) $\frac{7}{16}$ (G) $\frac{2}{3}$ (H) $\frac{3}{8}$

Answer: (A)

4. Use the Midpoint Rule with $n = 2$ to approximate the integral $\int_0^1 x^3 \, dx$.

(A) $\frac{1}{4}$ (B) $\frac{1}{2}$ (C) $\frac{7}{32}$ (D) $\frac{3}{2}$

(E) $\frac{5}{16}$ (F) $\frac{5}{32}$ (G) $\frac{7}{16}$ (H) $\frac{5}{2}$

Answer: (C)

5. Use Simpson's Rule with $n = 4$ to approximate the integral $\int_1^5 \frac{1}{x} \, dx$.

(A) $\frac{73}{45}$ (B) $\frac{71}{48}$ (C) $\frac{61}{35}$ (D) $\frac{73}{48}$

(E) $\frac{61}{36}$ (F) $\frac{59}{36}$ (G) $\frac{59}{35}$ (H) $\frac{71}{45}$

Answer: (A)

6. Use the Trapezoidal Rule with $n = 4$ to approximate the integral $\int_1^5 \frac{1}{x} \, dx$.

(A) $\frac{496}{315}$ (B) $\frac{73}{45}$ (C) $\frac{7}{32}$ (D) $\frac{3}{2}$

(E) $\frac{5}{16}$ (F) $\frac{101}{60}$ (G) $\frac{7}{16}$ (H) $\frac{5}{2}$

Answer: (F)

7. Use the Midpoint Rule with $n = 4$ to approximate the integral $\int_1^5 \frac{1}{x} \, dx$.

(A) $\frac{496}{315}$ (B) $\frac{1}{2}$ (C) 12   (D) 6

(E) $\frac{5}{16}$ (F) $\frac{101}{60}$ (G) $\frac{7}{16}$ (H) $\frac{5}{2}$

Answer: (A)

8. Use Simpson's Rule with $n = 4$ to approximate the integral $\int_{-2}^2 2^x \, dx$.

(A) $\frac{65}{4}$ (B) $\frac{1}{2}$ (C) $\frac{45}{8}$ (D) $\frac{3}{2}$

(E) $\frac{65}{12}$ (F) $\frac{45}{4}$ (G) $\frac{7}{16}$ (H) $\frac{5}{2}$

Answer: (E)

9. Use the Trapezoidal Rule with $n = 4$ to approximate the integral $\int_{-2}^2 2^x \, dx$.

(A) $\frac{65}{4}$ (B) $\frac{1}{2}$ (C) $\frac{45}{8}$ (D) $\frac{3}{2}$

(E) $\frac{65}{12}$ (F) $\frac{45}{4}$ (G) $\frac{7}{16}$ (H) $\frac{5}{2}$

Answer: (C)

10. Use the Midpoint Rule with $n = 4$ to approximate the integral $\int_{-2}^2 2^x \, dx$.

(A) 16.25   (B) 0.505   (C) 5.4167   (D) 1.5

(E) 5.625   (F) 11.25   (G) 5.3033   (H) 2.5

Answer: (G)

11. Suppose using $n = 10$ to approximate the integral of a certain function by the Trapezoidal Rule results in an upper bound for the error equal to $\frac{1}{10}$. What will the upper bound become if we change to $n = 20$?

(A) $\frac{1}{10,000}$ (B) $\frac{1}{100}$ (C) $\frac{1}{80}$ (D) $\frac{1}{160}$

(E) $\frac{1}{1000}$ (F) $\frac{1}{20}$ (G) $\frac{1}{40}$ (H) $\frac{1}{100,000}$

Answer: (G)

12. Suppose using $n = 10$ to approximate the integral of a certain function by Simpson's Rule results in an upper bound for the error equal to $\frac{1}{10}$. What will the upper bound become if we change to $n = 20$?

(A) $\frac{1}{100}$ (B) $\frac{1}{10,000}$ (C) $\frac{1}{40}$ (D) $\frac{1}{1000}$

(E) $\frac{1}{160}$ (F) $\frac{1}{20}$ (G) $\frac{1}{100,000}$ (H) $\frac{1}{80}$

Answer: (E)

13. Use Simpson's Rule with $n = 6$ to approximate $\int_0^2 \sqrt{x^3 + 2}\, dx$.

Answer: ≈ 3.86

14. Use Simpson's Rule with $n = 4$ to approximate $\int_0^1 \frac{1}{1 + x^2}\, dx$.

Answer: ≈ 0.785

15. Use the Midpoint Rule with 2 equal subdivisions to get an approximation for $\ln 5$.

Answer: $\ln 5 \approx 1.5$

16. Use (a) the Trapezoidal Rule with $n = 8$ and (b) Simpson's Rule with $n = 8$ to approximate $\int_0^2 e^x\, dx$. Round your answers to six decimal places.

Answer: (a) $T = 6.422298$ (b) $S = 6.389194$

17. Estimate $\int_1^3 \frac{1}{x^2}\, dx$ using the Trapezoidal Rule with $n = 4$. Then use the error bound $|E_T| \leq \frac{k(b-a)^3}{12n^2}$ to estimate the accuracy.

Answer: $|E_T| \leq \frac{1}{4}$

18. Estimate $\int_1^3 \frac{1}{x^2}\, dx$ using the Midpoint Rule with $n = 4$. Then use the error bound $|E_M| \leq \frac{k(b-a)^3}{24n^2}$ to estimate the accuracy.

Answer: $|E_M| \leq \frac{1}{8}$

19. Estimate $\int_1^3 \frac{1}{x^2}\, dx$ using Simpson's Rule with $n = 4$. Then use the error bound $|E_S| \leq \frac{k(b-a)^5}{180n^4}$ to estimate the accuracy.

Answer: $|E_S| \leq \frac{1}{12}$

20. Consider the integral $\int_0^{0.5} \cos(x^3)\, dx$. Approximating it by the Midpoint Rule with n equal subintervals, give an estimate for n which guarantees that the error is bounded by $\frac{1}{10^4}$.

Answer: $n > 15$ (answers may vary)

21. (a) Estimate $\ln 2 = \int_1^2 \frac{1}{x}\, dx$ using Simpson's Rule with $n = 4$.

    (b) Estimate the error of the approximation in part (a).

    (c) How large should we take n to guarantee that the estimate by Simpson's Rule is accurate to within 0.001?

    Answer: (a) 0.693 (b) $\frac{1}{1920}$ (c) $n = 4$

22. Two students use Simpson's Rule to estimate $\int_0^1 \left(x^2 + 4x - 5\right) dx$. One divides the interval into 30 equal subintervals and the other into 60 equal subintervals. How will the accuracy of their estimates compare?
    Answer: Since $f(x) = x^2 + 4x - 5$, the graph of f is a parabola. Therefore, Simpson's Rule gives an exact answer for the integral.

23. Two students use Simpson's Rule to estimate $\int_1^2 \left(x^3 + 2x^2 - x + 1\right) dx$. One divides the interval into 30 equal subintervals and the other into 60 equal subintervals. How will the accuracy of their estimates compare?
    Answer: Since $f^{(4)}(x) = 0$, $|E_S| = 0$, therefore using Simpson's Rule gives an exact answer for the integral.

24. The widths (in meters) of a kidney-shaped swimming pool were measured at 2-meter intervals as indicated in the figure. Use Simpson's Rule to estimate the area of the pool.

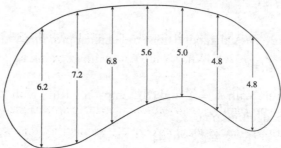

    Answer: $84.2\overline{6}$ m^2

25. Below is a table of values for a continuous function f.

x	-1	-0.5	0	0.5	1
$f(x)$	2.0	1.5	-1.0	0.5	-3.0

    (a) Use the Trapezoidal Rule with $n = 4$ to approximate $\int_{-1}^{1} f(x)\, dx$.

    (b) Use Simpson's Rule with $n = 4$ to approximate $\int_{-1}^{1} f(x)\, dx$.

    Answer: (a) $\frac{1}{4}$ (b) $\frac{5}{6}$

26. The following table shows the speedometer readings of a truck, taken at ten minute intervals during one hour of a trip.

Time (min)	0	10	20	30	40	50	60
Speed (mi/h)	40	45	50	60	70	65	60

Use the table and the indicated technique to estimate the distance that the truck traveled in the hour.

    (a) The Trapezoidal Rule

    (b) The Midpoint Rule

    (c) Simpson's Rule

Answer: (a) $\frac{170}{3}$ miles   (b) $\frac{170}{3}$ miles   (c) $\frac{170}{3}$ miles

27. Intelligence Quotient (IQ) scores are assumed to be normally distributed in the population. The probability that a person selected at random from the general population will have an IQ between 100 and 120 is given by $\int_0^2 p(x)\,dx$. Use the graph of $p(x)$ graphed below to answer the questions which follow:

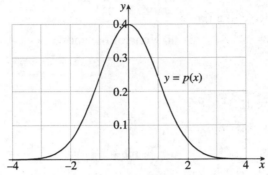

(a) Use Simpson's Rule with $n = 4$ to approximate $\int_0^2 p(x)\,dx$.

(b) The probability that a person selected from the general population will have an IQ score between 80 and 120 is given by $\int_{-2}^2 p(x)\,dx$. What is the approximate value of $\int_{-2}^2 p(x)\,dx$?

(c) Since $p(x)$ represents a probability distribution, the entire area of the region under the graph is exactly 1. Using this information, what is the approximate probability that a person selected at random from the general population will have an IQ score over 120?

Answer: (a) ≈ 0.47 (b) ≈ 0.94 (c) ≈ 0.03

5.10 Improper Integrals

1. Which one of the following is *not* an improper integral?

(A) $\displaystyle\int_{-4}^2 \frac{1}{x+2}\,dx$

(B) $\displaystyle\int_{-2}^2 \frac{1}{x^2-2}\,dx$

(C) $\displaystyle\int_0^\infty \frac{1}{x+2}\,dx$

(D) $\displaystyle\int_{-2}^2 \frac{1}{x^2+2}\,dx$

(E) $\displaystyle\int_{-\infty}^1 \frac{1}{x-2}\,dx$

(F) $\displaystyle\int_{-2}^2 \frac{1}{x+2}\,dx$

(G) $\displaystyle\int_{-\infty}^\infty \frac{1}{x^2+2}\,dx$

(H) $\displaystyle\int_{-2}^2 \frac{1}{x-2}\,dx$

Answer: (D)

195

2. Which one of the following integrals is improper?

(A) $\int_0^2 2\sqrt{x}\,dx$ (B) $\int_{-2}^2 \frac{1}{x^2-2}\,dx$

(C) $\int_0^3 \frac{1}{x+2}\,dx$ (D) $\int_1^2 \ln x\,dx$

(E) $\int_0^1 3^x\,dx$ (F) $\int_{-2}^2 \frac{1}{x^4+1}\,dx$

(G) $\int_{-5}^5 \frac{1}{x^2+2}\,dx$ (H) None of the above

Answer: (B)

3. Evaluate the improper integral $\int_1^\infty x^{-2}\,dx$.

(A) $\frac{1}{4}$ (B) 1 (C) 2 (D) 4

(E) $\frac{1}{2}$ (F) 3 (G) $\frac{1}{3}$ (H) Divergent

Answer: (B)

4. Evaluate the improper integral $\int_0^1 x^{-2}\,dx$.

(A) 3 (B) $\frac{1}{4}$ (C) 4 (D) 2

(E) $\frac{1}{3}$ (F) $\frac{1}{2}$ (G) 1 (H) Divergent

Answer: (H)

5. Evaluate the improper integral $\int_1^\infty x^{-1/2}\,dx$.

(A) 4 (B) 3 (C) $\frac{1}{4}$ (D) $\frac{1}{3}$

(E) $\frac{1}{2}$ (F) 2 (G) 1 (H) Divergent

Answer: (H)

6. Evaluate the improper integral $\int_0^1 x^{-1/2}\,dx$.

(A) $\frac{1}{3}$ (B) $\frac{1}{2}$ (C) 1 (D) 2

(E) $\frac{1}{4}$ (F) 3 (G) 4 (H) Divergent

Answer: (D)

7. Evaluate the improper integral $\int_1^\infty \frac{\ln x}{x}\,dx$.

(A) 2 (B) $\frac{1}{2}\ln 2$ (C) $\frac{1}{4}\ln 2$ (D) 1

(E) $\ln 2$ (F) $\frac{1}{2}$ (G) $2\ln 2$ (H) Divergent

Answer: (H)

8. Evaluate the improper integral $\int_0^1 \frac{\ln x}{x}\,dx$.

(A) $\frac{1}{2}$ (B) 1 (C) $\ln 2$ (D) $\frac{1}{4}\ln 2$

(E) $\frac{1}{2}\ln 2$ (F) $2\ln 2$ (G) 2 (H) Divergent

Answer: (H)

9. Evaluate the improper integral $\int_{-\infty}^{\infty} xe^{-x^2}\, dx$.

(A) e (B) $e^2 - 1$ (C) 0 (D) e^2

(E) e^{-1} (F) e^{-2} (G) 1 (H) $1 - e^{-2}$

Answer: (C)

10. Evaluate the improper integral $\int_0^{\infty} xe^{-x/2}\, dx$.

(A) 1 (B) 2 (C) 4 (D) $\frac{1}{4}$

(E) $\frac{1}{3}$ (F) 3 (G) $\frac{1}{2}$ (H) Divergent

Answer: (C)

11. Evaluate the improper integral $\int_0^{\infty} e^{-3x}\, dx$.

(A) 3 (B) $\frac{1}{3}$ (C) $-\frac{1}{3}$ (D) 1

(E) -1 (F) -3 (G) 0 (H) Divergent

Answer: (B)

12. Evaluate the improper integral $\int_0^{\infty} xe^{-x^2}\, dx$.

(A) 0 (B) 1 (C) e (D) e^{-1}

(E) $e - 1$ (F) $\frac{1}{2}$ (G) 2 (H) Divergent

Answer: (F)

13. Evaluate the improper integral $\int_1^{\infty} \frac{\ln x}{x^2}\, dx$.

(A) 3 (B) 2 (C) 1 (D) 0

(E) $\frac{1}{2}$ (F) $\frac{1}{3}$ (G) $\frac{1}{4}$ (H) Divergent

Answer: (C)

14. Evaluate the improper integral $\int_0^1 \frac{\ln x}{x^2}\, dx$.

(A) 3 (B) 2 (C) 1 (D) 0

(E) $\frac{1}{2}$ (F) $\frac{1}{3}$ (G) $\frac{1}{4}$ (H) Divergent

Answer: (H)

15. Evaluate the improper integral $\int_{-\infty}^{\infty} \frac{1}{4 + x^2}\, dx$.

(A) $\frac{\pi}{2}$ (B) $\frac{\pi}{4}$ (C) π (D) 2

(E) $\frac{\pi}{16}$ (F) $\frac{\pi}{8}$ (G) 1 (H) Divergent

Answer: (A)

16. Evaluate the improper integral $\int_0^{\infty} \cos x\, dx$.

(A) $\frac{\pi}{4}$ (B) $\frac{\pi}{4}$ (C) π (D) 2

(E) $\frac{\pi}{16}$ (F) $\frac{\sqrt{3}}{2}$ (G) 1 (H) Divergent

Answer: (H)

17. Evaluate the improper integral $\int_3^\infty \frac{1}{x^2 - x - 2}\,dx$.

(A) $\frac{1}{2}\ln 4$ (B) $\ln 4$ (C) $-\ln 4$ (D) $-\frac{1}{3}\ln 4$

(E) $\frac{1}{3}\ln 4$ (F) $\ln 2$ (G) $-\frac{1}{2}\ln 4$ (H) Divergent

Answer: (E)

18. Determine whether each integral is convergent or divergent. Evaluate those that are convergent.

(a) $\int_{-\infty}^2 \frac{1}{x^2 + 4}\,dx$ (b) $\int_1^\infty \frac{1}{x^{1.0001}}\,dx$ (c) $\int_1^\infty \frac{1}{x^{0.9999}}\,dx$

Answer: (a) $\frac{3\pi}{4}$ (b) 10,000   (c) Divergent

19. Determine whether each integral is convergent or divergent. Evaluate those that are convergent.

(a) $\int_3^\infty \frac{1}{x^{3/2}}\,dx$ (b) $\int_e^\infty \frac{1}{x(\ln x)}\,dx$ (c) $\int_0^\infty \frac{x}{(x^2+5)^2}\,dx$

Answer: (a) $\frac{2}{\sqrt{3}}$ (b) Divergent   (c) $\frac{1}{10}$

20. Determine whether each integral is convergent or divergent. Evaluate those that are convergent.

(a) $\int_1^\infty x^{-5/4}\,dx$ (b) $\int_{-\infty}^1 \frac{1}{\sqrt{x}}\,dx$ (c) $\int_0^\infty xe^{-2x}\,dx$

Answer: (a) 4   (b) Divergent   (c) $\frac{1}{4}$

21. Determine whether each integral is convergent or divergent. Evaluate those that are convergent.

(a) $\int_0^1 \frac{1}{(x-1)^2}\,dx$ (b) $\int_0^1 \frac{1}{\sqrt{1-x}}\,dx$ (c) $\int_0^4 \frac{1}{(x-2)^{2/3}}\,dx$

Answer: (a) Divergent   (b) 2   (c) $6\sqrt[3]{2}$

22. Determine whether each integral is convergent or divergent. Evaluate those that are convergent.

(a) $\int_0^2 \frac{1}{x-1}\,dx$ (b) $\int_2^\infty \frac{1}{x(\ln x)^2}\,dx$ (c) $\int_0^1 \frac{\ln x}{\sqrt{x}}\,dx$

Answer: (a) Divergent   (b) $\frac{1}{\ln 2}$ (c) -4

23. Determine whether each integral is convergent or divergent. Evaluate those that are convergent.

(a) $\int_0^2 \frac{1}{(x-1)^2}\,dx$ (b) $\int_0^3 \frac{dx}{(x-1)^{2/3}}$ (c) $\int_0^\pi \sec^2 t\,dt$

Answer: (a) Divergent   (b) $3\sqrt[3]{2}+3$ (c) Divergent

24. Use the Comparison Theorem to determine whether $\int_1^\infty \frac{\cos^2 x}{x^3}\,dx$ is convergent or divergent. Justify your answer.

Answer: Convergent

25. Use the Comparison Theorem to determine whether $\int_2^\infty \frac{dx}{\sqrt{x+e^x}}$ is convergent or divergent. Justify your answer.

Answer: Convergent

26. Use the Comparison Theorem to determine whether $\int_2^\infty \dfrac{dx}{\sqrt{4x^2+1}}$ is convergent or divergent. Justify your answer.

Answer: Divergent

27. Use the Comparison Theorem to determine whether $\int_2^\infty \dfrac{dx}{\sqrt{4x^2-1}}$ is convergent or divergent. Justify your answer.

Answer: Divergent

28. Use the Comparison Theorem to determine whether $\int_0^\infty \dfrac{1}{\sqrt{x}+1}\,dx$ is convergent or divergent. Justify your answer.

Answer: Divergent

29. The area of the region under the $f(x) = \dfrac{1}{4+x^2}$ is defined to be $\int_{-\infty}^\infty f(x)\,dx$. Find this area.

Answer: $\frac{\pi}{2}$

30. The work done against gravity in propelling an object with mass m kg to an altitude of h m above the surface of the earth is given by

$$W = \int_{6.37\times10^6}^{6.37\times10^6+h} \frac{GM_E m}{r^2}\,dr$$

where 6.37×10^6 m is the radius of the earth, $G \approx 6.667 \times 10^{-11}$ N $\cdot$ m^2/kg^2, and $M_E \approx 5.90 \times 10^{24}$ kg is the mass of the earth.

(a) Find the work required to launch a 1000-kilogram satellite vertically to an altitude of 1000 km.

(b) The formula shows that the work is dependent on h. Show that $\int_{6.37\times10^6}^{\infty} \dfrac{GM_E m}{r^2}\,dr$ is convergent.

What is the physical significance of the fact that this improper integral is finite?

Answer:

(a) About 8.3787×10^9 J

(b) It is possible to launch an object out of the earth's gravitational field.

31. At the Dr. T. Bottling Company, the amount of soda dispensed into the cans is normally distributed so the probability that a can will contain a certain amount of soda may be calculated using the area under the curve $y = p(x)$, where $p(x) = \dfrac{1}{\sqrt{2\pi}}e^{-x^2/2}$. Use your graphing calculator to produce a graph of this function.

(a) The probability that a can will contain between 12.0 and 12.2 ounces of soda is given by $\int_{-0.22}^{0.22} \dfrac{1}{\sqrt{2\pi}}e^{-x^2/2}\,dx$. Use Simpson's Rule with $n=4$ to approximate this probability.

(b) The probability that a can will contain at least 12 ounces of soda is given by $\int_{-0.22}^{\infty} \dfrac{1}{\sqrt{2\pi}}e^{-x^2/2}\,dx$.

What is the approximate value of this integral?

Answer: (a) About 0.17 (b) About 0.585

6 Applications of Integration

6.1 | More About Areas

1. Find the area of the region bounded by the curves $y = x^2 + 1$ and $y = 2$.

(A) $\frac{4}{3}$ (B) $\frac{2}{3}$ (C) $\frac{11}{9}$ (D) $\frac{5}{3}$

(E) $\frac{8}{9}$ (F) 1   (G) $\frac{14}{9}$ (H) 2

Answer: (A)

2. Find the area of the region bounded by the curves $y = x^2 - 4x$ and $y = x - 4$.

(A) $\frac{8}{3}$ (B) $\frac{2}{3}$ (C) $\frac{1}{12}$ (D) $\frac{1}{2}$

(E) $\frac{1}{3}$ (F) $\frac{1}{9}$ (G) $\frac{9}{2}$ (H) $\frac{5}{6}$

Answer: (G)

3. Find the area of the region bounded by the curves $y = x^2 - 1$ and $y = -x^2$.

(A) $\frac{\sqrt{2}}{2}$ (B) $\frac{\sqrt{3}}{6}$ (C) $\frac{\sqrt{3}}{2}$ (D) $\frac{2\sqrt{2}}{3}$

(E) $\frac{\sqrt{3}}{3}$ (F) $\frac{\sqrt{3}}{4}$ (G) $\frac{\sqrt{2}}{4}$ (H) $\frac{\sqrt{2}}{6}$

Answer: (D)

4. Find the area of the region bounded by the curves $y = x^3 - 2x$ and $y = -x$.

(A) $\frac{1}{4}$ (B) $\frac{1}{9}$ (C) $\frac{1}{18}$ (D) $\frac{2}{15}$

(E) $\frac{1}{2}$ (F) $\frac{1}{6}$ (G) 4   (H) 2

Answer: (E)

5. Find the area of the region bounded by the curves $x = 4 - y^2$ and $x = -3y$.

(A) $\frac{115}{6}$ (B) $\frac{1}{4}$ (C) $\frac{1}{15}$ (D) 20

(E) $\frac{1}{9}$ (F) $\frac{125}{6}$ (G) $\frac{1}{12}$ (H) $\frac{43}{2}$

Answer: (F)

6. Find the area of the region bounded by the parabolas $y = 2x - x^2$ and $y = x^2$.

(A) $\frac{1}{2}$ (B) $\frac{2}{3}$ (C) $\frac{3}{4}$ (D) $\frac{2}{5}$

(E) $\frac{1}{3}$ (F) $\frac{1}{4}$ (G) $\frac{1}{5}$ (H) $\frac{3}{5}$

Answer: (E)

7. Find the area of the region bounded by the parabola $x = y^2$ and the line $x - 2y = 3$.

(A) $\frac{29}{3}$ (B) $\frac{32}{3}$ (C) $\frac{35}{3}$ (D) $\frac{38}{3}$

(E) $\frac{41}{3}$ (F) $\frac{44}{3}$ (G) $\frac{47}{3}$ (H) $\frac{50}{3}$

Answer: (B)

8. Find the area of the region bounded by the curve $x = 4\cos t$, $y = 3\sin t$, $0 \leq t \leq \pi$, and the x-axis.

    (A) π (B) $6\pi^2$ (C) 3π (D) 6π

    (E) π^2 (F) $12\pi^2$ (G) $3\pi^2$ (H) 12π

    Answer: (D)

9. Find the area of the region bounded by the curve $x = 1 + \sin t$, $y = \sin t$, $0 \leq t \leq \pi$, and the x-axis.

    (A) 4π (B) $\frac{3\pi}{2}$ (C) 2π (D) $\frac{\pi}{4}$

    (E) $\frac{\pi}{2}$ (F) $\frac{\pi}{6}$ (G) π (H) $\frac{\pi}{3}$

    Answer: (E)

10. Find the area of the region bounded by $x = e^t \cos t$, $y = e^t \sin t$, $0 \leq t \leq \pi$, and the x-axis.

    (A) $\frac{1}{4}e^{2\pi}$ (B) $\frac{1}{2}e^{2\pi}$ (C) $\frac{1}{4}\left(e^{2\pi} + 1\right)$ (D) $\frac{1}{4}e^{\pi}$

    (E) $\frac{1}{4}\left(e^{2\pi} - 1\right)$ (F) $\frac{1}{2}\left(e^{2\pi} - 1\right)$ (G) $\frac{1}{2}\left(e^{\pi} - 1\right)$ (H) $e^{2\pi} - 1$

    Answer: (C)

11. Find the area of the region bounded by the curves $y = x^3 + x^2$ and $y = 2x^2 + 2x$.

    Answer: $\frac{37}{12}$

12. Find the area of the region bounded by the curves $y = (x - 2)^2 - 1$ and $y = 3 - x$.

    Answer: $\frac{9}{2}$

13. Find the area of the region bounded by the curves $y = x^2 - 1$ and $y = -x^2 + x + 2$.

    Answer: $\frac{125}{24}$

14. Find the area of the region bounded by the curves $x = 4 - y^2$ and $x = y^2 - 4$.

    Answer: $\frac{64}{3}$

15. Find the area of the region bounded by the curves $x = y^2 - 7$ and $x = y - 1$.

    Answer: $\frac{125}{6}$

16. Let R be the region bounded by: $y = x^3$, the tangent to $y = x^3$ at $(1, 1)$, and the x-axis. Find the area of R integrating

    (a) with respect to x.   (b) with respect to y.

    Answer: (a) $\frac{1}{12}$ (b) $\frac{1}{12}$

17. Find the area of the region bounded by the curves $f(x) = \frac{7}{2}x + 1$ and $g(x) = 2^x$.

    Answer: About 10.43

18. Find the area of the region bounded by the curves $f(x) = \sin x$ and $g(x) = \cos x$, for $\frac{\pi}{4} \leq x \leq \frac{5\pi}{4}$.

    Answer: $2\sqrt{2}$

19. Find the area of the region bounded by the curves $f(x) = 3 \cdot \sin\left(\frac{\pi}{4}x\right)$, $g(x) = 2^x - 1$ and $x \geq 0$.

    Answer: $2 + \dfrac{12}{\pi} - \dfrac{3}{\ln 2}$

20. Find the area of the shaded region:

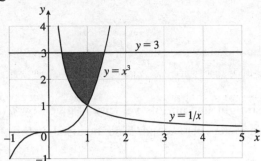

Answer: $\frac{9}{4}\sqrt[3]{3} - \ln 3 - \frac{3}{4}$

21. Find the area of the shaded region:

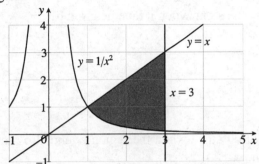

Answer: $\frac{10}{3}$

22. Find the area of the shaded region:

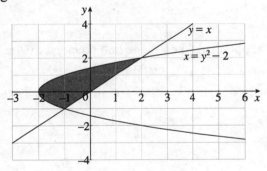

Answer: $\frac{9}{2}$

23. Find the area of the shaded region:

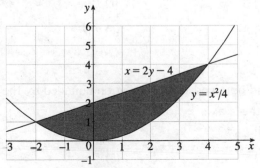

Answer: 9

24. Find the area of the region bounded by $y = x(x-1)(x-2)$ and the x-axis.

Answer: $\frac{1}{2}$

25. Find the area of the region bounded by the curves $y = x^3 - 6x$ and $y = -2x$.

Answer: 8

26. A particle is moving in a straight line and its velocity is given by $v(t) = 3t^2 - 12t + 9$, where t is measured in seconds and v in meters per second. Find the distance traveled by the particle during the time interval $[0, 5]$.

Answer: 28 m

27. A stone is thrown straight up from the top of a tower that is 80 ft tall with initial velocity 64 ft/s. What is the total distance traveled by the stone when it hits the ground?

Answer: 208 feet.

6.2 Volumes

1. Find the volume of the solid obtained when the region bounded by the x-axis, the y-axis, and the line $y + x = 3$ is rotated about the x-axis.

(A) 3π (B) 2π (C) 8π (D) 10π

(E) 9π (F) 12π (G) 4π (H) 6π

Answer: (E)

2. Find the volume of the solid obtained when the region bounded by the line $y = 2x$, the line $x = 3$, and the x-axis is rotated about the y-axis.

(A) 36π (B) 42π (C) 16π (D) 18π

(E) 24π (F) 30π (G) 48π (H) 27π

Answer: (A)

3. Suppose the disk method is used to find the volume of the solid obtained when the region bounded by the curve $x = y^2$, and the line $x = 4$ is rotated about the x-axis. What is the area of the largest cross-section?

(A) 6π (B) 3π (C) 12π (D) 10π

(E) 9π (F) 8π (G) 2π (H) 4π

Answer: (H)

4. Find the volume of the solid obtained when the region bounded by the curve $y = \sin x$, $0 \le x \le \pi$, and the x-axis is rotated about the x-axis.

(A) $\frac{1}{2}\pi^2$ (B) $\frac{1}{3}\pi^2$ (C) π (D) $\frac{\pi}{2}$

(E) $\frac{\pi}{4}$ (F) π^2 (G) $\frac{\pi}{3}$ (H) $\frac{1}{4}\pi^2$

Answer: (A)

5. The base of a solid S is the parabolic region $\{(x, y) \mid y^2 \le x \le 1\}$. Cross-sections perpendicular to the x-axis are squares. Find the volume of S.

(A) 1.5   (B) 1.6   (C) 1.7   (D) 1.8

(E) 1.9   (F) 2.0   (G) 2.1   (H) 2.2

Answer: (F)

6. Find the volume of the solid obtained by rotating about the line $y = 1$, the region bounded by $y = \cos x$, $y = 0$, $x = 0$, and $x = \frac{\pi}{2}$.

(A) π (B) π^2 (C) $\pi^2 - \frac{\pi}{2}$ (D) $\pi^2 - \pi$

(E) $\pi^2 - 2\pi$ (F) $2\pi - \frac{1}{4}\pi^2$ (G) $2\pi - \frac{1}{2}\pi^2$ (H) $\pi - \frac{1}{4}\pi^2$

Answer: (F)

7. Find the volume of the solid obtained by rotating the region bounded by the curves $y = 2 - x^2$ and $y = 1$ about the x-axis.

(A) $\frac{\pi}{15}$ (B) $2 - \pi^2$ (C) 15π (D) $\frac{7}{15}$

(E) $3 - \pi^2$ (F) 4π (G) $\frac{56\pi}{15}$ (H) $\frac{128\pi}{15}$

Answer: (G)

8. A solid has a circular base of radius 1. Parallel cross-sections perpendicular to the base are equilateral triangles. Find the volume of the solid.

(A) $\frac{\pi}{2}$ (B) $\frac{\sqrt{3}}{2}$ (C) $\frac{3\pi}{2}$ (D) $\frac{3\sqrt{3}}{2}$

(E) $\frac{2\pi}{3}$ (F) $\frac{4\sqrt{3}}{3}$ (G) $\frac{3\pi}{4}$ (H) $\frac{2\sqrt{2}}{3}$

Answer: (F)

9. Find the volume of the solid obtained when the region bounded by the curve $y = \sin x$, $0 \le x \le \pi$, and the x-axis is rotated about the y-axis.

(A) $\frac{1}{2}\pi^3$ (B) π^2 (C) π^3 (D) $4\pi^2$

(E) $2\pi^2$ (F) $2\pi^3$ (G) $\frac{1}{2}\pi^2$ (H) $4\pi^3$

Answer: (E)

10. Find the volume of the solid obtained when the region above the x-axis, bounded by the x-axis and the curve $y = x - x^3$, is rotated about the y-axis.

(A) $\frac{2}{7}\pi$ (B) $\frac{8}{35}\pi$ (C) $\frac{4}{15}\pi$ (D) $\frac{8}{15}\pi$

(E) $\frac{4}{35}\pi$ (F) $\frac{2}{5}\pi$ (G) $\frac{4}{5}\pi$ (H) $\frac{4}{7}\pi$

Answer: (C)

11. Find the volume of the solid obtained when the region bounded by the curves $y = x^2 + 1$, $y = 1$, and $x = 1$ is rotated about the line $x = 1$.

(A) $\frac{\pi}{12}$ (B) 8π (C) $\frac{\pi}{2}$ (D) $\frac{\pi}{4}$

(E) $\frac{\pi}{3}$ (F) $\frac{\pi}{6}$ (G) 4π (H) $\frac{10\pi}{3}$

Answer: (F)

12. Find the volume of the solid obtained when the region bounded by the curves $y = x^3$, $x = 1$, and the x-axis is rotated about the line $x = -1$.

    (A) $\frac{127\pi}{3}$ (B) $\frac{62\pi}{3}$ (C) $\frac{\pi}{2}$ (D) $\frac{\pi}{4}$

    (E) $\frac{2\pi}{5}$ (F) $\frac{\pi}{5}$ (G) $\frac{9\pi}{10}$ (H) $\frac{31\pi}{3}$

    Answer: (G)

13. Find the volume of the solid obtained by rotating the region bounded by the curves $y = \sqrt{x - 2}$, $y = 0$, and $x = 6$ about the x-axis.

    Answer: 8π

14. Find the volume of the solid obtained by rotating the region bounded by the curves $y = 2x^2$, $x = 0$, and $y = 2$ about the y-axis.

    Answer: π

15. Consider the region in the xy-plane between $x = 0$ and $x = \frac{\pi}{2}$, bounded by $y = 0$ and $y = \sin x$. Find the volume of the solid generated by rotating this region about the x-axis.

    Answer: $\frac{\pi^2}{4}$

16. Find the volume of the solid formed when the region bounded by the curves $y = x^3 + 1$, $x = 1$ and $y = 0$ is rotated about the x-axis.

    Answer: $\frac{23\pi}{14}$

17. Find the volume of the solid generated by rotating about the line $y = -1$ the region bounded by the graphs of the equations $y = x^2 - 4x + 5$ and $y = 5 - x$.

    Answer: $\frac{162\pi}{5}$

18. Find the volume of the solid obtained by rotating the region bounded by the curves $y = 3 - x^2$ and $y = 2$ about the line $y = 2$.

    Answer: $\frac{16\pi}{15}$

19. Find the volume of the solid obtained by rotating the region bounded by the curves $y = \sqrt{9 - x^2}$, $x = 0$, and $y = 1$ about the x-axis.

    Answer: $\frac{32\sqrt{2}\pi}{3}$

20. Find the volume of the solid obtained by rotating the region bounded by the curves $y = x^3$, $y = 0$, and $x = 1$ about the line $x = 2$.

    Answer: $\frac{3\pi}{5}$

21. Find the volume of the solid obtained by rotating the region bounded by the curve $y = \sqrt{1 - x^2}$ and the x-axis about the line $y = 2$.

    Answer: $2\pi^2 - \frac{4\pi}{3}$

22. Let R be the region bounded by the graph of $f(x) = x^2$, $g(x) = 1/x$, and the line $y = 3$.

    (a) Find the volume of the solid obtained by rotating R about the x-axis.

    (b) Find the volume of the solid obtained by rotating R about the y-axis.

    (c) Find the volume of the solid obtained by rotating R about the line $y = 3$.

    (d) Find the volume of the solid obtained by rotating R about the line $x = 2$.

Answer: (a) $\frac{\pi}{5}\left(36\sqrt{3}-24\right)$ (b) $\frac{10\pi}{3}$ (c) $\pi\left(\frac{24\sqrt{3}}{5}+\frac{4}{5}-6\ln 3\right)$ (d) $\pi\left(8\sqrt{3}-6-4\ln 3\right)$

23. Let R be the region bounded by the curve $4y=x^2$, and $x=2y-4$.

    (a) Find the volume of the solid obtained by rotating R about the x-axis.

    (b) Find the volume of the solid obtained by rotating R about the line $x=5$.

    (c) Find the volume of the solid obtained by rotating R about the line $y=-1$.

    Answer: (a) $\frac{144\pi}{5}$ (b) 72π (c) $\frac{234\pi}{5}$

24. The region R is given by the shaded area in the figure below:

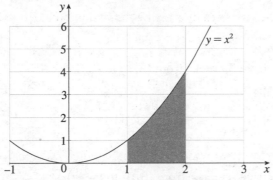

    (a) Find the area of the shaded region R.

    (b) Find the volume of the solid obtained by rotating R about

        (i) the x-axis.   (ii) the y-axis.   (iii) the line $x=2$.   (iv) the line $y=4$.

    Answer: (a) $\frac{7}{3}$ (b)(i) $\frac{31}{5}\pi$ (ii) $\frac{15}{2}\pi$ (iii) $\frac{11}{6}\pi$ (iv) $\frac{187}{15}\pi$

25. A hole of radius 6 cm is drilled through the center of a sphere of radius 10 cm. How much of the ball's volume is removed?

    Answer: $\frac{1952\pi}{3}$

26. Find the volume of the solid generated by rotating the region bounded by $y=\dfrac{1}{x}$, $x=1$, and the x-axis about the x-axis.

    Answer: π

27. The base of a certain solid is a plane region R enclosed by the x-axis and the curve $y=1-x^2$. Each cross-section of the solid perpendicular to the y-axis is an isosceles triangle of height 4 with its base lying in R. Find the volume of the solid.

    Answer: $\frac{8}{3}$

28. The base of a certain solid is a plane region R enclosed by the x-axis and the curve $y=1-x^2$. Each cross-section of the solid perpendicular to the y-axis is an equilateral triangle with its base lying in R. Find the volume of the solid.

    Answer: $\frac{\sqrt{3}}{2}$

29. The base of a certain solid is a plane region R enclosed by the x-axis and the curve $y=1-x^2$. Each cross-section of the solid perpendicular to the y-axis is an isosceles right triangle with hypotenuse lying in R. Find the volume of the solid.

    Answer: $\frac{1}{2}$

30. The base of a certain solid is the triangular region with vertices $(0,0)$, $(1,1)$, and $(2,0)$. Cross-sections perpendicular to the x-axis are semicircles. Find the volume of the solid.

Answer: $\frac{\pi}{12}$

31. The base of a certain solid is an elliptical region with boundary curve $\frac{x^2}{16} + \frac{y^2}{9} = 1$. Cross-sections perpendicular to the x-axis are squares. Find the volume of the solid.

Answer: 192

6.3 Arc Length

1. Find the arc length of the curve $3y = 4x$ from $(3,4)$ to $(9,12)$.

(A) 13   (B) 10   (C) 8   (D) 14

(E) 9   (F) 15   (G) 11   (H) 12

Answer: (B)

2. Find the arc length of the curve $y^2 = x^3$ from $(0,0)$ to $\left(\frac{1}{4}, \frac{1}{8}\right)$.

(A) $\frac{65}{216}$ (B) $\frac{29}{108}$ (C) $\frac{59}{216}$ (D) $\frac{37}{108}$

(E) $\frac{61}{216}$ (F) $\frac{31}{108}$ (G) $\frac{35}{108}$ (H) $\frac{71}{216}$

Answer: (E)

3. Find the arc length of the curve $y = \sqrt{4 - x^2}$, $-2 \le x \le 2$.

(A) 2π (B) $\frac{3\pi}{4}$ (C) π (D) $\frac{7\pi}{4}$

(E) $\frac{3\pi}{2}$ (F) $\frac{\pi}{2}$ (G) $\frac{9\pi}{4}$ (H) $\frac{5\pi}{4}$

Answer: (A)

4. Find the arc length of the curve $y = \ln(\cos x)$, $0 \le x \le \frac{\pi}{3}$.

(A) $\ln\left(2 + \sqrt{2}\right)$ (B) $\ln\left(1 + \sqrt{3}\right)$ (C) $\ln\left(2 - \sqrt{2}\right)$ (D) $\ln\left(2 - \sqrt{3}\right)$

(E) $\ln\left(1 + \sqrt{2}\right)$ (F) $\ln\left(2 + \sqrt{3}\right)$ (G) $\ln\left(\sqrt{3} - 1\right)$ (H) $\ln\left(\sqrt{2} - 1\right)$

Answer: (F)

5. Find the length of the curve $y = \frac{2}{3}(x - 4)^{3/2}$, $7 \le x \le 12$.

(A) 19   (B) $\frac{65}{2}$ (C) $\frac{55}{2}$ (D) 55

(E) $\frac{19}{2}$ (F) $\frac{38}{3}$ (G) 38   (H) 65

Answer: (F)

6. Find the length of the curve $x = t^3 - 3t^2$, $y = t^3 + 3t^2$, $0 \le t \le \sqrt{5}$.

(A) 81   (B) $\sqrt{5}$ (C) $\frac{171}{2}$ (D) $\sqrt{28}$

(E) 57   (F) $\sqrt{15}$ (G) $\sqrt{30}$ (H) $105\sqrt{5}$

Answer: (E)

7. Find the length of the curve $x = 2t^2 - 1$, $y = 4t^2 + 3$, $0 \le x \le 1$.

(A) $4\sqrt{5}$ (B) $8\sqrt{5}$ (C) $8\sqrt{3}$ (D) $2\sqrt{3}$

(E) $2\sqrt{5}$ (F) $4\sqrt{3}$ (G) $16\sqrt{3}$ (H) $16\sqrt{5}$

Answer: (E)

8. Find the length of the curve $x = \cos^2 t$, $y = \sin^2 t$, $0 \le t \le \frac{\pi}{2}$.

(A) $\frac{\pi}{2}$ (B) $4\sqrt{2}$ (C) $\frac{\pi}{4}$ (D) $\frac{1}{\sqrt{2}}$

(E) $2\sqrt{2}$ (F) π (G) 2π (H) $\sqrt{2}$

Answer: (H)

9. Give a definite integral representing the length of the parametric curve $x = t^3$, $y = t^4$, $0 \le t \le 1$.

(A) $\int_0^1 \left(t^3 + t^4 \right) dt$ (B) $\int_0^1 \sqrt{t^3 + t^4}\, dt$

(C) $\int_0^1 \sqrt{1 + 3t^2}\, dt$ (D) $\int_0^1 \sqrt{t^2 + 4t^3}\, dt$

(E) $\int_0^1 \sqrt{9t^4 + 16t^6}\, dt$ (F) $\int_0^1 \sqrt{4t^4 + 9t^6}\, dt$

(G) $\int_0^1 \sqrt{t^5 + t^7}\, dt$ (H) $\int_0^1 \sqrt{8t^6 + 6t^8}\, dt$

Answer: (E)

10. Give a definite integral representing the length of the curve with parametric equations $x = f(t)$, $y = g(t)$, $a \le t \le b$.

(A) $\int_a^b 2\pi t\, f(t)\, dt$ (B) $\int_a^b \pi \left[f(t) \right]^2 dt$

(C) $\int_a^b \left(1 + [f'(t)]^2 \right) dt$ (D) $\int_a^b [1 + f'(t)]^2\, dt$

(E) $\int_a^b \sqrt{1 + [f'(t)]^2}\, dt$ (F) $\int_a^b \sqrt{1 + [g'(t)]^2}\, dt$

(G) $\int_a^b \sqrt{[f'(t)]^2 + [g'(t)]^2}\, dt$ (H) $\int_a^b [f'(t) + g'(t)]^2\, dt$

Answer: (G)

11. Give a definite integral representing the length of the curve $y = 1/x$, $1 \le x \le 2$.

(A) $\displaystyle\int_1^2 \sqrt{1 + \frac{1}{x^2}}\, dx$ (B) $\displaystyle\int_1^2 \sqrt{1 + \frac{1}{x^4}}\, dx$

(C) $\displaystyle\int_1^2 \sqrt{1 + (\ln x)^2}\, dx$ (D) $\displaystyle\int_1^2 \sqrt{1 + \frac{1}{x}}\, dx$

(E) $\displaystyle\int_1^2 \frac{1}{x^2}\, dx$ (F) $\displaystyle\int_1^4 \sqrt{1 + \frac{1}{x^4}}\, dx$

(G) $\displaystyle\int_1^2 x\sqrt{1 + \frac{1}{x^2}}\, dx$ (H) $\displaystyle\int_1^4 \frac{1}{x^4}\, dx$

Answer: (B)

12. Find the arc length of the curve $y = 2x^{3/2}$ between $x = 0$ and $x = 3$.

Answer: $\frac{2}{27}\left(28^{3/2} - 1 \right)$

13. Set up, but do not evaluate, the equations and/or integrals to find the perimeter of the region bounded by the curve $y = x^2 - 2x$ and the x-axis.

Answer: $P = 2 + \int_0^2 \sqrt{1 + (2x - 2)^2}\, dx$

14. Find the length of $y = \ln(\sin x)$ for $\frac{\pi}{6} \le x \le \frac{\pi}{3}$.

Answer: $\ln\left(1 + \frac{2}{\sqrt{3}}\right)$

15. Set up, but do not evaluate, an integral for the length of $y = x^4 - x^2$, $-1 \le x \le 2$.

Answer: $L = \int_{-1}^{2} \sqrt{16x^6 - 16x^4 + 4x^2 + 1}\, dx$

16. Set up, but do not evaluate, an integral for the length of $y = \tan x$, $0 < x < \frac{\pi}{4}$.

Answer: $L = \int_0^{\pi/4} \sqrt{1 + \sec^4 x}\, dx$

17. Find the length of the curve $3x = 2y^{3/2}$ from $(0,0)$ to $\left(\frac{2}{3}, 1\right)$.

Answer: $\frac{2}{3}\left(2\sqrt{2} - 1\right)$

18. Find the distance traveled by a particle with position $(x, y) = \left(\cos^2 t, \cos t\right)$ as t varies in the time interval $[0, 4\pi]$. Compare with the length of the curve.

Answer: distance $= 4\sqrt{5} + 2\ln\left(\sqrt{5} + 2\right)$; $L = \sqrt{5} + \frac{1}{2}\ln\left(\sqrt{5} + 2\right)$

19. If $x = \cos 2t$, $y = \sin^2 t$, and (x, y) represents the position of a particle, find the distance the particle travels as t moves from 0 to $\frac{\pi}{2}$.

Answer: $\sqrt{5}$

20. Compute the length of the curve given parametrically by $x = \frac{1}{3}t^3$ and $y = \frac{1}{2}t^2$ for $0 \le t \le 2$.

Answer: $\dfrac{5\sqrt{5} - 1}{3}$

21. The equation of a curve in parametric form is $x = 4\cos 3t$, $y = 4\sin 3t$. Find the arc length of the curve from $t = 0$ to $t = \frac{\pi}{8}$.

Answer: $\frac{3\pi}{2}$

22. A curve is written parametrically as $x = 3t - t^3$, $y = 3t^2$. Find the length of the curve from $t = 0$ to $t = 1$.

Answer: 4

23. Find the arc length of the curve $y = \frac{2}{3}(x - 1)^{3/2}$, $1 \le x \le 4$.

Answer: $\frac{14}{3}$

24. Find the arc length of the curve $y = x^2 - \frac{1}{8}\ln x$, $1 \le x \le 3$.

Answer: $\frac{1}{8}\ln 3 + 8$

25. Find the arc length of the curve $x = t\cos t - \sin t$, $y = t\sin t + \cos t$, $0 \le t \le \pi$.

Answer: $\frac{\pi^2}{2}$

6.4 Average Value of a Function

1. Find the average value of the function $f(x) = 2 + 3x$ on the interval $[0, 2]$.

(A) 2   (B) 4   (C) 16   (D) 10

(E) 14   (F) 5   (G) 6   (H) 12

Answer: (F)

2. The density of a rod 9 meters long is $\sqrt{x}$ kg/m at a distance of x meters from one end of the rod. Find the average density of the rod.

(A) 6   (B) $\frac{4}{3}$ (C) 3   (D) 1

(E) 2   (F) $\frac{16}{3}$ (G) 4   (H) $\frac{8}{3}$

Answer: (E)

3. Find the average value of the function $f(x) = \sin 3x$ on the interval $\left[0, \frac{\pi}{3}\right]$.

(A) 1   (B) $\frac{3}{2}$ (C) 2   (D) 6

(E) $\frac{1}{\pi}$ (F) $\frac{2}{\pi}$ (G) 0   (H) $\frac{5}{2\pi}$

Answer: (F)

4. Find the average value of the function $f(x) = \sqrt{4 - x^2}$ on the interval $[-2, 2]$.

(A) $\frac{\pi}{2}$ (B) π (C) 8π (D) 3π

(E) 2π (F) 4π (G) 16π (H) 6π

Answer: (A)

5. Find the average value of $f(x) = x^3 - x$ on the interval $[1, 3]$.

Answer: 8

6. Find the average value of $f(x) = \sqrt{x}$ on the interval $[4, 9]$.

Answer: $\frac{38}{15}$

7. Find the average value of $f(x) = x\sqrt{25 - x^2}$ on the interval $[0, 5]$. At how many points in the interval does $f(x)$ have this value?

Answer: $\frac{25}{3}$, 2

8. The temperature (in °F) in a certain city t hours after 9 A.M. is approximated by the function $T(t) = 50 + 14 \sin\left(\frac{\pi}{12}t\right)$. Find the average temperature during the period from 9 A.M. to 9 P.M..

Answer: 59 °F

9. The temperature (in °C) of a metal rod 5 m long is $4x$ at a distance x meters from one end of the rod. What is the average temperature of the rod?

Answer: 10 °C

10. A stone is dropped from a bell tower 100 feet tall. Find the average velocity of the stone from the instant it is dropped until it strikes the ground. (Assume that the acceleration due to gravity is 32 ft/s².)

Answer: 40 ft/s

11. A culture of bacteria is doubling every hour. What is the average population over the first two hours if we assume that the culture initially contained two million organisms?

Answer: $\frac{3}{\ln 2}$ million $\approx 4,328,085$

12. Find the average value of $f(x) = 6 - |x|$ on the interval $[-2, 2]$.

Answer: 5

13. A particle is moving along a straight line so that its velocity at time t is $v(t) = 3t^2$. At what time t during the interval $0 < t < 3$ is its velocity the same as its average velocity over the entire interval?

Answer: $t = \sqrt{3}$

14. The following table shows the velocity of a car (in mi/h) during the first five seconds of a race.

t (s)	0	1	2	3	4	5
v (mi/h)	0	20	32	46	54	62

Determine the average velocity of the car during this five-second interval.

Answer: Answer may vary between 30.4 mph and 42.8 mph.

15. The graph of a continuous function $g(x)$ is given below:

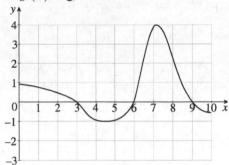

List from smallest to largest:

(a) The average value of g over $[0, 10]$

(b) The average rate of change of g over $[0, 10]$

(c) $g'(6)$

(d) $\int_3^5 g(x)\,dx$

(e) $\int_0^{10} g(x)\,dx$

(f) $\int_3^6 g(x)\,dx$

Answer: (f) < (d) < (b) < (a) < (c) < (e)

16. Consider the region R bounded by $y = \frac{1}{2}\sqrt{x}$, $y = 1$, and the y-axis.

(a) Find the area of R.

(b) Find the average height of R.

(c) Find the volume, V, of the solid obtained by rotating R about the x-axis.

(d) A cross section of the solid generated in part (c) taken perpendicular to the x-axis is a washer. Determine the average area of the cross sections of the solid.

Answer: (a) $\frac{4}{3}$ (b) $\frac{1}{3}$ (c) 2π (d) $\frac{\pi}{2}$

17. The voltage (in volts) at an electrical outlet is a function of time (in seconds) given by $V(t) = V_0 \cos(120\pi t)$ where V_0 is a constant representing the maximum voltage.

(a) What is the average value of the voltage over one second?

(b) How many times does the voltage reach a maximum in one second?

(c) Define a new function $S(t) = (V(t))^2$. Compute $\overline{S}$, the average value of $S(t)$ over one cycle.

(d) Instead of the average voltage, engineers use the root mean square $V_{rms} = \sqrt{\overline{S}}$. Determine V_{rms} in terms of V_0.

(e) The standard household voltage in the United States is 100 volts. This means that $V_{rms} = 110$. What is the value of V_0?

Answer: (a) 0   (b) 61 for $0 \le t \le 1$ (c) $\frac{1}{2}V_0^2$ (d) $V_{rms} = \frac{1}{\sqrt{2}}V_0$ (e) $V_0 = \sqrt{2} \cdot 110 \approx 156$ volts

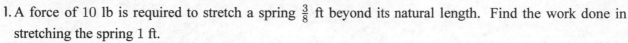

6.5 | Applications to Physics and Engineering

1. A force of 10 lb is required to stretch a spring $\frac{3}{8}$ ft beyond its natural length. Find the work done in stretching the spring 1 ft.

   (A) $\frac{80}{3}$ lb-ft   (B) $\frac{40}{9}$ lb-ft   (C) 10 lb-ft   (D) 20 lb-ft

   (E) 15 lb-ft   (F) $\frac{80}{9}$ lb-ft   (G) $\frac{40}{3}$ lb-ft   (H) 50 lb-ft

   Answer: (G)

2. A spring stretches 1 foot beyond its natural position under a force of 100 pounds. How much work in foot-pounds is done in stretching it 3 feet beyond its natural position?

   (A) 600   (B) 30   (C) 1500   (D) 450

   (E) 100   (F) 900   (G) 150   (H) 300

   Answer: (D)

3. A rope 100 feet long weighing 2 pounds per foot hangs over the edge of a building 100 feet tall. How much work in foot-pounds is done in pulling the rope to the top of the building?

   (A) 7500   (B) 5000   (C) 1000   (D) 500

   (E) 10,000   (F) 750   (G) 1250   (H) 12,500

   Answer: (E)

4. Find the work done in raising 500 lb of ore from a mine that is 1000 ft deep. Assume that the cable used to raise the ore weighs 2 lb/ft.

   (A) 5×10^5 lb-ft   (B) 2.5×10^6 lb-ft   (C) 2×10^6 lb-ft   (D) 6×10^5 lb-ft

   (E) 10^6 lb-ft   (F) 1.5×10^6 lb-ft   (G) 7×10^5 lb-ft   (H) 4×10^5 lb-ft

   Answer: (F)

5. A right circular cylinder tank of height 1 foot and radius 1 foot is full of water. Taking the density of water to be a nice round 60 pounds per cubic foot, how much work in foot-pounds is required to pump all of the water up and over the top of the tank?

   (A) 8π (B) 24π (C) 16π (D) 6π

   (E) 5π (F) 4π (G) 30π (H) 18π

   Answer: (G)

6. Find the x-coordinate $\overline{x}$ at the center of mass of a system consisting of a mass $m_1 = 1$ at $(-1, 0)$ and a mass $m_2 = 2$ at $(2, 0)$.

   (A) $\frac{5}{4}$ (B) $\frac{11}{6}$ (C) $\frac{7}{6}$ (D) 1

   (E) $\frac{7}{4}$ (F) 0   (G) $\frac{5}{3}$ (H) $\frac{4}{3}$

   Answer: (D)

7. Find the center of mass of the linear system $m_1 = 2$, $x_1 = -3$, $m_2 = 8$, $x_2 = -1$, $m_3 = 3$, $x_3 = 1$, $m_4 = 5$, $x_4 = 4$.

(A) 9   (B) $\frac{1}{2}$ (C) $-\frac{1}{2}$ (D) 0

(E) $\frac{2}{3}$ (F) $-\frac{2}{3}$ (G) -9 (H) 18

Answer: (B)

8. Find the center of mass of the system $m_1 = 5$, $P_1(-3, 1)$, $m_2 = 9$, $P_2(-1, -1)$, $m_3 = 6$, $P_3(1, 1)$, $m_4 = 8$, $P_4(3, -2)$.

(A) $\left(\frac{3}{14}, -\frac{1}{2}\right)$ (B) $\left(-\frac{1}{2}, \frac{3}{14}\right)$ (C) $\left(\frac{3}{14}, \frac{1}{2}\right)$ (D) $\left(-\frac{3}{14}, \frac{1}{2}\right)$

(E) $(6, -14)$ (F) $(-14, 6)$ (G) $(14, -6)$ (H) $(-14, -6)$

Answer: (A)

9. Consider a flat plate of uniform density $p = 1$ bounded by the curves $y = x^2$ and $y = 1$. Find the moment M_x.

(A) 1.0   (B) 0.6   (C) 1.3   (D) 0.7

(E) 1.1   (F) 0.8   (G) 1.2   (H) 0.9

Answer: (F)

10. Find the y-coordinate of the centroid of the region bounded by the curves $y = x^2$ and $y = 1$.

(A) 0.85   (B) 0.70   (C) 0.60   (D) 0.50

(E) 0.75   (F) 0.55   (G) 0.80   (H) 0.65

Answer: (C)

11. Find the x-coordinate $\bar{x}$ at the centroid of the region bounded by the x-axis and the lines $y = 3x$ and $x = 2$.

(A) $\frac{4}{3}$ (B) $\frac{7}{6}$ (C) $\frac{10}{7}$ (D) $\frac{5}{3}$

(E) $\frac{11}{7}$ (F) $\frac{11}{6}$ (G) $\frac{5}{4}$ (H) $\frac{7}{4}$

Answer: (A)

12. An aquarium 1 foot high, 1 foot wide, and 2 feet long is filled with water. For simplicity, take the density of water to be 60 lb/ft^3. Find the hydrostatic force in pounds on one of the 1 foot by 2 foot sides of the aquarium.

(A) 336   (B) 30   (C) 168   (D) 240

(E) 60   (F) 120   (G) 28   (H) 14

Answer: (E)

13. A gate in an irrigation canal is in the form of a trapezoid 3 feet wide at the bottom, 5 feet wide at the top, with height equal to 2 feet. It is placed vertically in the canal with the water extending to its top. For simplicity, take the density of water to be 60 lb/ft^3. Find the hydrostatic force in pounds on the gate.

(A) 360   (B) 380   (C) 440   (D) 420

(E) 400   (F) 460   (G) 500   (H) 480

Answer: (C)

14. A right circular cylinder tank of height 1 foot and radius 1 foot is full of water. Taking the density of water to be a nice round 60 pounds per cubic foot, find the hydrostatic force in pounds on the side of the tank.

(A) 30π (B) 60   (C) 240π (D) 240

(E) 30   (F) 120π (G) 60π (H) 120

Answer: (G)

15. A swimming pool 24 feet long and 15 feet wide has a bottom that is an inclined plane, the shallow end having a depth of 3 feet, and the deep end 10 feet. The pool is filled with water. For simplicity, take the density of water to be 60 lb/ft^3. Find the hydrostatic force in pounds on the bottom of the pool.

(A) 145,750   (B) 146,250   (C) 147,000   (D) 147,250

(E) 146,500   (F) 147,500   (G) 146,750   (H) 146,000

Answer: (B)

16. Find the work done in stretching a spring 6 inches beyond its natural length, if the spring constant is $k = 20$ lb/ft.

Answer: 2.5 ft-lbs

17. A force of 8 dynes is required to stretch a spring from its natural length of 10 cm to a length of 15 cm. How much work is done

  (a) in stretching the spring to a length of 25 cm?

  (b) in stretching the spring from a length of 20 cm to a length of 25 cm?

Answer: (a) 180 dynes-cm   (b) 100 dynes-cm

18. A force of 10 pounds is required to stretch a spring from its natural length of 8 inches to a length of 10 inches. How much work is done in stretching the spring to a length of 12 inches?

Answer: 40 lb-inches

19. How much work is done to bring a load of ore to the surface if a miner uses a cable weighing 2 lb/ft to haul a 100 lb bucket of ore up a mine shaft 800 feet deep?

Answer: $720,000$ ft-lb

20. A 100-foot length of steel chain weighing 5 lb/ft is dangling from the drum of a winch.

  (a) How much work is required to wind the chain onto the drum?

  (b) How much work is required to wind the first 30 feet of chain onto the drum?

Answer: (a) $25,000$ ft-lb   (b) $12,750$ ft-lb

21. A hemispherical tank with radius 8 feet is filled with water to a depth of 6 feet. Find the work required to empty the tank by pumping the water to the top of the tank.

Answer: $900\pi w$ ft-lbs, where w is the weight of 1 ft^3 of water, in lbs

22. Suppose a hemispherical tank of radius 10 feet is filled with a liquid whose density is 62 pounds per cubic foot. Find the work required to pump all of the liquid out through the top of the tank.

Answer: $155,000\pi$ ft-lbs

23. A tank 5 feet long has cross-sections in the shape of a parabola $y = x^2$, for $-2 \leq x \leq 2$ (where x and y are in feet). Suppose that the tank is filled to a depth of 3 feet with liquid weighing 15 lb/ft^3. How much work is required to empty the tank by pumping the liquid over the edge of the tank?

Answer: $660\sqrt{3}$ ft-lb

24. The tank in the figure below is full of water with a density of 62.5 lb/ft^3.

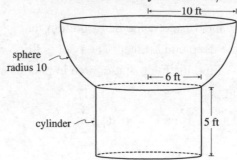

How much work is required to empty the tank by pumping water to a point 4 feet above the top of the tank?

Answer: $\frac{1,369,375}{3}\pi \approx 1.434 \times 10^6$ ft-lb

25. Find the total hydraulic force on a dam in the shape of an equilateral triangle with one vertex pointing down, if the side of the triangle is 100 feet and the water is even with the top.

Answer: 7,812,500 lb

26. A flat plate of negligible thickness is in the shape of a right triangle with base 5 ft and height 10 ft. The plate is submerged in a tank of water. Find the force on the face of the plate under the following conditions: (Use 62.4 lb/ft^3 as the density of water.)

(a) The plate is submerged horizontally so that it rests flat on the bottom of the tank at a depth of 14 ft.

(b) The plate is submerged vertically, base edge up and base at a depth of 3 ft.

Answer: (a) 21,840 lb   (b) 9880 lb

27. A swimming pool 5 m wide, 10 m long, and 3 m deep is filled with seawater of density 1030 kg/m^3 to a depth of 2.5 m. Find

(a) the hydrostatic pressure at the bottom of the pool.

(b) the hydrostatic force on the bottom.

(c) the hydrostatic force on one end of the pool.

Answer: (a) 25.2 kPa   (b) 1.26×10^6 N   (c) 1.58×10^5 N

28. A tank contains water. The end of the tank is vertical and has the shape below. Find the hydrostatic force against the end of the tank.

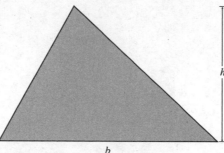

Answer: $\dfrac{1000gbh^2}{3}$ (metric units assumed)

29. A tank contains water. The end of the tank is vertical and has the shape below. Find the hydrostatic force against the end of the tank.

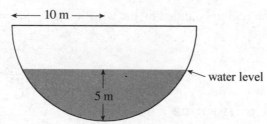

Answer: 1.23×10^6 N

30. A tank contains water. The end of the tank is vertical and has the shape below. Find the hydrostatic force against the end of the tank.

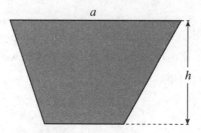

Answer: $\frac{500}{3}gh^2(a+2b)$ N

31. The masses m_i are located at the points P_i: $m_1 = 3$, $m_2 = 3$, $m_3 = 4$; $P_1(5,1)$, $P_2(3,-2)$, $P_3(-2,4)$. Find the moments M_x and M_y and the center of mass of the system.

Answer: $M_x = 13$; $M_y = 16$; Center of mass $\left(\frac{8}{5}, \frac{13}{10}\right)$

32. Calculate the center of mass of a lamina with the given density and shape:

   (a) $\rho = 4$ (b) $\rho = 1$ (c) $\rho = 1$

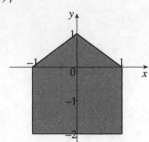 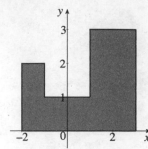 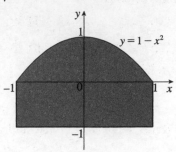

Answer: (a) $\left(0, -\frac{11}{15}\right)$ (b) $\left(\frac{9}{10}, \frac{6}{5}\right)$ (c) $\left(0, -\frac{7}{50}\right)$

33. Find the centroid of the region bounded by $y = 1 - x^2$ and $y = 0$.

   Answer: $(\overline{x}, \overline{y}) = \left(0, \frac{2}{5}\right)$

34. Find the center of mass of the lamina of uniform density δ bounded by $y = \sqrt{1 - x^2}$ and the x-axis.

   Answer: Center of mass $\left(0, \frac{4}{3\pi}\right)$

35. Determine the centroid of the region bounded by the equation $y^2 - 9x = 0$ in the first quadrant between $x = 1$ and $x = 4$.

   Answer: $(2.65, 2.41)$

6.6   Applications to Economics and Biology

1. Suppose a company has estimated that the marginal cost of manufacturing x items is $c'(x) = 5 + 0.02x$ (measured in dollars per unit) with a fixed start-up cost of $c(0) = 10,000$. Find the cost of producing the first 500 items.

   (A) $15,000   (B) $5000   (C) $10,000   (D) $17,500

   (E) $25,000   (F) $6000   (G) $20,000   (H) $60,000

   Answer: (A)

2. Suppose a company has estimated that the marginal cost of manufacturing x pairs of a new line of jeans is $c'(x) = 3 + 0.002x + 0.000006x^2$ (measured in dollars per pair) with a fixed start-up cost of $c(0) = 2000$. Find the cost of producing the first 1000 pairs of jeans.

   (A) $2000   (B) $4000   (C) $6000   (D) $10,000

   (E) $3000   (F) $5000   (G) $8000   (H) $15,000

   Answer: (G)

3. The demand function for a certain commodity is $p(x) = 4 - \frac{1}{30}x$. Find the consumer surplus when the sales level is 30.

   (A) 90   (B) 45   (C) 15   (D) 70

   (E) 30   (F) 60   (G) 20   (H) 80

   Answer: (C)

4. The demand function for a certain commodity is $p(x) = \dfrac{1800}{(x+5)^2}$. Find the consumer surplus when the selling price is \$18.

(A) 135   (B) 30   (C) 45   (D) 360

(E) 270   (F) 40   (G) 90   (H) 180

Answer: (G)

5. A supply function is given by $p_s(x) = 5 + \frac{1}{10}x$, where x is the number of units produced. Find the producer surplus when the selling price is \$15.

(A) 100   (B) 500   (C) 250   (D) 1000

(E) 800   (F) 400   (G) 200   (H) 2000

Answer: (B)

6. A rental estate management company manages an apartment complex with 20 units. The manager estimates that all 20 units can be rented if the rent is \$150 per unit per month and that for each increase in rent of \$10, one apartment will be vacated. Find the consumer surplus when 5 apartments are vacated.

(A) 3000   (B) 2250   (C) 1250   (D) 1000

(E) 1125   (F) 6000   (G) 2500   (H) 3500

Answer: (E)

7. The marginal revenue from selling x items is $90 - 0.02x$. The revenue from the sale of the first 100 items is \$8800. What is the revenue from the sale of the first 200 items?

Answer: \$17,500

8. The marginal revenue for a company when sales are q units is given by $\dfrac{dR}{dq} = 12 - 0.06q$. Find the increase in revenue when the sales level increases from 100 to 200 units.

Answer: \$300

9. The marginal cost for a company is given by $C'(q) = 2 - 0.01q + 0.005q^2$ where q is the number of units produced. What is the total cost to raise production from 100 to 200 units?

Answer: \$11,716.60

10. The marginal cost for the production of the new Super Widget at Widgets International is given by $C'(q) = 15 - 0.0002q$, whereas the marginal revenue is $R'(q) = 20 - 0.003q$, where in both cases q represents the number of units produced.

(a) Determine the change in profits when sales are increased from 700 to 1700 units.

(b) What is the change in profit when sales increase from 1700 to 2700 units? Discuss your answer.

Answer: (a) \$1640   (b) $-$\$1160. The company should change its production level.

11. The demand function for a certain commodity is $p = 5 - \dfrac{x}{10}$. Find the consumer's surplus when the sales level is 30. Illustrate by drawing the demand curve and identifying the consumer's surplus as an area.

Answer: $45

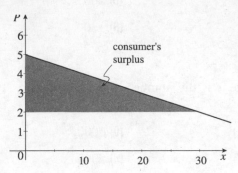

12. The demand function for producing a certain commodity is given by $p = 1000 - 0.1x - 0.0001x^2$. Find the consumer surplus when the sale level is 500.

Answer: $20,833.\overline{3}$

13. A manufacture has been selling 1000 ceiling fans at $60 each. A market survey indicates that for every $10 that price is reduced, the number of sets sold will increase by 100. Find the demand function and calculate the consumer surplus when the selling price is set at $50.

Answer: Demand function $p(x) = 160 - 0.1x$, Consumer surplus = $60,500

14. The dye dilution method is used to measure cardiac output with 6 mg of dye. The dye concentrations, in mg/L, are modeled by $c(t) = \frac{1}{15}t(15 - t)$, $0 \le t \le 15$, where t is measured in seconds. Find the cardiac output.

Answer: 0.16 L/sec

15. The following table shows the relationship between price and demand for milk produced in a large dairy.

q (billions of pounds of milk per year)	45	50	55	60	65	70	75
p (price in dollars per pound)	1.00	0.90	0.80	0.70	0.60	0.50	0.40

Determine the consumer's surplus when the sales quantity is 65 billion pounds of milk in a year. Illustrate your answer by drawing the corresponding demand curve and identifying the consumer's surplus as a region.

Answer: $42.25

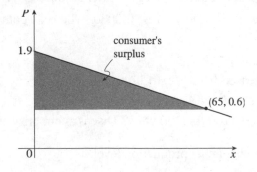

6.7 Probability

1. Find k so that the function $f(x) = \begin{cases} kx(1-x) & \text{if } 0 < x < 1 \\ 0 & \text{otherwise} \end{cases}$ can serve as the probability density function of a random variable X.

(A) $\frac{1}{3}$ (B) $\frac{1}{6}$ (C) $\frac{1}{2}$ (D) 1

(E) 3   (F) 6   (G) 2   (H) 0

Answer: (F)

2. Find k so that the function $f(x) = \begin{cases} \dfrac{k}{x(\ln x)^3} & \text{if } x > e \\ 0 & \text{otherwise} \end{cases}$ can serve as the probability density function of a random variable X.

(A) $\frac{1}{3}$ (B) $\frac{1}{6}$ (C) $\frac{1}{2}$ (D) 1

(E) 3   (F) 6   (G) 2   (H) 0

Answer: (G)

3. Let X be a continuous random variable with density function

$$f(X) = \begin{cases} c \cdot e^{-cX} & \text{if } X \geq 0 \\ 0 & \text{otherwise} \end{cases}$$

If the median of this distribution is $\frac{1}{3}$, then c is:

(A) $\frac{1}{3}\ln\frac{1}{2}$ (B) $\frac{1}{3}\ln 2$ (C) $2\ln\frac{3}{2}$ (D) $3\ln 2$

(E) 3   (F) $\frac{1}{3}$ (G) $2 \cdot \dfrac{\ln 3}{\ln 2}$ (H) $3\ln\frac{1}{2}$

Answer: (D)

4. Let X be a continuous random variable with density function

$$p(X) = \begin{cases} \frac{1}{9}X(4-X) & \text{if } 0 \leq X \leq 3 \\ 0 & \text{otherwise} \end{cases}$$

What is the mean of X?

(A) $\frac{4}{9}$ (B) 1   (C) $\frac{3}{2}$ (D) $\frac{2}{9}$

(E) $\frac{2}{3}$ (F) $\frac{1}{3}$ (G) $\frac{7}{4}$ (H) $\frac{9}{4}$

Answer: (G)

221

5. Find c so that the following can serve as the probability density function of a random variable X:

$$f(x) = \begin{cases} c \cdot X \cdot e^{-4X^2} & \text{if } X \geq 0 \\ 0 & \text{otherwise} \end{cases}$$

(A) 8   (B) 4   (C) $\frac{1}{8}$ (D) $\frac{1}{4}$

(E) 1   (F) 16   (G) $\frac{1}{16}$ (H) 2

Answer: (A)

6. (a) Show that $f(x) = \begin{cases} 4x + 12x^2 & \text{if } 0 \leq x \leq \frac{1}{2} \\ 0 & \text{otherwise} \end{cases}$ is the probability density function of a random variable.

(b) What is the mean for this distribution?

(c) Calculate the median of f.

Answer: (a) $\int_{-\infty}^{\infty} f(x)\,dx = \int_0^{1/2} 4x + 12x^2\,dx = 1$ (b) $\frac{17}{48}$ (c) About 0.3774

7. (a) Show that $p(x) = \begin{cases} (2-k)\,x^{-3+k} & \text{if } x \geq 1 \\ 0 & \text{otherwise} \end{cases}$ where k is fixed and $0 < k < 1$ is a probability density function.

(b) What is the mean for this distribution?

(c) Calculate the median of p.

Answer: (a) $\int_{-\infty}^{\infty} p(x)\,dx = \int_1^{\infty} (2-k)\,x^{-3+k}\,dx = 1$ (b) $\dfrac{2-k}{1-k}$ (c) $2^{1/2-k}$

8. (a) Explain why the function defined by the graph below is a probability density function.

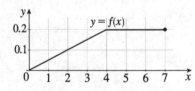

(b) Use the graph to find the following probabilities:

(i) $P(x < 2)$

(ii) $P(2 \leq x \leq 5)$

(c) Calculate the median for this distribution.

Answer: (a) $\int_{-\infty}^{\infty} f(x)\,dx = 1$ (b) (i) 0.1   (ii) 0.5   (c) 4.5

9. Assume the daily consumption of electric power (in millions of kilowatt-hours) of a certain city has the probability density $p(x) = \begin{cases} \frac{1}{9}xe^{-x/3} & \text{if } x \geq 0 \\ 0 & \text{if } x < 0 \end{cases}$

If the city's power plant has a daily capacity of 12 million kilowatt-hours, what is the probability that the available power supply will be inadequate on any given day?

Answer: $5 \cdot e^{-4} \approx 0.09$

10. Suppose that the mileage (in thousands of miles) which car owners can obtain from a certain kind of tire

    has the probability density $p(x) = \begin{cases} \frac{1}{100} \cdot e^{-x/100} & \text{if } x \geq 0 \\ 0 & \text{if } x < 0 \end{cases}$

    Find the probability that a tire chosen at random will last

    (a) at most 10,000 miles.

    (b) between 15,000 and 25,000 miles.

    (c) at least 30,000 miles.

    Answer: (a) $1 - \dfrac{1}{e^{100}}$ (b) $\dfrac{1}{e^{150}} - \dfrac{1}{e^{250}} \approx 7 \times 10^{-66}$ (c) $\dfrac{1}{e^{300}}$

11. Assume the weights of adult males are normally distributed with a mean weight of 150 pounds and a standard deviation of 20 pounds. Use Simpson's Rule or the Midpoint Rule to estimate the following:

    (a) What is the probability that an adult male chosen at random will weigh between 120 pounds and 180 pounds?

    (b) What percentage of the adult male population weighs more than 200 pounds?

    Answer: (a) About 0.87   (b) About 0.006

12. IQ scores are assumed to be normally distributed with a mean $\mu = 100$ and standard deviation $\sigma = 15$. Use either Simpson's Rule or the Midpoint Rule to approximate the probability that a person selected at random from the general population will have an IQ score

    (a) between 70 and 130.

    (b) over 130.

    Answer: (a) About 0.9544   (b) About 0.0228

13. Let $f(x) = \begin{cases} \dfrac{k \ln x}{x^4} & \text{if } x > 1 \\ 0 & \text{otherwise} \end{cases}$

    (a) Find k so that f can serve as the probability density function of a random variable X.

    (b) Find $P(X > e)$.

    (c) Find the mean.

    Answer: (a) $k = 9$ (b) $\dfrac{4}{e^3} \approx 0.199$ (c) $\frac{9}{4}$

14. The density function for the life of a certain type of battery is modeled by $p(t) = 0.2e^{-0.2t}$, $t > 0$ and is measured in months.

    (a) What is the probability that a battery will wear out during the first month of use?

    (b) What is the probability that a battery is functioning for more than 12 months?

    Answer: (a) About 0.181   (b) About 0.09

15. The density function for the life of a certain type of battery is modeled by $p(t) = 0.2e^{-0.2t}$, $t > 0$ and is measured in months.

  (a) Find the median life of the batteries.

  (b) Find the mean life of the batteries.

  (c) Sketch the graph of the density function showing the median and mean.

Answer:

  (a) $5 \ln 2 \approx 3.466$ months

  (b) 5 months

  (c)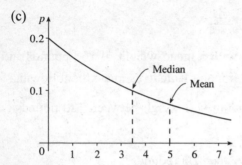

16. The density function for the waiting time at a bank is modeled by $p(t) = 0.1e^{-0.1t}$, $t > 0$ and is measured in minutes.

  (a) What is the probability that a customer will be served within the first 5 minutes?

  (b) What is the probability that a customer has to wait for more than 15 minutes?

Answer:

  (a) About 0.39

  (b) About 0.22

17. The density function for the waiting time at a bank is modeled by $p(t) = 0.1e^{-0.1t}$, $t > 0$ and is measured in minutes.

  (a) Find the median waiting time.

  (b) Find the mean waiting time.

  (c) Sketch the graph of the density function showing the median and mean.

Answer:

  (a) $10 \ln 2 \approx 6.93$ minutes

  (b) 10 minutes

  (c)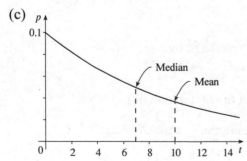

7   Differential Equations

7.1   Modeling with Differential Equations

1. Which of the following equations is satisfied by the function $x = \sin 2t$?

    (A) $x' - 2t = 0$ **(B)** $x' - 4xt = 0$ **(C)** $x'' + 4x = 0$ **(D)** $x'' + x = 0$

    (E) $x' - 4x = 0$ **(F)** $x' + 4x = 0$ **(G)** $x'' - 4x = 0$ **(H)** $x'' - x = 0$

    Answer: (C)

2. Which of the following equations is satisfied by the function $x = e^{2t}$?

    (A) $x' - 2t = 0$ **(B)** $x' - 4xt = 0$ **(C)** $x'' + 4x = 0$ **(D)** $x'' + x = 0$

    (E) $x' - 4x = 0$ **(F)** $x' + 4x = 0$ **(G)** $x'' - 4x = 0$ **(H)** $x'' - x = 0$

    Answer: (G)

3. Which of the following equations is satisfied by the function $x = e^{2t^2}$?

    (A) $x' - 2t = 0$ **(B)** $x' - 4xt = 0$ **(C)** $x'' + 4x = 0$ **(D)** $x'' + x = 0$

    (E) $x' - 4x = 0$ **(F)** $x' + 4x = 0$ **(G)** $x'' - 4x = 0$ **(H)** $x'' - x = 0$

    Answer: (B)

4. Which of the following is a solution of the differential equation $\dfrac{dy}{dx} + 4y = 0$?

    (A) $y = e^{-4x}$ **(B)** $y = 4x$ **(C)** $y = e^{2x^2}$ **(D)** $y = \sin 2x$

    (E) $y = e^{2x}$ **(F)** $y = 2x^2$ **(G)** $y = \dfrac{1}{4x+1}$ **(H)** $y = e^{4x}$

    Answer: (A)

5. Which of the following is a solution of the differential equation $\dfrac{dy}{dx} - 4y = 0$?

    (A) $y = e^{-4x}$ **(B)** $y = 4x$ **(C)** $y = e^{2x^2}$ **(D)** $y = \sin 2x$

    (E) $y = e^{2x}$ **(F)** $y = 2x^2$ **(G)** $y = \dfrac{1}{4x+1}$ **(H)** $y = e^{4x}$

    Answer: (H)

6. Which of the following is a solution of the differential equation $\dfrac{dy}{dx} + 4y^2 = 0$?

    (A) $y = e^{-4x}$ **(B)** $y = 4x$ **(C)** $y = e^{2x^2}$ **(D)** $y = \sin 2x$

    (E) $y = e^{2x}$ **(F)** $y = 2x^2$ **(G)** $y = \dfrac{1}{4x+1}$ **(H)** $y = c^{4x}$

    Answer: (G)

7. Which of the following is a solution of the differential equation $\dfrac{dy}{dx} - 4xy = 0$?

(A) $y = e^{-4x}$ (B) $y = 4x$ (C) $y = e^{2x^2}$ (D) $y = \sin 2x$

(E) $y = e^{2x}$ (F) $y = 2x^2$ (G) $y = \dfrac{1}{4x + 1}$ (H) $y = e^{4x}$

Answer: (C)

8. Which of the following is a solution of the differential equation $\dfrac{d^2y}{dx^2} + 4y = 0$?

(A) $y = e^{-4x}$ (B) $y = 4x$ (C) $y = e^{2x^2}$ (D) $y = \sin 2x$

(E) $y = e^{2x}$ (F) $y = 2x^2$ (G) $y = \dfrac{1}{4x + 1}$ (H) $y = e^{4x}$

Answer: (D)

9. Which of the following is a solution of the differential equation $\dfrac{d^2y}{dx^2} - 4y = 0$?

(A) $y = e^{-4x}$ (B) $y = 4x$ (C) $y = e^{2x^2}$ (D) $y = \sin 2x$

(E) $y = e^{2x}$ (F) $y = 2x^2$ (G) $y = \dfrac{1}{4x + 1}$ (H) $y = e^{4x}$

Answer: (E)

10. Which of the following is a solution of the differential equation $\dfrac{dy}{dx} - 4x = 0$?

(A) $y = e^{-4x}$ (B) $y = 4x$ (C) $y = e^{2x^2}$ (D) $y = \sin 2x$

(E) $y = e^{2x}$ (F) $y = 2x^2$ (G) $y = \dfrac{1}{4x + 1}$ (H) $y = e^{4x}$

Answer: (F)

11. Which of the following is a solution of the differential equation $\dfrac{dy}{dx} - 4 = 0$?

(A) $y = e^{-4x}$ (B) $y = 4x$ (C) $y = e^{2x^2}$ (D) $y = \sin 2x$

(E) $y = e^{2x}$ (F) $y = 2x^2$ (G) $y = \dfrac{1}{4x + 1}$ (H) $y = e^{4x}$

Answer: (B)

12. (a) Show that every member of the family of functions $y = ce^{(1/3)x^3}$ is a solution of the differential equation $y' = x^2 y$.

    (b) Find a solution of the differential equation $y' = x^2 y$ that satisfies the initial condition $y(0) = 8$.

    (c) Find a solution of the differential equation $y' = x^2 y$ that satisfies the initial condition $y(8) = 0$.

Answer:

    (a) $y' = \left(ce^{x^3/3}\right)' = cx^2 e^{x^3/3} = x^2 \left(ce^{x^3/3}\right) = x^2 y$ (b) $y = 8e^{x^3/3}$ (c) $y = 0$

13. (a) What can you conclude about the functions which satisfy $y' = y^2$ just by looking at the differential equation?

    (b) Verify that $y = -\dfrac{1}{x+c}$ are solutions of the equation in part (a).

    (c) Is there a solution of the equation in part (a) that is not a member of the family of functions in part (b)? Justify your answer.

    (d) Find a solution to the equation in part (a) with the additional condition that $y(0) = \frac{1}{3}$.

Answer:

(a) $y = 0$ is a constant solution and if $y \neq 0$, $\dfrac{dy}{dx} > 0$. Therefore solutions of the differential equation are increasing functions.

(b) $y' = \dfrac{1}{(x+c)^2} = \left(-\dfrac{1}{x+c}\right)^2 = y^2$ (c) $y = 0$ is not included in part (b). (d) $y = \dfrac{-1}{x-3} = \dfrac{1}{3-x}$

14. (a) What can you conclude about the graph of the solution of the equation $\dfrac{dy}{dx} = -\dfrac{x}{y}$ just by looking at the differential equation?

    (b) Use implicit differentiation to verify all members of the family $x^2 + y^2 = c^2$ are solutions of the equation in part (a).

    (c) Find a solution of the equation in part (a) with the additional condition that $y(3) = 4$.

Answer:

(a) Let $(x, y(x))$ be a graph of a solution of the differential equation. Then $\dfrac{dy}{dx} \cdot \dfrac{y}{x} = -\dfrac{x}{y} \cdot \dfrac{y}{x} = -1$, so the slope of the tangent of $y(x)$ is perpendicular to the line passing through $(0,0)$ and $(x, y(x))$.

(b) $2x + 2y\dfrac{dy}{dx} = 0 \implies \dfrac{dy}{dx} = -\dfrac{x}{y}$ (c) $x^2 + y^2 = 25$

15. A function $y(x)$ satisfies the differential equation $\dfrac{dy}{dx} = y^2 - 4y + 3$.

    (a) What are the constant solutions of the equation?

    (b) For what values of y is y increasing?

    (c) The equation shows that $\dfrac{dy}{dx}$ is independent of x. Using this observation, what can you say about the relationship of the graphs of the non-constant solutions of the equation?

Answer:

(a) $y = 1$ and $y = 3$.   (b) For $y < 1$ or $y > 3$, $y(x)$ is increasing.

(c) The slopes corresponding to two different points with the same y-coordinates must be equal. This means that if we know one solution to the equation, then we can obtain infinitely many others just by shifting the graph of the known solution to the right or left.

227

16. The study of free fall provides one context to consider differential equations. In the simplest case, in the absence of air or other resistance, physicists assume that the rate of change of velocity of a body is constant.

    (a) Write an equation for $\dfrac{dv}{dt}$.

    (b) As the time t increases without bound, what happens to the velocity v?

Answer:

    (a) $\dfrac{dv}{dt} = a$ where a is a constant.

    (b) Since $v(t) = at + v_0$, where v_0 is a constant, therefore as t increases without bound, $v(t)$ will increase without bound.

17. The study of free fall provides one context to consider differential equations. In the simplest case, in the absence of air or other resistance, physicists assume that the rate of change of velocity of a body is constant. But it is more realistic to consider the presence of air resistance. Assume that g is the constant of acceleration due to earth's gravity. Suppose that air resistance is proportional to the velocity of the falling body.

    (a) Explain why the differential equation $\dfrac{dv}{dt} = g - kv$, where k is a positive constant, would be a reasonable model for velocity under these conditions.

    (b) When does v increase most rapidly? Justify your answer.

    (c) Consider the equation in part (i). What would happen to the rate of change of velocity, $\dfrac{dv}{dt}$, as t increases? Justify your conclusion.

    (d) Make a sketch of a possible solution for this differential equation.

Answer:

    (a) $\dfrac{dv}{dt} = g - kv$ shows that the ratio at which the velocity increases, decreases at a rate proportional to the velocity.

    (b) $v'(0) = g > g - kv$ for $v > 0$. Therefore $v(t)$ increases most rapidly at $t = 0$.

    (c) As t increases, $\dfrac{dv}{dt}$ will approach 0. That means the force of resistance is just equal to the gravity. Therefore, the velocity will approach a limiting value.

    (d)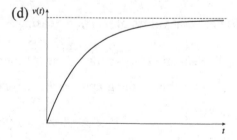

MEX3

18. In paleontology, the phenomenon of radioactive decay is commonly used to date fossil remains. This method uses the fact that the rate of decay $\frac{dA}{dt}$ of an element will be proportional to the amount A of the radioactive element that exists at time t.

(a) Determine a differential equation that $A(t)$ must satisfy.

(b) What can you say about $A(t)$ as $t \to \infty$?

(c) Find a solution to your differential equation.

(d) How long will it take for half of the original amount of the radioactive element to decay?

Answer:

(a) $\frac{dA}{dt} = -kA$, where k is a positive constant.

(b) Since $\frac{dA}{dt} < 0$, $A(t)$ will approach 0 as $t \to \infty$.

(c) $A(t) = ce^{-kt}$

(d) $t = \dfrac{\ln 2}{k}$

19. In biology, it is often assumed that the number of people that will contract a certain disease is directly proportional to the product of the number of people y who are currently infected with the disease at a particular time t and the number of people x who, at the same time, are not yet infected but who are susceptible to it. Assume that the total population, P, in the study is a constant.

(a) What does $\frac{dy}{dt}$ mean?

(b) Determine a differential equation that $y(t)$ must satisfy.

(c) What happens to y as $t \to \infty$?

Answer:

(a) $\frac{dy}{dt}$ is the infection rate.

(b) $\frac{dy}{dt} = ky(P - y)$

(c) Since $\frac{dy}{dt} > 0$, as $t \to \infty$, $y(t) \to P$.

20. A ball is thrown directly upward from the ground with an initial speed 24 ft/s.

(a) Determine the differential equation that the position function $y(t)$ satisfies.

(b) What are the initial conditions?

(c) How high does the ball rise?

Answer:

(a) $y''(t) = -32$ (b) $v(0) = 24$, $y(0) = 0$ (c) 9 feet

21. The brakes of a car traveling 60 mph decelerate the car at the rate of 20 ft/s^2.

    (a) Determine the differential equation that the position function $y(t)$ satisfies.

    (b) What are the initial conditions?

    (c) If the car is 175 feet from a barrier when the brakes are applied, will it hit the barrier?

Answer:

(a) $y''(t) = -20$ ft/s^2 (b) $v(0) = 88$ ft/s, $y(0) = 0$

(c) Yes, because the car needs 193.6 feet in order to stop.

7.2   Direction Fields and Euler's Method

1. A direction field is given below. Which of the following represents its differential equation?

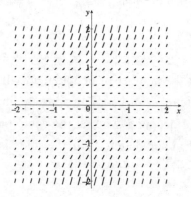

(A) $dy/dx = \sin x$ (B) $dy/dx = -y$ (C) $dy/dx = y - \frac{1}{2}y^2$ (D) $dy/dx = x + y$

(E) $dy/dx = x^2$ (F) $dy/dx = 1$ (G) $dy/dx = y^2$ (H) $dy/dx = x^2 + y^2$

Answer: (G)

2. A direction field is given below. Which of the following represents its differential equation?

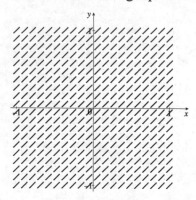

(A) $dy/dx = \sin x$ (B) $dy/dx = -y$ (C) $dy/dx = y - \frac{1}{2}y^2$ (D) $dy/dx = x + y$

(E) $dy/dx = x^2$ (F) $dy/dx = 1$ (G) $dy/dx = y^2$ (H) $dy/dx = x^2 + y^2$

Answer: (F)

3. A direction field is given below. Which of the following represents its differential equation?

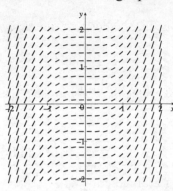

(A) $dy/dx = \sin x$ (B) $dy/dx = -y$ (C) $dy/dx = y - \frac{1}{2}y^2$ (D) $dy/dx = x + y$

(E) $dy/dx = x^2$ (F) $dy/dx = 1$ (G) $dy/dx = y^2$ (H) $dy/dx = x^2 + y^2$

Answer: (E)

4. A direction field is given below. Which of the following represents its differential equation?

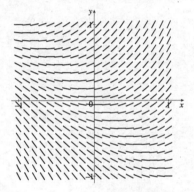

(A) $dy/dx = \sin x$ (B) $dy/dx = -y$ (C) $dy/dx = y - \frac{1}{2}y^2$ (D) $dy/dx = x + y$

(E) $dy/dx = x^2$ (F) $dy/dx = 1$ (G) $dy/dx = y^2$ (H) $dy/dx = x^2 + y^2$

Answer: (D)

5. A direction field is given below. Which of the following represents its differential equation?

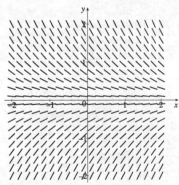

(A) $dy/dx = \sin x$ (B) $dy/dx = -y$ (C) $dy/dx = y - \frac{1}{2}y^2$ (D) $dy/dx = x + y$

(E) $dy/dx = x^2$ (F) $dy/dx = 1$ (G) $dy/dx = y^2$ (H) $dy/dx = x^2 + y^2$

Answer: (B)

6. A direction field is given below. Which of the following represents its differential equation?

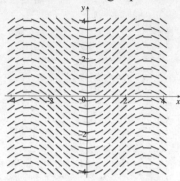

(A) $dy/dx = \sin x$ (B) $dy/dx = -y$ (C) $dy/dx = y - \frac{1}{2}y^2$ (D) $dy/dx = x + y$

(E) $dy/dx = x^2$ (F) $dy/dx = 1$ (G) $dy/dx = y^2$ (H) $dy/dx = x^2 + y^2$

Answer: (A)

7. Which of the given differential equations matches the given direction field?

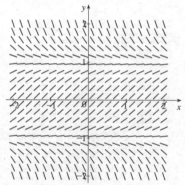

(A) $dy/dx = x - 1$ (B) $dy/dx = 1 - y^2$ (C) $dy/dx = 1 + y$ (D) $dy/dx = x^2 - y^2$

(E) $dy/dx = y - 1$ (F) $dy/dx = y^2 - x^2$ (G) $dy/dx = 1 - x$ (H) $dy/dx = y^2 - 1$

Answer: (B)

8. Which of the given differential equations matches the given direction field?

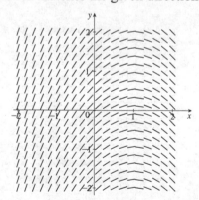

(A) $dy/dx = x - 1$ (B) $dy/dx = 1 - y^2$ (C) $dy/dx = 1 + y$ (D) $dy/dx = x^2 - y^2$

(E) $dy/dx = y - 1$ (F) $dy/dx = y^2 - x^2$ (G) $dy/dx = 1 - x$ (H) $dy/dx = y^2 - 1$

Answer: (G)

9. Which of the given differential equations matches the given direction field?

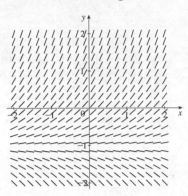

(A) $dy/dx = x - 1$ (B) $dy/dx = 1 - y^2$ (C) $dy/dx = 1 + y$ (D) $dy/dx = x^2 - y^2$

(E) $dy/dx = y - 1$ (F) $dy/dx = y^2 - x^2$ (G) $dy/dx = 1 - x$ (H) $dy/dx = y^2 - 1$

Answer: (C)

10. Which of the given differential equations matches the given direction field?

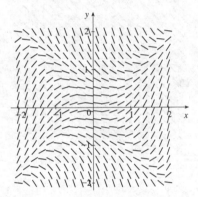

(A) $dy/dx = x - 1$ (B) $dy/dx = 1 - y^2$ (C) $dy/dx = 1 + y$ (D) $dy/dx = x^2 - y^2$

(E) $dy/dx = y - 1$ (F) $dy/dx = y^2 - x^2$ (G) $dy/dx = 1 - x$ (H) $dy/dx = y^2 - 1$

Answer: (D)

11. A direction field for a differential equation is given below:

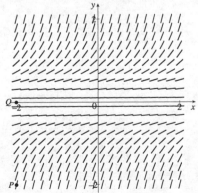

(a) Sketch the graphs of the solutions that have initial condition P and initial condition Q.

(b) Determine whether the differential equation is autonomous. Explain your answer.

233

Answer:

(a)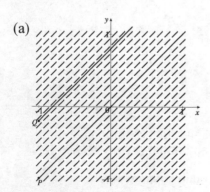

(b) It is autonomous since $\dfrac{dy}{dx}$ is independent of x.

12. A direction field for a differential equation is given below:

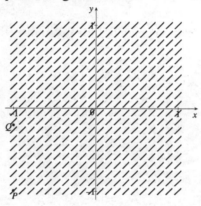

(a) Sketch the graphs of the solutions that have initial condition P and initial condition Q.

(b) Determine whether the differential equation is autonomous. Explain your answer.

Answer:

(a)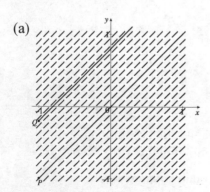

(b) It is autonomous since $\dfrac{dy}{dx}$ is constant and independent of x.

13. A direction field for a differential equation is given below:

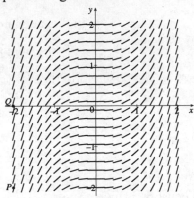

(a) Sketch the graphs of the solutions that have initial condition P and initial condition Q.

(b) Determine whether the differential equation is autonomous. Explain your answer.

Answer:

(a)

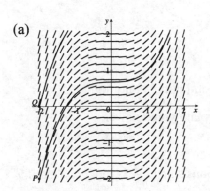

(b) It is not autonomous since $\dfrac{dy}{dx}$ is not independent of x.

14. A direction field for a differential equation is given below:

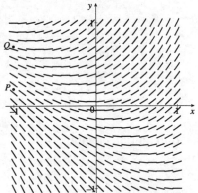

(a) Sketch the graphs of the solutions that have initial condition P and initial condition Q.

(b) Determine whether the differential equation is autonomous. Explain your answer.

235

Answer:

(a)

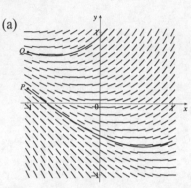

(b) It is not autonomous since $\dfrac{dy}{dx}$ is dependent on both x and y.

15. A direction field for a differential equation is given below:

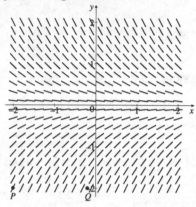

(a) Sketch the graphs of the solutions that have initial condition P and initial condition Q.

(b) Determine whether the differential equation is autonomous. Explain your answer.

Answer:

(a)

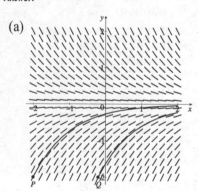

(b) It is autonomous since $\dfrac{dy}{dx}$ is independent of x.

16. A population is modeled by the differential equation $\dfrac{dP}{dt} = 0.4P\left(1 - \dfrac{P}{250}\right)$ where $P(t)$ is the population at time t.

   (a) What are the equilibrium solutions?

   (b) For what values of P is the population increasing?

   (c) For what values of P is the population decreasing?

   (d) Use the information from above to sketch the direction field for the given differential equation.

Answer:

(a) $P = 0$, $P = 250$

(b) $0 < P < 250$

(c) $0 < P < 250$

(d)

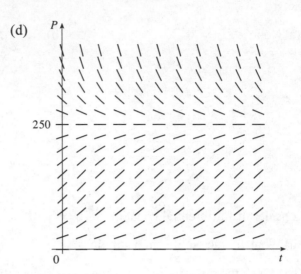

17. Consider the differential equation $\dfrac{dy}{dt} = y^3 - 2y^2 - 15y$.

   (a) What are the equilibrium solutions?

   (b) For what values of y is $y(t)$ increasing?

   (c) For what values of y is $y(t)$ decreasing?

   (d) Use the information from above to sketch the direction field for the given differential equation.

Answer:

(a) $y = 0$, $y = -3$, $y = 5$

(b) $-3 < y < 0$ or $y > 5$

(c) $y < -3$ or $0 < y < 5$

(d)

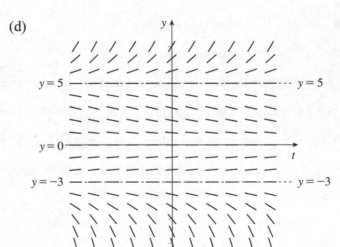

18. Consider the differential equation $\dfrac{dy}{dt} = t + 1$.

   (a) What are the equilibrium solutions?

   (b) Sketch the direction field for the given differential equation.

Answer:

(a) None

(b)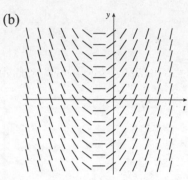

19. Consider the differential equation $\dfrac{dy}{dt} = t^2 - 1$.

(a) What are the equilibrium solutions?

(b) Sketch the direction field for the given differential equation.

Answer:

(a) None

(b)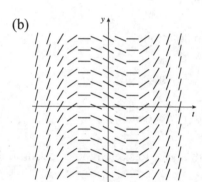

20. Consider the differential equation $\dfrac{dy}{dt} = y - t$.

(a) What are the equilibrium solutions?

(b) What are the points in the ty-plane at which the slope of the solution curve is 0?

(c) What are the points in the ty-plane at which the slope of the solution curve is 1?

(d) What are the points in the ty-plane at which the slope of the solution curve is -1?

(e) Use the information from above to sketch the direction field for the given differential equation.

Answer:

(a) None

(b) $\{(t, t) \mid t \in \mathbb{R}\}$

(c) $\{(t, t + 1) \mid t \in \mathbb{R}\}$

(d) $\{(t, t - 1) \mid t \in \mathbb{R}\}$

(e)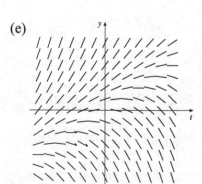

21. Make a rough sketch of a directional field for the autonomous differential equation $y' = f(y)$ where f is the function graphed below.

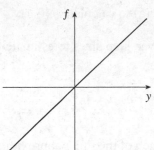

Answer:

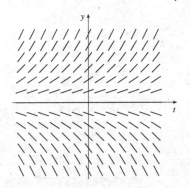

22. Make a rough sketch of a directional field for the autonomous differential equation $y' = f(y)$ where f is the function graphed below.

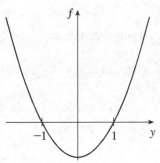

Answer:

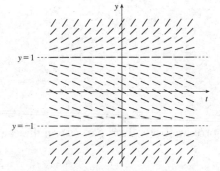

23. (a) Determine the solution of the differential equation $\dfrac{dy}{dx} = -y$ where $y(0) = 1$.

 (b) Use the solution $y(x)$ from part (a) to calculate $y(0.4)$.

 (c) Use Euler's Method with the given step sizes to estimate the value of $y(0.4)$ for the equation given in part (a).

  (i) $h = 0.4$ (ii) $h = 0.2$ (iii) $h = 0.1$

 (d) Sketch $y(x)$ from part (b) and each of the Euler approximations from part (c) on the same set of axes.

Answer:

(a) $y = e^{-x}$

(b) $y(0.4) = e^{-0.4} \approx 0.67032$

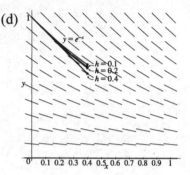

(d)

(c) (i) $y(0) = 1$ and $y'(0) = -y = -1$ $\Rightarrow$ $y = -x + 1$

    $\Rightarrow$ $y(0.4) = 0.6$

 (ii) $y(0) = 1$, $y'(0) = -1$ $\Rightarrow$ $y = -x + 1$ $\Rightarrow$

    $y(0.2) = 0.8$, $y'(0.2) = -y(0.2) = -0.8$ $\Rightarrow$

    $y = -0.8x + 0.96$ $\Rightarrow$ $y(0.4) = 0.64$

 (iii) $y(0) = 1$, $y'(0) = -1$ $\Rightarrow$ $y = -x + 1$ $\Rightarrow$

    $y(0.1) = 0.9$, $y'(0.1) = -y(0.1) = -0.9$ $\Rightarrow$

    $y = -0.9x + .99$ $\Rightarrow$ $y(0.2) = 0.81$,

    $y'(0.2) = -0.81$ $\Rightarrow$ $y = -0.81x + 0.972$ $\Rightarrow$

    $y(0.3) = 0.729$, $y'(0.3) = -0.729$ $\Rightarrow$

    $y = -0.729x + 0.9477$ $\Rightarrow$ $y(0.4) = 0.6561$

24. (a) Determine the solution of the differential equation $\dfrac{dy}{dx} = 2y$ where $y(0) = 2$.

 (b) Use the solution $y(x)$ from part (a) to calculate $y(0.4)$.

 (c) Use Euler's Method with the given step sizes to estimate the value of $y(0.4)$ for the equation given in part (a).

  (i) $h = 0.4$

  (ii) $h = 0.2$

  (iii) $h = 0.1$

 (d) Sketch $y(x)$ from part (b) and each of the Euler approximations from part (c) on the same coordinate plane.

Answer:

(a) $y(x) = 2e^{2x}$

(b) $y(0.4) = 2e^{2 \cdot 0.4} = 2e^{0.8} \approx 4.4510819$

(c) (i) $y(0) = 2$ and $y'(0) = 4 \quad \Rightarrow \quad y = 4x + 2 \quad \Rightarrow$
$y(0.4) = 3.6$

(ii) $y(0) = 2$ and $y'(0) = 4 \quad \Rightarrow \quad y = 4x + 2 \quad \Rightarrow$
$y(0.2) = 2.8, y'(0.2) = 5.6 \quad \Rightarrow \quad y = 5.6x + 1.68$
$\Rightarrow \quad y(0.4) = 3.92$

(iii) $y(0) = 2$ and $y'(0) = 4 \quad \Rightarrow \quad y = 4x + 2 \quad \Rightarrow$
$y(0.1) = 2.4, y'(0.1) = 4.8 \quad \Rightarrow \quad y = 4.8x + 1.92$
$\Rightarrow \quad y(0.2) = 2.88, y'(0.2) = 5.76 \quad \Rightarrow$
$y = 5.76x + 1.728 \quad \Rightarrow \quad y(0.3) = 3.456,$
$y'(0.3) = 6.912 \quad \Rightarrow \quad y = 6.912x + 1.3824 \quad \Rightarrow$
$y(0.4) = 4.1472$

(d)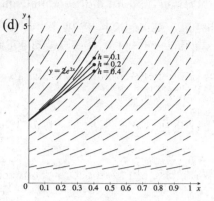

25. A direction field for a differential equation is given below. Use a straightedge to draw the graphs of the Euler approximations to the solution curve over the interval $[0, 1.2]$ that passes through $y(0) = 1$. Use as step sizes $h = 1.2$, $h = 0.6$, and $h = 0.2$.

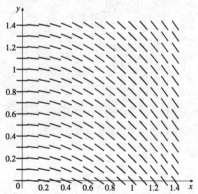

Answer:

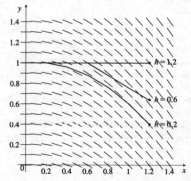

26. A direction field for a differential equation is given below. Use a straightedge to draw the graphs of the Euler approximations to the solution curve over the interval $[0, 1.2]$ that passes through $y(0) = 0.1$. Use as step sizes $h = 1.2$, $h = 0.6$, and $h = 0.2$.

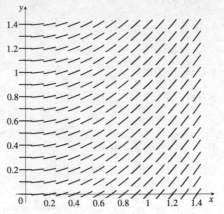

Answer:

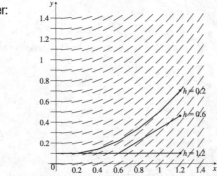

27. A direction field for a differential equation is given below. Use a straightedge to draw the graphs of the Euler approximations to the solution curve over the interval $[0, 4]$ that passes through $y(0) = 1$. Use as step sizes $h = 4$, $h = 2$, $h = 1$ and $h = 0.5$.

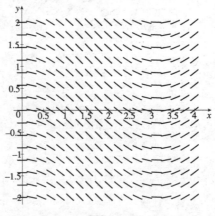

Answer:

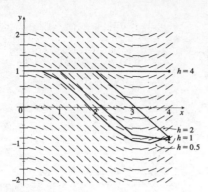

28. Consider the differential equation $\dfrac{dy}{dx} = 2x + y$.

   (a) Sketch the direction field. Indicate where the slopes are $-1, 0$, or 1. Draw some other slopes as well.

   (b) If the point $(1, 2)$ is on the graph of a solution, use Euler's Method with step size 0.5 to estimate the value of the solution at $x = 2.5$.

Answer:

(a)

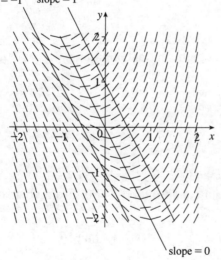

(b) $y = f(2.5) \approx 13.25$

29. Consider the differential equation $x\dfrac{dy}{dx} - 3y = 0$.

   (a) Sketch the direction field. Indicate where the slopes are $-1, 0$, or 1. Draw some other slopes as well.

   (b) If the point $(1, 2)$ is on the graph of a solution, use Euler's Method with step size 0.5 to estimate the value of the solution at $x = 2$.

Answer:

(a)

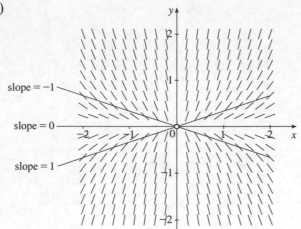

(b) $y = f(2) \approx 10$

slope = −1

slope = 0

slope = 1

7.3 Separable Equations

1. Solve the differential equation $y' = x^2$ subject to the initial condition $y(0) = 3$. From your solution, find the value of $y(1)$.

   (A) $\frac{7}{2}$ (B) $\frac{7}{3}$ (C) $\frac{10}{3}$ (D) $\frac{8}{3}$

   (E) $\frac{9}{2}$ (F) $\frac{5}{2}$ (G) 4   (H) 3

   Answer: (C)

2. Solve the differential equation $y' = 5y(1000 - y)$ subject to the initial condition $y(0) = 500$. From your solution, find the value of the limit $\lim_{t \to \infty} y(t)$.

   (A) 5000   (B) 2500   (C) 1000   (D) 2000

   (E) 200   (F) 20000   (G) 100   (H) 500

   Answer: (C)

3. Solve the differential equation $y' = y$ subject to the initial condition $y(0) = 0$. From your solution, find the value of $y(e)$.

   (A) e^e (B) e (C) $e^e - 1$ (D) $\ln 2$

   (E) $e^e - e$ (F) 0   (G) e^2 (H) 1

   Answer: (F)

4. Solve the differential equation $y' = y$ subject to the initial condition $y(0) = 1$. From your solution, find the value of $y(e)$.

   (A) e^e (B) e (C) $e^e - 1$ (D) $\ln 2$

   (E) $e^e - e$ (F) 0   (G) e^2 (H) 1

   Answer: (A)

5. A tank contains 100 L of brine with 5 kg of dissolved salt. Pure water enters the tank at a rate of 10 L/min. The solution is kept thoroughly mixed and drains from the tank at the same rate. How much salt is in the tank after 6 minutes?

(A) $5e^6$ kg   (B) $5e^{-6}$ kg   (C) $5e^{-0.6}$ kg   (D) $5e^{0.006}$ kg

(E) $5e^{-0.006}$ kg   (F) $5e^{-0.06}$ kg   (G) $5e^{0.06}$ kg   (H) $5e^{0.6}$ kg

Answer: (C)

6. Find the solution of the initial-value problem $y' = \dfrac{\ln x}{xy}$, $y(1) = 2$.

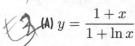

(A) $y = \dfrac{1+x}{1+\ln x}$ (B) $y = \dfrac{8x}{(1+x)^2}$

(C) $y = 2 + 2\ln x$ (D) $y = \sqrt{4 + (\ln x)^2}$

(E) $y = x\ln x + 2x$ (F) $y = x\left(1 + x^2\right)$

(G) $y = x + \sqrt{1 + \ln x}$ (H) $y = \sqrt{x}\,(1 + x)$

Answer: (D)

7. Find the solution of the initial-value problem $\dfrac{dy}{dt} = 2ty^2 + 3y^2$, $y(0) = 1$.

(A) $y = -\dfrac{1}{1 - 3t - t^2}$ (B) $y = \dfrac{1}{1 - 3t + t^2}$

(C) $\dfrac{1}{1 + 3t - t^2}$ (D) $y = \dfrac{1}{1 - 3t - t^2}$

(E) $y = 1 + 3t - t^2$ (F) $y = 1 - 3t - t^2$

(G) $y = 1 - 3t + t^2$ (H) $y = -1 + 3t + t^2$

Answer: (D)

8. Solve the initial-value problem $\dfrac{dy}{dt} = 2ty^2 + 3y^2$, $y(0) = 1$. Then use your solution to evaluate $y(1)$.

(A) -3 (B) 1 (C) $-\frac{1}{3}$ (D) $\frac{1}{3}$

(E) 1 (F) 3 (G) $-\frac{1}{5}$ (H) $\frac{1}{5}$

Answer: (C)

9. Find the solution of the initial-value problem $\dfrac{dy}{dt} = \dfrac{2t}{y^2 + t^2 y^2}$, $y(0) = 3$.

(A) $y = 3\ln\left(1 + t^2\right) + 3C$ (B) $y = \sqrt[3]{3\ln\left(1 + t^2\right) + 3C}$

(C) $y = 3\ln\left(1 + t^2\right) + 9$ (D) $y = \sqrt[3]{3\ln\left(1 + t^2\right) + 9}$

(E) $y = 3\ln\left(1 + t^2\right) + 27$ (F) $y = \sqrt[3]{3\ln\left(1 + t^2\right) + 27}$

(G) $y = 3\ln\left(1 + t^2\right)$ (H) $y = \sqrt[3]{3\ln\left(1 + t^2\right)}$

Answer: (F)

10. Solve the initial-value problem $\dfrac{dy}{dt} = \dfrac{2t}{y^2 + t^2y^2}$, $y(0) = 3$. Then use your solution to evaluate $y\left(\sqrt{e-1}\right)$.

(A) $\sqrt[3]{30}$ (B) $\sqrt[3]{12}$ (C) 30   (D) 1

(E) $\sqrt[3]{3}$ (F) $\sqrt[3]{10}$ (G) 12   (H) 27

Answer: (A)

11. Find the solution of the initial-value problem $\dfrac{dy}{dt} = 3y + 1$, $y(0) = 2$.

(A) $y = \frac{1}{3}\left(7e^t - 1\right)$ (B) $y = \left(7e^t - 5\right)$

(C) $y = \frac{1}{3}\left(e^{3t} - 1\right)$ (D) $y = \left(3e^{3t} - 1\right)$

(E) $y = \frac{1}{3}\left(5e^{3t} + 1\right)$ (F) $y = \left(5e^{3t} + 1\right)$

(G) $y = \frac{1}{3}\left(7e^{3t} - 1\right)$ (H) $y = \left(7e^{3t} - 1\right)$

Answer: (G)

12. Solve the solution of the initial-value problem $\dfrac{dy}{dt} = 3y + 1$, $y(0) = 2$. Then use your solution to evaluate $y(\ln 2)$.

(A) $\frac{3}{13}$ (B) $\frac{3}{55}$ (C) $\frac{7}{3}$ (D) $\frac{41}{3}$

(E) $\frac{13}{3}$ (F) $\frac{55}{3}$ (G) $\frac{3}{7}$ (H) 9

Answer: (F)

13. Find the solution of the initial-value problem $\dfrac{dy}{dt} = \dfrac{y + t^2y}{t^2}$, $y(1) = 2$.

(A) $y = 2e^{t+(1/t)}$ (B) $y = 3e^{t-(1/t)}$ (C) $y = 2e^t$ (D) $y = 2e^{1+(1/t^2)}$

(E) $y = 2e^{1/t}$ (F) $y = ce^{t-(1/t)}$ (G) $y = ce^{t+(1/t)}$ (H) $y = 2e^{t-(1/t)}$

Answer: (H)

14. Solve the initial-value problem $t\dfrac{dy}{dt} = y(y-1)$, $y(2) = 4$.

(A) $y = -\dfrac{8}{8 + 3t}$ (B) $y^2 - y = 6t$

(C) $y = -\dfrac{8}{8 - 3t}$ (D) $y^2 - y = 6t$

(E) $y = \dfrac{8}{8 - 3t}$ (F) $y^2 = 8t$

(G) $y = \dfrac{1}{1 - t}$ (H) $y^2 + y = 6t$

Answer: (E)

15. Consider the differential equation $y' = xy$.

(a) Find the general solution to the differential equation.

(b) Find the equation of the solution passing through the point $(0, 2)$.

Answer: (a) $y = ce^{x^2/2}$ (b) $y = 2e^{x^2/2}$

246

16. Consider the differential equation $\dfrac{dx}{dt} = \dfrac{2tx + x}{t^2 + t}$.

    (a) Find the general solution to the differential equation.

    (b) Find the solution that satisfies the initial condition $x(1) = 2$.

    Answer: (a) $x = c\left(t^2 + t\right)$ (b) $x = t^2 + t$

17. Consider the differential equation $x^2 y' = y^3$.

    (a) Find the general solution to the differential equation.

    (b) Find the solution that satisfies the initial condition $y(1) = 1$.

    Answer: (a) $y = 0$ or $y^2 = \dfrac{x}{2 + cx}$ (b) $y = \sqrt{\dfrac{x}{2 - x}}$

18. Find the solution to the differential equation $xy' = \sqrt{1 - y^2}$, $x > 0$ that satisfies the initial condition $y(1) = 1$.
    Answer: $y = \sin\left(\ln x + \frac{\pi}{2}\right)$

19. Find the solution to the differential equation $\dfrac{dy}{dx} = e^{x-y}$ that satisfies the initial condition $y(0) = 1$.
    Answer: $y = \ln\left(e^x + e - 1\right)$

20. The graph of a direction field for the differential equation $\dfrac{dy}{dx} = 1 - y$ is given below:

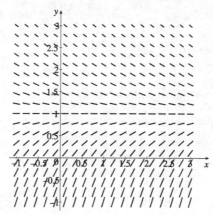

    (a) Sketch a solution curve that satisfies the given condition, but without solving the differential equation:

       (i) $y(0) = 1$ (ii) $y(2) = 1$ (iii) $y(0) = 0$

    (b) Solve the differential equation for each of the conditions in part (a). Compare your answers to the curves you produced in part (a).

    (c) What is the relationship between the curves (i) and (ii) in part (a)? Explain why this occurs.

Answer:

(a)

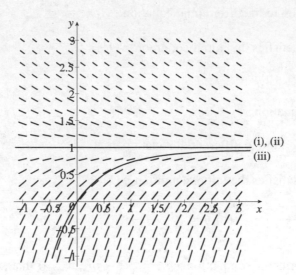

(i) $y(0) = 1$ (ii) $y(2) = 1$ (iii) $y(0) = 0$

(b) $y = 1$; $y = 1$; $y = 1 - e^{-x}$

(c) The solutions to (i) and (ii) are the same.

21. Find the orthogonal trajectories of the family of curves $xy = k$.

Answer: $xy = k \Rightarrow x\dfrac{dy}{dx} + y = 0 \Rightarrow \dfrac{dy}{dx} = -\dfrac{y}{x} \Rightarrow$ slope field for orthogonal trajectories is

$\dfrac{dy}{dx} = \dfrac{x}{y} \Rightarrow$ solve the equation $y\,dy = x\,dx \Rightarrow y^2 - x^2 = c$.

22. Find the orthogonal trajectories of the family of curves $x^2 + y^2 = k$.

Answer: $x^2 + y^2 = k \Rightarrow 2x + 2y\dfrac{dy}{dx} = 0 \Rightarrow \dfrac{dy}{dx} = -\dfrac{x}{y} \Rightarrow$ slope field for orthogonal trajectories

is $\dfrac{dy}{dx} = \dfrac{y}{x} \Rightarrow$ solve the equation $\dfrac{1}{y}\,dy = \dfrac{1}{x}\,dx \Rightarrow y = kx$.

23. In the presence of air resistance for an object in free fall, the velocity is the solution of the differential

equation $\dfrac{dv}{dt} = g - kv$ where g is the constant of acceleration due to earth's gravity and k is a positive constant.

(a) Find the solution for the equation that satisfies the initial value that $v(0) = 0$.

(b) As time, t, increases without bound, what is the limiting velocity. (Note: the limiting velocity during free fall is called the terminal velocity.)

(c) Sketch your solution from part (a).

Answer:

(a) $\dfrac{dv}{dt} = g - kv \Longrightarrow \dfrac{dv}{g - kv} = dt \Longrightarrow$

$v(t) = \dfrac{g}{k}\left(1 - e^{-kt}\right)$

(b) $\lim\limits_{t \to \infty} v(t) = \dfrac{g}{k}$

(c)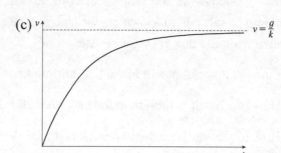

24. In a model of epidemics, let $y(t)$, in thousands, be the number of infected individuals in the population at time t, in days. If we assume that the infection spreads to all those who are susceptible, one possible solution for $y(t)$ is given by $\dfrac{dy}{dt} = k(P - y) \cdot y$ where k is a positive constant which measures the rate of infection and P, in thousands, is the total population in this situation.

   (a) Determine the solution of this differential equation if $y(0) = 1$.

   (b) Discuss what $y(0) = 1$ means.

   (c) As the time increases without bound, what happens to y? (That is, what does $\lim\limits_{t \to \infty} y$ mean?)

   (d) Sketch the solution of the differential equation in part (a).

Answer:

(a) $y(t) = \dfrac{P}{1 + (P - 1)\,e^{-P \cdot kt}}$

(b) At initial time there were 1000 infected individuals.

(c) $\lim\limits_{t \to \infty} y(t) = P$, which is the total population in this situation.

(d)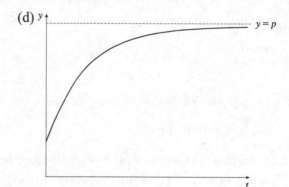

25. A model of the seasonal changes in daylight hours x is given by $\dfrac{dx}{dt} = kx \cos(wt)$, where k and w are constants.

   (a) Determine the general solution for this differential equation.

   (b) Discuss the practical meaning of the solution of this equation.

Answer:

(a) 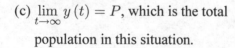 $x(t) = ce^{(k/w)\sin(wt)}$

(b) The solutions are periodic functions which model seasonal change in daylight hours.

26. A tank is filled with 200 gallons of brine in which is dissolved 5 pounds of salt. Brine containing 0.1 pound of salt per gallon enters the tank at a rate of 2 gallons per minute, and the well-stirred mixture is drawn from the talk at the same rate.

   (a) Find the amount of salt in the tank at time t.

   (b) How much salt is present in the tank after 20 minutes?

   (c) How much salt is present after a long time? What is the concentration then?

   Answer:

   (a) $\dfrac{ds}{dt} = 0.2 - \dfrac{s}{200}$ $\Rightarrow$ $s(t) = 40 - 35e^{-(1/200)t}$

   (b) $s(20) = 40 - 35e^{-0.1} \approx 8.33$ lb

   (c) 40 lb; 20%

27. A tank contains 10 gallons of water and 4 pounds of a chemical, Z, per gallon. To decrease the concentration of Z, pure water is added to the container at a rate of 2 gallons per minute, and the well stirred mixture is drawn from the tank at the same rate.

   (a) Find the amount of chemical Z in the tank at time t.

   (b) How much chemical Z is present after 10 minutes?

   (c) How long does it take for the concentration of chemical Z to be reduced to 0.1 pound per gallon?

   Answer:

   (a) $\dfrac{dZ}{dt} = -\dfrac{Z}{5}$ $\Rightarrow$ $Z(t) = 4e^{-(1/5)t}$

   (b) $Z(20) = 4e^{-4} \approx 0.073$ lb

   (c) $t = 5\ln 4 \approx 6.93$ min

28. A tank contains 500 liters of brine with 10 kg of dissolved salt. Pure water enters the tank at a rate of 10 liters per minute. The solution is kept thoroughly mixed and drains from the tank at the same rate. How much salt is in the tank

   (a) after t minutes?

   (b) after 10 minutes?

   Answer: (a) $\dfrac{ds}{dt} = -\dfrac{s}{50}$ $\Rightarrow$ $s(t) = 10e^{-(1/50)t}$ (b) $s(10) = 10e^{-1/5} \approx 8.19$ kg

29. A tank contains 500 liters of brine with 10 kg of dissolved salt. Pure water enters the tank at a rate of 10 liters per minute. The well-mixed solution drains from the tank 8 liters per minute. Determine the differential equation that the amount of salt in the tank at time t must satisfy.

   Answer: $\dfrac{dy}{dt} = -\dfrac{8y}{500 + 2t}$ with initial condition $y(0) = 10$

30. A tank contains 1000 liters of pure water. Brine that contains 0.05 kg of salt per liter of water enters the tank at a rate of 8 liters per minute. Brine that contains 0.04 kg of salt per liter of water enters the tank at a rate of 5 liters per minute. The well-mixed solution drains from the tank at a rate of 13 liters per minute. How much salt is in the tank after

(a) t minutes?

(b) half an hour?

(c) a very long time?

Answer:

(a) $\dfrac{ds}{dt} = 0.6 - \dfrac{13s}{1000} \quad \Rightarrow \quad s(t) = \dfrac{600}{13}\left(1 - e^{-3/1000\,t}\right)$

(b) $s(30) = \dfrac{600}{13}\left(1 - e^{-9/100}\right) \approx 3.97 \text{ kg}$

(c) $\dfrac{600}{13} \text{ kg}$

31. The discharge value on a 1000 liter tank that is filled with water is opened at time $t = 0$ and the water flows out at a rate of 10 liters per second. At the same time a 1% chlorine mixture enters the tank at a rate of 6 liters per second. Assuming that the solution is well-mixed throughout the tank, what is the concentration of chlorine when the tank is half full?

Answer: $\dfrac{dc}{dt} = \dfrac{3}{50} - \dfrac{10c}{1000 - 4t}, \; c(t) = \dfrac{1}{50}\left[500 - 2t - \dfrac{(500 - 2t)^{5/2}}{500^{3/2}}\right], \; c(125) \approx 3.23$

32. Newton's Law of Cooling states that the rate at which a body changes temperature is proportional to the difference between its temperature and the temperature of the surrounding medium. Suppose that a body has an initial temperature of 250 °F and that after one hour the temperature is 200 °F. Assuming that the surrounding air is kept at a constant temperature of 72 °F, determine the temperature of the body at time t.

Answer: $\dfrac{dT}{dt} = k(T - 72), \, T(0) = 250\,°\text{F}, \, T(1) = 200\,°\text{F} \quad \Rightarrow \quad T(t) = 72 + 178\left(\dfrac{128}{178}\right)^t$

33. According to Newton's Law of Cooling, the temperature T of a warm object decreases at a rate proportional to the difference between T and the temperature T_0 of its surroundings.

(a) Write down this law as a differential equation.

(b) Assume the room temperature is 70 °F. If it takes 2 minutes for a cup of hot coffee to cool down to 180 °F, find how long it takes to cool a cup of coffee from 200 °F to 100 °F.

Answer:

(a) $\dfrac{dT}{dt} = k(T_0 - T) \quad k > 0$

(b) $\dfrac{dT}{dt} = k(70° - T(t)) \quad T(0) = 200\,°\text{F}, \, T(t) = 70 + 130\left(\tfrac{11}{13}\right)^{t/2} \quad t \approx 17.56 \text{ minutes}$

34. According to Newton's Law of Heating, the temperature T of a cold object increases at a rate proportional to the difference between T and the temperature T_0 of its surroundings.

   (a) Write down this law as a differential equation.

   (b) Assume the room temperature is 70 °F. If it takes 10 minutes for a can of soda to warm up from 30 °F to 35 °F, find how long it takes to warm up a can of soda from 30 °F to 40 °F.

Answer:

(a) $\dfrac{dT}{dt} = k\left(T_0 - T\right) \quad k > 0$

(b) $\dfrac{dT}{dt} = k\left(70° - T\left(t\right)\right) \quad T\left(0\right) = 30\ °F, \ T\left(t\right) = 70 - 40\left(\frac{7}{8}\right)^{t/10} \quad t \approx 21.5$ minutes

---

7.4 Exponential Growth and Decay

1. The radioactive isotope Bismuth-210 has a half-life of 5 days. How many days does it take for 87.5% of a given amount to decay?

   (A) 15 days   (B) 8 days   (C) 10 days   (D) 13 days

   (E) 11 days   (F) 9 days   (G) 12 days   (H) 14 days

   Answer: (A)

2. A bacteria culture starts with 200 bacteria and triples in size every half hour. After 2 hours, how many bacteria are there?

   (A) 17,800   (B) 16,200   (C) 23,500   (D) 24,000

   (E) 19,300   (F) 14,800   (G) 15,700   (H) 21,000

   Answer: (B)

3. A bacteria culture starts with 200 bacteria and in 1 hour contains 400 bacteria. How many hours does it take to reach 2000 bacteria?

   (A) $\ln 400$ (B) $\ln 10$ (C) 10   (D) $\ln 1600$

   (E) $\ln 2000$ (F) $\ln 200$ (G) 5   (H) $\dfrac{\ln 10}{\ln 2}$

   Answer: (H)

4. When a child was born, her grandparents placed \$1000 in a savings account at 10% interest compounded continuously, to be withdrawn at age 20 to help pay for college. How much money is in the account at the time of withdrawal?

   (A) $1000e$ (B) $500e$ (C) $500e^2$ (D) $2000e^2$

   (E) $4000e$ (F) $2000e$ (G) $1000e^2$ (H) $4000e^2$

   Answer: (G)

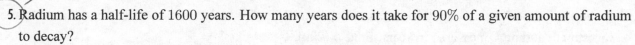

$Ex\ \mathcal{B}$

5. Radium has a half-life of 1600 years. How many years does it take for 90% of a given amount of radium to decay?

(A) $\dfrac{1600}{\ln 5}$ (B) $1600 \ln 2$ (C) $\dfrac{1600 \ln 10}{\ln 2}$ (D) $1600 \ln 5$

(E) $1600 \ln 10$ (F) $\dfrac{1600}{\ln 2}$ (G) $1500 \ln 6$ (H) $\dfrac{1600 \ln 2}{\ln 10}$

Answer: (C)

6. Carbon 14, with a half-life of 5700 years, is used to estimate the age of organic materials. What fraction of the original amount of carbon 14 would an object have if it were 2000 years old?

(A) $e^{-(57/20)\ln 2}$ (B) $\frac{57}{20}\ln 2$ (C) $e^{-(20/57)\ln 2}$ (D) $\frac{20}{57}\ln 2$

(E) $e^{(57/20)\ln 2}$ (F) $\frac{1}{57}\ln 20$ (G) $e^{(20/57)\ln 2}$ (H) $\frac{1}{20}\ln 57$

Answer: (C)

7. An object cools at a rate (measured in °C/min) equal to k times the difference between its temperature and that of the surrounding air. Suppose the object takes 10 minutes to cool from 60 °C to 40 °C in a room kept at 20 °C. Find the value of k.

(A) e^{-20} (B) $\ln 2$ (C) $10e^{-20}$ (D) $40 \ln 10$

(E) $\frac{1}{2}$ (F) $e^{-1/20}$ (G) $\frac{1}{10}\ln\frac{1}{2}$ (H) $60 \ln\frac{1}{2}$

Answer: (G)

8. A bacteria population grows at a rate proportional to its size. The initial count was 400 and 1600 after 1 hour. In how many minutes does the population double?

(A) 20   (B) 25   (C) 30   (D) 35

(E) 40   (F) 45   (G) 50   (H) 55

Answer: (C)

9. An object cools at a rate (in ° C/min) equal to $\frac{1}{10}$ of the difference between its temperature and that of the surrounding air. If a room is kept at 20° C and the temperature of the object is 28° C, what is the temperature of the object 5 minutes later?

(A) 22   (B) 24   (C) $20 + 5e^{-1/10}$ (D) $20 + 8e^{-1/2}$

(E) $20 + 5e^{-4/5}$ (F) $20 + 8e^{-1/10}$ (G) $28 - 8e^{-1/10}$ (H) $28 - 10e^{-1/2}$

Answer: (D)

10. A thermometer is taken outside from a room where the temperature is 72° F. Outdoors, the temperature is 48° F. After one minute, the thermometer reads 55° F. After how many minutes does the thermometer read 50° F?

(A) 2.107   (B) 1.107   (C) 3.100   (D) 1.503

(E) 2.017   (F) 1.017   (G) 3.010   (H) 1.013

Answer: (E)

11. 1 cent is invested at 6% annual interest, compounded continuously. Let $A(t)$ be the amount of the investment at time t, measured in years. Find $A(200)$.

(A) \$1627.55   (B) \$16.28   (C) \$160   (D) \$140

(E) \$162.76   (F) \$162,755   (G) \$150   (H) \$130

Answer: (A)

12. The growth of a population is modeled by the differential equation $\dfrac{dP}{dt} = 0.2P^{1.01}$, and the initial population is $P(0) = 2$. Find $P(50)$.

(A) 37   (B) 90   (C) 44,053   (D) 81,350

(E) 30   (F) 80   (G) 90,000   (H) 37,648

Answer: (D)

13. In an experiment, a tissue culture has been subjected to ionizing radiation. It was found that the number A of undamaged cells depends on the exposure time, in hours, according to the formula $A = A_0 e^{kt}$, $t \geq 0$. If 5000 cells were present initially and 3000 survived a 2-hour exposure, find the elapsed time of exposure after which only half the original cells survive.

Answer: 2.71 hours

14. A lettuce leaf collected from the salad bar at the college cafeteria contains $\frac{99}{100}$ as much carbon-14 as a freshly cut lettuce leaf. How old is it? (Use 5700 years for the half-life of ^{14}C.)

Answer: About 83 years old

15. Assume that the rate of growth of a population of fruit flies is proportional to the size of the population at each instant of time. If 100 fruit flies are present initially and 200 are present after 5 days, how many will be present after 10 days?

Answer: 400

16. Assume the half-life of carbon 14 is 5700 years. A wooden statue is measured with 70% of the carbon-14. How old is the statue?

Answer: About 2933 years old

17. It takes money 20 years to triple at a certain rate of interest. How long does it take for money to double at this rate?

Answer: 12.62 years

18. In 1970, the Brown County groundhog population was 100. By 1980, there were 900 groundhogs in Brown County. If the rate of population growth of these animals is proportional to the population size, how many groundhogs might one expect to see in 1995?

Answer: 24,300

19. In a certain medical treatment, a tracer dye is injected into a human organ to measure its function rate and the rate of change of the amount of dye is proportional to the amount present at any time. If a physician injects 0.5 g of dye and 30 minutes later 0.1 g remains, how much dye will be present in $1\frac{1}{2}$ hours?

Answer: 0.004 g

20. In an idealized experiment, the following results were obtained for a population of bacteria during a 7 hour period. The initial population is 1000 bacteria.

Time (hours)	0.5	1.0	1.5	2.0	2.5	3.0	3.5
Number of Bacteria	10^3	10^3	3.2×10^3	10^4	3.2×10^4	10^5	3.2×10^5

Time (hours)	4.0	4.5	5.0	5.5	6.0	6.5	7.0
Number of Bacteria	10^6	3.2×10^6	10^7	3.2×10^7	10^8	3.2×10^8	10^9

(a) Identify the period where there is no change in the number of bacteria. (This is called the period of adaptation.)

(b) Identify the period of growth.

(c) Assume that the growth rate of bacteria is proportional to the population. Find an exponential model for the data during the period of growth.

(d) Add an additional line to the table using your population model to generate the entries for the given time values. Compare these entries with the given data and explain any discrepancy.

Answer:

(a) $0 \leq t \leq 1$

(b) $1 < t \leq 7$

(c) $P(t) = 0.1 \cdot 10^{t+3}$ (Answer may vary.)

(d)

Time (hours)	Number of Bacteria	Population (from model)
0.5	1000	1000
1.0	1000	1000
1.5	3200	3162
2.0	10,000	10,000
2.5	32,000	31,623
3.0	100,000	100,000
3.5	320,000	316,228
4.0	1,000,000	1,000,000
4.5	3,200,000	3,162,000
5.0	10,000,000	10,000,000
5.5	32,000,000	31,623,000
6.0	100,000,000	100,000,000
6.5	320,000,000	316,228,000
7.0	1,000,000,000	1,000,000,000

21. The following data approximate the results obtained by subjecting Hela-S cells to 250 kvp x-rays:

Dose (rads)	0	100	150	200	250	300	400	450	500	550	600
Fraction Surviving	1	0.5	0.4	0.3	0.17	0.13	0.03	0.02	0.01	0.006	0.005

Assume that these data fit an exponential model.

(a) Find the appropriate exponential model.

(b) Add another line to the table using your population model for the given doses of radiation.

(c) Compare the model entries to the given data and explain any discrepancy.

Answer:

(a) $1.515912177 \cdot 0.9904346579^x$

(b)

Dose (rads)	0	100	150	200	250	300	400	450	500	550	600
Fraction Surviving (actual)	1	0.5	0.4	0.3	0.17	0.13	0.03	0.02	0.01	0.006	0.005
Fraction Surviving (model)	1.52	0.58	0.36	0.22	0.137	0.085	0.032	0.02	0.0124	0.0077	0.0047

(c) Answers may vary. The model does not fit well at $x = 0$, but fits better for larger doses.

22. $2000 is invested at 3% annual interest. Find the value at the end of 10 years if

(a) the interest compounds annually.

(b) the interest compounds continuously.

Answer: (a) About $2687.83   (b) About $2699.72

23. $2000 is invested at 5% annual interest. Find the value at the end of 18 years if

(a) the interest compounds monthly.

(b) the interest compounds continuously.

Answer: (a) About $4910.02   (b) About $4919.21

7.5 The Logistic Equation

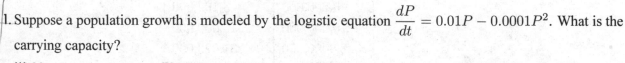

1. Suppose a population growth is modeled by the logistic equation $\dfrac{dP}{dt} = 0.01P - 0.0001P^2$. What is the carrying capacity?

(A) 90   (B) 10   (C) 50   (D) 1000

(E) 100   (F) 60   (G) 20   (H) 10,000

Answer: (E)

2. Suppose a population growth is modeled by the logistic equation $\dfrac{dP}{dt} = 0.0001P(100 - P)$. What is the relative growth rate?

(A) 0.0001   (B) −0.01   (C) 0.001   (D) 0.01

(E) 0.0002   (F) −0.02   (G) 0.002   (H) 0.02

Answer: (D)

3. Suppose a population growth is modeled by the logistic differential equation with the carrying capacity 2000 and the relative growth rate $k = 0.06$ per year. If the initial population is $P(0) = 500$, find $P(10)$.

(A) 309   (B) 756   (C) 310   (D) 757

(E) 308   (F) 755   (G) 307   (H) 800

Answer: (B)

4. Suppose a population growth is modeled by the logistic equation $\dfrac{dP}{dt} = 0.01P - 0.0002P^2$. Solve this differential equation with the initial condition $P(0) = 20$.

Answer: $P(t) = \dfrac{50}{1 + 1.5e^{-0.01t}}$

5. Suppose that a population of bacteria grows according to the logistic equation $\dfrac{dP}{dt} = 0.01P - 0.0002P^2$, where P is the population measured in thousands and t is time measured in days.

(a) What is the carrying capacity? What is the value of k?

(b) A direction field for this equation is given below. Where are the slopes close to 0? Where are the slope values the largest? Where are the solutions increasing? Where are the solutions decreasing?

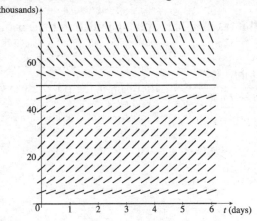

(c) Use the direction field to sketch solutions for initial populations of 10, 30, 50, and 70. What do these solutions have in common? How do they differ? Which solutions have inflection points? At what population levels do they occur?

(d) What are the equilibrium solutions? How are the other solutions related to these solutions?

Answer:

(a) 50 thousand; $k = 0.01$

(b) Near $P = 0$ or $P = 50$ thousand, the slopes are close to 0. At $P = 25$ thousand, the slope value is the largest. The solutions are increasing for $0 < P < 50$. The solutions are decreasing for $P > 50$.

(c) The solution curves that start below $P = 50$ are increasing and those that start above $P = 50$ are decreasing. The solution curves that start below $P = 25$ have an inflection point when $P = 25$.

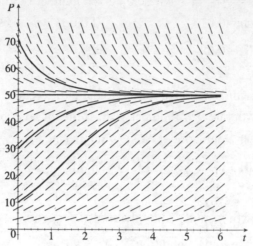

(d) $P = 0$ and $P = 50$. The solutions move away from $P = 0$ and move towards $P = 50$.

6. A rumor tends to spread according to the logistic differential equation $\dfrac{dy}{dt} = 0.3y - 0.0001y^2$, where y is the number of people in the community who have heard the rumor and t is the time in days.

(a) Describe the population for this sociological study.

(b) Assume that there were 10 people who knew the rumor at initial time $t = 0$. Find the solution for the differential equation.

(c) How many days will it take for half of the population to hear the rumor?

Answer:

(a) $P(t) = \dfrac{3000}{1 + \left(\dfrac{3000 - P_0}{P_0}\right)e^{-0.3t}}$ where P_0 is the population who heard the rumor when $t = 0$.

(b) $P(t) = \dfrac{3000}{1 + 299e^{-0.3t}}$

(c) $\dfrac{10\ln 299}{3} \approx 19$ days

7. In a model of epidemics, the number of infected individuals in a population at a time is a solution of the logistic differential equation $\dfrac{dy}{dt} = 0.6y - 0.0002y^2$, where y is the number of infected individuals in the community and t is the time in days.

(a) Describe the population for this situation.

(b) Assume that 10 people were infected at the initial time $t = 0$. Find the solution for the differential equation.

(c) How many days will it take for half of the population to be infected?

Answer:

(a) $P(t) = \dfrac{3000}{1 + \left(\dfrac{3000 - P_0}{P_0}\right) e^{-0.6t}}$ where P_0 is the number of infected population when $t = 0$.

(b) $P(t) = \dfrac{3000}{1 + 299e^{-0.6t}}$

(c) $\dfrac{10 \ln 299}{6} \approx 9.5$ days

8. The following table contains population data for a Minnesota county for the decades from 1900 to 1980:

Year	Clay County Population	Population Estimate (Exponential Model)	Population Estimate (Logistic Model)
1900	17,942		
1910	19,640		
1920	21,780		
1930	23,120		
1940	25,337		
1950	30,363		
1960	39,080		
1970	46,585		
1980	49,327		

(a) Produce a scatter plot for the data.

(b) Find an exponential model using the data from 1900 through 1950.

(c) Find a logistic model using the data from 1900 through 1950. (Assume the carrying capacity is 440,000.)

(d) Use your models to estimate the population for 1960, 1970, and 1980. Enter your data in the table provided above.

Answer:

(a)

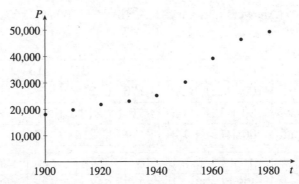

(b) $P = ab^t$, where $a = 17{,}729.92014$ and $b = 1.009918005$ (Answers may vary.)

(c) $P = \dfrac{440000}{1 + \frac{422{,}058}{17{,}942}\left(\frac{19{,}640}{17{,}942}\right)^{-x/10}}$, where x is the year since 1900. (Answers may vary.)

(d)

Year	Clay County Population	Population Estimate (Exponential Model)	Population Estimate (Logistic Model)
1900	17,942	17,730	17,942
1910	19,640	19,569	19,564
1920	21,780	21,599	21,326
1930	23,120	23,839	23,238
1940	25,337	26,312	25,311
1950	30,363	29,041	27,556
1960	39,080	32,053	29,986
1970	46,585	35,378	32,614
1980	49,327	39,048	35,451

Note: Answers for (b) and (c) may vary. None of the models is a good fit in this situation. The aim for the problem is to practice the procedure of using data to fit the exponential and logistic models.

9. An outbreak of a previously unknown influenza occurred on the campus of the University of Northern South Dakota at Roscoe during the first semester. Due to the contagious nature of the disease, the campus was quarantined and the disease was allowed to run its course. The table below shows the total number P of infected students for the first four weeks of the outbreak on this campus of 2,500 students.

t (days)	0	2	4	6	8	10	12	14	16	18	20	22	24	26	28
P	100	121	146	176	212	254	304	361	428	503	589	683	787	899	1017
Logistic															
Exponential															

(a) Find a logistic model for the data. Complete the table with predicted values using this model.

(b) Find an exponential model for these data. Complete the table with predicted values using this model.

(c) Compare your findings in parts (a) and (b) above. For what values would you consider both models to be a good fit for the data? Which model provides the best fit for the data? Justify your choice.

Answer:

(a) $P = \dfrac{2500}{1 + 24e^{-0.1t}}$ (Answers may vary.)   (b) $P = 100 \cdot 1.1^x$ (Answers may vary.)

(c)

t (days)	0	2	4	6	8	10	12	14
P	100	121	146	176	212	254	304	361
Logistic	100	121	146	176.4	212.1	254.3	303.8	361.3
Exponential	100	121	146	177	214	259	314	380

t (days)	16	18	20	22	24	26	28
P	428	503	589	683	787	899	1017
Logistic	427.6	503.3	588.5	683.2	786.8	898.4	1016.5
Exponential	459	556	673	814	985	1192	1442

Both models fit well for $0 \le t \le 10$. For $t > 10$, the logistic model fits better.

10. Suppose that a certain population grows according to an exponential model.

    (a) Write the differential equation for this situation with a relative growth rate of $k = 0.01$. Produce a solution for the initial condition $t = 0$ (in hours) and population $P = 1$ (in thousands).

    (b) Find the population when $t = 10$ hours, $t = 100$ hours, and $t = 1000$ hours.

    (c) After how many hours does the population reach 2 thousand? 30 thousand? 55 thousand?

    (d) As the time t increases without bound, what happens to the population?

    (e) Sketch the graph of the solution of the differential equation.

    Answer:

    (a) $\dfrac{dP}{dt} = 0.01P$ and $P(t) = e^{0.01t}$

    (b) $P(10) \approx 1.105$ thousand, $P(100) \approx 2.718$ thousand, $P(1000) \approx 22{,}026.466$ thousand

    (c) The population will reach 2 thousand in about 69.3 hours. The population will reach 30 thousand in about 340.12 hours. The population will reach 55 thousand in about 400.74 hours.

    (d) As $t \to \infty$, $P(t) \to \infty$

    (e)

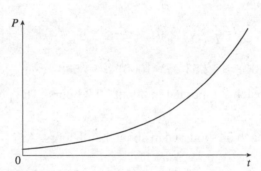

11. Suppose that a population grows according to a logistic model.

    (a) Write the differential equation for this situation with $k = 0.01$ and carrying capacity of 60 thousand.

    (b) Solve the differential equation in part (a) with the initial condition $t = 0$ (hours) and population $P = 1$ thousand.

    (c) Find the population for $t = 10$ hours, $t = 100$ hours, and $t = 1000$ hours.

    (d) After how many hours does the population reach 2 thousand? 30 thousand? 55 thousand?

    (e) As the time t increases without bound, what happens to the population?

    (f) Sketch the graph of the solution of the differential equation.

    Answer:

    (a) $\dfrac{dP}{dt} = 0.01P\left(1 - \dfrac{P}{60}\right)$

    (b) $P(t) = \dfrac{60}{1 + 59e^{-0.01t}}$

    (c) $P(10) \approx 1.103$, $P(100) \approx 2.643$, $P(1000) \approx 59.840$

    (d) The population will reach 2 thousand in about 71.03 hours. The population will reach 30 thousand in about 407.75 hours. The population will reach 55 thousand in about 647.55 hours.

(e) As $t \to \infty$, $P(t) \to 60$ thousand

(f)

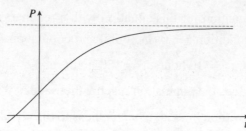

12. Suppose that a population, P, grows at a rate given by the equation $dP/dt = bPe^{-kt}$, where P is the population (in thousands) at time t (in hours), and b and k are positive constants.

(a) Find the solution to the differential equation when $b = 0.04$, $k = 0.01$ and $P(0) = 1$.

(b) Find $P(10)$, $P(100)$, and $P(1000)$.

(c) After how many hours does the population reach 2 thousand? 30 thousand? 54 thousand?

(d) As time t increases without bound, what happens to the population?

(e) Sketch the graph of the solution of the differential equation.

Answer:

(a) $\dfrac{dP}{dt} = 0.04Pe^{-0.01t}$ $\Rightarrow$ $P(t) = e^{4(1-e^{-0.01t})}$

(b) $P(10) \approx 1.463$, $P(100) \approx 12.534$, $P(1000) \approx 54.588$

(c) The population will reach 2 thousand in about 19.3 hours. The population will reach 30 thousand in about 190 hours.

The population will reach 54 thousand in about 590.3 hours. As $t \to \infty$, $P(t) \to e^4 \approx 54.59815$ (thousand)

(e)

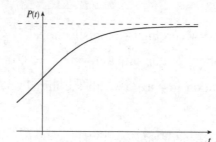

13. Assume that a population grows at a rate summarized by the equation $\dfrac{dP}{dt} = \dfrac{bkPe^{-kt}}{1 - be^{-kt}}$, where b and k are positive constants ($b > 1$), and P is the population at time t. Show that $P = \dfrac{P_0}{1-b}\left(1 - be^{-kt}\right)$ is the general solution for the differential equation (where P_0 is the initial population). [*Note:* This is known as the monomolecular growth curve.]

Answer: Either solve the equation or substitute $P(t)$ into the equation to verify. *Note:* When $t = \dfrac{\ln b}{k}$ then $P = 0$ for this model.

14. (a) Solve the differential equation $\dfrac{dP}{dt} = \dfrac{bkPe^{-kt}}{1 - be^{-kt}}$, with $b = 2$ and $k = 0.1$, and $P_0 = 1$.

(b) Sketch a graph of the solution you produced for part (a) and discuss the major characteristics of this monomolecular growth curve.

Answer:

(a) $P(t) = \dfrac{1}{1-2}\left(1 - 2e^{-0.1t}\right) = 2e^{-0.1t} - 1$

(b)

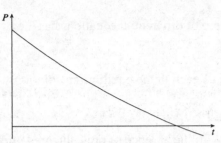

$P(t)$ is a decreasing function and when $t = 10\ln 2$, $P = 0$.

7.6 Predator-Prey Systems

1. Suppose that we model populations of aphids and ladybugs with the system of differential equations:

$$\frac{dA}{dt} = 3A - 0.01AL$$

$$\frac{dL}{dt} = -0.5L + 0.0001AL$$

Find the equilibrium solution.

(A) $A = 5000$, $L = 300$ (B) $A = 100$, $L = 6$

(C) $A = 30{,}000$, $L = 50$ (D) $A = 60$, $L = 100$

(E) $A = 300$, $L = 5000$ (F) $A = 6$, $L = 100$

(G) $A = 50$, $L = 30{,}000$ (H) $A = 100$, $L = 60$

Answer: (A)

2. Suppose that we model populations of predators and preys (in millions) with the system of differential equations

$$\frac{dx}{dt} = 2x - 1.2xy$$

$$\frac{dy}{dt} = -y + 0.9xy$$

Find the equilibrium solution.

(A) $x = \frac{10}{9}$, $y = \frac{3}{5}$ (B) $x = \frac{9}{10}$, $y = \frac{3}{5}$

(C) $x = \frac{5}{9}$, $y = \frac{3}{10}$ (D) $x = \frac{5}{3}$, $y = \frac{10}{9}$

(E) $x = \frac{10}{9}$, $y = \frac{5}{3}$ (F) $x = \frac{10}{3}$, $y = \frac{9}{5}$

(G) $x = \frac{3}{9}$, $y = \frac{3}{5}$ (H) $x = \frac{3}{5}$, $y = \frac{10}{9}$

Answer: (E)

3. A predator-prey system is modeled by the system of differential equations $dx/dt = ax - bxy$, $dy/dt = -cy + dxy$, where a, b, c, and d are positive constants.

(a) Which variable, x or y, represents the predator? Defend your choice.

(b) Show that the given system of differential equations has the two equilibrium solutions $\{x = 0, y = 0\}$ and $\{x = c/d, y = a/b\}$.

(c) Explain the significance of each of the equilibrium solutions.

Answer:

(a) y represents the predator. In the absence of prey, the predators will die out.

(b) Solve $\begin{cases} ax - bxy = 0 \\ -cy + dxy = 0 \end{cases}$ to get these solutions.

(c) $x = 0$ and $y = 0$ implies that there is neither predator nor prey. The population of both predator and prey are not changing if $x = \dfrac{c}{d}$ and $y = \dfrac{a}{b}$.

4. Consider the predator-prey system $dx/dt = 2x - xy$, $dy/dt = -4y + xy$, where x and y are in millions of creatures and t represents time in years.

(a) Find equilibrium solutions for this system.

(b) Explain why it is reasonable to approximate this predator-prey system as $dx/dt \approx 2x$, $dy/dt \approx -4y$, if the initial conditions are $x(0) = 0.001$ and $y(0) = 0.002$.

(c) Describe what this approximate system tells about the rate of change of each of the specie populations $x(t)$ and $y(t)$ near $(0, 0)$.

(d) Find the solution for the approximate system given in part (b).

(e) Sketch $x(t)$ and $y(t)$ as determined in part (d) on the same coordinate plane.

(f) Sketch a phase trajectory through $(0.001, 0.002)$ for the predator-prey system. Describe in words what happens to each population of species and the interaction between them.

Answer:

(a) $\begin{cases} x = 0 \\ y = 0 \end{cases}$ or $\begin{cases} x = 4 \\ y = 2 \end{cases}$

(b) Near $t = 0$, $xy \approx 0.001 \cdot 0.002 = 2 \times 10^{-6}$

(c) Near $t = 0$, the prey population increases exponentially, and the predator population decreases exponentially.

(d) $x(t) = 0.001e^{2t}$ $y(t) = 0.002e^{-4t}$

(e)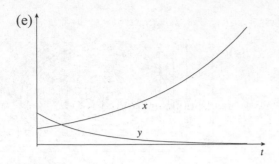

(f)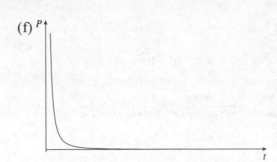

As the population of predator decreases,

the population of prey increases.

5. Consider the following predator-prey system where x and y are in millions of creatures and t represents time in years:

$$\frac{dx}{dt} = 2x - xy$$

$$\frac{dy}{dt} = -4y + xy$$

(a) Show that $(4, 2)$ is the nonzero equilibrium solution.

(b) Find an expression for $\frac{dy}{dx}$.

(c) The direction field for the differential equation is given below:

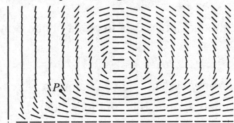

   (i) Locate $(4, 2)$ on the graph.

   (ii) Sketch a rough phase trajectory through P indicated in the graph.

(d) With the aid of the phase trajectory, answer the following questions:

   (i) For the region $0 < x < 4$ and $0 < y < 2$, is $x(t)$ increasing or decreasing? Is $y(t)$ increasing or decreasing? Describe in words how the two species interact with one another.

   (ii) For the region $x > 4$ and $0 < y < 2$, is $x(t)$ increasing or decreasing? Is $y(t)$ increasing or decreasing? Describe in words how the two species interact with one another.

   (iii) For the region $x > 4$ and $y > 2$, is $x(t)$ increasing or decreasing? Is $y(t)$ increasing or decreasing? Describe in words how the two species interact with one another.

   (iv) For the region $0 < x < 4$ and $y > 2$, is $x(t)$ increasing or decreasing? Is $y(t)$ increasing or decreasing? Describe in words how the two species interact with one another.

(e) Suggest a pair of species which might interact in the manner described by this system.

Answer:

(a) Solve the system of equations $\begin{cases} 2x - xy = 0 \\ -4y + xy = 0 \end{cases}$

(b) $\dfrac{dy}{dx} = \dfrac{-4y + xy}{2x - xy}$

(c)

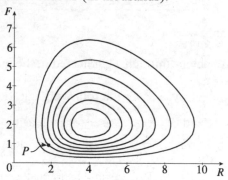

(d) (i) $\dfrac{dx}{dt} > 0$ and $\dfrac{dy}{dt} < 0$

In this region the number of predator decreases because of the lack of prey, whereas the prey population can increase due to lack of predators.

(ii) $\dfrac{dx}{dt} > 0$ and $\dfrac{dy}{dt} > 0$

In this region the prey population has increased so much that the predator population can also increase.

(iii) $\dfrac{dx}{dt} < 0$ and $\dfrac{dy}{dt} > 0$

In this region the predator population has increased so much that the prey population is in decline.

(iv) $\dfrac{dx}{dt} < 0$ and $\dfrac{dy}{dt} < 0$

In this region, due to the lack of prey, both predator and prey are in decline.

(e) Wolves and rabbits

6. A phase portrait of a predator-prey system is given below in which F represents the population of foxes (in thousands) and R the population of rabbits (in thousands).

(a) Referring to the graph, what is a reasonable non-zero equilibrium solution for the system?

(b) Write down a possible system of differential equations which could have been used to produce the given graph.

(c) Describe how each population changes as time passes, using the initial condition P indicated on the graph.

(d) Use your description in part (c) to make a rough sketch of the graph of R and F as functions of time.

Answer:

(a) $(4, 2)$

(b) $\begin{cases} \dfrac{dx}{dt} = 2x - xy \\[2mm] \dfrac{dy}{dt} = -4y + xy \end{cases}$ (Answers may vary.)

(c) Initially, the numbers of both species increase. At a certain point, the rabbit population begins a steep decline, followed closely by the fox population. Then the rabbit population begins to increase, again followed by the fox population, and the cycle begins anew.

(d)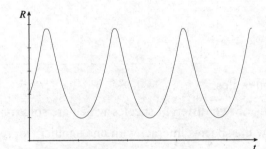

7. The population of two species is modeled by the system of equations $\begin{cases} \dfrac{dx}{dt} = 2x - xy \\[2mm] \dfrac{dy}{dt} = -4y + xy \end{cases}$

(a) Find an expression for $\dfrac{dy}{dx}$.

(b) A possible direction field for the differential equation in part (a) is given below:

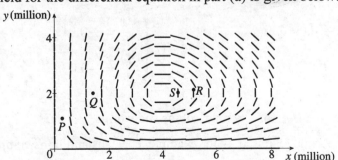

Use this graph to sketch a phase portrait with each of P, Q, R, and S as an initial condition. Describe the behavior of the trajectories near the nonzero equilibrium solutions.

(c) Graph x and y as function of t. What happens to the population of the two species as the time t increases without bound?

Answer:

(a) $\dfrac{dy}{dx} = \dfrac{-4y + xy}{2x - xy}$

(b)

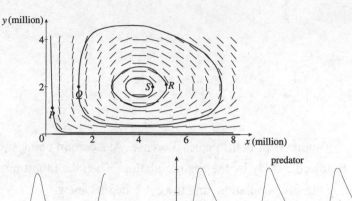

(c)

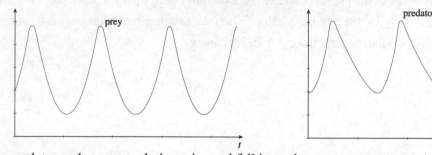

The predator and prey populations rise and fall in cycles.

8. In each of the given systems, x and y are populations of two different species which are solutions to the differential equations. For each system, describe how the species interact with one another (for example, do they compete for the same resources, or cooperate for mutual benefit?) and suggest a pair of species that might interact in a manner consistent with the given system of equations.

(a) $\begin{cases} \dfrac{dx}{dt} = -0.01x + 0.0002xy \\[2mm] \dfrac{dy}{dt} = -0.2y - 0.004xy \end{cases}$

(d) $\begin{cases} \dfrac{dx}{dt} = 0.01x\,(1 - 0.02x) + 0.01xy \\[2mm] \dfrac{dy}{dt} = 0.02y\,(1 - 0.01y) + 0.01xy \end{cases}$

(b) $\begin{cases} \dfrac{dx}{dt} = 0.01x - 0.0002xy \\[2mm] \dfrac{dy}{dt} = 0.2y - 0.004xy \end{cases}$

(e) $\begin{cases} \dfrac{dx}{dt} = 0.08x\,(1 - 0.0001x) - 0.002xy \\[2mm] \dfrac{dy}{dt} = -0.02y + 0.002xy \end{cases}$

(c) $\begin{cases} \dfrac{dx}{dt} = 0.01x + 0.0002xy \\[2mm] \dfrac{dy}{dt} = 0.2y + 0.004xy \end{cases}$

(f) $\begin{cases} \dfrac{dx}{dt} = -0.01x \\[2mm] \dfrac{dy}{dt} = -0.02y \end{cases}$

Answer:

(a) Predator-prey system — for example, robins and worms.

(b) Compete for the same resource — for example, cheetahs and lions compete for wildebeest.

(c) Cooperate for mutual benefit — for example, clownfish and anemone.

(d) Cooperate for mutual benefit — for example, clownfish and anemone.

(e) Predator-prey system — for example, whales and krills.

(f) No interaction — for example, whales and tigers.

8.1 | Sequences

1. Find a formula for the general term a_n of the sequence $\left\{1, -\frac{1}{2}, \frac{1}{4}, -\frac{1}{8}, \cdots\right\}$.

(A) 2^{1-n} (B) 2^{n-1} (C) $(-2)^n$ (D) $(-2)^{n-1}$

(E) $(-1)^{2n}$ (F) $(-2)^{1-n}$ (G) $(-2)^{2n}$ (H) 2^{-n}

Answer: (F)

2. Find a formula for the general term a_n of the sequence $\{1, 6, 120, 5040, \cdots\}$.

(A) $3^n (n+1)!$ (B) $3^n n!$ (C) $(n+1)!$ (D) $(n+2)!$

(E) $(2n)!$ (F) $n!$ (G) $(2n-1)!$ (H) $2^n n!$

Answer: (G)

3. Determine the limit of the sequence $a_n = \dfrac{\sqrt{n+1} - \sqrt{n}}{\sqrt{n+1} + \sqrt{n}}$.

(A) $\frac{1}{4}$ (B) $\sqrt{2}$ (C) 4 (D) $\frac{1}{\sqrt{2}}$

(E) 0 (F) Divergent   (G) 2 (H) $\frac{1}{2}$

Answer: (E)

4. Determine the limit of the sequence $a_n = \dfrac{(n+1)!}{n!}$.

(A) 2 (B) 1 (C) $\frac{1}{3}$ (D) $\frac{1}{2}$

(E) Divergent   (F) 3 (G) e (H) 0

Answer: (E)

5. Find the limit of the sequence $a_n = \dfrac{e^n}{n!}$.

(A) $\dfrac{e^2 - 1}{e}$ (B) $\sqrt{e}$ (C) e (D) e^2

(E) 0 (F) $\dfrac{e-1}{e}$ (G) Divergent   (H) 1

Answer: (E)

6. Find the limit of the sequence $\left\{\sqrt{3}, \sqrt{3\sqrt{3}}, \sqrt{3\sqrt{3\sqrt{3}}}, \ldots\right\}$.

(A) 1 (B) e^3 (C) $e^{3/2}$ (D) 3

(E) $\frac{1}{3}$ (F) $e^{\sqrt{3}}$ (G) π (H) Divergent

Answer: (D)

7. If $a_1 = 1$ and $a_{n+1} = \sqrt{1 + a_n}$ for $n \geq 1$, and $\lim\limits_{n \to \infty} a_n = L$ is assumed to exist, then what must L be?

(A) $\sqrt{2}$ (B) $\sqrt{3}$ (C) $\sqrt{5}$ (D) $\sqrt{7}$

(E) $\dfrac{1 + \sqrt{2}}{2}$ (F) $\dfrac{2 + \sqrt{3}}{4}$ (G) $\dfrac{1 + \sqrt{5}}{2}$ (H) $\dfrac{3 + \sqrt{7}}{2}$

Answer: (G)

8. Determine the limit of the sequence $a_n = \dfrac{(-1)^n}{\sqrt{n}}$.

(A) -1 (B) 0 (C) $\frac{1}{2}$ (D) 1

(E) $\sqrt{2}$ (F) 2 (G) e (H) Divergent

Answer: (B)

9. Determine the limit of the sequence $a_n = \dfrac{(-2)^n}{n}$.

(A) -2 (B) 0 (C) $\ln 2$ (D) $\sqrt{2}$

(E) e^2 (F) $-\frac{1}{2}$ (G) 1 (H) Divergent

Answer: (H)

10. Determine the limit of the sequence $a_n = \dfrac{5 \cos n}{n}$.

(A) 0 (B) 1 (C) 2 (D) 3

(E) 4 (F) 5 (G) 6 (H) Divergent

Answer: (A)

11. Determine the limit of the sequence $a_n = [\ln(n + 1) - \ln(n)]$.

(A) $\dfrac{1}{e}$ (B) 1 (C) 2 (D) 0

(E) e (F) $\frac{1}{4}$ (G) $\ln 2$ (H) Divergent

Answer: (D)

12. Determine the limit of the sequence $a_n = \dfrac{\sin n}{\sqrt{n}}$.

(A) 0 (B) 1 (C) 2 (D) 3

(E) 4 (F) 5 (G) $\sqrt{e}$ (H) Divergent

Answer: (A)

13. If $a_1 = 1$ and $a_{n+1} = 3 - \left(\dfrac{1}{a_n}\right)$ for $n \geq 1$, find the limit of the sequence a_n.

(A) 2 (B) $\sqrt{2}$ (C) $\sqrt{3}$ (D) $\sqrt{5}$

(E) $\dfrac{2 + \sqrt{3}}{4}$ (F) $\dfrac{3 + \sqrt{5}}{2}$ (G) $\dfrac{5 + \sqrt{7}}{2}$ (H) $\dfrac{5 + 2\sqrt{2}}{3}$

Answer: (F)

14. Determine the limit of the sequence $a_n = \dfrac{2^n}{n!}$.

   (A) 0   (B) 1   (C) 2   (D) 3

   (E) 4   (F) 5   (G) 6   (H) Divergent

   Answer: (A)

15. Determine the limit of the sequence $a_n = \dfrac{n!}{(n+3)!}$.

   (A) 0   (B) 1   (C) 2   (D) e

   (E) 3   (F) $\frac{1}{2}$ (G) $\frac{1}{3}$ (H) Divergent

   Answer: (A)

16. Determine the limit of the sequence $a_n = \dfrac{\sqrt{n+1} - \sqrt{n}}{\sqrt{n+1} + \sqrt{n}}$.

   (A) $\frac{1}{4}$ (B) $\sqrt{2}$ (C) 4   (D) $\frac{1}{\sqrt{2}}$

   (E) 0   (F) Divergent   (G) 2   (H) $\frac{1}{2}$

   Answer: (E)

17. Determine the limit of the sequence $a_n = (-1)^n \left(1 - \dfrac{1}{\sqrt{n}} \right)$.

   (A) -2 (B) 0   (C) $\ln 2$ (D) $\sqrt{2}$

   (E) e^2 (F) $-\frac{1}{2}$ (G) 1   (H) Divergent

   Answer: (H)

18. Determine the limit of the sequence $a_n = \dfrac{5 \cos n + n}{n^2}$.

   (A) 0   (B) 1   (C) 2   (D) 3

   (E) 4   (F) 5   (G) 6   (H) Divergent

   Answer: (A)

19. Find a formula for the nth term of the sequence $\frac{1}{4}, -\frac{2}{9}, \frac{3}{16}, -\frac{4}{25}, \ldots$.

   (A) $\dfrac{2^n}{n+1}$ (B) $\dfrac{n}{(n+1)^2}$ (C) $(-1)^n \dfrac{n}{(n+1)^2}$ (D) $(-1)^{n-1} \dfrac{n}{(n+1)^2}$

   (E) $(-1)^n \dfrac{2^n}{n+1}$ (F) $\dfrac{1}{(n+1)^2}$ (G) $\dfrac{1}{n^2}$ (H) $\dfrac{(-1)^{n-1}}{n^2}$

   Answer: (D)

20. A sequence is defined by $a_n = 0.9999^n$.

   (a) Calculate a_{10^3} and a_{10^5}.

   (b) Determine whether a_n converges or diverges. If it converges, find the limit.

   Answer: (a) $a_{10^3} \approx 0.905$, $a_{10^5} \approx 4.5 \times 10^{-5}$ (b) Converges to 0

21. A sequence is defined by $b_n = 1.0001^n$.

   (a) Calculate b_{10^3} and b_{10^5}.

   (b) Determine whether b_n converges or diverges. If it converges, find the limit.

   Answer: (a) $b_{10^3} \approx 1.105$, $b_{10^5} \approx 22015$ (b) Diverges

22. A sequence is defined by $a_n = r^n$, where r is a constant. For what values of r will the sequence converge? What is the limit?

Answer: For $|r| < 1$, $\lim\limits_{n \to \infty} r^n = 0$

23. Consider the recursive sequence defined by $x_1 = 1$; $x_{n+1} = \dfrac{x_n^2 + 2}{2x_n}$, $n > 1$. Evaluate the first three terms of this sequence.

Answer: $x_1 = 1$; $x_2 = \frac{3}{2}$; $x_3 = \frac{17}{12}$

24. Consider the recursive sequence defined by $x_1 = 1$; $x_{n+1} = \dfrac{x_n^2 + 2}{2x_n}$, $n > 1$. You may assume the sequence to be monotonic (after the first term) and bounded and hence convergent. Find its limit.

Answer: $L = \sqrt{2}$

25. Consider the recursive sequence defined by $a_1 = 1$; $a_{n+1} = \frac{1}{2}(a_n + 4)$, $n > 1$.

    (a) Evaluate the first four terms of this sequence.

    (b) Show that the sequence converges.

    (c) Find the limit.

Answer:

   (a) $a_1 = 1$, $a_2 = \frac{5}{2}$, $a_3 = \frac{13}{4}$, $a_4 = \frac{29}{8}$

   (b) Use mathematical induction to show that the sequence is decreasing and bounded.

   (c) 4

26. Determine whether $a_n = \sin\left(\dfrac{n\pi}{2}\right)$ converges or diverges. If it converges, find the limit.

Answer: Diverges

27. Determine whether $a_n = \dfrac{n \cos n}{n^2 + 1}$ converges or diverges. If it converges, find the limit.

Answer: Converges to 0

28. Consider the recursive sequence defined by $a_1 = 2$; $a_{n+1} = \dfrac{2}{3 - a_n}$, $n > 1$.

    (a) Evaluate the first four terms of this sequence.

    (b) Show that the sequence converges.

    (c) Find the limit.

Answer:

   (a) $a_1 = 2$, $a_2 = 2$, $a_3 = 2$, $a_4 = 2$

   (b) $a_n = 2$ for all $n \geq 1$.

   (c) 2

29. Determine whether $a_n = \dfrac{3n + 4}{2n + 5}$ is increasing, decreasing, or not monotonic.

Answer: Increasing

30. Determine whether $a_n = \dfrac{3 + (-1)^n}{n}$ is increasing, decreasing, or not monotonic.

Answer: Not monotonic

272

31. Determine whether $a_n = \dfrac{\sqrt{n+1}}{5n+3}$ is increasing, decreasing, or not monotonic.

Answer: Decreasing

32. If $\dfrac{3n-1}{n+1} < x_n < \dfrac{3n^2+6n+2}{n^2+2n+1}$ for all positive integers n, then find $\lim\limits_{n\to\infty} x_n$.

Answer: $\lim\limits_{n\to\infty} x_n = 3$

33. Write the first five terms of the sequence: $a_n = \left\{ \dfrac{(-7)^{n+1}}{n!} \right\}$.

Answer: $\left\{ 49, -\dfrac{343}{2}, \dfrac{2401}{6}, -\dfrac{16807}{24}, \dfrac{117649}{120}, \cdots \right\}$

34. Find a formula for the general term a_n of $\left\{ \dfrac{1}{2}, \dfrac{1}{4}, \dfrac{1}{6}, \dfrac{1}{8}, \ldots \right\}$ assuming the pattern of the first few terms continues.

Answer: $a_n = \dfrac{1}{2n}$

35. Find a formula for the general term a_n of $\left\{ \dfrac{3}{2}, -\dfrac{9}{4}, \dfrac{27}{8}, -\dfrac{81}{16}, \ldots \right\}$ assuming the pattern of the first few terms continues.

Answer: $a_n = (-1)^{n+1}\left(\dfrac{3}{2} \right)^n$

36. Consider the sequence defined by $a_n = \left(\dfrac{2}{3} \right)^n$. ($n$ starts at 1)

    (a) Write the first five terms of the sequence.

    (b) Determine the limit of the sequence.

    (c) Let $b_n = \dfrac{a_{n+1}}{a_n}$. Write the first five terms of this sequence.

    (d) Determine the limit of b_n.

Answer: (a) $\dfrac{2}{3}, \dfrac{4}{9}, \dfrac{8}{27}, \dfrac{16}{81}, \dfrac{32}{243}$ (b) Converges to 0

(c) $\dfrac{2}{3}, \dfrac{2}{3}, \dfrac{2}{3}, \dfrac{2}{3}, \dfrac{2}{3}$ (d) Converges to $\dfrac{2}{3}$

37. Consider the sequence defined by $a_n = \left(-\dfrac{3}{4} \right)^n$. ($n$ starts at 1)

    (a) Write the first five terms of the sequence.

    (b) Determine the limit of the sequence.

    (c) Let $b_n = \dfrac{a_{n+1}}{a_n}$. Write the first five terms of this sequence.

    (d) Determine the limit of b_n.

Answer: (a) $-\dfrac{3}{4}, \dfrac{9}{16}, -\dfrac{27}{64}, \dfrac{81}{256}, -\dfrac{243}{1024}$ (b) Converges to 0

(c) $-\dfrac{3}{4}, -\dfrac{3}{4}, -\dfrac{3}{4}, -\dfrac{3}{4}, -\dfrac{3}{4}$ (d) Converges to $-\dfrac{3}{4}$

38. Consider the sequence defined by $a_n = \left(\dfrac{3}{2} \right)^n$. ($n$ starts at 1)

    (a) Write the first five terms of the sequence.

    (b) Determine the limit of the sequence.

    (c) Let $b_n = \dfrac{a_{n+1}}{a_n}$. Write the first five terms of this sequence.

    (d) Determine the limit of b_n.

Answer: (a) $\dfrac{3}{2}, \dfrac{9}{4}, \dfrac{27}{8}, \dfrac{81}{16}, \dfrac{243}{32}$ (b) Diverges to ∞

(c) $\dfrac{3}{2}, \dfrac{3}{2}, \dfrac{3}{2}, \dfrac{3}{2}, \dfrac{3}{2}$ (d) Converges to $\dfrac{3}{2}$

39. Consider the sequence defined by $a_n = (-1)^n$. (n starts at 1)

    (a) Write the first five terms of the sequence.

    (b) Determine the limit of the sequence.

    (c) Let $b_n = \dfrac{a_{n+1}}{a_n}$. Write the first five terms of this sequence.

    (d) Determine the limit of b_n.

    (e) Let $c_n = \sum\limits_{k=1}^{n} a_k$. Write the first five terms of this sequence.

    (f) Determine the limit of c_n.

    Answer: (a) $-1, 1, -1, 1, -1$ (b) Does not exist (c) $-1, -1, -1, -1, -1$

    (d) Converges to -1 (e) $-1, 0, -1, 0, -1$ (f) Diverges

40. A sequence of right triangles, $A_1, A_2, A_3, \ldots$ is given in the figure below:

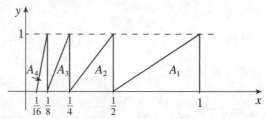

    (a) Let $a_n = \text{area}\,(A_n)$. Determine an expression for a_n and find the limit of a_n.

    (b) Let $b_n = \sum\limits_{k=1}^{n} a_k$. Use geometric reasoning to determine the limit of b_n.

    Answer: (a) $\left\{ a_n = \dfrac{1}{2^n} \right\}_{n=2}^{\infty}$ $a_n \to 0$ (b) Converges to $\frac{1}{2}$

41. Consider a sequence of rectangles, $R_1, R_2, R_3, \ldots$ illustrated in the figure below:

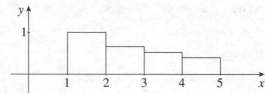

    (a) The height L_n of R_n is given by $L_n = f(n)$ where $f(x) = \dfrac{1}{x}$. Write down the first five terms of $\{L_n\}$ and determine the limit of $\{L_n\}$.

    (b) Let $b_n = \sum\limits_{k=1}^{n} L_k$. Compare b_n to $\int_1^{n+1} (1/x)\,dx$.

    (c) Determine whether $\{b_n\}$ converges or diverges. Justify your answer.

    Answer: (a) $1, \frac{1}{2}, \frac{1}{3}, \frac{1}{4}, \frac{1}{5}$; $L_n = \dfrac{1}{n} \to 0$

    (b) For any n, the region whose area is given by $\int_1^{n+1} (1/x)\,dx$ is completely contained in the union of rectangles whose area is given by b_n. So $b_n > \int_1^{n+1} (1/x)\,dx$.

    (c) Since $\displaystyle\int_1^{\infty} (1/x)\,dx$ diverges, $\{b_n\}$ also diverges.

42. Suppose that $1,000$ is deposited in a bank at 3% interest, compounded annually. Let $B(n)$ denote the balance after the nth year. Find an expression for the sequence $B(n)$.

Answer: $B(n) = 1000\left(1 + \frac{3}{1000}\right)^n$

43. Suppose a 600 milligram dose of a drug is injected into a patient and that the patient's kidneys remove 20% of the drug from the bloodstream every hour. Let $D(n)$ denote the amount of the drug left in the patient's body after n hours.

   (a) Find an expression for $D(n)$.

   (b) How long will it take for the drug level to drop below 200 milligrams?

   (c) How long will it take to bring the drug level below 10% of the original dosage?

Answer: (a) $D(n) = 600(0.8)^n$ (b) About 4.9 hours   (c) About 10.3 hours

44. Consider the sequence defined by $a_n = \dfrac{n!}{2 \cdot 5 \cdot 8 \cdots (3n-1)}, n \geq 1.$

   (a) Evaluate the first three terms of this sequence.

   (b) Find the limit.

Answer:

   (a) $a_1 = \frac{1}{2}$, $a_2 = \frac{1}{5}$, $a_3 = \frac{3}{40}$

   (b) 0

45. Evaluate $\displaystyle\lim_{n\to\infty}\left(1 - \frac{2}{n}\right)^n.$

Answer: $\dfrac{1}{e^2}$

8.2   Series

1. Find the sum of the series $2 + \frac{1}{2} + \frac{1}{8} + \frac{1}{32} + \cdots$.

   (A) $\frac{15}{7}$ (B) $\frac{8}{3}$ (C) $\frac{7}{3}$ (D) $\frac{13}{6}$

   (E) $\frac{16}{7}$ (F) $\frac{5}{2}$ (G) $\frac{17}{6}$ (H) Divergent

Answer: (B)

2. Find the sum of the series $\displaystyle\sum_{n=1}^{\infty} \frac{1}{n(n+2)}$.

   (A) $\frac{3}{4}$ (B) $\frac{1}{2}$ (C) $\frac{3}{5}$ (D) $\frac{9}{10}$

   (E) $\frac{7}{10}$ (F) $\frac{4}{5}$ (G) $\frac{2}{3}$ (H) Divergent

Answer: (A)

3. Express the number $1.363636\ldots$ as a ratio of integers.

   (A) $\frac{17}{13}$ (B) $\frac{31}{19}$ (C) $\frac{30}{19}$ (D) $\frac{15}{13}$

   (E) $\frac{17}{11}$ (F) $\frac{22}{17}$ (G) $\frac{15}{11}$ (H) $\frac{21}{17}$

Answer: (G)

4. Find the values of x for which the series $\sum\limits_{n=1}^{\infty} (x-1)^n$ converges.

(A) $0 < x \le 2$ (B) $-2 \le x < 0$ (C) $-2 < x \le 0$ (D) $0 \le x < 2$

(E) $-2 < x < 0$ (F) $0 < x < 2$ (G) $0 \le x \le 2$ (H) $-2 \le x \le 0$

Answer: (F)

5. A rubber ball is dropped from a height of 10 feet and bounces to $\frac{3}{4}$ its height after each fall. If it continues to bounce until it comes to rest, find the total distance in feet it travels.

(A) 55   (B) 70   (C) 40   (D) 65

(E) 35   (F) 45   (G) 50   (H) 60

Answer: (B)

6. Find the sum of the series $\sum\limits_{n=1}^{\infty} (-1)^{n+1} \dfrac{2^n}{3^n}$.
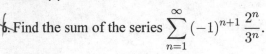

(A) $\frac{1}{3}$ (B) $\frac{1}{2}$ (C) $\frac{3}{5}$ (D) 1

(E) $\frac{3}{2}$ (F) $\frac{2}{5}$ (G) 3   (H) Divergent

Answer: (F)

7. Find the sum of the series $0.9 + 0.09 + 0.009 + 0.0009 + \cdots$.

(A) 9   (B) 0   (C) 0.999   (D) 0.9999

(E) 9.9   (F) 2   (G) 1   (H) Divergent

Answer: (G)

8. Find the sum of the series $\sum\limits_{n=1}^{\infty} \dfrac{(-3)^{n-1}}{4^n}$.

(A) $-\frac{3}{4}$ (B) $-\frac{1}{4}$ (C) $-\frac{1}{7}$ (D) $\frac{1}{7}$

(E) $\frac{1}{4}$ (F) $\frac{3}{4}$ (G) 0   (H) Divergent

Answer: (D)

9. Find the sum of the series $\sum\limits_{n=0}^{\infty} 3\left[\left(\frac{1}{2}\right)^n + \left(-\frac{1}{2}\right)^n\right]$.

(A) $\frac{4}{3}$ (B) $\frac{5}{3}$ (C) 8   (D) 3

(E) 4   (F) 5   (G) 6   (H) Divergent

Answer: (C)

10. Find the sum of the series $\sum\limits_{n=4}^{\infty} \ln\left(\dfrac{n+1}{n}\right)$.

(A) $\frac{1}{4}$ (B) $\frac{1}{3}$ (C) 0   (D) $\ln 2$

(E) $\frac{3}{4}$ (F) $\ln(n+1)$ (G) $\ln \frac{3}{2}$ (H) Divergent

Answer: (H)

11. Find the value of $\frac{2}{9} - \frac{4}{27} + \cdots + \dfrac{(-1)^{n+1} \cdot 2^n}{3^{n+1}} + \cdots$.

Answer: $\frac{2}{15}$

12. Determine whether the series $\sum\limits_{n=1}^{\infty} \dfrac{n-1}{5n+1}$ is convergent or divergent. If it is convergent, find the sum.

    Answer: Diverges

13. Determine whether the series $\sum\limits_{n=1}^{\infty} \cos\left(\dfrac{\pi}{2n^2-1}\right)$ is convergent or divergent. If it is convergent, find the sum.

    Answer: Diverges

14. Find the value of $\sum\limits_{n=2}^{\infty} \dfrac{3^n+5^n}{15^n}$.

    Answer: $S = \frac{13}{60}$

15. Determine whether the series $\sum\limits_{n=1}^{\infty} \dfrac{n}{\sqrt{3n+2}}$ is convergent or divergent. If it is convergent, find the sum.

    Answer: Diverges

16. Determine whether the series $1 - \frac{1}{2} + \frac{1}{4} - \frac{1}{8} + \cdots$ is convergent or divergent. If it is convergent, find its sum.

    Answer: Converges with sum $\frac{2}{3}$

17. Determine whether the series $\frac{1}{2^6} + \frac{1}{2^8} + \frac{1}{2^{10}} + \frac{1}{2^{12}} + \cdots$ is convergent or divergent. If it is convergent, find its sum.

    Answer: Converges with sum $\frac{1}{48}$

18. Determine whether the series $\sum\limits_{n=1}^{\infty} \ln\left(\dfrac{2n-1}{2n+1}\right)$ is convergent or divergent. If it is convergent, find the sum.

    Answer: Diverges

19. Determine whether the series $\sum\limits_{n=1}^{\infty} \dfrac{1}{(3n-1)(3n+2)}$ is convergent or divergent. If it is convergent, find the sum.

    Answer: Converges with sum $\frac{1}{6}$

20. Determine whether the series $-\frac{81}{100} + \frac{9}{10} - 1 + \frac{10}{9} - \cdots$ is convergent or divergent. If it is convergent, find its sum.

    Answer: Diverges

21. Determine whether the series $\sum\limits_{n=2}^{\infty} \ln \dfrac{n^2}{(n+1)(n-1)}$ is convergent or divergent. If it is convergent, find the sum.

    Answer: Converges to $\ln 2$

22. Determine whether the series $\sum\limits_{n=1}^{\infty} \dfrac{3+(-1)^n}{3^n}$ is convergent or divergent. If it is convergent, find the sum.

    Answer: Converges to $\frac{5}{4}$

23. Determine whether the series $\sum_{n=1}^{\infty} \dfrac{1}{e^{2n}}$ is convergent or divergent. If it is convergent, find its sum.

Answer: Converges to $\dfrac{1}{e^2 - 1}$

24. Determine whether the series $\sum_{n=1}^{\infty} (0.9999)^n$ is convergent or divergent. If it is convergent, find the sum.

Answer: Converges to 9999

25. Determine whether the series $\sum_{n=1}^{\infty} (1.0001)^n$ is convergent or divergent. If it is convergent, find the sum.

Answer: Diverges

26. Determine whether the series $\sum_{n=1}^{\infty} \dfrac{n^2}{3\,(n+1)\,(n+2)}$ is convergent or divergent. If it is convergent, find its sum.

Answer: Diverges by the Test for Divergence

27. If $\sum_{n=2}^{\infty} \left(\dfrac{a}{1+a} \right)^n = 3$ and $a > 0$, determine the value of a.

Answer: $a = \dfrac{3 + \sqrt{21}}{2}$

28. Determine whether the series $\sum_{n=1}^{\infty} (-1)^{n-1} \dfrac{3^{2n}}{2^{3n+1}}$ is convergent or divergent. If it is convergent, find its sum.

Answer: Diverges

29. Let $\sum a_n$ and $\sum b_n$ be two series. Determine whether each of the following statements is true or false. Justify your answer.

(a) If $\sum a_n$ converges, then $a_n \to 0$.

(b) If $a_n \to 0$, then $\sum a_n$ converges.

(c) If $\sum a_n$ converges, and $\sum b_n$ diverges, then $\sum (a_n + b_n)$ diverges.

(d) If $\sum a_n$ diverges, and $\sum b_n$ diverges, then $\sum (a_n + b_n)$ diverges.

(e) If $\sum a_n$ converges, and $\lim_{n \to \infty} b_n = 0$ the $\sum (a_n + b_n)$ converges.

Answer: (a) True   (b) False. For example, $\dfrac{1}{n} \to 0$, but $\sum \dfrac{1}{n}$ diverges.   (c) True

(d) False. For example, $\sum_{n=0}^{\infty} (-1)^n$ and $\sum_{n=0}^{\infty} (-1)^{n+1}$ both diverge, but $\sum_{n=0}^{\infty} \left[(-1)^n + (-1)^{n+1} \right] = 0$, which is convergent.

(e) False. For example, $\sum \dfrac{1}{2^n}$ converges and $\dfrac{1}{n} \to 0$, but $\sum \left(\dfrac{1}{2^n} + \dfrac{1}{n} \right)$ diverges by part (c).

30. A series $\sum_{k=1}^{\infty} a_k$ has partial sums, s_n, given by $s_n = \dfrac{7n-2}{n}$.

(a) Is $\sum_{k=1}^{\infty} a_k$ convergent? If it is, find the sum.

(b) Find $\lim_{n \to \infty} a_k$.

(c) Find $\sum_{k=1}^{200} a_k$.

Answer: (a) $s_n \to 7$, which is the sum of $\sum_{k=1}^{\infty} a_k$. (b) Since $\sum_{k=1}^{\infty} a_k$ converges, $a_k \to 0$. (c) $\frac{699}{100}$

31. Let $a_n = \dfrac{1+3^n}{1+4 \cdot 3^n}$.

(a) Find $\lim_{n \to \infty} a_n$.

(b) Is $\sum a_n$ convergent? Justify your answer.

Answer: (a) $a_n \to \frac{1}{4}$ (b) $\sum a_n$ diverges by the Test for Divergence.

32. Express the number $0.\overline{307}$ as a ratio of integers.

Answer: $\frac{307}{999}$

33. Express the number $0.2\overline{15}$ as a ratio of integers.

Answer: $\frac{213}{990}$

34. A superball is dropped from a height of 8 ft. Each time it strikes the ground after falling from a height of t ft. it rebounds to a height of $\frac{3}{4}t$ feet. Find the total distance traveled by the ball.

Answer: 56 ft

35. A superball is dropped from a height of 8 ft. Each time it strikes the ground after falling from a height of t ft. it rebounds to a height of $\frac{3}{4}t$ feet. How long does it take for the ball to come to rest? (Use $g = 32$ ft/s^2.)

Answer: About 9.849 s

36. Find $\sum_{n=2}^{\infty} \left(\sum_{m=2}^{\infty} \dfrac{1}{n^m} \right)$.

Answer: 1

37. Determine whether each of the following series is convergent or divergent.

(a) $\sum_{n=1}^{\infty} \dfrac{1}{2+3^{-n}}$

(b) $\sum_{n=0}^{\infty} \dfrac{\pi^n}{3^n}$

(c) $\sum_{n=1}^{\infty} \dfrac{e^n}{3^n}$

Answer: (a) Divergent (b) Divergent (c) Convergent

38. Determine whether each of the following series is convergent or divergent.

(a) $\sum_{n=1}^{\infty} \dfrac{1}{n}$

(b) $\sum_{n=0}^{\infty} n \sin\left(\dfrac{1}{n}\right)$

(c) $\sum_{n=0}^{\infty} (-1)^n \dfrac{3^n}{5^n}$

Answer: (a) Divergent (b) Divergent (c) Convergent

39. Here is a two-player game: Two players take turns flipping a fair coin. The first player to get a head wins the game. What is the probability that the person who starts first wins the game?

Answer: $\frac{2}{3}$

40. Here is a two-player game: Two players take turns tossing a fair die. The first player to get a 5 wins the game. What is the probability that the player who starts first wins the game?

    Answer: $\frac{6}{11}$

41. Let $X = \{1, 2, 3, \ldots, n, \ldots\}$ be a discrete random variable with probability density function $f(n) = r(1-r)^{n-1}$, where $0 < r < 1$.

    (a) Show that $\sum_{n=1}^{\infty} f(n) = 1$. Explain the significance of the value 1.

    (b) The expected value of the random variable X is defined by $E(X) = \sum_{n=1}^{\infty} nf(n)$. Show that $E(X) = \frac{1}{r}$. The distribution of X is known as the *geometric distribution*.

42. Let $X = \{0, 1, 2, 3, \ldots, n, \ldots\}$ be a discrete random variable with probability density function $f(n) = e^{-\mu}\frac{\mu^n}{n!}$, where $0 < \mu$.

    (a) Show that $\sum_{n=0}^{\infty} f(n) = 1$. Explain the significance of the value 1.

    (b) The expected value of the random variable X is defined by $E(X) = \sum_{n=0}^{\infty} nf(n)$. Show that $E(X) = \mu$. The distribution of X is known as the *Poisson distribution*.

8.3 The Integral and Comparison Tests; Estimating Sums

1. Which of the three series below converges?

$$1) \sum_{n=1}^{\infty} \frac{1}{n} \qquad 2) \sum_{n=1}^{\infty} \frac{1}{n^{1.1}} \qquad 3) \sum_{n=1}^{\infty} \frac{1}{n^{0.9}}$$

(A) 1, 2   (B) 1   (C) None   (D) 3

(E) 2   (F) 2, 3   (G) 1, 2, 3   (H) 1, 3

Answer: (E)

2. Which of the three series below converges?

$$1) \sum_{i=2}^{\infty} \frac{1}{n \ln n} \qquad 2) \sum_{i=2}^{\infty} \frac{1}{n(\ln n)^2} \qquad 3) \sum_{i=2}^{\infty} \frac{1}{n(\ln n)^3}$$

(A) 2   (B) 1, 2, 3   (C) 1, 3   (D) 2, 3

(E) 3   (F) None   (G) 1, 2   (H) 1

Answer: (D)

3. According to the estimates found in the justification for the Integral Test, the sum of the series $\sum\limits_{n=1}^{\infty} \dfrac{1}{n^{1.001}}$ must lie between what two values?

(A) 101 and 102   (B) 102 and 103   (C) 999 and 1000   (D) 1001 and 1002

(E) 1002 and 1003   (F) 1000 and 1001   (G) 99 and 100   (H) 100 and 101

Answer: (F)

4. What is the value of p that marks the boundary between convergence and divergence of the series $\sum\limits_{n=2}^{\infty} \dfrac{1}{n\,(\ln n)^p}$?

(A) $\frac{1}{2}$ (B) $\frac{1}{3}$ (C) Diverges for all p (D) $\ln 2$

(E) 1   (F) $\ln 3$ (G) Converges for all p (H) $\dfrac{1}{e}$

Answer: (E)

5. Which of the three series below converges?

$$1)\ \sum_{n=1}^{\infty} \frac{1}{n^4} \qquad 2)\ \sum_{n=1}^{\infty} \frac{n^2}{2n^2+1} \qquad 3)\ \sum_{n=1}^{\infty} \left(\sqrt{2}\right)^n$$

(A) None   (B) 1   (C) 2   (D) 3

(E) 1, 2   (F) 1, 3   (G) 2, 3   (H) 1, 2, 3

Answer: (B)

6. The series $\sum\limits_{n=1}^{\infty} \dfrac{1}{n^{\alpha}}$ converges if and only if

(A) $\alpha < 1$ (B) $-1 < \alpha < 1$ (C) $\alpha \le 1$ (D) $\alpha > 1$

(E) $\alpha \ge 1$ (F) $\alpha < -1$ (G) $\alpha > -1$ (H) $-1 > \alpha > 1$

Answer: (D)

7. Which of the three series below converges?

$$1)\ \sum_{n=1}^{\infty} \frac{n}{n+1} \qquad 2)\ \sum_{n=1}^{\infty} \frac{\pi^n}{3^n} \qquad 3)\ \sum_{n=1}^{\infty} \frac{1}{n\sqrt{n}}$$

(A) None   (B) 1   (C) 2   (D) 3

(E) 1, 2   (F) 1, 3   (G) 2, 3   (H) 1, 2, 3

Answer: (D)

8. Which of the following three tests will establish that the series $\displaystyle\sum_{n=1}^{\infty} \frac{3}{n\,(n+2)}$ converges?

1) Comparison Test with $\displaystyle\sum_{n=1}^{\infty} 3n^{-2}$ 　　　　　2) Limit Comparison Test with $\displaystyle\sum_{n=1}^{\infty} n^{-2}$

3) Comparison Test with $\displaystyle\sum_{n=1}^{\infty} 3n^{-1}$

(A) None 　　　　(B) 1 　　　　(C) 2 　　　　(D) 3

(E) 1, 2 　　　　(F) 1, 3 　　　　(G) 2, 3 　　　　(H) 1, 2, 3

Answer: (E)

9. Which of the following three tests will establish that the series $\displaystyle\sum_{n=1}^{\infty} \frac{n}{\sqrt{2n^5 + 1}}$ converges?

1) Comparison Test with $\displaystyle\sum_{n=1}^{\infty} n^{-5/2}$ 　　　　2) Comparison Test with $\displaystyle\sum_{n=1}^{\infty} n^{-3/2}$

3) Comparison Test with $\displaystyle\sum_{n=1}^{\infty} n^{-1/2}$

(A) None 　　　　(B) 1 　　　　(C) 2 　　　　(D) 3

(E) 1, 2 　　　　(F) 1, 3 　　　　(G) 2, 3 　　　　(H) 1, 2, 3

Answer: (C)

10. Which of the following three tests will establish that the series $\displaystyle\sum_{n=1}^{\infty} \frac{n}{\sqrt{7n^3 + 46}}$ diverges?

1) Limit Comparison Test with $\displaystyle\sum_{n=1}^{\infty} n^{-1}$ 　　　　2) Comparison Test with $\displaystyle\sum_{n=1}^{\infty} n^{-1}$

3) Comparison Test with $\displaystyle\sum_{n=1}^{\infty} n^{-1/2}$

(A) None 　　　　(B) 1 　　　　(C) 2 　　　　(D) 3

(E) 1, 2 　　　　(F) 1, 3 　　　　(G) 2, 3 　　　　(H) 1, 2, 3

Answer: (C)

11. Which of the following series converges?

1) $\displaystyle\sum_{n=1}^{\infty} \frac{1}{n^2 + \sqrt{n}}$ 　　　2) $\displaystyle\sum_{n=1}^{\infty} \frac{\sqrt{n}}{n^2 + \ln n}$ 　　　3) $\displaystyle\sum_{n=1}^{\infty} \frac{n}{\sqrt{n^3 + 2n^2}}$

(A) None 　　　　(B) 1 　　　　(C) 2 　　　　(D) 3

(E) 1, 2 　　　　(F) 1, 3 　　　　(G) 2, 3 　　　　(H) 1, 2, 3

Answer: (E)

12. Which of the following series converges?

$$1) \sum_{n=1}^{\infty} n^{-n} \qquad 2) \sum_{n=1}^{\infty} e^{100-n} \qquad 3) \sum_{n=1}^{\infty} \frac{n^n}{n!}$$

(A) None   (B) 1   (C) 2   (D) 3

(E) 1, 2   (F) 1, 3   (G) 2, 3   (H) 1, 2, 3

Answer: (E)

13. Which of the following series converges?

$$1) \sum_{n=1}^{\infty} \frac{1}{\ln(n+1)} \qquad 2) \sum_{n=1}^{\infty} \frac{1}{[\ln(n+1)]^2} \qquad 3) \sum_{n=1}^{\infty} \frac{1}{[\ln(n+1)]^3}$$

(A) None   (B) 1   (C) 2   (D) 3

(E) 1, 2   (F) 1, 3   (G) 2, 3   (H) 1, 2, 3

Answer: (A)

14. Which of the following series converges?

$$1) \sum_{n=1}^{\infty} \frac{1}{e^n} \qquad 2) \sum_{n=1}^{\infty} \frac{1}{\sqrt{e^n}} \qquad 3) \sum_{n=1}^{\infty} \frac{1}{\sqrt[3]{e^n}}$$

(A) None   (B) 1   (C) 2   (D) 3

(E) 1, 2   (F) 1, 3   (G) 2, 3   (H) 1, 2, 3

Answer: (H)

15. Which of the following series converges?

$$1) \sum_{n=1}^{\infty} \frac{3^{2n}}{2^{3n}} \qquad 2) \sum_{n=1}^{\infty} \frac{1}{(n+1)^3} \qquad 3) \sum_{n=1}^{\infty} \frac{n+1}{\sqrt{n^3+2}}$$

(A) None   (B) 1   (C) 2   (D) 3

(E) 1, 2   (F) 1, 3   (G) 2, 3   (H) 1, 2, 3

Answer: (C)

16. Which of the following series converges?

$$1) \sum_{n=1}^{\infty} (-1)^n \qquad 2) \sum_{n=1}^{\infty} 2^n \qquad 3) \sum_{n=1}^{\infty} \frac{1}{2+n^3}$$

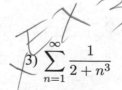

(A) None   (B) 1   (C) 2   (D) 3

(E) 1, 2   (F) 1, 3   (G) 2, 3   (H) 1, 2, 3

Answer: (D)

17. Which of the following series converges?

$$1) \sum_{n=1}^{\infty} \frac{n}{\sqrt{n^3 + n^2}} \qquad 2) \sum_{n=2}^{\infty} \frac{n}{n\sqrt{n} - 1} \qquad 3) \sum_{n=1}^{\infty} \frac{1}{n^2 + n + 1}$$

(A) None   (B) 1   (C) 2   (D) 3

(E) 1, 2   (F) 1, 3   (G) 2, 3   (H) 1, 2, 3

Answer: (D)

18. Use the Integral Test to determine if the following series converges or diverges: $\sum_{n=1}^{\infty} \frac{n}{(n^2 + 1)^2}$.

Answer: The integral has a value of $\frac{1}{4}$. Since it is finite, the series converges.

19. Determine whether or not $\sum_{k=2}^{\infty} \frac{1}{k(\ln k)^2}$ converges.

Answer: Converges

20. Determine whether $\sum_{n=1}^{\infty} 3ne^{-n^2}$ converges or diverges.

Answer: Converges

21. Use the integral test to show that the series $\sum_{k=2}^{\infty} \frac{1}{k(\ln k)^p}$ converges if $p > 1$ and diverges if $p \le 1$.

Hint: Consider the two cases $p = 1$ and $p \ne 1$.

Answer: Suppose that $p = 1$. Using the integral test with $\int_2^{\infty} \frac{dx}{x \ln k}$ gives $\lim_{l \to +\infty} (\ln(\ln x))_2^l = \infty$ and

the series diverges. If $p \ne 1$, then using the integral test with $\int_2^{\infty} \frac{dx}{x(\ln x)^p}$ gives $\lim_{l \to \infty} \left[\frac{(\ln x)^{1-p}}{1 - p} \right]_2^l$.

Since $\ln x \to \infty$ as $x \to \infty$, the convergence of the series depends on whether $\ln x$ is in the numerator or denominator of the limit above. If $p > 1$, the $\ln x$ is in the denominator and the series converges. If $p > 1$, the $\ln x$ is in the numerator and the series diverges. So we have convergence if $p > 1$ and divergence if $p \le 1$.

22. Determine whether $\sum_{n=1}^{\infty} \frac{\cos n + 3^n}{n^2 + 5^n}$ is convergent or divergent.

Answer: Convergent

23. Determine whether the series $\sum_{n=0}^{\infty} \frac{1 + \sin^2 n}{5^n}$ converges.

Answer: Converges

24. Determine whether the given series is convergent or divergent. Indicate the test you use and show any necessary computation.

(a) $\displaystyle\sum_{n=1}^{\infty} \frac{2n^2+1}{5n^3-n+4}$

(e) $\displaystyle\sum_{n=1}^{\infty} \tan^{-1} n$

(i) $\displaystyle\sum_{n=1}^{\infty} \frac{4^n}{2^n+3^n}$

(b) $\displaystyle\sum_{n=1}^{\infty} \left(\frac{1+\sin n}{n}\right)^2$

(f) $\displaystyle\sum_{n=1}^{\infty} \frac{1}{n\sqrt{1+\ln n}}$

(j) $\displaystyle\sum_{n=1}^{\infty} \ln\left(1+\frac{1}{n}\right)$

(c) $\displaystyle\sum_{n=1}^{\infty} n \cdot \sin\left(\frac{1}{n}\right)$

(g) $\displaystyle\sum_{n=1}^{\infty} \frac{\ln n}{(n+1)^3}$

(k) $\displaystyle\sum_{n=1}^{\infty} n \cdot e^{-n^2}$

(d) $\displaystyle\sum_{n=1}^{\infty} \left(\frac{2}{n\sqrt{n}}+\frac{3}{n^3}\right)$

(h) $\displaystyle\sum_{n=1}^{\infty} \frac{\ln n}{n}$

Answer: (a) Diverges   (b) Converges   (c) Diverges   (d) Converges   (e) Diverges   (f) Diverges

(g) Converges   (h) Diverges   (i) Diverges   (j) Diverges   (k) Converges

25. Consider the two series: (a) $\displaystyle\sum_{k=2}^{\infty} \frac{\ln k}{k}$ and (b) $\displaystyle\sum_{k=2}^{\infty} \frac{1}{k \ln k}$. Suppose you compare (a) and (b) to the series

$\displaystyle\sum_{k=1}^{\infty} \frac{1}{k}$. What (if anything) can you conclude about the convergence or divergence of (a) and (b) using *only* the Comparison Test?

Answer: $\displaystyle\sum_{k=1}^{\infty} \frac{1}{k}$ diverges to ∞. Since $\ln k > 1$ for $k \geq 3$, we have (a) $\dfrac{\ln k}{k} > \dfrac{1}{k}$ and (b) $\dfrac{1}{k \ln k} < \dfrac{1}{k}$.

From (a) we conclude that $\displaystyle\sum_{k=2}^{\infty} \frac{\ln k}{k}$ also diverges to ∞. However, nothing can be concluded from (b).

The comparison test yields no useful information about the series $\displaystyle\sum_{k=2}^{\infty} \frac{1}{k \ln k}$.

26. For the series $\displaystyle\sum_{n=2}^{\infty} \frac{n^{1/n}}{\ln n}$, tell whether or not it converges, and indicate what test you used. If the test involves a limit, give the limit. If the test involves a comparison, give the comparison.

Answer: It diverges by the Comparison Test: Because $\displaystyle\sum_{n=2}^{\infty} \frac{1}{n}$ diverges and $\dfrac{n^{1/n}}{\ln n} > \dfrac{1}{n}$ for all $n > 1$, the given series also diverges.

27. Use the sum of the first 10 terms to approximate the sum of the series $\displaystyle\sum_{n=1}^{\infty} \frac{1}{n^4+1}$. Estimate the error involved in this approximation.

Answer: $S_{10} \approx 0.57819$; $R_{10} \leq \frac{1}{3000} \approx 0.00034$. (Answers for R_{10} may vary.)

28. Estimate $\displaystyle\sum_{n=1}^{\infty} \frac{1}{n^4+1}$ to within 0.01.

Answer: $\dfrac{1}{1^4+1} + \dfrac{1}{2^4+1} + \dfrac{1}{3^4+1} + \dfrac{1}{4^4+1} \approx 0.575$

29. Use the sum of the first 10 terms to approximate the sum of the series $\displaystyle\sum_{n=1}^{\infty} \frac{1}{n(\ln(2n))^4 + 1}$. Estimate the error involved in this approximation.

Answer $S_{10} \approx 0.995\,51$; $R_{10} \leq \dfrac{1}{3\,(\ln 20)^3} \approx 0.0124$.

30. Which one of the following series converges?

(a) $\displaystyle\sum_{n=1}^{\infty} \frac{1}{n^{1.0001}}$ (b) $\displaystyle\sum_{n=1}^{\infty} \frac{1}{n}$ (c) $\displaystyle\sum_{n=1}^{\infty} \frac{1}{n^{0.99}}$ (d) $\displaystyle\sum_{n=1}^{\infty} \frac{1}{n^{-4}}$ (e) None of these

Answer: (a)

31. Which one of the following series converges?

(a) $\displaystyle\sum_{n=1}^{\infty} \frac{1}{n^{3/4}}$ (b) $\displaystyle\sum_{n=1}^{\infty} \frac{1}{n}$ (c) $\displaystyle\sum_{n=1}^{\infty} \frac{1}{n^{0.99}}$ (d) $\displaystyle\sum_{n=1}^{\infty} \frac{1}{n^{-4}}$ (e) None of these

Answer: (e)

32. Which one of the following series diverges?

(a) $\displaystyle\sum_{n=1}^{\infty} \frac{1}{n^{1.0001}}$ (b) $\displaystyle\sum_{n=1}^{\infty} \left(\frac{\pi}{4}\right)^n$ (c) $\displaystyle\sum_{n=1}^{\infty} \frac{1}{n + \ln n}$ (d) $\displaystyle\sum_{n=1}^{\infty} \frac{1}{n^4}$ (e) None of these

Answer: (c)

33. Which one of the following series diverges?

(a) $\displaystyle\sum_{n=1}^{\infty} \frac{1}{n^{1.0001}}$ (b) $\displaystyle\sum_{n=1}^{\infty} \left(\frac{\pi}{4}\right)^n$ (c) $\displaystyle\sum_{n=1}^{\infty} \frac{1}{n + e^n}$ (d) $\displaystyle\sum_{n=1}^{\infty} \frac{n + n^3}{n^4 + 1}$ (e) None of these

Answer: (d)

34. Which one of the following series diverges?

(a) $\displaystyle\sum_{n=1}^{\infty} \frac{n}{e^n}$ (b) $\displaystyle\sum_{n=1}^{\infty} (-1)^n \left(\frac{2}{3}\right)^n$ (c) $\displaystyle\sum_{n=1}^{\infty} \frac{n + n^3}{n^4}$ (d) $\displaystyle\sum_{n=1}^{\infty} \frac{1}{n\,(\ln n)^2}$ (e) None of these

Answer: (c)

8.4 Other Convergence Tests

1. Which of the following are alternating series?

1) $\dfrac{(-1)^{2n}}{n}$ 2) $\displaystyle\sum_{n=1}^{\infty} \frac{(-1)^{n-1}}{n}$ 3) $\displaystyle\sum_{n=1}^{\infty} \frac{\cos n\pi}{n}$

(A) None (B) 1 (C) 2 (D) 3

(E) 1, 2 (F) 1, 3 (G) 2, 3 (H) 1, 2, 3

Answer: (G)

2. Which of the following series converges?

1) $\displaystyle\sum_{n=1}^{\infty} \frac{(-1)^n}{\ln(n+1)}$ 2) $\displaystyle\sum_{n=1}^{\infty} (-1)^n \ln(n+1)$ 3) $1 - \frac{1}{2} + \frac{2}{3} - \frac{3}{4} + \frac{4}{5} - \frac{5}{6} + \cdots$

(A) None (B) 1 (C) 2 (D) 3

(E) 1, 2 (F) 1, 3 (G) 2, 3 (H) 1, 2, 3

Answer: (B)

3. If we add the first 100 terms of the alternating series $1 - \frac{1}{2} + \frac{1}{3} - \frac{1}{4} + \frac{1}{5} - \cdots$, how close can we determine the partial sum s_{100} to be to the sum s of the series?

(A) $s_{100} > s$, with $s_{100} - s < \frac{1}{101}$ (B) $s_{100} > s$, with $s_{100} - s < \frac{1}{e^{100}}$

(C) $s_{100} > s$, with $s_{100} - s < \frac{1}{100}$ (D) $s_{100} < s$, with $s - s_{100} < \frac{1}{e^{101}}$

(E) $s_{100} > s$, with $s_{100} - s < \frac{1}{e^{101}}$ (F) $s_{100} < s$, with $s - s_{100} < \frac{1}{101}$

(G) $s_{100} < s$, with $s - s_{100} < \frac{1}{100}$ (H) $s_{100} < s$, with $s - s_{100} < \frac{1}{e^{100}}$

Answer: (F)

4. How many terms of the alternating series $\displaystyle\sum_{n=1}^{\infty} (-1)^{n+1} n^{-2}$ must we add in order to be sure that the partial sum s_n is within 0.0001 of the sum s?

(A) 10 (B) 300 (C) 30,000 (D) 30

(E) 3 (F) 10,000 (G) 100 (H) 1000

Answer: (G)

5. Which of the following series converges?

 1) $\displaystyle\sum_{n=1}^{\infty} \frac{(-1)^n n}{n+1}$ 2) $\displaystyle\sum_{n=1}^{\infty} \frac{\sqrt{n+1}}{n^2+2}$ 3) $\displaystyle\sum_{n=1}^{\infty} \frac{(-1)^{n-1}}{\sqrt{n+1}}$

(A) None (B) 1 (C) 2 (D) 3

(E) 1, 2 (F) 1, 3 (G) 2, 3 (H) 1, 2, 3

Answer: (G)

6. Which of the following series converges?

1) $\displaystyle\sum_{n=1}^{\infty} \frac{1}{n}$ 2) $\displaystyle\sum_{n=1}^{\infty} \frac{(-1)^n n}{\ln n}$ 3) $\displaystyle\sum_{n=1}^{\infty} \frac{(-1)^n}{n}$

(A) None (B) 1 (C) 2 (D) 3

(E) 1, 2 (F) 1, 3 (G) 2, 3 (H) 1, 2, 3

Answer: (D)

7. Which one of the following series diverges?

(A) $\displaystyle\sum_{n=1}^{\infty} \left(\frac{3}{\pi}\right)^n$

(B) $\displaystyle\sum_{n=2}^{\infty} \frac{1}{\sqrt{n^3+1}}$

(C) $\displaystyle\sum_{n=4}^{\infty} \frac{(-1)^n}{\ln n}$

(D) $\displaystyle\sum_{n=2}^{\infty} \frac{3}{n \ln n}$

(E) $\displaystyle\sum_{n=1}^{\infty} \left(\frac{1}{n} - \frac{1}{n+1}\right)$

(F) $\displaystyle\sum_{n=1}^{\infty} \left(\frac{2}{e}\right)^n$

(G) $\displaystyle\sum_{n=1}^{\infty} \frac{3}{n^2 \ln n}$

(H) $\displaystyle\sum_{n=1}^{\infty} 3n^{-3/2}$

Answer: (D)

8. Which of the following series converges?

1) $\displaystyle\sum_{n=1}^{\infty} \left(\frac{n}{2+3n}\right)^n$

2) $\displaystyle\sum_{n=2}^{\infty} \frac{n+1}{\sqrt{n^4-1}}$

3) $\displaystyle\sum_{n=1}^{\infty} \frac{1}{1+n^2}$

(A) None

(B) 1

(C) 2

(D) 3

(E) 1, 2

(F) 1, 3

(G) 2, 3

(H) 1, 2, 3

Answer: (F)

9. Which of the following series diverges?

1) $\displaystyle\sum_{n=1}^{\infty} \frac{n+2}{n^2+1}$

2) $\displaystyle\sum_{n=1}^{\infty} \frac{n!}{2^n}$

3) $\displaystyle\sum_{n=1}^{\infty} \left(\frac{2n-1}{n+3}\right)^n$

(A) None

(B) 1

(C) 2

(D) 3

(E) 1, 2

(F) 1, 3

(G) 2, 3

(H) 1, 2, 3

Answer: (H)

10. Which of the following series is absolutely convergent?

1) $\displaystyle\sum_{n=1}^{\infty} \frac{(-1)^n}{n^2}$

2) $\displaystyle\sum_{n=1}^{\infty} \frac{(-1)^n}{n}$

3) $\displaystyle\sum_{n=1}^{\infty} \frac{1}{n^3}$

(A) None

(B) 1

(C) 2

(D) 3

(E) 1, 2

(F) 1, 3

(G) 2, 3

(H) 1, 2, 3

Answer: (F)

11. Which of the following series can be shown to be convergent using the Ratio Test?

$$1) \sum_{n=1}^{\infty} \frac{1}{n^2} \qquad 2) \sum_{n=1}^{\infty} \frac{n}{3^n} \qquad 3) \sum_{n=1}^{\infty} \frac{2^n}{n!}$$

(A) None   (B) 1   (C) 2   (D) 3

(E) 1, 2   (F) 1, 3   (G) 2, 3   (H) 1, 2, 3

Answer: (G)

12. Which one of the following series is divergent?

(A) $\sum_{n=1}^{\infty} \left(\frac{2}{3}\right)^n$ (B) $\sum_{n=1}^{\infty} \frac{1}{n^2+1}$

(C) $\sum_{n=1}^{\infty} \frac{1}{n5^n}$ (D) $\sum_{n=2}^{\infty} \frac{n}{n^2-1}$

(E) $\sum_{n=1}^{\infty} \frac{n^3}{n^5+2}$ (F) $\sum_{n=1}^{\infty} \frac{2^n}{n!}$

(G) $\sum_{n=1}^{\infty} \frac{\pi}{n^2}$ (H) $\sum_{n=1}^{\infty} (-1)^{n-1} \frac{\pi}{n}$

Answer: (D)

13. Examine the two series below for absolute convergence (A), convergence that is not absolute (C), or divergence (D).

$$1) \sum_{n=1}^{\infty} (-1)^n \qquad 2) \sum_{n=1}^{\infty} (-1)^{n-1} n^{-1}$$

(A) 1A, 2A   (B) 1A, 2C   (C) 1A, 2D   (D) 1C, 2A

(E) 1C, 2C   (F) 1C, 2D   (G) 1D, 2A   (H) 1D, 2C

Answer: (H)

14. Examine the two series below for absolute convergence (A), convergence that is not absolute (C), or divergence (D).

$$1) \sum_{n=1}^{\infty} (-1)^{n-1} n^{-1} \qquad 2) \sum_{n=1}^{\infty} (-1)^{n-1} n^{-2}$$

(A) 1A, 2A   (B) 1A, 2C   (C) 1A, 2D   (D) 1C, 2A

(E) 1C, 2C   (F) 1C, 2D   (G) 1D, 2A   (H) 1D, 2C

Answer: (D)

15. Which of the following series will, when rearranged, converge to different values?

$$1) \sum_{n=1}^{\infty} n^{-1} \qquad 2) \sum_{n=1}^{\infty} (-1)^{n-1} n^{-1} \qquad 3) \sum_{n=1}^{\infty} (-1)^{n-1} n^{-2}$$

(A) None   (B) 1   (C) 2   (D) 3

(E) 1, 2   (F) 1, 3   (G) 2, 3   (H) 1, 2, 3

Answer: (C)

16. Which of the following series are convergent, but not absolutely convergent?

$$1) \sum_{n=1}^{\infty} (-e)^{-n} \qquad 2) \sum_{n=1}^{\infty} (-1)^{-n} n^{-1} \qquad 3) \sum_{n=1}^{\infty} (-1)^{-n} n^{-2}$$

(A) None   (B) 1   (C) 2   (D) 3

(E) 1, 2   (F) 1, 3   (G) 2, 3   (H) 1, 2, 3

Answer: (C)

17. Examine the two series below for absolute convergence (A), convergence that is not absolute (C), or divergence (D).

$$1) \sum_{n=1}^{\infty} (-1)^{n-1} \frac{(n+2)\, 3^n}{2^{2n+1}} \qquad 2) \sum_{n=1}^{\infty} (-1)^{n-1} \frac{(n+3)\, 2^{2n}}{3^{n+100}}$$

(A) 1A, 2A   (B) 1A, 2C   (C) 1A, 2D   (D) 1C, 2A

(E) 1C, 2C   (F) 1C, 2D   (G) 1D, 2A   (H) 1D, 2C

Answer: (C)

18. Examine the two series below for absolute convergence (A), convergence that is not absolute (C), or divergence (D).

$$1) \sum_{n=1}^{\infty} \frac{(-1)^{n-1}}{\ln(n+1)} \qquad 2) \sum_{n=1}^{\infty} \frac{(-1)^{n-1}}{(\ln(n+1))^2}$$

(A) 1A, 2A   (B) 1A, 2C   (C) 1A, 2D   (D) 1C, 2A

(E) 1C, 2C   (F) 1C, 2D   (G) 1D, 2A   (H) 1D, 2C

Answer: (E)

19. Examine the two series below for absolute convergence (A), convergence that is not absolute (C), or divergence (D).

$$1) \sum_{n=1}^{\infty} (-1)^{n-1} \frac{n+1}{\ln(n+1)} \qquad 2) \sum_{n=1}^{\infty} (-1)^{n-1} \frac{\ln(n+1)}{n+1}$$

(A) 1A, 2A   (B) 1A, 2C   (C) 1A, 2D   (D) 1C, 2A

(E) 1C, 2C   (F) 1C, 2D   (G) 1D, 2A   (H) 1D, 2C

Answer: (H)

20. Which of the following series are convergent, but not absolutely convergent?

$$\text{1) } \sum_{n=1}^{\infty} \frac{(-1)^n}{\sqrt[3]{n}} \qquad \text{2) } \sum_{n=1}^{\infty} \frac{(-1)^{n-1}}{\sqrt{n}\ln n} \qquad \text{3) } \sum_{n=1}^{\infty} \frac{\cos n}{2^n}$$

(A) None   (B) 1   (C) 2   (D) 3

(E) 1, 2   (F) 1, 3   (G) 2, 3   (H) 1, 2, 3

Answer: (E)

21. Which of the following series are convergent, but not absolutely convergent?

$$\text{1) } \sum_{n=1}^{\infty} (-1)^{n+1} \frac{n+2}{n^2+1} \qquad \text{2) } \sum_{n=1}^{\infty} \frac{(-1)^n}{n^4} \qquad \text{3) } \sum_{n=1}^{\infty} \frac{(-1)^n \, n}{n+1}$$

(A) None   (B) 1   (C) 2   (D) 3

(E) 1, 2   (F) 1, 3   (G) 2, 3   (H) 1, 2, 3

Answer: (B)

22. Which one of the following series diverges?

(A) $\sum_{n=1}^{\infty} \dfrac{1}{n(2n+1)}$ (B) $\sum_{n=1}^{\infty} \dfrac{2n}{n+1}$

(C) $\sum_{n=1}^{\infty} \dfrac{1}{(n+1)(n+3)}$ (D) $\sum_{n=1}^{\infty} \dfrac{1}{3^n}$

(E) $\sum_{n=1}^{\infty} \dfrac{n-2}{n2^n}$ (F) $\sum_{n=1}^{\infty} \dfrac{2n}{n!}$

(G) $\sum_{n=1}^{\infty} \dfrac{n^{100}}{n!}$ (H) $\sum_{n=1}^{\infty} \dfrac{n^{100}}{2^n}$

Answer: (B)

23. Which of the following series converges?

$$\text{1) } \sum_{n=1}^{\infty} \sin\left(\frac{1}{n^2}\right) \qquad \text{2) } \sum_{n=1}^{\infty} \frac{(-1)^n}{\sqrt[3]{n}} \qquad \text{3) } \sum_{n=1}^{\infty} \left(\frac{3n+1}{2n+1}\right)^n$$

(A) None   (B) 1   (C) 2   (D) 3

(E) 1, 2   (F) 1, 3   (G) 2, 3   (H) 1, 2, 3

Answer: (E)

24. Which of the following series converges?

$$1) \sum_{n=1}^{\infty} \frac{4^n}{3^n + 2^n} \qquad 2) \sum_{n=1}^{\infty} \frac{3^n}{n + 5^n} \qquad 3) \sum_{n=1}^{\infty} \frac{n}{1 + 4n}$$

(A) None   (B) 1   (C) 2   (D) 3

(E) 1, 2   (F) 1, 3   (G) 2, 3   (H) 1, 2, 3

Answer: (C)

25. Use the Ratio Test to examine the two series below, stating: absolute convergence (A), divergence (D), or Ratio Test inconclusive (I).

$$1) \sum_{n=1}^{\infty} n^{-100} \qquad 2) \sum_{n=1}^{\infty} 100^{-n}$$

(A) 1A, 2A   (B) 1A, 2D   (C) 1A, 2I   (D) 1D, 2A

(E) 1D, 2D   (F) 1D, 2I   (G) 1I, 2A   (H) 1I, 2D

Answer: (G)

26. Use the Ratio Test to examine the two series below, stating: absolute convergence (A), divergence (D), or Ratio Test inconclusive (I).

$$1) \sum_{n=1}^{\infty} (-1)^{n-1} \frac{2^{2n+1}}{5^n} \qquad 2) \sum_{n=1}^{\infty} (-1)^{n-1} \frac{5^n}{2^{2n+1}}$$

(A) 1A, 2A   (B) 1A, 2D   (C) 1A, 2I   (D) 1D, 2A

(E) 1D, 2D   (F) 1D, 2I   (G) 1I, 2A   (H) 1I, 2D

Answer: (B)

27. For which of the following series will the Test for Divergence establish divergence?

$$1) \sum_{n=1}^{\infty} (-1)^n \qquad 2) \sum_{n=1}^{\infty} n^{-1} \qquad 3) \sum_{n=1}^{\infty} \frac{n+1}{2n}$$

(A) None   (B) 1   (C) 2   (D) 3

(E) 1, 2   (F) 1, 3   (G) 2, 3   (H) 1, 2, 3

Answer: (F)

28. For which of the following series will the Ratio Test fail to give a definite answer (i.e., be inconclusive)?

$$1) \sum_{n=1}^{\infty} \left(\frac{99}{100}\right)^n \qquad 2) \sum_{n=1}^{\infty} \left(\frac{100}{99}\right)^n \qquad 3) \sum_{n=1}^{\infty} n^{-100}$$

(A) None   (B) 1   (C) 2   (D) 3

(E) 1, 2   (F) 1, 3   (G) 2, 3   (H) 1, 2, 3

Answer: (D)

29. Tell which of the following three series can be compared with geometric series to establish convergence.

$$1) \sum_{n=1}^{\infty} \frac{1}{2+3^n} \qquad 2) \sum_{n=1}^{\infty} \frac{n}{n^3+4} \qquad 3) \sum_{n=1}^{\infty} \frac{n^2}{3^n}$$

(A) None   (B) 1   (C) 2   (D) 3

(E) 1, 2   (F) 1, 3   (G) 2, 3   (H) 1, 2, 3

Answer: (F)

30. Tell which of the following three series cannot be found convergent by the Ratio Test but can be found convergent by comparison with a p-series.

$$1) \sum_{n=1}^{\infty} \frac{1}{2+3^n} \qquad 2) \sum_{n=1}^{\infty} \frac{n}{n^3+4} \qquad 3) \sum_{n=1}^{\infty} \frac{\sqrt{n}}{n^2+n}$$

(A) None   (B) 1   (C) 2   (D) 3

(E) 1, 2   (F) 1, 3   (G) 2, 3   (H) 1, 2, 3

Answer: (G)

31. Test the following series for convergence or divergence: $5 - \frac{5}{2} + \frac{5}{5} - \frac{5}{8} + \frac{5}{11} - \frac{5}{14} + \cdots$.

Answer: Converges by the Alternating Series Test

32. Test the following series for convergence or divergence: $\dfrac{1}{\ln 2} - \dfrac{1}{\ln 3} + \dfrac{1}{\ln 4} - \dfrac{1}{\ln 5} + \dfrac{1}{\ln 6} - \cdots$.

Answer: Converges by the Alternating Series Test

33. Test the following series for convergence or divergence: $\displaystyle\sum_{n=1}^{\infty} \frac{(-1)^n}{\sqrt{n+3}}$.

Answer: Converges by the Alternating Series Test

34. Test the following series for convergence or divergence: $\displaystyle\sum_{n=2}^{\infty} \frac{(-1)^{n-1}}{n \ln n}$.

Answer: Converges by the Alternating Series Test

35. Test the following series for convergence or divergence: $\displaystyle\sum_{n=1}^{\infty} (-1)^n \frac{n^2}{n^2+1}$.

Answer: Diverges by the Divergence Test

36. Test the following series for convergence or divergence: $\displaystyle\sum_{n=1}^{\infty} (-1)^{n-1} \frac{(n+9)(n+10)}{n(n+1)}$.

Answer: Diverges

37. Test the following series for convergence or divergence: $\displaystyle\sum_{n=1}^{\infty} (-1)^n \cos\left(\frac{\pi}{n}\right)$.

Answer: Diverges

38. Approximate the sum $\displaystyle\sum_{n=1}^{\infty} \frac{(-1)^{n+1}}{n^4}$ with error < 0.001.

Answer: 0.948

293

39. Approximate the sum $\sum_{n=0}^{\infty} \frac{(-1)^n n}{4^n}$ with error < 0.002.

Answer: -0.161

40. Consider the series $\sum_{n=0}^{\infty} (-1)^n \frac{1}{(4n)!}$.

(a) Show that $\sum_{n=0}^{\infty} (-1)^n \frac{1}{(4n)!}$ is absolutely convergent.

(b) Calculate the sum of the first 3 terms to approximate the sum of the series.

(c) Estimate the error involved in the approximation from part (b).

Answer: (b) About 0.958358 (c) $R_3 \le \frac{1}{12!} \approx 2 \times 10^{-9}$

41. Consider the series $\sum_{n=1}^{\infty} (-1)^{n-1} \frac{n}{4^n}$.

(a) Show that the series is absolutely convergent.

(b) Calculate the sum of the first 3 terms to approximate the sum of the series.

(c) Is the approximation in part (b) an overestimate or an underestimate?

(d) Estimate the error involved in the approximation from part (b).

Answer: (b) About 0.17 (c) Overestimate   (d) $R_3 \le \frac{1}{64} \approx 0.016$

42. Consider the series $\sum_{n=1}^{\infty} (-1)^{n-1} \frac{n}{n^2 + 1}$.

(a) Show that the series is convergent, but not absolutely convergent.

(b) Calculate the sum of the first 8 terms to approximate the sum of the series.

(c) Is the approximation in part (b) an overestimate or an underestimate?

(d) Estimate the error involved in the approximation from part (b).

Answer: (b) About 0.21 (c) Underestimate   (d) $R_8 \le \frac{9}{82} \approx 0.11$

43. Consider the series $\sum_{n=1}^{\infty} (-1)^{n-1} \frac{1}{2n - 1}$.

(a) Show that the series is convergent, but not absolutely convergent.

(b) Calculate the sum of the first 9 terms to approximate the sum of the series.

(c) Is the approximation in part (b) an overestimate or an underestimate?

(d) Estimate the error involved in the approximation from part (b).

Answer: (b) About 0.81 Overestimation   (d) $R_9 \le \frac{1}{19} \approx 0.053$

44. Estimate $\sum_{n=1}^{\infty} \frac{(-1)^{n-1}}{n^4 + 1}$ to within 0.01.

Answer: $\frac{1}{2} - \frac{1}{17} + \frac{1}{82} \approx 0.453$

45. Which of the following series is convergent, but not absolutely convergent?

    (a) $\displaystyle\sum_{n=1}^{\infty} \frac{1}{n}$
    (b) $\displaystyle\sum_{n=1}^{\infty} \frac{\sin n}{n^2}$
    (c) $\displaystyle\sum_{n=1}^{\infty} \frac{(-1)^n}{\sqrt{n}}$
    (d) $\displaystyle\sum_{n=1}^{\infty} \frac{3^n}{2^n + \sqrt{n}}$
    (e) $\displaystyle\sum_{n=1}^{\infty} \frac{1-2n}{n+1}$

    Answer: (c) is convergent by the Alternating Series Test, but not absolutely convergent since $\displaystyle\sum_{0}^{\infty} \left| \frac{(-1)^n}{\sqrt{n}} \right| =$

    $\displaystyle\sum_{n=1}^{\infty} \frac{1}{n^{1/2}}$ is a divergent p-series.

46. Determine whether the given series is convergent (but not absolutely convergent), absolutely convergent, or divergent.

    $$\sum_{k=2}^{\infty} \frac{(-1)^{k+1}}{\ln k}$$

    Answer: Convergent, but not absolutely convergent

47. Determine whether the given series is convergent (but not absolutely convergent), absolutely convergent, or divergent.

    $$\sum_{n=1}^{\infty} \frac{(-1)^{n+1} n}{n^2 + 1}$$

    Answer: Convergent, but not absolutely convergent

48. Estimate $\displaystyle\sum_{n=0}^{\infty} \frac{(-1)^n}{(2n)!}$ to within 0.0001.

    Answer: $1 - \frac{1}{2} + \frac{1}{24} - \frac{1}{720} \approx 0.54028$

49. Show that the series $\displaystyle\sum_{n=1}^{\infty} \frac{(-1)^{n-1}}{3n+1}$ is convergent. How many terms of the series do we need to add to find the sum to within 0.01?

    Answer: $n \geq 32$

50. Show that the series $\displaystyle\sum_{n=1}^{\infty} \frac{(-1)^{n-1}}{4n}$ is convergent. How many terms of the series do we need to add to find the sum to within 0.01?

    Answer: $n \geq 24$

51. Determine whether each of the following series converges. Justify your answer by specifying which test you are using and showing any necessary computation.

(a) $\displaystyle\sum_{n=1}^{\infty} \frac{2 + (-1)^n}{2^n}$

(b) $\displaystyle\sum_{n=1}^{\infty} \frac{n^2 + 1}{3n^3 - n + 2}$

(c) $\displaystyle\sum_{n=1}^{\infty} \left(\frac{1 + \sin n}{n} \right)^2$

(d) $\displaystyle\sum_{n=1}^{\infty} \frac{n!}{1 \cdot 3 \cdot 5 \cdot \cdots \cdot (2n - 1)}$

(e) $\displaystyle\sum_{n=1}^{\infty} \frac{n!}{n^n}$

(f) $\displaystyle\sum_{n=1}^{\infty} \left(\frac{\ln n}{n} \right)^n$

(g) $\displaystyle\sum_{n=1}^{\infty} \frac{1}{n\sqrt{1 + \ln n}}$

(h) $\displaystyle\sum_{n=1}^{\infty} \frac{\ln n}{(n + 1)^3}$

(i) $\displaystyle\sum_{n=1}^{\infty} 3^n \sin\left(\frac{\pi}{4^n} \right)$

(j) $\displaystyle\sum_{n=1}^{\infty} \tan^{-1} n$

(k) $\displaystyle\sum_{n=1}^{\infty} (-1)^n \frac{\ln n}{n}$

(l) $\displaystyle\sum_{n=1}^{\infty} \ln\left(1 + \frac{1}{n} \right)$

(m) $\displaystyle\sum_{n=1}^{\infty} \frac{2^n n!}{2 \cdot 5 \cdot 8 \cdot \ldots \cdot (3n - 1)}$

(n) $\displaystyle\sum_{n=1}^{\infty} \frac{\sqrt{n + 1} - \sqrt{n}}{n}$

Answer: (a) Converges (b) Diverges (c) Converges (d) Converges (e) Converges (f) Converges (g) Diverges (h) Converges (i) Converges (j) Diverges (k) Converges (l) Diverges (m) Converges (n) Converges

8.5 Power Series

1. Find the radius of convergence of $\displaystyle\sum_{n=0}^{\infty} 3x^n$.

(A) 2   (B) $\frac{1}{2}$ (C) 6   (D) $\frac{1}{6}$

(E) 3   (F) 1   (G) $\frac{1}{3}$ (H) 0

Answer: (F)

2. Find the radius of convergence of $\displaystyle\sum_{n=0}^{\infty} (3x)^n$.

(A) 3   (B) 0   (C) 2   (D) $\frac{1}{6}$

(E) 6   (F) $\frac{1}{3}$ (G) 1   (H) $\frac{1}{2}$

Answer: (F)

3. Find the interval of convergence of $\displaystyle\sum_{n=0}^{\infty} \frac{x^n}{3n + 1}$.

(A) $[-3, 3]$ (B) $(-1, 1)$ (C) $(-3, 3)$ (D) $[-1, 1]$

(E) $(-1, 1]$ (F) $(-3, 3]$ (G) $[-3, 3)$ (H) $[-1, 1)$

Answer: (H)

4. Find the interval of convergence of $\displaystyle\sum_{n=0}^{\infty} \frac{(-3x)^n}{3n + 1}$.

(A) $\left(-\frac{1}{3}, \frac{1}{3}\right)$ (B) $\left(-\frac{1}{3}, \frac{1}{3}\right]$ (C) $\left[-\frac{1}{3}, \frac{1}{3}\right)$ (D) $\left[-\frac{1}{3}, \frac{1}{3}\right]$

(E) $(-3, 3)$ (F) $(-3, 3]$ (G) $[-3, 3)$ (H) $[-3, 3]$

Answer: (B)

5. Find the interval of convergence of $\sum_{n=0}^{\infty} \frac{x^n}{2n^2}$.

(A) $[-1, 1]$ (B) $(-1, 1]$ (C) $(-1, 1)$ (D) $[-1, 1)$

(E) $[-2, 2]$ (F) $(-2, 2]$ (G) $(-2, 2)$ (H) $[-2, 2)$

Answer: (A)

6. Find the radius of convergence of $\sum_{n=0}^{\infty} \frac{x^n}{n!}$.

(A) $\frac{1}{e}$ (B) ∞ (C) 2 (D) 0

(E) $\frac{1}{(2e)}$ (F) $\frac{1}{2}$ (G) e (H) $2e$

Answer: (B)

7. Find the radius of convergence of $\sum_{n=0}^{\infty} \frac{4^n}{n!} (x - 2)^n$.

(A) 0 (B) $\frac{1}{4}$ (C) $\frac{1}{2}$ (D) 1

(E) 2 (F) 4 (G) 8 (H) ∞

Answer: (H)

8. Find the radius of convergence of $\sum_{n=1}^{\infty} \frac{(x + 2)^n}{n^2 3^n}$.

(A) 0 (B) 1 (C) 2 (D) 3

(E) 4 (F) 5 (G) 6 (H) ∞

Answer: (D)

9. Find the radius of convergence of $\sum_{n=0}^{\infty} \frac{n!}{4^n} (x + 3)^n$.

(A) 0 (B) 1 (C) 2 (D) 3

(E) 4 (F) 5 (G) 6 (H) ∞

Answer: (A)

10. Find the interval of convergence of $\sum_{n=0}^{\infty} \frac{n}{4^n} (x + 3)^n$.

(A) $(-3, 3)$ (B) $[-3, 3)$ (C) $[-3, 3]$ (D) $(-3, 3]$

(E) $(-7, 1)$ (F) $[-7, 1)$ (G) $[-7, 1]$ (H) $(-7, 1]$

Answer: (E)

11. Find the radius of convergence of $\sum_{n=1}^{\infty} (2n)! x^n$.

(A) 0 (B) 2 (C) 4 (D) 6

(E) $\frac{1}{2}$ (F) $\frac{1}{4}$ (G) $\frac{1}{6}$ (H) ∞

Answer: (A)

12. Find the radius of convergence of $\sum_{n=1}^{\infty} \dfrac{n!x^n}{n^n}$.

(A) 0   (B) ∞ (C) $1/e$ (D) $\frac{1}{2}$

(E) 1   (F) e (G) 2   (H) 3

Answer: (F)

13. Find the radius of convergence of $\sum_{n=0}^{\infty} \dfrac{(-1)^n \, x^{2n+1}}{(2n+1)!}$.

(A) 1   (B) $\frac{1}{2}$ (C) 2   (D) 0

(E) ∞ (F) $\frac{1}{4}$ (G) 4   (H) 8

Answer: (E)

14. Find the radius of convergence of $\sum_{n=1}^{\infty} \dfrac{(-1)^n \, (x+2)^n}{\sqrt{n}3^n}$.

(A) 0   (B) 1   (C) 2   (D) 3

(E) 4   (F) 5   (G) 6   (H) ∞

Answer: (D)

15. Find the interval of convergence of $\sum_{n=1}^{\infty} \dfrac{(-1)^n \, (x+2)^n}{\sqrt{n}3^n}$.

(A) $(-\infty, \infty)$ (B) $(-5, 1]$ (C) $[-5, 1)$ (D) $[-5, 1]$

(E) $(-4, 0]$ (F) $[-4, 0)$ (G) $[-4, 0]$ (H) $(-3, -1)$

Answer: (B)

16. Find the radius of convergence of $\sum_{n=1}^{\infty} \dfrac{(x-2)^n}{n3^n}$.

(A) 0   (B) 1   (C) 2   (D) 3

(E) 4   (F) 5   (G) 6   (H) ∞

Answer: (D)

17. Find the interval of convergence of $\sum_{n=1}^{\infty} \dfrac{(x-2)^n}{n3^n}$.

(A) $(1, 3)$ (B) $[1, 3)$ (C) $(2, 4]$ (D) $[2, 4]$

(E) $(-1, 5)$ (F) $[-1, 5)$ (G) $(-2, 6]$ (H) $(-\infty, \infty)$

Answer: (F)

18. Find the radius of convergence of $\sum_{n=0}^{\infty} \dfrac{(-3)^n \, (x-1)^n}{\sqrt{n+1}}$.

(A) 0   (B) $\frac{1}{3}$ (C) $\frac{1}{2}$ (D) 1

(E) 2   (F) 3   (G) 4   (H) ∞

Answer: (B)

19. Find the interval of convergence of $\displaystyle\sum_{n=0}^{\infty} \frac{(-3)^n (x-1)^n}{\sqrt{n+1}}$.

(A) $\left(\frac{2}{3}, \frac{4}{3}\right]$ (B) $\left[\frac{2}{3}, \frac{4}{3}\right)$ (C) $\left(\frac{1}{2}, \frac{3}{2}\right)$ (D) $\left[\frac{1}{2}, \frac{3}{2}\right]$

(E) $(0, 2]$ (F) $[0, 2)$ (G) $(-1, 3)$ (H) $[-2, 4]$

Answer: (A)

20. Find the interval of convergence of the power series $\displaystyle\sum_{k=0}^{\infty} \frac{(-1)^k k^2}{5^k} (x-2)^k$.

Answer: $(-3, 7)$

21. Find the interval of convergence for $\displaystyle\sum_{n=1}^{\infty} \frac{x^n}{4n^2}$.

Answer: $[-1, 1]$

22. Find the interval of convergence for $\displaystyle\sum_{n=1}^{\infty} \frac{x^n}{n2^n}$.

Answer: $[-2, 2)$

23. Find the interval of convergence of the power series $\displaystyle\sum_{n=1}^{\infty} \frac{(-1)^n (x-2)^n}{\sqrt[3]{n}}$.

Answer: $(1, 3]$

24. Consider the power series $\displaystyle\sum_{k=1}^{\infty} \frac{(-1)^k}{k} x^k$.

(a) Find the radius of convergence.

(b) Determine what happens at the end points (absolute or conditional convergence, or divergence).

Answer: (a) $r = 1$ (b) for $x = 1$, converges conditionally; for $x = -1$, diverges

25. Find the interval of convergence for $\displaystyle\sum_{k=0}^{\infty} \left(\frac{e^k}{k+1}\right) x^k$.

Answer: $\dfrac{-1}{e} \leq x < \dfrac{1}{e}$

26. Find the interval of convergence for $\displaystyle\sum_{k=1}^{\infty} \frac{(-1)^k (x-3)^k}{5^k (k+1)}$.

Answer: $(-2, 8]$

27. The power series $\displaystyle\sum_{n=1}^{\infty} a_n (x-2)^n$ and $\displaystyle\sum_{n=1}^{\infty} b_n (x-3)^n$ both converge at $x = 6$. Find the largest interval over which both series must converge.

Answer: $0 < x \leq 6$

28. Find the radius of convergence of the series $\displaystyle\sum_{n=1}^{\infty} \frac{3^n (x-2)^{2n+1}}{n!}$.

Answer: $r = \infty$; that is, the series converges for all real x.

29. Find the radius of convergence of $\displaystyle\sum_{n=1}^{\infty} \frac{2 \cdot 5 \cdot 8 \cdots (3n-1)}{n!} x^n$.

Answer: $\frac{1}{3}$

30. Find the radius of convergence of $\displaystyle\sum_{n=1}^{\infty} \frac{n}{2 \cdot 5 \cdot 8 \cdots (3n-1)} x^n$.

Answer: ∞

31. Find the radius of convergence of $\displaystyle\sum_{n=1}^{\infty} \frac{2 \cdot 5 \cdot 8 \cdots (3n-1)}{n} x^n$.

Answer: 0

32. Construct an example of a power series that has $[-3, 5]$ as its interval of convergence.

Answer: There are many such series. One is $\displaystyle\sum_{n=1}^{\infty} \frac{(x-1)^n}{4^n n^2}$.

33. Construct an example of a power series that has $[-3, 5)$ as its interval of convergence.

Answer: There are many such series. One is $\displaystyle\sum_{n=1}^{\infty} \frac{(x-1)^n}{4^n n}$.

34. Construct an example of a power series that has $(-3, 5)$ as its interval of convergence.

Answer: There are many such series. One is $\displaystyle\sum_{n=1}^{\infty} \frac{n(x-1)^n}{4^n}$.

8.6   Representations of Functions as Power Series

1. Find a power series representation for the function $f(x) = \dfrac{1-x}{1+x}$ and give its interval of convergence.

Answer: $1 - 2 \displaystyle\sum_{n=0}^{\infty} (-1)^n x^{n+1}$, interval of convergence $|x| < 1$

2. Find a power series representation for $f(x) = \dfrac{x}{x+5}$ and find its interval of convergence.

Answer: $\displaystyle\sum_{n=0}^{\infty} (-1)^n \left(\frac{x}{5}\right)^{n+1}$, interval of convergence $|x| < 5$

3. Find a power series representation for the function $f(x) = \ln\sqrt{1-x}$ and determine the radius of convergence.

Answer: $-\frac{1}{2} \displaystyle\sum_{n=0}^{\infty} \frac{x^{n+1}}{n+1}$, radius of convergence 1

4. Find a power series representation for $f(x) = \arctan(3x)$ and determine its radius of convergence.

Answer: $3 \displaystyle\sum_{n=0}^{\infty} \frac{(-9)^n x^{2n+1}}{2n+1}$, radius of convergence $\frac{1}{3}$

5. Evaluate $\int \dfrac{1}{1+x^5}\, dx$ as a power series.

Answer: $C + \displaystyle\sum_{n=0}^{\infty} \dfrac{(-1)^n\, x^{5n+1}}{5n+1}$

6. Find a power series representation for $\ln\left(1+x^2\right)$.

Hint: What is $\dfrac{d}{dx}\ln\left(1+x^2\right)$?

Answer: $\displaystyle\sum_{n=1}^{\infty} \dfrac{(-1)^{n+1}\, x^{2n}}{n}$

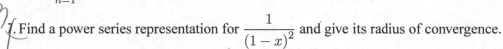

7. Find a power series representation for $\dfrac{1}{(1-x)^2}$ and give its radius of convergence.

Answer: $\displaystyle\sum_{n=0}^{\infty} (n+1)\, x^n$; radius of convergence 1

8. Approximate the definite integral $\int_0^1 e^{-x^2}\, dx$ accurate to six decimal places.

Answer: 0.746824

9. Show that $f(x) = \displaystyle\sum_{n=0}^{\infty} \dfrac{(8x)^n}{n!}$ is a solution to the differential equation $\dfrac{dy}{dx} = 8y$.

10. Find the sum of the series $\displaystyle\sum_{n=2}^{\infty} (n-1)\, x^n$, where $|x| < 1$.

Answer: $\dfrac{x^2}{(x-1)^2}$

11. Find a power series representation for the function $f(x) = \dfrac{x^2}{1-3x}$.

Answer: $\displaystyle\sum_{n=0}^{\infty} 3^n x^{n+2}$

12. Approximate the definite integral $\displaystyle\int_0^{0.1} \dfrac{1}{x^5+1}\, dx$ accurate to six decimal places.

Answer: 0.100000

13. Approximate the definite integral $\displaystyle\int_0^{0.5} \dfrac{\ln(1+x)}{x}\, dx$ accurate to six decimal places.

Answer: 0.448414

14. Find the sum of the series $\displaystyle\sum_{n=1}^{\infty} \dfrac{n^2}{3^n}$.

Answer: $\dfrac{3}{2}$

15. Given that the power series for $\dfrac{1}{1-x}$ is $\displaystyle\sum_{n=0}^{\infty} x^n$, find the power series for $\dfrac{1}{(1-x)^2}$ in terms of powers of x.

Answer: $\displaystyle\sum_{n=1}^{\infty} n x^{n-1}$

16. Find the power series for $f(x) = \dfrac{5x + 7}{x^2 + 2x - 3}$ in terms of powers of x.

Hint: Express $f(x)$ in terms of partial fractions.

Answer: $\dfrac{2}{3} \sum\limits_{n=0}^{\infty} (-1)^n \left(\dfrac{x}{3}\right)^n - 3 \sum\limits_{n=0}^{\infty} x^n$

17. Find a power series representation for $\displaystyle\int \dfrac{x}{x^3 + 1}\, dx$.

Answer: $\sum\limits_{n=0}^{\infty} \dfrac{x^{3n+2}}{3n + 2} + C$

8.7 Taylor and Maclaurin Series

1. Find the coefficient of x^3 in the Maclaurin series for $f(x) = \sin 2x$.

(A) $-\dfrac{2}{3}$ (B) $-\dfrac{4}{3}$ (C) $\dfrac{4}{3}$ (D) $-\dfrac{8}{3}$

(E) $\dfrac{2}{3}$ (F) $\dfrac{8}{3}$ (G) $-\dfrac{1}{3}$ (H) $\dfrac{1}{3}$

Answer: (B)

2. Find the radius of convergence of the Maclaurin series for $f(x) = \dfrac{1}{4 + x^2}$.

(A) 1 (B) $\dfrac{1}{8}$ (C) ∞ (D) $\dfrac{1}{4}$

(E) $\dfrac{1}{2}$ (F) 4 (G) 8 (H) 2

Answer: (H)

3. Find the coefficient of x^2 in the Maclaurin series for e^{x-1}.

(A) e (B) $\dfrac{1}{e}$ (C) $\dfrac{1}{(2e)}$ (D) 2

(E) $\dfrac{1}{2}$ (F) 0 (G) 1 (H) $\dfrac{e}{2}$

Answer: (C)

4. Find the coefficient of x^2 in the Maclaurin series for $f(x) = e^{-x^2}$.

(A) $\dfrac{1}{4}$ (B) -1 (C) $\dfrac{1}{2}$ (D) -2

(E) 1 (F) $-\dfrac{1}{4}$ (G) $-\dfrac{1}{2}$ (H) 2

Answer: (B)

5. Find the coefficient of x^5 in the Maclaurin series for $f(x) = \int \cos\left(x^2\right) dx$.

Note: The series is unique except for the constant of integration.

(A) $-\dfrac{1}{10}$ (B) $\dfrac{1}{15}$ (C) $-\dfrac{1}{5}$ (D) $\dfrac{2}{5}$

(E) $-\dfrac{2}{5}$ (F) $-\dfrac{1}{15}$ (G) $\dfrac{1}{5}$ (H) $\dfrac{1}{10}$

Answer: (A)

6. Find the terms in the Maclaurin series for the function $f(x) = \ln(1 + x)$, as far as the term in x^3.

(A) $1 - x + x^2 - x^3$

(B) $x - x^2 + x^3$

(C) $1 - x + \frac{1}{2}x^2 - \frac{1}{6}x^3$

(D) $x - \frac{1}{2}x^2 + \frac{1}{3}x^3$

(E) $1 + \frac{1}{2}x + \frac{2}{3}x^2 + \frac{5}{6}x^3$

(F) $x + \frac{1}{2}x^2 + \frac{1}{6}x^3$

(G) $1 + \frac{x}{2} + \frac{1}{6}x^2 + \frac{1}{24}x^3$

(H) $x - \frac{1}{24}x^2 + \frac{1}{120}x^3$

Answer: (D)

7. Find the terms in the Maclaurin series for the function $f(x) = e^{-x}$, as far as the term in x^3.

(A) $1 - x + \frac{1}{2}x^2 - \frac{1}{6}x^3$

(B) $1 + x + \frac{1}{2}x^2 - \frac{1}{6}x^3$

(C) $1 - x + x^2 - x^3$

(D) $1 + x + x^2 + x^3$

(E) $1 - x + \frac{1}{2}x^2 - \frac{1}{3}x^3$

(F) $1 + x + \frac{1}{2}x^2 + \frac{1}{3}x^3$

(G) $-x + x^3$

(H) $x - x^3$

Answer: (A)

8. Find the first four terms in the Maclaurin series for $f(x) = xe^{-x}$.

(A) $x - x^2 + x^3 - x^4$

(B) $x - \frac{1}{2}x^2 + \frac{1}{3}x^3 - \frac{1}{4}x^4$

(C) $x - x^2 + \frac{1}{2}x^3 - \frac{1}{6}x^4$

(D) $x - 2x^2 + 3x^3 - 4x^4$

(E) $x + \frac{1}{2}x^2 + \frac{1}{6}x^3 + \frac{1}{24}x^4$

(F) $x + x^2 + \frac{1}{3}x^3 + \frac{1}{8}x^4$

(G) $x + x^2 + \frac{1}{2}x^3 + \frac{1}{6}x^4$

(H) $\frac{1}{2}x - \frac{1}{6}x^2 + \frac{1}{24}x^3 - \frac{1}{120}x^4$

Answer: (C)

9. Find the terms of the Maclaurin series for $\dfrac{1}{\sqrt{1-x}}$, as far as the term in x^3.

(A) $1 - x + x^2 - x^3$

(B) $1 - \frac{1}{2}x + \frac{1}{4}x^2 + \frac{1}{8}x^3$

(C) $1 + \frac{1}{2}x + \frac{3}{8}x^2 + \frac{5}{16}x^3$

(D) $1 - \frac{1}{2}x + \frac{3}{4}x^2 - \frac{5}{8}x^3$

(E) $1 + \frac{1}{2}x + \frac{1}{4}x^2 + \frac{1}{6}x^3$

(F) $1 - \frac{1}{2}x + \frac{1}{6}x^2 + \frac{1}{24}x^3$

(G) $1 + \frac{1}{2}x + \frac{3}{4}x^2 + \frac{15}{16}x^3$

(H) $1 - \frac{1}{2}x + \frac{3}{8}x^2 + \frac{7}{24}x^3$

Answer: (C)

10. Find the terms of the Maclaurin series for $f(x) = \dfrac{1}{\sqrt{1+2x}}$, as far as the term in x^3.

(A) $1 - x + x^2 - x^3$

(B) $1 + x - \frac{1}{2}x^2 + \frac{1}{3}x^3$

(C) $1 - x + \frac{3}{2}x^2 - \frac{5}{2}x^3$

(D) $1 + x + 3x^2 + 5x^3$

(E) $1 - x + \frac{3}{2}x^2 - \frac{7}{3}x^3$

(F) $1 + x + \frac{1}{2}x^2 + \frac{7}{3}x^3$

(G) $1 - x + \frac{5}{2}x^2 - \frac{7}{3}x^3$

(H) $1 + x + \frac{7}{2}x^2 + \frac{11}{3}x^3$

Answer: (C)

11. Give the Taylor series expansion of $f(x) = \sin x$ about the point $c = \frac{\pi}{4}$.

Answer: $\frac{\sqrt{2}}{2} + \frac{\sqrt{2}}{2}\left(x - \frac{\pi}{4}\right) - \frac{\sqrt{2}}{2} \cdot \frac{1}{2!}\left(x - \frac{\pi}{4}\right)^2 - \frac{\sqrt{2}}{2} \cdot \frac{1}{3!}\left(x - \frac{\pi}{4}\right)^3 + \cdots$

12. Find the Taylor series for $y = \ln x$ at 2.

Answer: $\ln 2 + \displaystyle\sum_{n=1}^{\infty} \frac{(-1)^{n-1}}{n} \left(\frac{x-2}{2}\right)^n$

13. Find the Taylor polynomial of degree 4 at 0 for the function defined by $f(x) = \ln(1+x)$. Then compute the value of $\ln(1.1)$ accurate to as many decimal places as the polynomial of degree 4 allows.

Answer: $\ln(1+x) = x - \frac{1}{2}x^2 + \frac{1}{3}x^3 - \frac{1}{4}x^4$; $\ln(1.1) = 0.09531$, accurate to five decimal places

14. Find the Maclaurin series expansion for $f(x) = \ln(1-x)$ and determine the interval of convergence.

Answer: $\displaystyle\sum_{n=1}^{\infty} -\frac{1}{n}x^n$; converges for all x such that $-1 \le x < 1$

15. If the Maclaurin series for $f(x)$ is $1 - 9x + 16x^2 - 25x^3 + \cdots$, find $f^3(0)$.

Answer: -150

16. Find the Taylor series of degree 5 about $x = 0$ for $y = \tan^2 x$.

Answer: $x^2 + \frac{2}{3}x^4 + \cdots$

17. Find the Taylor series for $x \cos x$ about the origin.

Answer: $\displaystyle\sum_{n=0}^{\infty} \frac{(-1)^n x^{2n+1}}{(2n)!}$

18. Derive the Taylor series about $x = 0$ for $f(x) = e^x$.

Answer: $\displaystyle\sum_{k=0}^{\infty} \frac{x^k}{k!}$

19. Use the result of the last question to obtain the series expansion for e^{-x^2}.

Answer: $1 - x^2 + \dfrac{x^4}{2!} - \dfrac{x^6}{3!} + \dfrac{x^8}{4!} - \cdots$

20. Use the result of the last question to obtain $\int_0^1 e^{-x^2}\, dx$ to two decimal place accuracy.

Answer: 0.75

21. Find the fourth-degree Maclaurin polynomial for $f(x) = \log \sec x$.

Answer: $\dfrac{x^2}{2} + \dfrac{x^4}{12}$

22. Find the Maclaurin series expansion with $n = 5$ for $f(x) = 2^x$. Use this expansion to approximate 2^{1}.

Answer: $1 + (\ln 2)x + \dfrac{(\ln 2)^2 x^2}{2!} + \dfrac{(\ln 2)^3 x^3}{3!} + \dfrac{(\ln 2)^4 x^4}{4!} + \dfrac{(\ln 2)^5 x^5}{5!} + \cdots$; $2^{0.1} \approx 1.0718$

23. Find the coefficient of x^2 in the Maclaurin series for $f(x) = 1/(x+2)$.

Answer: $\frac{1}{8}$

24. Find the sum of the series $\displaystyle\sum_{n=0}^{\infty} \frac{(-1)^n \pi^{2n+1}}{3^{2n}(2n+1)!}$.

Answer: $\frac{3\sqrt{3}}{2}$

25. Find the sum of the series $\displaystyle\sum_{n=1}^{\infty} \frac{(-1)^n}{n!}$.

Answer: $\dfrac{1}{e} - 1$

26. Find the sum of the series $\displaystyle\sum_{n=1}^{\infty} \frac{n3^n}{4^n}$.

Answer: 12

27. Find the sum of the series $\displaystyle\sum_{n=0}^{\infty} \frac{1}{(2n)!}$.

Answer: $\dfrac{1}{2}\left(e + \dfrac{1}{e}\right)$

28. If $f(x) = e^{x^2}$, compute $f^{(11)}(0)$.

Answer: 0

29. If $f(x) = e^{x^2}$, compute $f^{(10)}(0)$.

Answer: $\dfrac{10!}{5!} = 30{,}240$

30. Let $f(x) = \dfrac{x}{1 + \frac{1}{4}x^2}$, compute $f^{(23)}(0)$.

Answer: $-\dfrac{23!}{4^{11}}$

8.8 The Binomial Series

1. Find the coefficient of x^3 in the binomial series for $(1 + x)^5$.

(A) 3   (B) 6   (C) 15   (D) 20

(E) 10   (F) 5   (G) 16   (H) 12

Answer: (E)

2. Find the coefficient of x in the binomial series for $\sqrt{1 + x}$.

(A) 2   (B) -1 (C) 1   (D) $-\frac{1}{2}$

(E) $\frac{1}{2}$ (F) $-\sqrt{2}$ (G) -2 (H) $\sqrt{2}$

Answer: (E)

3. Find the coefficient of x^3 in the binomial series for $\sqrt{1 + x}$.

(A) $-\frac{1}{2}$ (B) $-\frac{1}{4}$ (C) $\frac{1}{8}$ (D) $\frac{1}{2}$

(E) $-\frac{1}{8}$ (F) $-\frac{1}{16}$ (G) $\frac{1}{16}$ (H) $\frac{1}{4}$

Answer: (G)

4. Use the binomial series to expand the function $\sqrt{4 + x}$ as a power series. Give the coefficient of x^2 in that series.

(A) $-\frac{1}{8}$ (B) $-\frac{1}{32}$ (C) $-\frac{1}{64}$ (D) $\frac{1}{8}$

(E) $\frac{1}{32}$ (F) $-\frac{1}{16}$ (G) $\frac{1}{64}$ (H) $\frac{1}{16}$

Answer: (C)

5. How many coefficients in the binomial series expansion of $(1+x)^7$ are divisible by 7?

(A) 0   (B) 5   (C) 7   (D) 3

(E) 2   (F) 6   (G) 1   (H) 4

Answer: (F)

6. Find the coefficient of x^3 in the binomial series for $\dfrac{1}{(1+x)^4}$.

(A) 6   (B) 20   (C) -6 (D) -10

(E) -20 (F) -12 (G) 10   (H) 12

Answer: (E)

7. Use the binomial series to expand $\dfrac{1}{(1+x)^3}$ as a power series. State the radius of convergence.

Answer: $1 + \displaystyle\sum_{n=1}^{\infty} \dfrac{(-1)^n\, 3 \cdot 4 \cdot 5 \cdots (n+2)\, x^n}{n!}$ with $R = 1$

8. Use the binomial series to expand $\sqrt[3]{1+x^2}$ as a power series. State the radius of convergence.

Answer: $1 + \dfrac{x^2}{3} + \displaystyle\sum_{n=2}^{\infty} \dfrac{(-1)^{n-1}\, 2 \cdot 5 \cdot 8 \cdots (3n-4)\, x^{2n}}{3^n n!}$ with $R = 1$

9. Use the binomial series to expand $\dfrac{x^2}{\sqrt{1-x^3}}$ as a power series. State the radius of convergence.

Answer: $x^2 + \displaystyle\sum_{n=1}^{\infty} \dfrac{1 \cdot 3 \cdot 5 \cdots (2n-1)\, x^{3n+2}}{2^n n!}$ with $R = 1$

10. Use the binomial series to expand $\sqrt[5]{x-1}$ as a power series. State the radius of convergence.

Answer: $-1 + \dfrac{x}{5} + \displaystyle\sum_{n=2}^{\infty} \dfrac{4 \cdot 9 \cdots (5n-6)\, x^n}{5^n n!}$ with $R = 1$

11. Use the binomial series formula to obtain the Maclaurin series for $f(x) = (1+x)^{1/3}$.

Answer: $1 + \dfrac{1}{3}x + \displaystyle\sum_{n=2}^{\infty} \dfrac{(-1)^{n+1} \cdot 2 \cdot 5 \cdot 8 \cdots (3n-4)\, x^n}{3^n \cdot n!}$, for $|x| < 1$

12. Use the binomial series to expand $\dfrac{1}{\sqrt{2+x}}$ as a power series. State the radius of convergence.

Answer: $\dfrac{\sqrt{2}}{2}\left[1 + \displaystyle\sum_{n=1}^{\infty} \dfrac{(-1)^n\, 1 \cdot 3 \cdot 5 \cdots (2n-1)\, x^n}{2^{2n} n!} \right]$ with $\left|\dfrac{x}{2}\right| < 1$ so $|x| < 2$ and $R = 2$.

13. Use the binomial series to expand $(4+x)^{3/2}$ as a power series. State the radius of convergence.

Answer: $8 + 3x + \displaystyle\sum_{n=2}^{\infty} \dfrac{(3)(1)(-1) \cdots (5-2n)\, x^n}{8^{n-1} n!}$ with $\left|\dfrac{x}{4}\right| < 1$ so $|x| < 4$ and $R = 4$.

14. Find the terms in the power series expansion for the function $f(x) = 1/\sqrt{1+x^2}$, as far as the term in x^3.

Answer: $1 - \frac{1}{2}x^2$

15. Find the terms of the Maclaurin series for $1/\sqrt{1+2x}$, as far as the term in x^3.

Answer: $1 - x + \frac{3}{2}x^2 - \frac{5}{2}x^3$

8.9 | Applications of Taylor Polynomials

1. According to Taylor's Formula, what is the maximum error possible in the use of the sum $\sum_{n=0}^{4} \dfrac{x^n}{n!}$ to approximate e^x in the interval $-1 \le x \le 1$?

(A) $\dfrac{e}{240}$ (B) $\dfrac{e}{48}$ (C) $\dfrac{e}{480}$ (D) $\dfrac{e}{24}$

(E) $\dfrac{e}{20}$ (F) $\dfrac{e}{120}$ (G) $\dfrac{e}{12}$ (H) $\dfrac{e}{60}$

Answer: (F)

2. Find the coefficient of $(x-2)^2$ in the Taylor polynomial $T_2(x)$ for the function x^3 at the number 2.

(A) 3 (B) 0 (C) 1 (D) 6

(E) 2 (F) 5 (G) 8 (H) 4

Answer: (D)

3. What is the smallest value of n that will guarantee (according to Taylor's Formula) that the Taylor polynomial T_n at the number 0 will be within 0.0001 of e^x for $0 \le x \le 1$?

(A) 4 (B) 5 (C) 8 (D) 6

(E) 7 (F) 2 (G) 3 (H) 9

Answer: (E)

4. Estimate the range of values of x for which the approximation $\dfrac{1}{x} = 1 - (x-1) + (x-1)^2$ is accurate to within 0.01.

(A) $[0.68, 1.41]$ (B) $[0.61, 1.54]$ (C) $[0.995, 1.005]$ (D) $[1.51, 2.59]$

(E) $[0.95, 1.05]$ (F) $[0.80, 1.23]$ (G) $[0.980, 1.023]$ (H) $[0.89, 1.14]$

Answer: (F)

5. Estimate the range of values of x for which the approximation $\ln x = \ln 2 + \frac{1}{2}(x-2) - \frac{1}{8}(x-2)^2$ is accurate to within 0.01.

(A) $[1.08, 3.20]$ (B) $[1.80, 2.20]$ (C) $[0.89, 3.56]$ (D) $[1.43, 2.66]$

(E) $[0.45, 1.78]$ (F) $[0.71, 1.33]$ (G) $[1.90, 2.10]$ (H) $[1.99, 2.01]$

Answer: (D)

6. Estimate the range of values of x for which the approximation $\sqrt{x^2+3} = 2 + \frac{1}{2}(x-1) + \frac{3}{16}(x-1)^2$ is accurate to within 0.0002.

Answer: $[0.84, 1.16]$

7. Estimate the range of values of x for which the approximation $e^x \cos x = 1 + x - \frac{1}{3}x^3$ is accurate to within 0.001.

Answer: $[-0.282, 0.274]$

8. Find the second-degree Taylor polynomial of the function $f(x) = xe^x$ at $a = -1$.

Answer: $-\dfrac{1}{e} + \dfrac{1}{2e}(x+1)^2$

9. Find the Taylor polynomial $T_3(x)$ for the function $f(x) = \dfrac{5x}{2+4x}$ at the point $x_0 = 0$.

Answer: $T_3(x) = \frac{5}{2}x - 5x^2 + 10x^3$

10. Consider the function $f(x) = 3x^4 - 24x^3 + 72x^2 - 96x + 49$.

   (a) Find the fourth-degree Taylor polynomial of f at $a = 2$.

   (b) What is the remainder?

   (c) What is the absolute minimum value of f, and where does it occur?

Answer:

   (a) $T_4(x) = 1 + 3(x-2)^4$

   (b) 0

   (c) As we can see from the form of $T_4(x) = f(x)$, f has the absolute minimum value $f(2) = 1$.

11. Write the fourth-degree Taylor polynomial centered about the origin for the function $f(x) = e^{-2x}$.

Answer: $T_4(x) = 1 - 2x + 2x^2 - \frac{4}{3}x^3 + \frac{2}{3}x^4$

12. Find the second-degree Taylor polynomial for $f(x) = \sqrt{x}$, centered about $a = 100$. Also obtain a bound for the error in using this polynomial to approximate $\sqrt{100.1}$.

Answer: $T_2(x) = 10 + \frac{1}{20}(x-100) - \frac{1}{8000}(x-100)^2$; $|\text{error}| \leq 6 \times 10^{-10}$

13. Find an approximation for $\sin(0.1)$ accurate to 6 decimal places.

   (*Note:* sin's argument is measured in radians.)

Answer: 0.099833

14. Give the 4th-degree Taylor polynomial for $f(x) = \sqrt{x}$ about the point $x = 4$. Using this polynomial, approximate $\sqrt{4.2}$. Give the maximum error for this approximation.

Answer: $T_4(x) = 2 + \dfrac{x-4}{4} + \dfrac{(x-4)^2}{64} + \dfrac{(x-4)^3}{512} - \dfrac{5(x-4)^4}{16384} + R_4$; $\sqrt{4.2} \approx 2.049390137$; $R_4 \approx 0.0000000171$

15. Use the 3rd-degree Taylor polynomial of $f(x) = \sqrt{x}$ about $x = 4$ to approximate $\sqrt{6}$. Use the remainder term to give an upper bound for the error in this approximation.

Answer: $\sqrt{6} \approx T_3(6) = 2 + \frac{2}{4} - \frac{2^2}{64} + \frac{2^3}{512} = 2.453125$; $|\text{error}| \leq 0.005$

16. Write the Taylor polynomial at 0 of degree 4 for $f(x) = \ln(1+x)$.

Answer: $x - \frac{1}{2}x^2 + \frac{1}{3}x^3 - \frac{1}{4}x^4$

17. The first three derivatives of $f(x) = (x+4)^{3/2}$ are $f'(x) = \dfrac{3(x+4)^{1/2}}{2}$, $f''(x) = \dfrac{3}{4(x+4)^{1/2}}$ and

$f'''(x) = \dfrac{-3}{8(x+4)^{3/2}}$.

(a) Give the first four terms of the Taylor series associated with f at $a = -3$.

(b) Give the second-order Taylor polynomial, $T_2(x)$, associated with f at $a = 0$.

(c) Suppose that $x \geq 0$ and that $T_2(x)$ from part (b) is used to approximate $f(x)$. Prove that the error in

this approximation does not exceed $\dfrac{x^3}{128}$.

Answer: (a) $1 + \frac{3}{2}(x+3) + \frac{3}{8}(x+3)^2 - \frac{1}{16}(x+3)^3$ (b) $8 + 3x + \frac{3}{16}x^2$

(c) Error $\leq \dfrac{Mx^3}{3!}$ where $M = \max\left|f^{(3)}(x)\right| = \frac{3}{64}$. So error $\leq \dfrac{3}{64 \cdot 6}x^3 = \dfrac{x^3}{128}$

18. Given $f(x) = \tan x$ and $a = 0$,

    (a) calculate $T_1(x; 0)$.   (b) calculate $T_3(x; 0)$.   (c) calculate $T_5(x; 0)$.

Answer: (a) x (b) $x + \dfrac{x^3}{3}$ (c) $x + \dfrac{x^3}{3} + \dfrac{2}{15}x^5$

19. Find the third Taylor polynomial associated with $f(x) = 2 + x^2 - 5x^3$ at $a = 0$. What is the remainder?

Answer: $2 + x^2 - 5x^3$. The remainder is 0.

20. (a) Find the third-order Taylor polynomial associated with $f(x) = \sin^{-1} x$ at $a = 0$.

(b) Use the Taylor polynomial from part (a) to find an approximation of $\sin^{-1} 0.2$.

(c) Compare the value you calculated in part (b) with your calculator's value for $\sin^{-1} 0.2$.

Answer: (a) $x + \dfrac{x^3}{6}$ (b) About 0.201333   (c) A calculator gives 0.2013579.

21. (a) Use series to compute $\int_0^1 x \cos x \, dx$ correct to three decimal places.

(b) Use integration by parts to compute $\int_0^1 x \cos x \, dx$.

(c) Compare your answers in parts (a) and (b) above.

Answer: (a) About 0.382   (b) $\cos 1 + \sin 1 - 1$ (c) $\cos 1 + \sin 1 - 1 \approx 0.38177$

22. Use series to compute $\int_0^1 \cos \sqrt{x} \, dx$ correct to four decimal places.

Answer: About 0.7635

23. Find the third-degree Taylor polynomial centered at $x = 1$ for $f(x) = \ln x$. Use this result to approximate $\ln 1.2$.

Answer: $T_3(x) = (x-1) - \frac{1}{2!}(x-1)^2 + \frac{2}{3!}(x-1)^3$; $\ln(1.2) \approx 0.18266$

24. Find the third-degree Taylor polynomial of the function $f(x) = \int_0^x \sin t^2 \, dt$ at $a = 0$.

Answer: $\frac{1}{3}x^3$

25. Find the third-degree Taylor polynomial of the function $f(x) = e^{x^2} - x^2 \cos \sqrt{x}$ at $a = 0$.

Answer: $1 + \dfrac{x^3}{2}$

26. Find the second-degree Taylor polynomial of the function $f(x) = x \ln x$ at $a = \dfrac{1}{e}$.

Answer: $-\dfrac{1}{e} + \dfrac{e}{2}\left(x - \dfrac{1}{e}\right)^2$

9 Vectors and the Geometry of Space

9.1 Three-Dimensional Coordinate Systems

1. Find the distance from the point $(1, 2, 3)$ to the origin $(0, 0, 0)$.

(A) $\sqrt{13}$ (B) $\sqrt{14}$ (C) $\sqrt{15}$ (D) 4

(E) $\sqrt{17}$ (F) $\sqrt{18}$ (G) $\sqrt{19}$ (H) $\sqrt{20}$

Answer: (B)

2. Find the distance from the point $(4, -3, 5)$ to the x-axis.

(A) 5 (B) $2\sqrt{5}$ (C) $\sqrt{34}$ (D) $\sqrt{5}$

(E) 50 (F) 3 (G) $\sqrt{41}$ (H) 4

Answer: (C)

3. Find the radius of the sphere whose equation is $x^2 + 2x + y^2 + z^2 = 4$.

(A) 1 (B) $\sqrt{2}$ (C) $\sqrt{3}$ (D) 2

(E) $\sqrt{5}$ (F) $\sqrt{6}$ (G) $\sqrt{7}$ (H) $2\sqrt{2}$

Answer: (E)

4. Find the center of the sphere whose equation is $x^2 + 2x + y^2 - y + z^2 = 0$.

(A) $(2, 1, 0)$ (B) $(2, -1, 0)$ (C) $(-2, 1, 0)$ (D) $(-2, -1, 0)$

(E) $\left(1, \frac{1}{2}, 0\right)$ (F) $\left(-1, \frac{1}{2}, 0\right)$ (G) $\left(1, -\frac{1}{2}, 0\right)$ (H) $\left(-1, -\frac{1}{2}, 0\right)$

Answer: (F)

5. Find the distance from the center of the sphere whose equation is $x^2 + 2x + y^2 + 4y + z^2 + 6z = 0$ to the xz-plane.

(A) $\sqrt{14}$ (B) 4 (C) $\sqrt{10}$ (D) 3

(E) 1 (F) $\sqrt{13}$ (G) 2 (H) $\sqrt{5}$

Answer: (A)

6. What region of $\mathbb{R}^3$ is represented by the inequality $x^2 + y^2 \leq 1$?

   (A) points inside a circular cylinder with axis the x-axis

   (B) points inside a circular cylinder with axis the y-axis

   (C) points inside a circular cylinder with axis the z-axis

   (D) points inside a sphere of radius 1

   (E) points inside a sphere of radius $\sqrt{2}$

   (F) points inside a sphere of radius 2

   (G) points inside a sphere of radius $\sqrt{3}$

   (H) points inside a sphere of radius 3

   Answer: (C)

7. What region of $\mathbb{R}^3$ is represented by the equation $z = 3$?

   (A) line parallel to the xy-plane   (B) line parallel to the xz-plane

   (C) line parallel to the yz-plane   (D) plane parallel to the xz-plane

   (E) plane parallel to the xy-plane   (F) line perpendicular to the xy-plane

   (G) line perpendicular to the xz-plane (H) line perpendicular to the yz-plane

   Answer: (E)

8. The center of the sphere $x^2 + y^2 + z^2 + 4x - 2y - 6z = 0$ is

   (A) $(1, 1, 1)$ (B) $(0, 0, 0)$ (C) $(4, -2, 9)$ (D) $(2, -1, -3)$

   (E) $(-2, 1, 3)$ (F) $(-2, -1, 3)$ (G) $(2, 1, 3)$ (H) $(-4, 2, 6)$

   Answer: (E)

9. Find the equation of the sphere, in standard form, one of whose diameters has $(-5, 2, 9)$ and $(3, 6, 1)$ as endpoints.

   Answer: $x^2 + y^2 + z^2 + 2x + 4y - 10z + 14 = 0$

10. Find the lengths of the sides of the triangle ABC and determine whether the triangle is isosceles, a right triangle, both, or neither given: $A(5, 5, 1)$, $B(3, 3, 2)$, $C(1, 4, 4)$.

    Answer: $AB = 3$; $BC = 3$; $CA = \sqrt{26}$; isosceles but not right

11. Find an equation of the sphere with center $P(6, -2, 4)$ that is tangent to the xz-plane.

    Answer: $(x - 6)^2 + (y + 2)^2 + (z - 4)^2 = 4$

12. Describe in words the region of $\mathbb{R}^3$ represented by the inequality $1 \leq x^2 + y^2 + z^2 \leq 25$.

    Answer: All points on and between the concentric spheres with radii one and five and center $(0, 0, 0)$.

13. Find an equation of the set of all points P such that the distance from P to $A(0, 0, 0)$ is twice the distance from P to $B(0, 0, 1)$. Describe the set.

    Answer: $x^2 + y^2 + \left(z - \frac{4}{3}\right)^2 = \frac{4}{9}$, a sphere with center $\left(0, 0, \frac{4}{3}\right)$ and radius $\frac{2}{3}$

14. Determine whether the points $A(2, 2, 4)$, $B(-1, 1, 2)$, and $C(8, 4, 8)$ lie on a straight line.

    Answer: Yes

9.2 Vectors

1. Find the length of the vector $\langle 2, 2, 3 \rangle$.

(A) $\sqrt{13}$ (B) $\sqrt{14}$ (C) $\sqrt{15}$ (D) 4

(E) $\sqrt{17}$ (F) $\sqrt{18}$ (G) $\sqrt{19}$ (H) $\sqrt{20}$

Answer: (E)

2. Find the length of the vector $2\mathbf{i} + \mathbf{j} - 2\mathbf{k}$.

(A) $\sqrt{2}$ (B) $\sqrt{3}$ (C) 2   (D) $\sqrt{5}$

(E) $\sqrt{6}$ (F) $\sqrt{7}$ (G) $\sqrt{8}$ (H) 3

Answer: (H)

3. Find the length of the vector from the point $P(1, 2)$ to the point $Q(3, 4)$.

(A) $\sqrt{8}$ (B) 5   (C) 3   (D) 7

(E) 8   (F) $\sqrt{52}$ (G) $\sqrt{3}$ (H) $\sqrt{7}$

Answer: (A)

4. Find the length of the vector $\mathbf{a} - \mathbf{b}$, where $\mathbf{a} = \langle 1, 3 \rangle$ and $\mathbf{b} = \langle 5, 2 \rangle$.

(A) $\sqrt{13}$ (B) $\sqrt{17}$ (C) $\sqrt{19}$ (D) $\sqrt{21}$

(E) $2\sqrt{13}$ (F) $2\sqrt{17}$ (G) $2\sqrt{19}$ (H) $2\sqrt{21}$

Answer: (B)

5. Find the length of the vector $2\mathbf{a} + 3\mathbf{b}$, where $\mathbf{a} = \langle 1, 1 \rangle$ and $\mathbf{b} = \langle -1, 2 \rangle$.

(A) $\sqrt{51}$ (B) $\sqrt{53}$ (C) $\sqrt{57}$ (D) $\sqrt{65}$

(E) $\sqrt{71}$ (F) $\sqrt{73}$ (G) $\sqrt{82}$ (H) $\sqrt{87}$

Answer: (D)

6. Find a unit vector that has the same direction as the vector $\langle 6, -8 \rangle$.

(A) $\langle \frac{4}{5}, \frac{3}{5} \rangle$ (B) $\langle \frac{3}{5}, \frac{4}{5} \rangle$ (C) $\langle \frac{1}{3}, \frac{1}{4} \rangle$ (D) $\langle 4, -3 \rangle$

(E) $\langle -\frac{3}{5}, -\frac{4}{5} \rangle$ (F) $\langle -\frac{3}{5}, \frac{4}{5} \rangle$ (G) $\langle \frac{3}{5}, -\frac{4}{5} \rangle$ (H) $\langle 6, -8 \rangle$

Answer: (G)

7. Find a unit vector that has the same direction as the vector $\langle 2, 2, 1 \rangle$.

(A) $\langle 1, 1, 1 \rangle$ (B) $\langle 1, 0, 0 \rangle$ (C) $\langle 0, 1, 0 \rangle$ (D) $\langle 0, 0, 1 \rangle$

(E) $\langle 1, 1, 0 \rangle$ (F) $\langle \frac{2}{3}, \frac{2}{3}, \frac{1}{3} \rangle$ (G) $\langle \frac{1}{2}, \frac{1}{2}, 1 \rangle$ (H) $\langle \frac{1}{3}, \frac{1}{3}, 1 \rangle$

Answer: (F)

8. Find a unit vector that has the same direction as the vector from the point $P(1, -1, 1)$ to the point $Q(3, 2, -5)$.

(A) $\langle -\frac{1}{2}, \frac{1}{3}, -\frac{1}{6} \rangle$ (B) $\langle \frac{1}{2}, \frac{1}{3}, \frac{1}{6} \rangle$ (C) $\langle \frac{7}{2}, \frac{7}{3}, \frac{7}{6} \rangle$ (D) $\langle \frac{2}{7}, \frac{3}{7}, \frac{6}{7} \rangle$

(E) $\langle \frac{1}{3}, \frac{1}{4}, \frac{1}{5} \rangle$ (F) $\langle \frac{2}{7}, \frac{3}{7}, -\frac{6}{7} \rangle$ (G) $\langle \frac{2}{3}, -\frac{3}{4}, \frac{5}{6} \rangle$ (H) $\langle \frac{2}{3}, \frac{3}{4}, -\frac{5}{6} \rangle$

Answer: (F)

313

9. Find a unit vector that has the same direction as the vector $\langle 1, 1, 1 \rangle$.

(A) $\langle 1, 1, 1 \rangle$ (B) $\langle -1, -1, -1 \rangle$ (C) $\left\langle \sqrt{\frac{1}{3}}, \sqrt{\frac{1}{3}}, \sqrt{\frac{1}{3}} \right\rangle$ (D) $\left\langle \sqrt{\frac{1}{2}}, \sqrt{\frac{1}{2}}, \sqrt{\frac{1}{2}} \right\rangle$

(E) $\left\langle \frac{1}{3}, \frac{1}{3}, \frac{1}{3} \right\rangle$ (F) $\left\langle \frac{1}{2}, \frac{1}{2}, \frac{1}{2} \right\rangle$ (G) $\left\langle \frac{1}{4}, \frac{1}{4}, \frac{1}{4} \right\rangle$ (H) $\langle 1, -1, 1 \rangle$

Answer: **(C)**

10. Let $\mathbf{a} = \langle 5, -1, -2 \rangle$ and $\mathbf{b} = \langle 1, -4, 3 \rangle$.

(a) Compute $\mathbf{a} + 2\mathbf{b}$.

(b) Find $|\mathbf{a}|$.

(c) Find the unit vector in the direction of $\mathbf{b}$.

Answer: (a) $\langle 7, -9, 4 \rangle$ (b) $\sqrt{30}$ (c) $\left\langle \frac{1}{\sqrt{26}}, -\frac{4}{\sqrt{26}}, \frac{3}{\sqrt{26}} \right\rangle$

11. Find the component form of $\mathbf{a} + \mathbf{b}$ given that $\mathbf{a}$ and $\mathbf{b}$ are unit vectors.

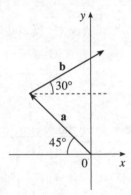

Answer: $\left\langle \frac{\sqrt{3}-\sqrt{2}}{2}, \frac{1+\sqrt{2}}{2} \right\rangle$

12. Given the points $P(-2, 5)$ and $Q(3, -3)$, find the unit vector in the direction of the displacement vector $\overrightarrow{PQ}$.

Answer: $\left\langle \frac{5}{\sqrt{89}}, -\frac{8}{\sqrt{89}} \right\rangle$

13. Find the coordinates of the point halfway between the midpoints of the vectors $\mathbf{a} = 3\mathbf{i} - 5\mathbf{j} + \mathbf{k}$ and $\mathbf{b} = 5\mathbf{i} + 3\mathbf{j} + \mathbf{k}$.

Answer: $\left(2, -\frac{1}{2}, \frac{1}{2} \right)$

14. Given $\langle -1, 2 \rangle$ and $\langle 5, 3 \rangle$, find their sum and illustrate geometrically.

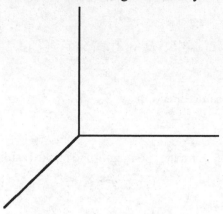

Answer:

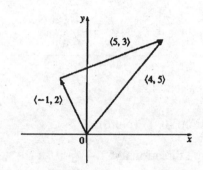

15. Given $\langle 0, 3, 2 \rangle$ and $\langle 1, 0, -3 \rangle$, find their sum and illustrate geometrically.

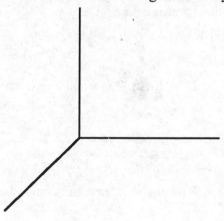

Answer:

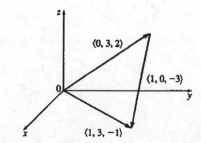

16. Find $|\mathbf{a}|$, $\mathbf{a} + \mathbf{b}$, $\mathbf{a} - \mathbf{b}$, $2\mathbf{a}$, and $3\mathbf{a} + 4\mathbf{b}$ given $\mathbf{a} = \langle -1, 2 \rangle$ and $\mathbf{b} = \langle 4, 3 \rangle$.

Answer: $|\mathbf{a}| = \sqrt{5}$, $\mathbf{a} + \mathbf{b} = \langle 3, 5 \rangle$, $\mathbf{a} - \mathbf{b} = \langle -5, -1 \rangle$, $2\mathbf{a} = \langle -2, 4 \rangle$, and $3\mathbf{a} + 4\mathbf{b} = \langle 13, 18 \rangle$

315

17. Find $|\mathbf{a}|$, $\mathbf{a} + \mathbf{b}$, $\mathbf{a} - \mathbf{b}$, $2\mathbf{a}$, and $3\mathbf{a} + 4\mathbf{b}$ given $\mathbf{a} = \langle 3, 2, -1 \rangle$ and $\mathbf{b} = \langle 0, 6, 7 \rangle$.

    Answer: $|\mathbf{a}| = \sqrt{14}$, $\mathbf{a} + \mathbf{b} = \langle 3, 8, 6 \rangle$, $\mathbf{a} - \mathbf{b} = \langle 3, -4, -8 \rangle$, $2\mathbf{a} = \langle 6, 4, -2 \rangle$, and $3\mathbf{a} + 4\mathbf{b} = \langle 9, 30, 25 \rangle$

18. Determine whether the points $A(1, 3, 5)$, $B(8, 4, 2)$, and $C(-13, 1, 11)$ lie on a straight line.

    Answer: Yes

19. Find a unit vector that has the same direction as $\langle 3, -5 \rangle$.

    Answer: $\left\langle \frac{3}{\sqrt{34}}, -\frac{5}{\sqrt{34}} \right\rangle$

20. For the given forces $\mathbf{F}_1$ and $\mathbf{F}_2$, compute the magnitude of the resulting force and its direction.

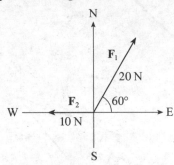

    Answer: $|\mathbf{F}_1 + \mathbf{F}_2| = 10\sqrt{3}$. Direction: $\langle 0, 1 \rangle$ (North)

21. Find a unit vector that has the same direction as $2\mathbf{i} - 4\mathbf{j} + 7\mathbf{k}$.

    Answer: $\frac{2}{\sqrt{69}}\mathbf{i} - \frac{4}{\sqrt{69}}\mathbf{j} + \frac{7}{\sqrt{69}}\mathbf{k}$

22. Which two of the following four vectors are parallel?

    (a) $\langle 0, 8, 2 \rangle$ (b) $\langle -1, 4, 1 \rangle$ (c) $\left\langle -\frac{1}{2}, 2, \frac{1}{2} \right\rangle$ (d) $\left\langle \frac{7}{2}, 5, -\frac{7}{2} \right\rangle$

    Answer: (b) and (c)

23. Given $\mathbf{a} = \langle 1, 1 \rangle$, $\mathbf{b} = \langle -4, 2 \rangle$, and $\mathbf{c} = \langle 5, 2 \rangle$, find s and t such that $\mathbf{c} = s\mathbf{a} + t\mathbf{b}$.

    Answer: $s = 3$, $t = -\frac{1}{2}$

24. Find a vector of length 6 with the same direction as $\mathbf{a} = \langle 2, 2, -1 \rangle$

    Answer: $\langle 4, 4, -2 \rangle$

25. Let $\mathbf{a}$ be the vector shown below. Find the horizontal component $\mathbf{b}$ and the vertical component $\mathbf{c}$ of $\mathbf{a}$ if $\mathbf{a} = 3$.

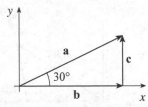

    Answer: $\mathbf{b} = \left\langle \frac{3\sqrt{3}}{2} \right\rangle$, $\mathbf{c} = \left\langle \frac{3}{2} \right\rangle$

26. Is the quadrilateral $ABCD$ formed by the points $A(-1, 2, 0)$, $B(3, 1, 1)$, $C(1, 2, 1)$, and $D(-3, 3, 0)$ a parallelogram?

    Answer: Yes

9.3 The Dot Product

1. Find the dot product of the vectors $\langle 1, 2 \rangle$ and $\langle 4, 5 \rangle$.

(A) 14   (B) 15   (C) 16   (D) 17

(E) 18   (F) 19   (G) 20   (H) 21

Answer: **(A)**

2. Find the dot product of the vectors $\langle 1, 2, 3 \rangle$ and $\langle 3, 0, -7 \rangle$.

(A) -24 (B) -21 (C) -18 (D) -16

(E) 24   (F) 21   (G) 18   (H) 16

Answer: **(C)**

3. What value of x will cause the two vectors $\langle 5x, -1, 2 \rangle$ and $\langle 3, 2x, -2 \rangle$ to be orthogonal?

(A) $-\frac{17}{4}$ (B) $-\frac{4}{17}$ (C) $\frac{13}{4}$ (D) $-\frac{13}{4}$

(E) $\frac{17}{4}$ (F) $\frac{4}{17}$ (G) $-\frac{4}{13}$ (H) $\frac{4}{13}$

Answer: **(H)**

4. Find the cosine of the angle between the two vectors $\langle 1, 2 \rangle$ and $\langle -2, 1 \rangle$.

(A) $\frac{1}{\sqrt{2}}$ (B) 0   (C) $\frac{1}{\sqrt{3}}$ (D) 1

(E) $\frac{1}{\sqrt{5}}$ (F) $\frac{1}{2}$ (G) $\frac{4}{3}$ (H) $\frac{3}{4}$

Answer: **(B)**

5. Find $\mathbf{a} \cdot \mathbf{b}$, given that $|\mathbf{a}| = 2$, $|\mathbf{b}| = 3$, and the angle between $\mathbf{a}$ and $\mathbf{b}$ is $\frac{5\pi}{6}$.

(A) $3\sqrt{2}$ (B) 3   (C) $3\sqrt{3}$ (D) $2\sqrt{3}$

(E) $-3\sqrt{2}$ (F) -3 (G) $-3\sqrt{3}$ (H) $-2\sqrt{3}$

Answer: **(G)**

6. Find the cosine of the acute angle between the two diagonals of a rectangle with length 3 and width 2.

(A) $-\frac{5}{13}$ (B) 5   (C) $\frac{2}{13}$ (D) $\frac{\sqrt{2}}{2}$

(E) $\frac{5}{13}$ (F) $\frac{5\sqrt{13}}{13}$ (G) $\frac{2}{5}$ (H) $\frac{\sqrt{3}}{5}$

Answer: **(E)**

7. Find the cosine of the angle between the two vectors $\langle 1, 1, 1 \rangle$ and $\langle 1, 4, 3 \rangle$.

(A) $8/\sqrt{41}$ (B) $8/\sqrt{53}$ (C) $8/\sqrt{69}$ (D) $8/\sqrt{78}$

(E) $4/\sqrt{41}$ (F) $4/\sqrt{53}$ (G) $4/\sqrt{69}$ (H) $4/\sqrt{78}$

Answer: **(D)**

8. A constant force with vector representation $\mathbf{F} = \mathbf{i} + 2\mathbf{j}$ moves an object along a straight line from the point $(2, 4)$ to the point $(5, 7)$. Find the work done in foot-pounds if force is measured in pounds and distance is measured in feet.

(A) 6   (B) 7   (C) 8   (D) 9

(E) 10   (F) 11   (G) 12   (H) 13

Answer: **(D)**

9. A person pushing a lawnmower exerts a force of 30 pounds in the direction of the handle, which makes an angle of $30°$ with the ground. How much work is done in moving the lawnmower 20 feet?

(A) $300\sqrt{3}$ (B) $\frac{300}{\sqrt{3}}$ (C) $200\sqrt{3}$ (D) $\frac{200}{\sqrt{3}}$

(E) 100   (F) 200   (G) 300   (H) 400

Answer: **(A)**

10. Let $\mathbf{a} = \langle 0, 1, 2 \rangle$, $\mathbf{b} = \langle -1, -1, 3 \rangle$, $\mathbf{c} = \langle 2, 4, -2 \rangle$, and $\mathbf{d} = \langle 1, 3, -3 \rangle$. Find $\mathbf{a} \cdot \mathbf{d} - \mathbf{b} \cdot \mathbf{c}$.

Answer: 9

11. Let $\mathbf{a} = \langle 0, 1, 2 \rangle$, $\mathbf{b} = \langle -1, -1, 3 \rangle$, $\mathbf{c} = \langle 2, 4, -2 \rangle$, and $\mathbf{d} = \langle 1, 3, -3 \rangle$. Find $(\mathbf{a} \cdot \mathbf{d})\, \mathbf{b} - (\mathbf{b} \cdot \mathbf{c})\, \mathbf{d}$.

Answer: $\langle 15, 39, -45 \rangle$

12. Let $\mathbf{a} = \langle 0, 1, 2 \rangle$, $\mathbf{b} = \langle -1, -1, 3 \rangle$, $\mathbf{c} = \langle 2, 4, -2 \rangle$, and $\mathbf{d} = \langle 1, 3, -3 \rangle$. Find $(2\mathbf{a} + \mathbf{b}) \cdot (2\mathbf{c} - \mathbf{d})$.

Answer: -5

13. Determine all values for a such that the vectors $\mathbf{x} = 2\mathbf{i} + \mathbf{j} + 2\mathbf{k}$ and $\mathbf{y} = \mathbf{i} + 2\mathbf{j} + a\mathbf{k}$ will form a $60°$ angle.

Answer: $a = \dfrac{-32 \pm 9\sqrt{11}}{7}$

14. Suppose $\mathbf{u} = \langle 1, 2, 3 \rangle$ and $\mathbf{v} = \langle 1, 1, -2 \rangle$. Find two vectors $\mathbf{a}$ and $\mathbf{b}$ such that $\mathbf{u} = \mathbf{a} + \mathbf{b}$, $\mathbf{a}$ is parallel to $\mathbf{v}$, and $\mathbf{b}$ is perpendicular to $\mathbf{v}$.

Answer: $\mathbf{a} = \left\langle -\frac{1}{2}, -\frac{1}{2}, 1 \right\rangle$ and $\mathbf{b} = \left\langle \frac{3}{2}, \frac{5}{2}, 2 \right\rangle$

15. Given a triangle with vertices $A(1, 2)$, $B(2, 3)$, and $C(5, 2)$, find the angle $\angle ABC$, correct to the nearest degree.

Answer: $117°$

16. Let $\mathbf{a} = 3\mathbf{i} - 2\mathbf{j} + \mathbf{k}$, $\mathbf{b} = \mathbf{i} - 3\mathbf{j} + 5\mathbf{k}$, and $\mathbf{c} = 2\mathbf{i} + \mathbf{j} - 4\mathbf{k}$. Do these vectors form a right triangle? Show why or why not.

Answer: Yes, the vectors form a right triangle since the dot product of $\mathbf{a}$ and $\mathbf{c}$ is 0, and $\mathbf{b} + \mathbf{c} = \mathbf{a}$.

17. Let $\mathbf{a} = \langle -2, 3, 1 \rangle$ and $\mathbf{b} = \langle 6, c, -3 \rangle$.

(a) Find the value of c such that $\mathbf{a}$ and $\mathbf{b}$ are orthogonal.

(b) Find the value of c such that $\mathbf{a}$ and $\mathbf{b}$ are parallel.

Answer: (a) $c = 5$ (b) $c = -9$

18. For which values of t are $\mathbf{a} = \langle t + 2, t, t \rangle$ and $\mathbf{b} = \langle t - 2, t + 1, t \rangle$ orthogonal?

Answer: $t = -\frac{4}{3}$ or $t = 1$

19. Let $\mathbf{a} = 3\mathbf{i} - \mathbf{j} + 2\mathbf{k}$ and $\mathbf{b} = \mathbf{i} - 2\mathbf{j} + 3\mathbf{k}$. Find the scalar projection of $\mathbf{a}$ onto $\mathbf{b}$.

Answer: $\dfrac{11}{\sqrt{14}}$

20. Find the projection of the vector $\langle 2, 3, -5 \rangle$ along the vector $\langle -1, 1, 2 \rangle$.

Answer: $\langle \frac{3}{2}, -\frac{3}{2}, -3 \rangle$

21. What does the fact that $\mathbf{a} \cdot \mathbf{a} = 0$ imply about the vector $\mathbf{a}$?

Answer: $\mathbf{a} = \mathbf{0}$

22. Given two distinct nonzero vectors $\mathbf{a}$ and $\mathbf{b}$, is it always true that $|\mathrm{proj}_{\mathbf{a}} \mathbf{b}| = |\mathrm{proj}_{\mathbf{b}} \mathbf{a}|$?

Answer: No

23. Let $\mathbf{v}$ and $\mathbf{w}$ be vectors which are both perpendicular to $\langle 1, 3, -1 \rangle$. Assuming that $\langle 0, -2, 1 \rangle = a\mathbf{v} + b\mathbf{w} + c \langle 1, 3, -1 \rangle$, find c.

Answer: $c = -\frac{7}{11}$

24. Let $\mathbf{a} = \langle -1, 2, 2 \rangle$ and suppose that $\mathbf{b}$ is a vector parallel to $\mathbf{a}$. Find $\mathrm{proj}_{\mathbf{b}} \mathbf{a}$.

Answer: $\mathrm{proj}_{\mathbf{b}} \mathbf{a} = \langle -1, 2, 2 \rangle$

25. Find two unit vectors that are orthogonal to both $\langle 1, -1, 1 \rangle$ and $\langle 0, 2, 2 \rangle$.

Answer: $\pm \left\langle \frac{\sqrt{6}}{3}, \frac{\sqrt{6}}{6}, -\frac{\sqrt{6}}{6} \right\rangle$

26. A suitcase is pulled along a straight path on the floor by a rope that applies a force of 70 lb at an angle of $60°$ with the floor. How much work is done in moving the suitcase 20 ft?

Answer: 700 lb-ft

9.4 | The Cross Product

1. Find the cross product $\langle 1, 2, 0 \rangle \times \langle 3, 4, 0 \rangle$.

(A) $\langle 0, 0, -2 \rangle$ (B) $\langle 0, 0, 2 \rangle$ (C) $\langle 3, 8, 0 \rangle$ (D) $\langle 8, 3, 0 \rangle$

(E) $\langle 0, 3, 8 \rangle$ (F) $\langle 0, 8, 3 \rangle$ (G) $\langle 3, 0, 8 \rangle$ (H) $\langle 8, 0, 3 \rangle$

Answer: (A)

2. Find $|\mathbf{a} \times \mathbf{b}|$, given that $|\mathbf{a}| = 2$, $|\mathbf{b}| = 5$, and the angle between $\mathbf{a}$ and $\mathbf{b}$ is $\frac{5\pi}{6}$.

(A) $5\sqrt{5}$ (B) $5\sqrt{2}$ (C) 10 (D) 5

(E) $5\sqrt{3}$ (F) $\frac{5\sqrt{2}}{2}$ (G) $-5\sqrt{5}$ (H) -5

Answer: (D)

3. Find the cross product $\mathbf{a} \times \mathbf{b}$, where $\mathbf{a} = -\mathbf{i} + 2\mathbf{j} + 4\mathbf{k}$ and $\mathbf{b} = 7\mathbf{i} + 3\mathbf{j}$.

(A) $15\mathbf{i} - 8\mathbf{j} + 10\mathbf{k}$ (B) $3\mathbf{i} + 11\mathbf{j} - 9\mathbf{k}$ (C) $7\mathbf{i} + 13\mathbf{j} + \mathbf{k}$ (D) $14\mathbf{i} + 5\mathbf{j} - 12\mathbf{k}$

(E) $-7\mathbf{i} - 23\mathbf{j} + 33\mathbf{k}$ (F) $-10\mathbf{i} + 27\mathbf{j} + 13\mathbf{k}$ (G) $-12\mathbf{i} + 28\mathbf{j} - 17\mathbf{k}$ (H) $18\mathbf{i} + 32\mathbf{j} + 7\mathbf{k}$

Answer: (G)

4. Find the length of the cross product of the vectors $\langle 1, 1, 1 \rangle$ and $\langle 1, 1, 2 \rangle$.

(A) $\frac{1}{\sqrt{5}}$ (B) $\frac{1}{2}$ (C) $\frac{1}{\sqrt{3}}$ (D) $\frac{1}{\sqrt{2}}$

(E) $\sqrt{5}$ (F) 2 (G) $\sqrt{3}$ (H) $\sqrt{2}$

Answer: (H)

5. Find the area of the triangle whose vertices are $A(1,-1,2)$, $B(4,0,1)$, and $C(2,-1,2)$.

(A) $\frac{\sqrt{30}}{2}$ (B) $\frac{\sqrt{3}}{2}$ (C) $\frac{\sqrt{2}}{2}$ (D) $\left|\sqrt{2}\right|$

(E) $\frac{4}{3}$ (F) $\sqrt{30}$ (G) 3   (H) $\sqrt{3}$

Answer: (C)

6. Find a unit vector orthogonal to both of the vectors $\langle 1,-1,0\rangle$ and $\langle 1,2,3\rangle$.

(A) $\left\langle\frac{1}{\sqrt{3}},\frac{1}{\sqrt{3}},\frac{1}{\sqrt{3}}\right\rangle$ (B) $\left\langle-\frac{1}{\sqrt{3}},\frac{1}{\sqrt{3}},\frac{1}{\sqrt{3}}\right\rangle$ (C) $\left\langle\frac{1}{\sqrt{3}},-\frac{1}{\sqrt{3}},\frac{1}{\sqrt{3}}\right\rangle$ (D) $\left\langle\frac{1}{\sqrt{3}},\frac{1}{\sqrt{3}},-\frac{1}{\sqrt{3}}\right\rangle$

(E) $\left\langle\frac{2}{3},\frac{2}{3},\frac{1}{3}\right\rangle$ (F) $\left\langle-\frac{2}{3},\frac{2}{3},\frac{1}{3}\right\rangle$ (G) $\left\langle\frac{2}{3},-\frac{2}{3},\frac{1}{3}\right\rangle$ (H) $\left\langle\frac{2}{3},\frac{2}{3},-\frac{1}{3}\right\rangle$

Answer: (D)

7. Find a unit vector orthogonal to the plane through the points $(1,0,0)$, $(0,1,0)$, and $(0,2,2)$.

(A) $\left\langle\frac{1}{\sqrt{3}},\frac{1}{\sqrt{3}},\frac{1}{\sqrt{3}}\right\rangle$ (B) $\left\langle-\frac{1}{\sqrt{3}},\frac{1}{\sqrt{3}},\frac{1}{\sqrt{3}}\right\rangle$ (C) $\left\langle\frac{1}{\sqrt{2}},\frac{1}{\sqrt{2}},0\right\rangle$ (D) $\left\langle-\frac{1}{\sqrt{2}},\frac{1}{\sqrt{2}},0\right\rangle$

(E) $\left\langle\frac{2}{3},\frac{2}{3},\frac{1}{3}\right\rangle$ (F) $\left\langle-\frac{2}{3},\frac{2}{3},\frac{1}{3}\right\rangle$ (G) $\left\langle\frac{2}{3},-\frac{2}{3},\frac{1}{3}\right\rangle$ (H) $\left\langle\frac{2}{3},\frac{2}{3},-\frac{1}{3}\right\rangle$

Answer: (H)

8. Find the volume of the parallelepiped determined by the vectors $\langle 1,0,1\rangle$, $\langle 2,1,3\rangle$, and $\langle 1,1,1\rangle$.

(A) 1   (B) 2   (C) 3   (D) 4

(E) 5   (F) 6   (G) 7   (H) 8

Answer: (A)

9. Find the volume of the parallelepiped with adjacent edges PQ, PR, and PS, where $P(-2,1,1)$, $Q(-1,0,2)$, $R(0,5,2)$, and $S(1,3,0)$.

(A) 19   (B) 22   (C) 38   (D) 80

(E) 20   (F) 40   (G) 44   (H) 72

Answer: (A)

10. Find the torque vector $\boldsymbol{\tau}$ of the force $\mathbf{F}=\langle 1,1,0\rangle$ acting on a rigid body at the point given by the position vector $\mathbf{r}=\langle 2,3,0\rangle$.

(A) $\langle-1,0,0\rangle$ (B) $\langle 0,-1,0\rangle$ (C) $\langle 0,0,-1\rangle$ (D) $\langle-1,1,0\rangle$

(E) $\langle 0,-1,1\rangle$ (F) $\langle 1,0,-1\rangle$ (G) $\langle-1,1,1\rangle$ (H) $\langle 1,-1,1\rangle$

Answer: (C)

11. Find the cross product $\mathbf{a}\times\mathbf{b}$, where $\mathbf{a}=\mathbf{i}+2\mathbf{j}+3\mathbf{k}$ and $\mathbf{b}=2\mathbf{i}-\mathbf{j}+\mathbf{k}$.

Answer: $5\mathbf{i}+5\mathbf{j}-5\mathbf{k}$

12. Consider the points $P=(1,2,3)$, $Q=(2,-1,0)$, and $R=(-1,4,1)$. Find the area of the triangle PQR.

Answer: $2\sqrt{14}$

13. Let $\mathbf{a}$ and $\mathbf{b}$ be vectors such that $|\mathbf{a}|=2$ and $|\mathbf{b}|=3$. Assume that the angle between a and b is $\frac{\pi}{3}$. Find $|(2\mathbf{a}+3\mathbf{b})\times(\mathbf{a}+4\mathbf{b})|$.

Answer: $15\sqrt{3}$

14. Find $\mathbf{a} \times \mathbf{b}$, where $\mathbf{a}$ and $\mathbf{b}$ are given in the figure.

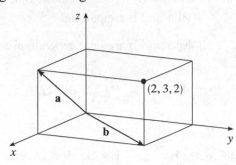

Answer: $\langle -6, 4, 6 \rangle$

15. Let $\mathbf{a}$ and $\mathbf{b}$ be vectors. Under what conditions is $\mathbf{a} \times \mathbf{b} = \mathbf{b} \times \mathbf{a}$? When is $(2\mathbf{a}) \times (3\mathbf{b}) = 6\,(\mathbf{a} \times \mathbf{b})$?

Answer: $\mathbf{a} \times \mathbf{b} = \mathbf{b} \times \mathbf{a}$ when (1) $\mathbf{a} = \mathbf{b}$, (2) $\mathbf{a} = 0$ or $\mathbf{b} = 0$, (3) $\mathbf{a}$ and $\mathbf{b}$ are parallel; in all cases $\mathbf{a} \times \mathbf{b} = 0$; $(2\mathbf{a}) \times (3\mathbf{b}) = 6\,(\mathbf{a} \times \mathbf{b})$ always.

16. Use the property of the cross product that $|\mathbf{u} \times \mathbf{v}| = |\mathbf{u}|\,|\mathbf{v}| \sin\theta$ to derive a formula for the distance d from a point P to a line l. Use this formula to find the distance from the origin to the line through $(2, 1, -4)$ and $(3, 3, -2)$.

Answer: Let $\mathbf{u}$ be a vector from l to P, $\mathbf{v}$ be a vector parallel to l and θ be the angle between $\mathbf{u}$ and $\mathbf{v}$. Note that $d = |\mathbf{u}| \sin\theta$. But $|\mathbf{u} \times \mathbf{v}| = |\mathbf{u}|\,|\mathbf{v}| \sin\theta$. So $|\mathbf{u} \times \mathbf{v}| = |\mathbf{v}|\,d = \dfrac{|\mathbf{u} \times \mathbf{v}|}{|\mathbf{v}|} \;\Rightarrow\; d = \frac{\sqrt{173}}{3}$.

17. Given the vectors $\mathbf{u} = 2\mathbf{i} + \mathbf{j} - \mathbf{k}$ and $\mathbf{w} = \mathbf{i} + \mathbf{j} + 4\mathbf{k}$, find a vector of length 2 which is orthogonal to both $\mathbf{u}$ and $\mathbf{w}$.

Answer: $\frac{10}{\sqrt{107}}\mathbf{i} - \frac{18}{\sqrt{107}}\mathbf{j} + \frac{2}{\sqrt{107}}\mathbf{k}$

18. Find $\mathbf{a} \times \mathbf{b}$, where $\mathbf{a}$ and $\mathbf{b}$ are given in the figure.

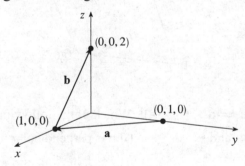

Answer: $\langle -2, -2, -1 \rangle$

19. Let $\mathbf{u} \times \mathbf{v} = \mathbf{i} - \mathbf{j} + 2\mathbf{k}$. Find $\mathbf{u} \cdot (\mathbf{u} \times \mathbf{v})$, if it exists.

Answer: 0

20. Let $\mathbf{u} \times \mathbf{v} = \mathbf{i} - \mathbf{j} + 2\mathbf{k}$. Find the area A of the parallelogram determined by $\mathbf{u}$ and $\mathbf{v}$, if it exists.

Answer: $A = \sqrt{6}$

21. Find the distance from the point $P\,(1, 1, 1)$ to the line passing through the points $Q\,(2, 0, 1)$ and $R\,(0, 3, 2)$.

Answer: $\sqrt{\frac{3}{14}}$

22. Give a counterexample showing that the statement "If $\mathbf{a} \times \mathbf{b} = \mathbf{a} \times \mathbf{c}$, then $\mathbf{b} = \mathbf{c}$" is not always true.

Answer: For example, if $\mathbf{a} = \mathbf{i}$, $\mathbf{b} = 2\mathbf{i}$, and $\mathbf{c} = 3\mathbf{i}$, then $\mathbf{a} \times \mathbf{b} = \mathbf{a} \times \mathbf{c} = 0$, but $\mathbf{b} \neq \mathbf{c}$.

23. For vectors **a** and **b**, given that $|\mathbf{a} \times \mathbf{b}| = |\mathbf{a}|\,|\mathbf{b}|$, which of the following statements is true?

(A) $\mathbf{a} = \mathbf{b}$ (B) **a** and **b** are parallel   (C) **a** and **b** are not parallel

(D) **a** and **b** are perpendicular   (E) **a** and **b** are not perpendicular

Answer: (D)

24. Use vectors to determine whether the points $P(0,0,0)$, $Q(5,0,0)$, $R(2,6,6)$, and $S(7,6,6)$ are coplanar.

Answer: Yes

25. If vector $\mathbf{a} = 3\mathbf{i} + 4\mathbf{j} - 2\mathbf{k}$, and vector $\mathbf{b} = 2\mathbf{i} - \mathbf{j} + 5\mathbf{k}$, find a vector perpendicular to both vectors.

Answer: Any scalar multiple of $18\mathbf{i} - 19\mathbf{j} - 11\mathbf{k}$ is perpendicular

26. Find the volume of the parallelepiped spanned by the vectors $2\mathbf{i} + 3\mathbf{j} + 5\mathbf{k}$, $3\mathbf{i} - \mathbf{j} + 4\mathbf{k}$, and $-\mathbf{i} - 2\mathbf{j} + 3\mathbf{k}$.

Answer: 64

27. Find the volume of the parallelepiped below given $P = (1, -3, 2)$, $Q = (3, -1, 3)$, $R = (2, 1, -4)$, and $S = (-1, 2, 1)$.

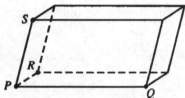

Answer: 91

28. Find the area of quadrilateral $ABCD$. Note that $ABCD$ is *not* a parallelogram.

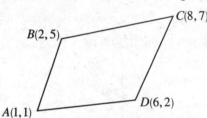

Answer: $\frac{45}{2}$

29. Suppose that $\mathbf{a} \perp \mathbf{b}$, and let $\mathbf{c} = [\mathbf{a} \times (\mathbf{b} \times \mathbf{a})]$. Which of the following statements is true?

(A) **c** is perpendicular to both **a** and **b**   (B) **c** is perpendicular to neither **a** nor **b**

(C) **c** is perpendicular to **a**   (D) **c** is perpendicular to **b**

Answer: (C)

30. Compute $|\mathbf{a} \times \mathbf{b}|$ if $|\mathbf{a}| = 3$, $|\mathbf{b}| = 7$, and $\mathbf{a} \cdot \mathbf{b} = 0$.

Answer: 21

31. If $\mathbf{b} = \langle 1, 0, 1 \rangle$, $\mathbf{c} = \langle 0, -1, 1 \rangle$, and $\mathbf{a} = \langle 2, -3, z \rangle$, find a value for z which guarantees that **a**, **b**, and **c** are coplanar.

Answer: $z = 5$

32. Find the distance from the point $P(-1, 0, 2)$ to the plane passing through the points $A(-2, 1, 1)$, $B(0, 5, 2)$, and $C(1, 3, 0)$.

Answer: $\frac{19}{5\sqrt{5}}$

33. If we know that $\mathbf{a} \times \mathbf{b} = \mathbf{a} \times \mathbf{c}$, which of the following statements is true?

(A) $\mathbf{b} = \mathbf{c}$ 　　　　(B) $|\mathbf{b}| = |\mathbf{c}|$ 　　　　(C) $\mathbf{b}$ and $\mathbf{c}$ are parallel

(D) $\mathbf{a}$ is parallel to $\mathbf{b} - \mathbf{c}$ 　　　　(E) $\mathbf{a}$ is a unit vector

Answer: (D)

9.5 Equations of Lines and Planes

1. Find a vector $\mathbf{v}$ for a vector equation $\mathbf{r} = \mathbf{r}_0 + t\mathbf{v}$ of the line passing through the points $(1, 2, 3)$ and $(4, 5, 6)$.

(A) $\langle 1, 1, 0 \rangle$ 　　　(B) $\langle 0, 1, 1 \rangle$ 　　　(C) $\langle 1, 0, 1 \rangle$ 　　　(D) $\langle 1, 1, 1 \rangle$

(E) $\langle 0, 0, 1 \rangle$ 　　　(F) $\langle 1, 0, 0 \rangle$ 　　　(G) $\langle 0, 1, 0 \rangle$ 　　　(H) $\langle 0, 0, 0 \rangle$

Answer: (D)

2. For the line l passing through the points $(1, 0, 1)$ and $(2, 4, 7)$, what is the value of c in the following symmetric equation for l? $\dfrac{x - 1}{1} = \dfrac{y - 0}{4} = \dfrac{z - 1}{c}$

(A) 1 　　　(B) 2 　　　(C) 3 　　　(D) 4

(E) 5 　　　(F) 6 　　　(G) 7 　　　(H) 8

Answer: (F)

3. Find the value d for which the plane $x - y + 2z = d$ passes through the point $(1, 2, 3)$.

(A) 2 　　　(B) 3 　　　(C) 4 　　　(D) 5

(E) 6 　　　(F) 7 　　　(G) 8 　　　(H) 9

Answer: (D)

4. Find a unit vector perpendicular to the plane $x - 2y - 2z = 10$.

(A) $\left\langle -\frac{2}{3}, -\frac{2}{3}, \frac{1}{3} \right\rangle$ 　　(B) $\left\langle -\frac{1}{3}, \frac{2}{3}, \frac{2}{3} \right\rangle$ 　　(C) $\left\langle \frac{1}{3}, \frac{2}{3}, \frac{2}{3} \right\rangle$ 　　(D) $\left\langle \frac{2}{3}, \frac{2}{3}, \frac{1}{3} \right\rangle$

(E) $\left\langle \frac{1}{\sqrt{2}}, \frac{1}{\sqrt{2}}, 0 \right\rangle$ 　　(F) $\left\langle \frac{1}{\sqrt{2}}, 0, \frac{1}{\sqrt{2}} \right\rangle$ 　　(G) $\left\langle 0, \frac{1}{\sqrt{2}}, \frac{1}{\sqrt{2}} \right\rangle$ 　　(H) $\langle -1, 0, 0 \rangle$

Answer: (B)

5. Find the point of intersection of the line $x = 2t$, $y = t - 1$, $z = 3t + 4$ and the plane $x - 5y + 3z = 47$.

(A) $(10, 4, 19)$ 　　(B) $(-10, 4, 19)$ 　　(C) $(0, -4, -1)$ 　　(D) $(10, -4, 19)$

(E) $(0, -1, 4)$ 　　(F) $(0, 1, -4)$ 　　(G) $(0, -1, -4)$ 　　(H) $(10, -4, -19)$

Answer: (A)

6. Find the cosine of the angle between the two planes $x + y + z = 0$ and $x + 2y + 3z = 1$.

(A) $4/\sqrt{35}$ 　　(B) $6/\sqrt{35}$ 　　(C) $7/\sqrt{35}$ 　　(D) $8/\sqrt{35}$

(E) $5/\sqrt{42}$ 　　(F) $6/\sqrt{42}$ 　　(G) $7/\sqrt{42}$ 　　(H) $8/\sqrt{42}$

Answer: (F)

7. Find direction numbers a, b, and c for the line of intersection of the two planes $x + y + z = 1$ and $x + z = 0$.

(A) $1, 1, 0$ (B) $1, 0, 1$ (C) $0, 1, 1$ (D) $1, -1, 1$

(E) $1, 1, 1$ (F) $1, -1, 0$ (G) $1, 0, -1$ (H) $0, 1, -1$

Answer: (G)

8. Find an equation for the plane consisting of all points that are equidistant from the two points $(1, 1, 0)$ and $(0, 1, 1)$.

(A) $x - z = 0$ (B) $x - z = 1$ (C) $x - y = 0$ (D) $x - y = 1$

(E) $x + z = 0$ (F) $x + z = 1$ (G) $x + y = 0$ (H) $x + y = 1$

Answer: (A)

9. Find the point at which the two lines $\mathbf{r} = \langle 1, 1, 0 \rangle + t \langle 1, -1, 2 \rangle$ and $\mathbf{r} = \langle 2, 0, 2 \rangle + s \langle -1, 1, 0 \rangle$ intersect.

(A) $(1, 0, 1)$ (B) $(2, 0, 2)$ (C) $(1, 1, 1)$ (D) $(2, 2, 2)$

(E) $(1, 1, 0)$ (F) $(2, 2, 0)$ (G) $(0, 1, 1)$ (H) $(0, 2, 2)$

Answer: (B)

10. Find an equation of the plane whose graph is given below.

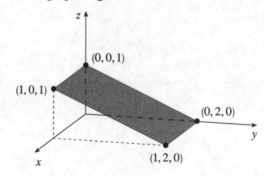

Answer: $2z + y = 2$

11. Find an equation of the plane passing through the points A, B, and C shown below.

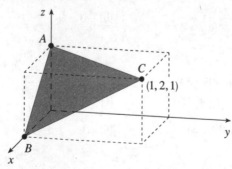

Answer: $2x - y + 2z = 2$

12. Let $\mathbf{a} = 2\mathbf{i} + \mathbf{j} - \mathbf{k}$ and $\mathbf{b} = \mathbf{i} + 2\mathbf{j} + 3\mathbf{k}$. Find an equation of the line parallel to $\mathbf{a} + \mathbf{b}$ and passing through the tip of $\mathbf{b}$.

Answer: $\mathbf{r}(t) = (1 + 3t)\mathbf{i} + (2 + 3t)\mathbf{j} + (3 + 2t)\mathbf{k}$

13. Find the cosine of the acute angle between the lines $x = 4 - 4t$, $y = 3 - t$, $z = 1 + 5t$ and $x = 4 - t$, $y = 3 + 2t$, $z = 1$.

Answer: $\frac{\sqrt{210}}{105}$

14. Find symmetric equations of the line passing through $(2, -3, 4)$ and parallel to the vector $\overrightarrow{AB}$, where A and B are the points $(-2, 1, 1)$ and $(0, 2, 3)$.

Answer: $\dfrac{x - 2}{2} = \dfrac{y + 3}{1} = \dfrac{z - 4}{2}$

15. Find the distance between the following two lines.

$$x = -t \qquad\qquad x = 3 + t$$
$$y = t \qquad \text{and} \qquad y = 3t$$
$$z = 2t \qquad\qquad z = 5 - 4t$$

Answer: $\dfrac{13}{\sqrt{30}}$

16. Let l and l' be two lines in space given by the equations

$$x = 3 + t \qquad\qquad x = -1 + t$$
$$l: \quad y = 1 - t \qquad l': \quad y = 2t$$
$$z = 2t \qquad\qquad z = 1 + kt$$

Find all values of k (if any) for which l and l' are parallel.

Answer: No value of k will work

17. Let l and l' be two lines in space given by the equations

$$x = 3 + t \qquad\qquad x = -1 + t$$
$$l: \quad y = 1 - t \qquad l': \quad y = 2t$$
$$z = 2t \qquad\qquad z = 1 + kt$$

Find all values of k (if any) for which l and l' are perpendicular.

Answer: $k = \frac{1}{2}$

18. Find parametric equations and symmetric equations of the line passing through the points A and B shown below.

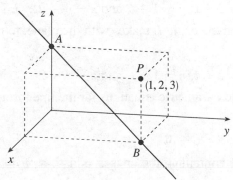

Answer: $x = t$, $y = 2t$, $z = 3 - 3t$; $x = \dfrac{y}{2} = \dfrac{z - 3}{-3}$

19. Find parametric equations and symmetric equations of the line passing through the points A and B shown below.

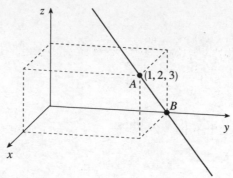

Answer: $x = t, y = 2, z = 3t; x = \dfrac{z}{3}, y = 2$

20. Find an equation of the plane through the point $P = (2, 1, -4)$ and perpendicular to the line $x = 2 + 3t$, $y = 1 - 4t, z = 3 + 3t$.

Answer: $3x - 4y + 3z = -10$

21. Find the intersection point of the line $\mathbf{r} = \langle 1, 0, 2 \rangle + \langle 2, -2, 1 \rangle\, t$ and the plane $3x + 4y + 6z = 7$.

Answer: $(-3, 4, 0)$

22. Find the intersections of the line passing through the points $(-1, 3, 4)$ and $(3, 5, 2)$ with the yz-plane, the xz-plane, and the xy-plane.

Answer: $(0, 3.5, 3.5), (-7, 0, 7), (7, 7, 0)$

23. Determine whether the lines $L_1: x = 1 + 7t, y = 3 + t, z = 5 - 3t$ and $L_2: x = 4 - t, y = 4, z = 7 + 2t$ are parallel, intersecting or skew. If they intersect, find the point of intersection.

Answer: Skew

24. Find the equation of the plane containing the points $(5, 3, 1)$, $(1, 8, 4)$, and $(-1, 3, -2)$.

Answer: $x + 2y - 2z = 9$

25. Determine whether the lines $L_1: x = 1 + t, y = 2 + 3t, z = 3 + t$ and $L_2: x = 1 + t, y = 3 + 4t$, $z = 4 + 2t$ are parallel, intersecting or skew. If they intersect, find the point of intersection.

Answer: They intersect at $(0, -1, 2)$

26. Find the normal vector to the plane which passes through the points $(1, 0, 0)$, $(0, 0, 1)$, and $(4, 3, -2)$.

Answer: $\langle -3, 1, -3 \rangle$

27. Let L be the line given by $x = 2 - t, y = 1 + t$, and $z = 1 + 2t$. L intersects the plane $2x + y - z = 1$ at the point $P = (1, 2, 3)$. Find the angle L makes with the plane, to the nearest degree.

Answer: $30°$

28. Let L be the line given by $x = 2 - t, y = 1 + t$, and $z = 1 + 2t$. L intersects the plane $2x + y - z = 1$ at the point $P = (1, 2, 3)$. Find parametric equations for the line through P which lies in the plane and is perpendicular to L.

Answer: $x = 1 + 3t, y = 2 - 3t, z = 3 + 3t$

29. Find the equation of the plane containing the lines $x = 4 - 4t, y = 3 - t, z = 1 + 5t$ and $x = 4 - t$, $y = 3 + 2t, z = 1$.

Answer: $10x - 5y + 7z - 32 = 0$

30. Given the points $A = (2, 3, 1)$, $B = (4, -1, 5)$, and $O = (0, 0, 0)$, find the distance from O to the line through A and B.

    Answer: $\frac{\sqrt{122}}{3}$

31. Find the distance between the two skew lines

    $$L_1 \colon \frac{x-1}{2} = \frac{y-3}{5} = \frac{z-1}{3} \qquad \text{and} \qquad L_2 \colon \frac{x-2}{4} = \frac{y+1}{2} = \frac{z+2}{3}$$

    Answer: $\frac{33\sqrt{373}}{373}$

32. Are the planes $3x - y + 5z = 13$ and $x + 7y - 2z = 4$ perpendicular to each other?

    Answer: No

33. Find the angle between the lines $\frac{x-2}{1} = \frac{1-y}{3} = \frac{z-3}{1}$ and $\frac{x}{2} = \frac{y+3}{-1} = \frac{z-1}{2}$.

    Answer: $\cos^{-1} \frac{7}{3\sqrt{11}} \approx 45.3°$ or 0.7904 radians

34. Find an equation of the plane containing $P(-1, 2, 1)$ and the line $\frac{x+1}{2} = \frac{y}{5} = \frac{z-3}{1}$.

    Answer: $3x - y - z + 6 = 0$

35. Let $P = (1, 3, 2)$ and let L be the line with parametric equations $x = 2 - t$, $y = -1 + 2t$, $z = 3 + t$. Use the vector cross product to find the distance from P to L.

    Answer: $\frac{\sqrt{66}}{3}$

36. Find a parametric equation of the line which is the intersection of the planes $-x + 3y + z = 7$ and $x + y = 1$.

    Answer: $\langle -1 + t, 2 - t, 4t \rangle$. (Other forms are possible.)

37. Do the two lines

    $$\mathbf{x}_1(t) = \langle 1, 1, 3 \rangle + t \langle -1, 0, 2 \rangle \qquad \text{and} \qquad \mathbf{x}_2(s) = \langle -1, 1, 4 \rangle + s \langle 2, 0, 1 \rangle$$

    intersect? If so, find the point of intersection.

    Answer: Yes; $\left(\frac{1}{5}, 1, \frac{23}{5} \right)$

38. Find the point at which the following three planes intersect:

    $$x - 2y + z = 5$$
    $$2x - y + z = 1$$
    $$-2x + y + z = 3$$

    Answer: $\left(-\frac{8}{3}, -\frac{10}{3}, 1 \right)$

39. Find an equation of the plane containing the lines

    $$\frac{x}{2} = \frac{y-2}{3} = \frac{z+1}{1} \qquad \text{and} \qquad \frac{x+1}{4} = \frac{y}{6} = \frac{z-3}{2}$$

    Answer: $14x - 9y - z + 17 = 0$

40. The lines $l_1 \colon \mathbf{r}_1 = \langle 2, 3, 1 \rangle + t \langle -1, 1, 1 \rangle$ and $l_2 \colon \mathbf{r}_2 = \langle 3, 1, 2 \rangle + s \langle -1, 2, -1 \rangle$ both contain the point $P(2, 3, 1)$. Find the value of s which gives the point of intersection P, and then compute the angle θ between the two lines.

    Answer: $s = 1$, $\theta \approx 61.9°$

41. The planes P_1: $x + 2y + 3z = 2$ and P_2: $-2x + 3y + 2z = -4$ both contain the point $P(2, 0, 0)$. Find a vector equation $\mathbf{r} = \overrightarrow{OP_0} + t\mathbf{d}$ for the line of intersection of these planes.

Answer: $\mathbf{r} = \langle 2, 0, 0 \rangle + t \langle -5, -8, 7 \rangle$

9.6 | Functions and Surfaces

1. Identify the surface $x = y^2 + 2z^2$.

(A) ellipsoid but not a sphere

(B) hyperboloid of one sheet

(C) hyperboloid of two sheets

(D) cylinder

(E) sphere

(F) elliptic but not circular paraboloid

(G) cone

(H) circular paraboloid (figure of revolution)

Answer: (F)

2. Identify the surface $x^2 + y^2 + z^2 = 4$.

(A) ellipsoid but not a sphere

(B) hyperboloid of one sheet

(C) hyperboloid of two sheets

(D) cylinder

(E) sphere

(F) elliptic but not circular paraboloid

(G) cone

(H) circular paraboloid (figure of revolution)

Answer: (E)

3. Identify the surface $x^2 = y^2 + z^2$.

(A) ellipsoid but not a sphere

(B) hyperboloid of one sheet

(C) hyperboloid of two sheets

(D) cylinder

(E) sphere

(F) elliptic but not circular paraboloid

(G) cone

(H) circular paraboloid (figure of revolution)

Answer: (G)

4. Identify the surface $2 = y^2 + z^2$.

(A) ellipsoid but not a sphere

(B) hyperboloid of one sheet

(C) hyperboloid of two sheets

(D) cylinder

(E) sphere

(F) elliptic but not circular paraboloid

(G) cone

(H) circular paraboloid (figure of revolution)

Answer: (D)

5. Identify the surface $x^2 + y^2 + z^2 = 3$.

   (A) ellipsoid but not a sphere

   (B) hyperboloid of one sheet

   (C) hyperboloid of two sheets

   (D) cylinder

   (E) sphere

   (F) elliptic but not circular paraboloid

   (G) cone

   (H) circular paraboloid (figure of revolution)

   Answer: (E)

6. Identify the surface $x^2 - y^2 + z^2 = 10$.

   (A) ellipsoid but not a sphere

   (B) hyperboloid of one sheet

   (C) hyperboloid of two sheets

   (D) cylinder

   (E) sphere

   (F) elliptic but not circular paraboloid

   (G) cone

   (H) circular paraboloid (figure of revolution)

   Answer: (B)

7. Identify the surface $-x^2 + y^2 - z^2 = 10$.

   (A) ellipsoid but not a sphere

   (B) hyperboloid of one sheet

   (C) hyperboloid of two sheets

   (D) cylinder

   (E) sphere

   (F) elliptic but not circular paraboloid

   (G) cone

   (H) circular paraboloid (figure of revolution)

   Answer: (C)

8. Identify the surface $x = y^2 - z^2$.

   (A) ellipsoid but not a sphere

   (B) hyperboloid of one sheet

   (C) hyperboloid of two sheets

   (D) cylinder

   (E) sphere

   (F) elliptic but not circular paraboloid

   (G) cone

   (H) hyperbolic paraboloid

   Answer: (H)

9. Identify the trace of the surface $x = y^2 + z^2$ in the plane $x = 1$.

   (A) ellipse but not a circle

   (B) parabola

   (C) hyperbola

   (D) circle

   (E) two parallel straight lines

   (F) two intersecting straight lines

   (G) point

   (H) straight line

   Answer: (D)

329

10. Identify the trace of the surface $x = y^2 + z^2$ in the plane $x = 0$.

    (A) ellipse but not a circle

    (C) hyperbola

    (E) two parallel straight lines

    (G) point

    (B) parabola

    (D) circle

    (F) two intersecting straight lines

    (H) straight line

    Answer: (G)

11. Identify the trace of the surface $x = y^2 + z^2$ in the plane $y = 0$.

    (A) ellipse but not a circle

    (C) hyperbola

    (E) two parallel straight lines

    (G) point

    (B) parabola

    (D) circle

    (F) two intersecting straight lines

    (H) straight line

    Answer: (B)

12. Identify the trace of the surface $x = y^2 + z^2$ in the plane $z = 1$.

    (A) ellipse but not a circle

    (C) hyperbola

    (E) two parallel straight lines

    (G) point

    (B) parabola

    (D) circle

    (F) two intersecting straight lines

    (H) straight line

    Answer: (B)

13. Identify the trace of the surface $x^2 = y^2 + z^2$ in the plane $z = 0$.

    (A) ellipse but not a circle

    (C) hyperbola

    (E) two parallel straight lines

    (G) point

    (B) parabola

    (D) circle

    (F) two intersecting straight lines

    (H) straight line

    Answer: (F)

14. Identify the trace of the surface $x^2 = y^2 + z^2$ in the plane $z = 1$.

    (A) ellipse but not a circle

    (C) hyperbola

    (E) two parallel straight lines

    (G) point

    (B) parabola

    (D) circle

    (F) two intersecting straight lines

    (H) straight line

    Answer: (C)

15. Identify the trace of the surface $x^2 = y^2 + z^2$ in the plane $y = 1$.

   (A) ellipse but not a circle

   (B) parabola

   (C) hyperbola

   (D) circle

   (E) two parallel straight lines

   (F) two intersecting straight lines

   (G) point

   (H) straight line

   Answer: (C)

16. Identify the trace of the surface $x^2 = y^2 + z^2$ in the plane $x = 0$.

   (A) ellipse but not a circle

   (B) parabola

   (C) hyperbola

   (D) circle

   (E) two parallel straight lines

   (F) two intersecting straight lines

   (G) point

   (H) straight line

   Answer: (G)

17. Identify the trace of the surface $x = y^2 + z^2$ in the plane $x = y$.

   (A) ellipse but not a circle

   (B) parabola

   (C) hyperbola

   (D) circle

   (E) two parallel straight lines

   (F) two intersecting straight lines

   (G) point

   (H) straight line

   Answer: (D)

18. Identify the trace of the surface $x = 2y^2 + 3z^2$ in the plane $x = 1$.

   (A) ellipse but not a circle

   (B) parabola

   (C) hyperbola

   (D) circle

   (E) two parallel straight lines

   (F) two intersecting straight lines

   (G) point

   (H) straight line

   Answer: (A)

19. Let $f(x, y) = x \sin y$. Find $f\left(2, \frac{\pi}{3}\right)$.

   (A) $\sqrt{3}$

   (B) $\sqrt{2}$

   (C) $\frac{\sqrt{3}}{2}$

   (D) $\frac{\sqrt{2}}{2}$

   (E) $\frac{1}{2}$

   (F) $\frac{1}{3}$

   (G) 1

   (H) 0

   Answer: (A)

20. Let $f(x, y) = x^2 + 2xy + y^2$. If $x = 2$, find $f(x, 2x)$.

   (A) 12

   (B) 16

   (C) 24

   (D) 28

   (E) 32

   (F) 36

   (G) 42

   (H) 48

   Answer: (F)

21. Let $f(x, y) = x \sin y$. If $x = \pi$, find $f(x, x/2)$.

   (A) $\frac{\pi}{6}$ (B) $\frac{\pi}{4}$ (C) $\frac{\pi}{3}$ (D) $\frac{\pi}{2}$

   (E) $\frac{2\pi}{3}$ (F) $\frac{3\pi}{4}$ (G) π (H) 2π

   Answer: (G)

22. Let $f(x, y) = (x^2 + y)^3$. If $x = 1$, find $f(x, 2x)$.

   (A) 1   (B) 2   (C) 3   (D) 4

   (E) 8   (F) 9   (G) 16   (H) 27

   Answer: (H)

23. Find the domain of the function $f(x, y) = \sqrt{x - y^2}$.

   (A) All points on or to the left of $x = y^2$ (B) All points on or to the right of $x = y^2$

   (C) All points to the left of $x = y^2$ (D) All points to the right of $x = y^2$

   (E) All points on or to the left of $x = 0$ (F) All points on or to the right of $x = 0$

   (G) All points to the left of $x = 0$ (H) All points in the xy-plane

   Answer: (B)

24. Find the range of the function $f(x, y) = \sqrt{x - y^2}$.

   (A) $(0, \infty)$ (B) $[0, \infty)$ (C) $(-\infty, 0)$ (D) $(-\infty, \infty)$

   (E) $(1, \infty)$ (F) $[1, \infty)$ (G) $(\sqrt{2}, \infty)$ (H) $[\sqrt{2}, \infty)$

   Answer: (B)

25. Find the domain of the function $f(x, y) = e^{x - y^2}$.

   (A) All points on or to the left of $x = y^2$ (B) All points on or to the right of $x = y^2$

   (C) All points to the left of $x = y^2$ (D) All points to the right of $x = y^2$

   (E) All points on or to the left of $x = 0$ (F) All points on or to the right of $x = 0$

   (G) All points to the left of $x = 0$ (H) All points in the xy-plane

   Answer: (H)

26. Find the range of the function $f(x, y) = e^{x - y^2}$.

   (A) $(0, \infty)$ (B) $[0, \infty)$ (C) $(-\infty, \infty)$ (D) $(-\infty, 0)$

   (E) $(1, \infty)$ (F) $[1, \infty)$ (G) $(\sqrt{2}, \infty)$ (H) $[\sqrt{2}, \infty)$

   Answer: (A)

27. Find the domain of the function $f(x, y) = \ln(x - y^2)$.

   (A) All points on or to the left of $x = y^2$ (B) All points on or to the right of $x = y^2$

   (C) All points to the left of $x = y^2$ (D) All points to the right of $x = y^2$

   (E) All points on or to the left of $x = 0$ (F) All points on or to the right of $x = 0$

   (G) All points to the left of $x = 0$ (H) All points in the x-y plane

   Answer: (D)

28. Find the range of the function $f(x, y) = \ln(x - y^2)$.

    (A) $(0, \infty)$ (B) $[0, \infty)$ (C) $(-\infty, \infty)$ (D) $(-\infty, 0)$

    (E) $(1, \infty)$ (F) $[1, \infty)$ (G) $(\sqrt{2}, \infty)$ (H) $[\sqrt{2}, \infty)$

    Answer: (C)

29. Identify the graph of the function $f(x, y) = 3 - x^2 - y^2$.

    (A) Cone   (B) Paraboloid

    (C) Ellipsoid   (D) Hyperboloid of one sheet

    (E) Hyperboloid of two sheets   (F) Hyperbolic cylinder

    (G) Elliptic cylinder   (H) Parabolic cylinder

    Answer: (B)

30. Let S be the quadric surface given by $x^2 + 2y^2 + 2x - z = 0$. What kind of surface is S?

    Answer: elliptic paraboloid

31. Let S be the quadric surface given by $x^2 + 2y^2 + 2x - z = 0$. What are the traces of S in each of the three coordinate planes?

    Answer: xy-plane: ellipse; yz-plane: parabola; xz-plane: parabola

32. Sketch the graph of $z = x^2 + y^2$ in $\mathbb{R}^3$, and name the surface.

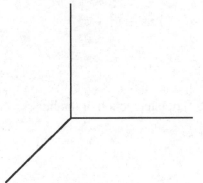

    Answer: Paraboloid

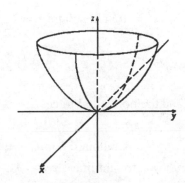

33. Sketch the graph of $\dfrac{x^2}{4} + y^2 - z^2 = 1$ in $\mathbb{R}^3$, and name the surface.

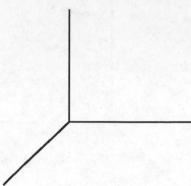

Answer: Elliptic hyperboloid of one sheet

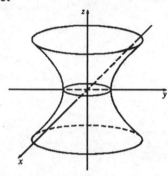

34. Which of the following is not a quadric surface?

(A) $x^2 + z^2 = 1$ (B) $z = x^2 + y^2$ (C) $y = x^3 + z$

(D) $z = x^2 - y^2$ (E) $x^2 + y^2 + z^2 = 1$

Answer: (C)

35. Find the coordinates of the point(s) of intersection of the line $x = 1 - t$, $y = 1 - t$, $z = 4t$ and the surface $z = x^2 + 2y^2$.

Answer: $(-2, -2, 12)$, $\left(\frac{2}{3}, \frac{2}{3}, \frac{4}{3}\right)$

36. Describe the trace of the surface $z = 4x^2 = 0$ in the plane $z = 1$.

Answer: $x = \pm\frac{1}{2}$; two straight lines

37. Describe the vertical traces $x = 0$ and the horizontal traces $z = -1$ (if any) for the surfaces $z = x^2 + y$ and $z^2 = x^2 + y^2$.

Answer: $z = x^2 + y^2$: $x = 0 \Rightarrow z = y^2$, a parabola; $z = -1 \Rightarrow x^2 + y^2 = -1$, no trace.
$z^2 = x^2 + y^2$: $x = 0 \Rightarrow z = \pm y$, two straight lines; $z = -1 \Rightarrow 1 = x^2 + y^2$, a circle

38. Sketch and identify the quadric surface given by $x^2 + y^2 - 2x = 0$.

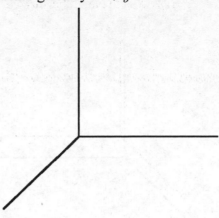

Answer: Circular cylinder

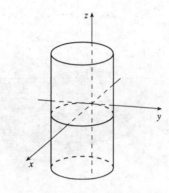

39. Sketch and identify the quadric surface given by the equation $z^2 - 2z - y = 0$.

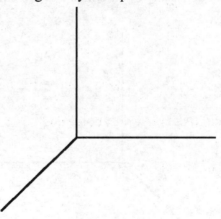

Answer: Parabolic cylinder

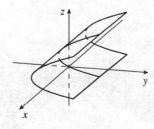

40. Find an equation of the surface consisting of all points that are equidistant from the point $(0, 1, 0)$ and the plane $y = -1$. Then sketch the surface.

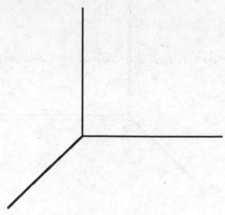

Answer: $y = \frac{1}{4}\left(x^2 + z^2\right)$

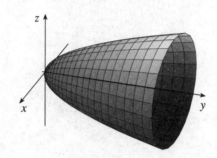

41. Find an equation of the surface consisting of all points that are equidistant from the y-axis and the xz-plane. Then sketch the surface.

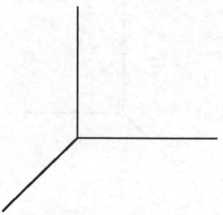

Answer: $y^2 = x^2 + z^2$

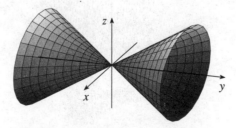

42. Sketch the region bounded by the surfaces with equations $x^2 + y^2 + z^2 - 4z = 0$ and $z = \sqrt{x^2 + y^2}$.

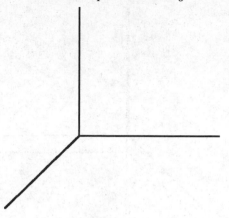

Answer:

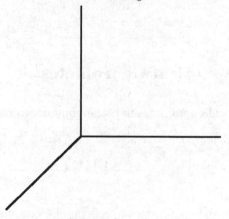

43. Sketch the curve of intersection of the two surfaces $z = y^2 - x^2$ and $x^2 + y^2 = 1$.

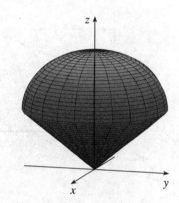

Answer:

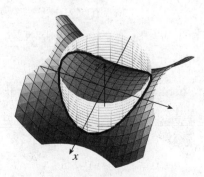

44. For the function $z = \sqrt{x^2 + y^2 - 1}$, sketch the portion of the surface in the first octant.

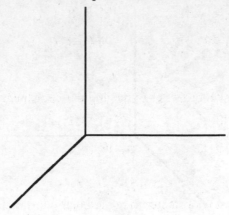

Answer:

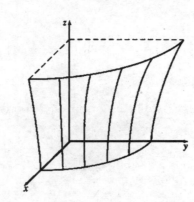

45. Describe the vertical traces $x = k$ and $y = k$ and the horizontal traces $z = k$ for the function $f(x, y) = x^2 - y^2$.

Answer: $x = k$: $z = k^2 - y^2$, parabola; $y = k$: $z = x^2 - k^2$, parabola; $z = k$: $x^2 - y^2 = k$, hyperbola

9.7   Cylindrical and Spherical Coordinates

1. Convert $(1, \pi, 1)$ from cylindrical coordinates to rectangular coordinates.

(A) $(1, 1, 1)$ (B) $(-1, 1, 1)$ (C) $(1, -1, 1)$ (D) $(1, 1, -1)$

(E) $(-1, 0, 1)$ (F) $(0, -1, 1)$ (G) $(1, 1, -1)$ (H) $(0, 1, 1)$

Answer: (E)

2. Convert $\left(2, \frac{5\pi}{4}, 3\right)$ from cylindrical coordinates to rectangular coordinates.

(A) $(1, 1, 3)$ (B) $(0, 2, 3)$ (C) $(2, 0, 3)$ (D) $\left(\sqrt{2}, \sqrt{2}, 3\right)$

(E) $(-1, -1, 3)$ (F) $(0, -2, 3)$ (G) $(-2, 0, 3)$ (H) $\left(-\sqrt{2}, -\sqrt{2}, 3\right)$

Answer: (H)

3. Convert $(1, 1, 1)$ from rectangular coordinates to cylindrical coordinates.

(A) $\left(\sqrt{2}, \frac{\pi}{2}, 1\right)$ (B) $\left(\sqrt{2}, \frac{\pi}{4}, 1\right)$ (C) $\left(1, \frac{\pi}{2}, 1\right)$ (D) $\left(1, \frac{\pi}{4}, 1\right)$

(E) $\left(1, \frac{\pi}{2}, \sqrt{2}\right)$ (F) $\left(1, \frac{\pi}{4}, \sqrt{2}\right)$ (G) $\left(1, \frac{\pi}{2}, 2\right)$ (H) $\left(1, \frac{\pi}{4}, 2\right)$

Answer: (B)

4. Convert $\left(1, -\sqrt{3}, \sqrt{3}\right)$ from rectangular coordinates to cylindrical coordinates.

(A) $\left(1, \frac{\pi}{3}, \sqrt{3}\right)$ (B) $\left(1, \frac{\pi}{6}, \sqrt{3}\right)$ (C) $\left(\sqrt{3}, \frac{\pi}{3}, 1\right)$ (D) $\left(\sqrt{3}, \frac{\pi}{6}, 1\right)$

(E) $\left(2, \frac{\pi}{3}, \sqrt{3}\right)$ (F) $\left(2, -\frac{\pi}{3}, \sqrt{3}\right)$ (G) $\left(\sqrt{3}, \frac{\pi}{3}, 2\right)$ (H) $\left(\sqrt{3}, \frac{\pi}{6}, 2\right)$

Answer: (F)

5. Convert $(1, \pi, \pi)$ from spherical coordinates to rectangular coordinates.

(A) $(0, 0, -1)$ (B) $(0, 0, 1)$ (C) $(0, 1, -1)$ (D) $(1, 0, -1)$

(E) $(1, 1, -1)$ (F) $(1, 0, 1)$ (G) $(0, 1, 1)$ (H) $(1, 1, 1)$

Answer: (A)

6. Convert $\left(1, \frac{\pi}{4}, \frac{\pi}{4}\right)$ from spherical coordinates to rectangular coordinates.

(A) $\left(\frac{1}{2}, \frac{1}{2}, \frac{1}{2}\right)$ (B) $\left(\frac{1}{2}, \frac{1}{2}, \frac{1}{\sqrt{2}}\right)$ (C) $\left(\frac{1}{2}, \frac{1}{\sqrt{2}}, \frac{1}{2}\right)$ (D) $\left(\frac{1}{\sqrt{2}}, \frac{1}{2}, \frac{1}{2}\right)$

(E) $\left(0, \frac{1}{\sqrt{2}}, \frac{1}{\sqrt{2}}\right)$ (F) $\left(\frac{1}{\sqrt{2}}, 1, \frac{1}{\sqrt{2}}\right)$ (G) $\left(\frac{1}{\sqrt{2}}, \frac{1}{\sqrt{2}}, 0\right)$ (H) $(1, 0, 0)$

Answer: (B)

7. Convert $\left(1, 1, \sqrt{2}\right)$ from rectangular coordinates to spherical coordinates.

(A) $\left(\sqrt{2}, \frac{\pi}{4}, \frac{\pi}{4}\right)$ (B) $\left(2, \frac{\pi}{4}, \frac{\pi}{4}\right)$ (C) $\left(\sqrt{2}, \frac{\pi}{2}, \frac{\pi}{4}\right)$ (D) $\left(2, \frac{\pi}{2}, \frac{\pi}{4}\right)$

(E) $\left(\sqrt{2}, \frac{\pi}{4}, \frac{\pi}{2}\right)$ (F) $\left(2, \frac{\pi}{4}, \frac{\pi}{2}\right)$ (G) $\left(\sqrt{2}, \frac{\pi}{2}, \frac{\pi}{2}\right)$ (H) $\left(2, \frac{\pi}{2}, \frac{\pi}{2}\right)$

Answer: (B)

8. Convert $\left(-1, \sqrt{3}, 2\right)$ from rectangular coordinates to spherical coordinates.

(A) $\left(2, \frac{\pi}{6}, \frac{\pi}{4}\right)$ (B) $\left(4, \frac{\pi}{6}, \frac{\pi}{4}\right)$ (C) $\left(\sqrt{2}, \frac{\pi}{6}, \frac{\pi}{4}\right)$ (D) $\left(\sqrt{8}, \frac{2\pi}{3}, \frac{\pi}{4}\right)$

(E) $\left(2, \frac{\pi}{3}, \frac{\pi}{4}\right)$ (F) $\left(4, \frac{\pi}{3}, \frac{\pi}{4}\right)$ (G) $\left(\sqrt{2}, \frac{4\pi}{3}, \frac{\pi}{4}\right)$ (H) $\left(\sqrt{8}, \frac{\pi}{3}, \frac{\pi}{4}\right)$

Answer: (D)

9. Describe the surface whose equation in cylindrical coordinates is $r = 3$.

(A) Cylinder with vertical axis   (B) Cylinder with horizontal axis

(C) Sphere   (D) Vertical plane or half-plane

(E) Horizontal plane or half-plane   (F) Paraboloid

(G) Cone or half-cone with vertical axis   (H) Cone or half-cone with horizontal axis

Answer: (A)

10. Describe the surface whose equation in cylindrical coordinates is $z = 3$.

(A) Cylinder with vertical axis   (B) Cylinder with horizontal axis

(C) Sphere   (D) Vertical plane or half-plane

(E) Horizontal plane or half-plane   (F) Paraboloid

(G) Cone or half-cone with vertical axis   (H) Cone or half-cone with horizontal axis

Answer: (E)

11. Describe the surface whose equation in cylindrical coordinates is $\theta = 3$.

    (A) Cylinder with vertical axis   (B) Cylinder with horizontal axis

    (C) Sphere   (D) Vertical plane or half-plane

    (E) Horizontal plane or half-plane   (F) Paraboloid

    (G) Cone or half-cone with vertical axis   (H) Cone or half-cone with horizontal axis

    Answer: (D)

12. Describe the surface whose equation in cylindrical coordinates is $z = 4r$.

    (A) Cylinder with vertical axis   (B) Cylinder with horizontal axis

    (C) Sphere   (D) Vertical plane or half-plane

    (E) Horizontal plane or half-plane   (F) Paraboloid

    (G) Cone or half-cone with vertical axis   (H) Cone or half-cone with horizontal axis

    Answer: (G)

13. Describe the surface whose equation in cylindrical coordinates is $z = r^2$.

    (A) Cylinder with vertical axis   (B) Cylinder with horizontal axis

    (C) Sphere   (D) Vertical plane or half-plane

    (E) Horizontal plane or half-plane   (F) Paraboloid

    (G) Cone or half-cone with vertical axis   (H) Cone or half-cone with horizontal axis

    Answer: (F)

14. Describe the surface whose equation in spherical coordinates is $\rho = 3$.

    (A) Cylinder with vertical axis   (B) Cylinder with horizontal axis

    (C) Sphere   (D) Vertical plane or half-plane

    (E) Horizontal plane or half-plane   (F) Paraboloid

    (G) Cone or half-cone with vertical axis   (H) Cone or half-cone with horizontal axis

    Answer: (C)

15. Describe the surface whose equation in spherical coordinates is $\theta = 3$.

    (A) Cylinder with vertical axis   (B) Cylinder with horizontal axis

    (C) Sphere   (D) Vertical plane or half-plane

    (E) Horizontal plane or half-plane   (F) Paraboloid

    (G) Cone or half-cone with vertical axis   (H) Cone or half-cone with horizontal axis

    Answer: (D)

16. Describe the surface whose equation in spherical coordinates is $\phi = 3$.

    (A) Cylinder with vertical axis   (B) Cylinder with horizontal axis

    (C) Sphere   (D) Vertical plane or half-plane

    (E) Horizontal plane or half-plane   (F) Paraboloid

    (G) Cone or half-cone with vertical axis   (H) Cone or half-cone with horizontal axis

    Answer: (G)

17. Describe the surface whose equation in spherical coordinates is $\rho = 4 \cos \phi$.

    (A) Cylinder with vertical axis   (B) Cylinder with horizontal axis

    (C) Sphere   (D) Vertical plane or half-plane

    (E) Horizontal plane or half-plane   (F) Paraboloid

    (G) Cone or half-cone with vertical axis   (H) Cone or half-cone with horizontal axis

    Answer: (C)

18. Describe the surface whose equation in spherical coordinates is $\rho = 3 \sec \phi$.

    (A) Cylinder with vertical axis   (B) Cylinder with horizontal axis

    (C) Sphere   (D) Vertical plane or half-plane

    (E) Horizontal plane or half-plane   (F) Paraboloid

    (G) Cone or half-cone with vertical axis   (H) Cone or half-cone with horizontal axis

    Answer: (E)

19. Describe the surface whose equation in spherical coordinates is $\phi = \pi$.

    (A) Cylinder with vertical axis   (B) Cylinder with horizontal axis

    (C) Sphere   (D) Positive z-axis

    (E) Negative z-axis   (F) Paraboloid

    (G) Cone or half-cone with vertical axis   (H) Cone or half-cone with horizontal axis

    Answer: (E)

20. If $P = \left(1, 1, \sqrt{2}\right)$ in rectangular coordinates, find the spherical coordinates of P.

    Answer: $\left(2, \frac{\pi}{4}, \frac{\pi}{4}\right)$

21. If $Q = \left(1, \frac{\pi}{2}, 3\right)$ in cylindrical coordinates, find rectangular coordinates of Q.

    Answer: $(0, 1, 3)$

22. Convert the point $\left(1, -\sqrt{3}, -2\right)$ to cylindrical and spherical coordinates.

    Answer: Cylindrical coordinates: $\left(2, \frac{-\pi}{3}, -2\right)$; spherical coordinates: $\left(2\sqrt{2}, \frac{-\pi}{3}, \frac{3\pi}{4}\right)$

23. Convert the point $(0, -5, 0)$ to cylindrical and spherical coordinates.

    Answer: Cylindrical coordinates: $\left(5, \frac{3\pi}{2}, 0\right)$; spherical coordinates: $\left(5, \frac{3\pi}{2}, \frac{\pi}{2}\right)$

24. Find rectangular and cylindrical equations for the surface whose equation in spherical coordinates is $\rho = 3$. Describe the surface.

    Answer: Rectangular: $x^2 + y^2 + z^2 = 9$; cylindrical: $r^2 + z^2 = 9$

25. Find rectangular and spherical equations for the surface whose equation in cylindrical coordinates is $\theta = \frac{\pi}{4}$. Describe the surface.

    Answer: Rectangular: $x = y$; spherical: $\theta = \frac{\pi}{4}$

26. Find cylindrical and spherical equations for the surface whose equation in rectangular coordinates is $x = 2$. Describe the surface.

    Answer: Cylindrical: $r \cos \theta = 2$; spherical: $\rho \sin \phi \cos \theta = 2$

27. Describe in words the solid represented in spherical coordinates by the inequality $2 \leq \rho \leq 5$.

    Answer: solid sphere of radius 5 centered at origin, with hollow ball inside of radius 2

28. Describe in words or sketch the solid represented in cylindrical coordinates by the inequalities $\frac{\pi}{6} \leq \theta \leq \frac{\pi}{3}$, $0 \leq r \leq 2$, $-1 \leq z \leq 1$.

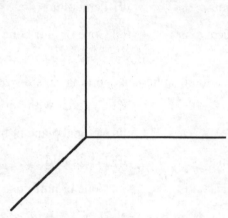

    Answer: Wedge of a circular cylinder with axis the z-axis

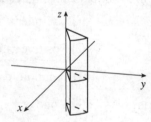

29. Describe the surface whose equation in cylindrical coordinates is $\theta = \frac{\pi}{2}$.

    Answer: Vertical plane

30. Describe the surface whose equation in cylindrical coordinates is $r = \sin \theta$.

    Answer: Circular cylinder with axis the z-axis

31. Describe the surface whose equation in spherical coordinates is $\sin \phi = \cos \phi$.

    Answer: Half-cone with axis the z-axis

32. New Orleans is situated at latitude 30° N and longitude 90° W, and New York is situated at latitude 41° N and longitude 74° W. Find the distance from New Orleans to New York, assuming that the radius of the earth is 3960 miles.

    Answer: About 1175 miles

33. Sketch the solid given in spherical coordinates by $0 \le \theta \le \pi, 0 \le \phi \le \frac{\pi}{4}, \rho \le 4 \sec \phi$.

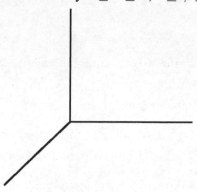

Answer:

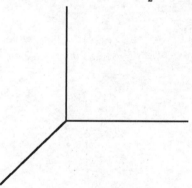

34. Sketch the solid given in cylindrical coordinates by $0 \le \theta \le \frac{\pi}{2}, 1 \le r \le 3, r \le z \le 3$.

Answer:

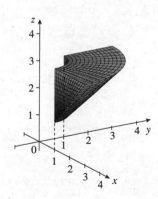

10   Vector Functions

10.1   Vector Functions and Space Curves

1. Find $\lim\limits_{t \to 0} \langle 2t, \cos t, e^t \rangle$.

  (A) $\langle 2, 1, 0 \rangle$ (B) $\langle 0, 0, 1 \rangle$ (C) $\langle 2, 0, 1 \rangle$ (D) $\langle 2, 1, 1 \rangle$

  (E) $\langle 1, 1, 1 \rangle$ (F) $\langle 1, 1, 0 \rangle$ (G) $\langle 1, 0, 1 \rangle$ (H) $\langle 0, 1, 1 \rangle$

Answer: (H)

2. Find $\lim\limits_{t \to \infty} \left[\dfrac{t+1}{t-1} \mathbf{i} + \left(1 + \dfrac{1}{t} \right)^t \mathbf{j} + \arctan t \, \mathbf{k} \right]$.

  (A) $\mathbf{i} + e\mathbf{j} + \frac{\pi}{4}\mathbf{k}$ (B) $\mathbf{i} + e\mathbf{j} + \frac{\pi}{2}\mathbf{k}$ (C) $\mathbf{i} + \frac{\pi}{4}\mathbf{k}$ (D) $\mathbf{i} + \frac{\pi}{2}\mathbf{k}$

  (E) $3\mathbf{i} + e\mathbf{j} + \frac{\pi}{4}\mathbf{k}$ (F) $3\mathbf{i} + e\mathbf{j} + \frac{\pi}{2}\mathbf{k}$ (G) $3\mathbf{i} + \frac{\pi}{4}\mathbf{k}$ (H) $3\mathbf{i} + \frac{\pi}{2}\mathbf{k}$

Answer: (B)

3. A curve is given by the vector equation $\mathbf{r}(t) = (2 + \cos t)\, \mathbf{i} + (1 + \sin t)\, \mathbf{j}$. Find a relation between x and y which has the same graph.

Answer: $(x - 2)^2 + (y - 1)^2 = 1$

4. The position of a particle at time t is given parametrically by $y = t^2$ and $x = \frac{1}{3}\left(t^3 - 3t\right)$. Show that the particle crosses the y-axis three times.

Answer: The particle crosses the y-axis when $x = 0$. That occurs at $t = -\sqrt{3}, 0,$ and $\sqrt{3}$

5. Consider the curve in the xy-plane defined parametrically by $x = t^3 - 3t$, $y = t^2$, $z = 0$. Sketch a rough graph of the curve.

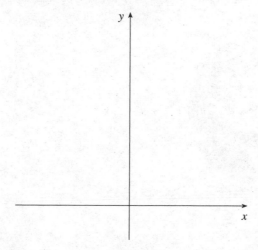

Answer:

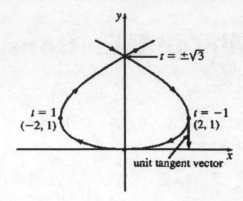

6. Find a space curve which parametrizes the intersection of the paraboloid $z = -x^2 - y^2$ and the plane $y = x$.

Answer: $\langle t, t, -2t^2 \rangle$

7. The graphs of which three of the following four vector functions lie along the line $y = 4 - x$?

(A) $x = 6 - t^2, y = t^2 - 2$ (B) $x = \cos^2 t, y = \sin^2 t + 3$

(C) $x = 2e^t, y = 2e^t - 8$ (D) $x_3 = \ln(1/t), y = \ln(e^4 t)$

Answer: (A), (B), and (D)

8. Consider the paraboloid $z = x^2 + y^2$. Which of the following space curves have as their range points lying on this paraboloid?

(A) $\mathbf{r}(t) = \langle t \sin t, t \cos t, t \rangle, t \in \mathbb{R}$ (B) $\mathbf{r}(t) = \langle t^2, t \sin t, t \cos t \rangle, t \in \mathbb{R}$

(C) $\mathbf{r}(t) = \langle t \cos t, t \sin t, t^2 \rangle, t \in \mathbb{R}$ (D) $\mathbf{r}(t) = \langle \sqrt{t} \sin t, t, \sqrt{t} \cos t \rangle, t > 0$

(E) $\mathbf{r}(t) = \langle \sqrt{t} \sin t, \sqrt{t} \cos t, t \rangle, t > 0$

Answer: (C) and (E)

9. Show that the curve with vector equation $\mathbf{r}(t) = 2\cos^2 t \, \mathbf{i} + \sin(2t) \, \mathbf{j} + 2\sin t \, \mathbf{k}$ is the curve of intersection of the surfaces $(x - 1)^2 + y^2 = 1$ and $x^2 + y^2 + z^2 = 4$. Use this fact to sketch the curve.

Answer:

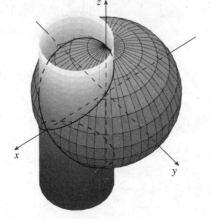

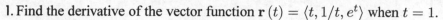

10.2 Derivatives and Integrals of Vector Functions

1. Find the derivative of the vector function $\mathbf{r}(t) = \langle t, 1/t, e^t \rangle$ when $t = 1$.

(A) $\langle 0, 1, 1 \rangle$ (B) $\langle 1, 0, 1 \rangle$ (C) $\langle 1, 1, e \rangle$ (D) $\langle 0, 0, e \rangle$

(E) $\langle -1, 1, e \rangle$ (F) $\langle 1, -1, e \rangle$ (G) $\langle 1, 1, -1 \rangle$ (H) $\langle 1, 1, 1 \rangle$

Answer: (F)

2. Find the derivative of the vector function $\mathbf{r}(t) = t\,\mathbf{i} + \sin t\,\mathbf{j}$ when $t = 0$.

(A) $\mathbf{i}$ (B) $\mathbf{j}$ (C) $-\mathbf{i}$ (D) $-\mathbf{j}$

(E) $-\mathbf{i} + \mathbf{j}$ (F) $\mathbf{i} - \mathbf{j}$ (G) $-\mathbf{i} - \mathbf{j}$ (H) $\mathbf{i} + \mathbf{j}$

Answer: (H)

3. Find the tangent vector $\mathbf{r}'(t)$ of the function $\mathbf{r}(t) = \left\langle t, \sqrt{t}, \dfrac{1}{2\sqrt{t}} \right\rangle$ when $t = \frac{1}{4}$.

(A) $\langle 1, 2, 4 \rangle$ (B) $\langle 1, 2, -2 \rangle$ (C) $\langle 1, 1, 4 \rangle$ (D) $\langle 1, 1, -2 \rangle$

(E) $\langle 1, 2, -4 \rangle$ (F) $\langle 1, 2, 2 \rangle$ (G) $\langle 1, 1, -4 \rangle$ (H) $\langle 1, 1, 2 \rangle$

Answer: (D)

4. Find the tangent vector $\mathbf{r}'(t)$ of the function $\mathbf{r}(t) = \sin 2t\,\mathbf{i} - \cos 2t\,\mathbf{j}$ when $t = \frac{\pi}{6}$.

(A) $\frac{1}{2}\mathbf{i} + \frac{\sqrt{3}}{2}\mathbf{j}$ (B) $\frac{1}{2}\mathbf{i} - \frac{\sqrt{3}}{2}\mathbf{j}$ (C) $\mathbf{i} + \sqrt{3}\mathbf{j}$ (D) $-\mathbf{i} - \sqrt{3}\mathbf{j}$

(E) $\frac{\sqrt{3}}{2}\mathbf{i} + \frac{1}{2}\mathbf{j}$ (F) $\frac{\sqrt{3}}{2}\mathbf{i} - \frac{1}{2}\mathbf{j}$ (G) $-\sqrt{3}\mathbf{i} + \mathbf{j}$ (H) $-\sqrt{3}\mathbf{i} - \mathbf{j}$

Answer: (C)

5. Find the unit tangent vector $\mathbf{T}(t)$ to the curve $\mathbf{r}(t) = \langle \sin t, 2t, t^2 \rangle$ when $t = 0$.

(A) $\left\langle -\frac{2}{\sqrt{5}}, -\frac{1}{\sqrt{5}}, 0 \right\rangle$ (B) $\left\langle \frac{2}{\sqrt{5}}, -\frac{1}{\sqrt{5}}, 0 \right\rangle$ (C) $\left\langle -\frac{2}{\sqrt{5}}, \frac{1}{\sqrt{5}}, 0 \right\rangle$ (D) $\left\langle \frac{2}{\sqrt{5}}, \frac{1}{\sqrt{5}}, 0 \right\rangle$

(E) $\left\langle -\frac{1}{\sqrt{5}}, -\frac{2}{\sqrt{5}}, 0 \right\rangle$ (F) $\left\langle \frac{1}{\sqrt{5}}, -\frac{2}{\sqrt{5}}, 0 \right\rangle$ (G) $\left\langle -\frac{1}{\sqrt{5}}, \frac{2}{\sqrt{5}}, 0 \right\rangle$ (H) $\left\langle \frac{1}{\sqrt{5}}, \frac{2}{\sqrt{5}}, 0 \right\rangle$

Answer: (H)

6. Find the unit tangent vector $\mathbf{T}(t)$ to the curve $\mathbf{r}(t) = t\,\mathbf{i} + t^2\,\mathbf{j}$ when $t = 0$.

(A) $\mathbf{i}$ (B) $\mathbf{j}$ (C) $\frac{1}{\sqrt{2}}\mathbf{i} + \frac{1}{\sqrt{2}}\mathbf{j}$ (D) $\frac{1}{\sqrt{2}}\mathbf{i} - \frac{1}{\sqrt{2}}\mathbf{j}$

(E) $\frac{2}{\sqrt{5}}\mathbf{i} + \frac{1}{\sqrt{5}}\mathbf{j}$ (F) $\frac{1}{\sqrt{5}}\mathbf{i} + \frac{2}{\sqrt{5}}\mathbf{j}$ (G) $\frac{2}{\sqrt{5}}\mathbf{i} - \frac{1}{\sqrt{5}}\mathbf{j}$ (H) $\frac{1}{\sqrt{5}}\mathbf{i} - \frac{2}{\sqrt{5}}\mathbf{j}$

Answer: (A)

7. Evaluate the integral $\int_0^1 \left(t\,\mathbf{i} - 2t^2\,\mathbf{j} + e^{-t}\,\mathbf{k} \right) dt$.

(A) $\mathbf{i}$ (B) $\mathbf{j}$

(C) $\mathbf{i} - \mathbf{j} + \left(\dfrac{1}{e} - 1 \right)\mathbf{k}$ (D) $\mathbf{i} - \frac{1}{2}\mathbf{j} + \left(1 - \dfrac{1}{e} \right)\mathbf{k}$

(E) $\frac{1}{2}\mathbf{i} - \mathbf{j}$ (F) $\frac{1}{2}\mathbf{i} - \frac{1}{2}\mathbf{j}$

(G) $\frac{1}{2}\mathbf{i} - \frac{2}{3}\mathbf{j} + \left(\dfrac{1}{e} - 1 \right)\mathbf{k}$ (H) $\frac{1}{2}\mathbf{i} - \frac{2}{3}\mathbf{j} + \left(1 - \dfrac{1}{e} \right)\mathbf{k}$

Answer: (H)

8. Find $\mathbf{r}(1)$ if $\mathbf{r}'(t) = t^2\,\mathbf{i} + t^3\,\mathbf{j}$ and $\mathbf{r}(0) = \mathbf{i}$.

(A) $\frac{1}{3}\mathbf{i} + \frac{1}{4}\mathbf{j}$ (B) $\frac{4}{3}\mathbf{i} + \frac{1}{4}\mathbf{j}$ (C) $\frac{2}{3}\mathbf{i} + \frac{1}{4}\mathbf{j}$ (D) $\mathbf{i} + \frac{1}{4}\mathbf{j}$

(E) $\frac{1}{3}\mathbf{i} + \frac{3}{4}\mathbf{j}$ (F) $\frac{4}{3}\mathbf{i} + \frac{3}{4}\mathbf{j}$ (G) $\frac{2}{3}\mathbf{i} + \frac{3}{4}\mathbf{j}$ (H) $\mathbf{i} + \frac{3}{4}\mathbf{j}$

Answer: (B)

9. Find the unit tangent vector to the curve $\mathbf{r}(t) = \left\langle e^{2t}\cos t, e^{2t}\sin t, e^{2t} \right\rangle$ at the point where $t = \frac{\pi}{2}$.

(A) $\left\langle \frac{2}{3}, -\frac{2}{3}, \frac{1}{3} \right\rangle$ (B) $\left\langle \frac{2}{3}, -\frac{1}{3}, \frac{2}{3} \right\rangle$ (C) $\left\langle -\frac{1}{3}, \frac{2}{3}, \frac{2}{3} \right\rangle$ (D) $\left\langle \frac{2}{3}, \frac{2}{3}, -\frac{1}{3} \right\rangle$

(E) $\left\langle \frac{3}{\sqrt{14}}, \frac{2}{\sqrt{14}}, -\frac{1}{\sqrt{14}} \right\rangle$ (F) $\left\langle -\frac{2}{\sqrt{14}}, \frac{1}{\sqrt{14}}, \frac{3}{\sqrt{14}} \right\rangle$ (G) $\left\langle \frac{1}{\sqrt{14}}, -\frac{3}{\sqrt{14}}, \frac{2}{\sqrt{14}} \right\rangle$ (H) $\left\langle \frac{1}{\sqrt{6}}, \frac{2}{\sqrt{6}}, \frac{1}{\sqrt{6}} \right\rangle$

Answer: (C)

10. Find parametric equations of the tangent line to the curve $\mathbf{r}(t) = e^{2t}\,\mathbf{i} + 2\sin 3t\,\mathbf{j}$ at $t = 0$.

Answer: $x = 1 + 2t$, $y = 6t$.

11. Find parametric equations of the tangent line to the curve $\mathbf{r}(t) = \left\langle t, \sqrt{2}\cos t, \sqrt{2}\sin t \right\rangle$ at $\left(\frac{\pi}{4}, 1, 1\right)$. Then sketch the curve and its tangent line.

Answer: $x = \frac{\pi}{4} + t$, $y = 1 - t$, $z = 1 + t$

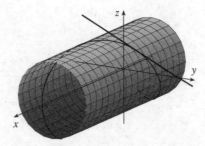

12. Let $\mathbf{u}(t) = 2t\,\mathbf{i} + \sin t\,\mathbf{j} - \cos t\,\mathbf{k}$ and $\mathbf{v}(t) = \mathbf{i} + t^2\,\mathbf{j} - t\,\mathbf{k}$. Find $\dfrac{d}{dt}\left[\mathbf{u}(t) \times \mathbf{v}(t)\right]$.

Answer: $\dfrac{d}{dt}\left[\mathbf{u}(t) \times \mathbf{v}(t)\right] = \left(t\cos t - \sin t - t^2\sin t\right)\mathbf{i} + \left(4t + \sin t\right)\mathbf{j} + \left(6t^2 - \cos t\right)\mathbf{k}$

13. Find an expression for $\dfrac{d}{dt}\left[(\mathbf{u}(t) \times \mathbf{v}(t)) \cdot \mathbf{w}(t)\right]$.

Answer: $(\mathbf{u}'(t) \times \mathbf{v}(t)) \cdot \mathbf{w}(t) + (\mathbf{u}(t) \times \mathbf{v}'(t)) \cdot \mathbf{w}(t) + (\mathbf{u}(t) \times \mathbf{v}(t)) \cdot \mathbf{w}'(t)$

14. Let $x = t^3$ and $y = 3t^2$. Find the point on the curve closest to $(0, 3)$.

Answer: $\left(\pm\left(\sqrt{15} - 3\right)^{3/2}, 3\sqrt{15} - 9 \right)$

15. Find the point(s) on the curve described by the vector function $\mathbf{r}(t) = \left\langle t^2 + 2t, t^3 - 12t \right\rangle$ where the tangent vector is horizontal or vertical.

Answer: Horizontal at $(0, 16)$ and $(8, -16)$, vertical at $(-1, 11)$

16. Let $\mathbf{r}(t) = \left\langle \cos 2t, \sin 2t, 3 \right\rangle$. Compute the tangent vector $\mathbf{r}'(t)$ and show that it is always orthogonal to $\mathbf{r}(t)$.

Answer: $\mathbf{r}'(t) = \left\langle -2\sin 2t, 2\cos 2t, 0 \right\rangle$; $\mathbf{r}'(t) \cdot \mathbf{r}(t) = 0$

17. Where does the tangent line to the curve $\mathbf{r}(t) = \left\langle e^{-2t}, \cos t, 3\sin t \right\rangle$ at $(1, 1, 0)$ intersects the yz-plane?

Answer: $\left(0, 1, \frac{3}{2}\right)$

18. If $\mathbf{u}(t) = \langle -\sqrt{t}\sin t, t, t^{2/3} \rangle$ and $\mathbf{v}(t) = \langle -\sqrt{t}\sin t, \cos^2 t, -t^{1/3} \rangle$, compute $\dfrac{d}{dt}(\mathbf{u}(t) \cdot \mathbf{v}(t))$ and $\dfrac{d}{dt}(\mathbf{u}(t) \cdot \mathbf{u}(t))$.

Answer: $\dfrac{d}{dt}(\mathbf{u}(t) \cdot \mathbf{v}(t)) = 0$, $\dfrac{d}{dt}(\mathbf{u}(t) \cdot \mathbf{u}(t)) = \sin^2 t + 2t\sin t\cos t + 2t + \frac{4}{3}t^{1/3}$

10.3 Arc Length and Curvature

1. Find the length of the curve $\mathbf{r}(t) = \langle 2t, \sin t, \cos t \rangle$, $0 \le t \le 2\pi$.

(A) $2\pi\sqrt{2}$ (B) $\pi\sqrt{10}$ (C) $2\pi\sqrt{3}$ (D) $\pi\sqrt{14}$

(E) 4π (F) $3\pi\sqrt{2}$ (G) $2\pi\sqrt{5}$ (H) $\pi\sqrt{22}$

Answer: (G)

2. Find the length of the curve $\mathbf{r}(t) = \langle 2t^{3/2}, 2t+1, \sqrt{5}t \rangle$, $0 \le t \le 3$.

(A) $3\sqrt{21}$ (B) 6 (C) 8 (D) 10

(E) 189 (F) 14 (G) 16 (H) 18

Answer: (F)

3. Find the unit tangent vector $\mathbf{T}(t)$ to the curve $\mathbf{r}(t) = \langle \sin t, t, \cos t \rangle$ when $t = 0$.

(A) $\langle -1, 0, 0 \rangle$ (B) $\langle 0, 0, -1 \rangle$ (C) $\langle 1, 0, 0 \rangle$ (D) $\langle 0, 0, 1 \rangle$

(E) $\left\langle 0, \frac{1}{\sqrt{2}}, \frac{1}{\sqrt{2}} \right\rangle$ (F) $\left\langle \frac{1}{\sqrt{2}}, 0, \frac{1}{\sqrt{2}} \right\rangle$ (G) $\left\langle \frac{1}{\sqrt{2}}, \frac{1}{\sqrt{2}}, 0 \right\rangle$ (H) $\left\langle \frac{1}{\sqrt{3}}, \frac{1}{\sqrt{3}}, \frac{1}{\sqrt{3}} \right\rangle$

Answer: (G)

4. Find the unit tangent vector $\mathbf{T}(t)$ to the curve $\mathbf{r}(t) = \langle t^2 - 1, 3t^2 - t^4, 2/t \rangle$ when $t = 1$.

(A) $\left\langle \frac{1}{\sqrt{3}}, \frac{1}{\sqrt{3}}, -\frac{1}{\sqrt{3}} \right\rangle$ (B) $\left\langle \frac{1}{\sqrt{3}}, -\frac{1}{\sqrt{3}}, -\frac{1}{\sqrt{3}} \right\rangle$ (C) $\langle 0, 1, 0 \rangle$ (D) $\langle 0, 0, 1 \rangle$

(E) $\left\langle \frac{1}{\sqrt{3}}, \frac{1}{\sqrt{3}}, \frac{1}{\sqrt{3}} \right\rangle$ (F) $\left\langle \frac{1}{\sqrt{2}}, 0, \frac{1}{\sqrt{2}} \right\rangle$ (G) $\left\langle \frac{1}{\sqrt{2}}, \frac{1}{\sqrt{2}}, 0 \right\rangle$ (H) $\left\langle \frac{1}{\sqrt{2}}, \frac{1}{\sqrt{2}}, \frac{1}{\sqrt{2}} \right\rangle$

Answer: (A)

5. Find the unit normal vector $\mathbf{N}(t)$ to the curve $\mathbf{r}(t) = \langle \sin t, t, \cos t \rangle$ when $t = 0$.

(A) $\langle -1, 0, 0 \rangle$ (B) $\langle 0, 0, -1 \rangle$ (C) $\langle 1, 0, 0 \rangle$ (D) $\langle 0, 0, 1 \rangle$

(E) $\left\langle 0, \frac{1}{\sqrt{2}}, \frac{1}{\sqrt{2}} \right\rangle$ (F) $\left\langle \frac{1}{\sqrt{2}}, 0, \frac{1}{\sqrt{2}} \right\rangle$ (G) $\left\langle \frac{1}{\sqrt{2}}, \frac{1}{\sqrt{2}}, 0 \right\rangle$ (H) $\left\langle \frac{1}{\sqrt{3}}, \frac{1}{\sqrt{3}}, \frac{1}{\sqrt{3}} \right\rangle$

Answer: (B)

6. Find the unit normal vector $\mathbf{N}(t)$ to the curve $\mathbf{r}(t) = \langle t, 2t, t^2 \rangle$ when $t = 1$.

(A) $\left\langle \frac{1}{3}, \frac{2}{3}, \frac{2}{3} \right\rangle$ (B) $\langle 1, 0, 0 \rangle$ (C) $\langle 0, 1, 0 \rangle$ (D) $\left\langle -\frac{2}{3\sqrt{5}}, -\frac{4}{3\sqrt{5}}, \frac{5}{3\sqrt{5}} \right\rangle$

(E) $\left\langle 0, \frac{1}{\sqrt{2}}, \frac{1}{\sqrt{2}} \right\rangle$ (F) $\left\langle \frac{1}{\sqrt{2}}, 0, \frac{1}{\sqrt{2}} \right\rangle$ (G) $\left\langle \frac{1}{\sqrt{2}}, \frac{1}{\sqrt{2}}, 0 \right\rangle$ (H) $\left\langle \frac{1}{\sqrt{2}}, \frac{1}{\sqrt{2}}, \frac{1}{\sqrt{2}} \right\rangle$

Answer: (D)

7. Find the curvature κ of the curve $y = 2x^2$ at $x = 0$.

(A) 0 (B) $\frac{1}{8}$ (C) $\frac{1}{4}$ (D) $\frac{1}{2}$

(E) 1 (F) 2 (G) 4 (H) 8

Answer: (G)

8. Find the curvature κ of the curve $\mathbf{r}(t) = \langle t, t, 1 - t^2 \rangle$ when $t = 0$.

(A) 0   (B) $\frac{1}{8}$ (C) $\frac{1}{4}$ (D) $\frac{1}{2}$

(E) 1   (F) 2   (G) 4   (H) 8

Answer: (E)

9. Find the curvature κ of the curve $\mathbf{r}(t) = \langle \sin 2t, 3t, \cos 2t \rangle$ when $t = \frac{\pi}{2}$.

(A) $\frac{3}{13}$ (B) $\frac{4}{13}$ (C) $\frac{6}{13}$ (D) $\frac{8}{13}$

(E) $\frac{1}{3}$ (F) $\frac{4}{9}$ (G) $\frac{2}{3}$ (H) $\frac{8}{9}$

Answer: (B)

10. Find the length of the curve $\mathbf{r}(t) = \langle \sin 2t, \cos 2t, 2t^{3/2} \rangle$, $0 \le t \le 1$.

(A) $\frac{2}{27}\left(13\sqrt{13} - 8\right)$ (B) $\frac{13}{9}$ (C) $\frac{13\sqrt{13} - 6}{27}$ (D) $\frac{16}{9}$

(E) $\frac{10}{27}\left(\sqrt{13} - 2\right)$ (F) $\frac{19}{9}$ (G) $\frac{4}{9}\left(7\sqrt{7} - 2\right)$ (H) $\frac{22}{9}$

Answer: (A)

11. Find the unit tangent and the unit normal to the graph of the vector function $\mathbf{r}(t) = \langle t^2 - 2, 2t - t^3 \rangle$ at $t = 1$.

Answer: Unit tangent: $\frac{1}{\sqrt{5}}\langle 2, -1 \rangle$; unit normal: $\frac{1}{\sqrt{5}}\langle 1, 2 \rangle$

12. At what point does the curve $\mathbf{r}(t) = \langle t, t, 1 - at^2 \rangle$, $a > 0$ have maximum curvature? What is the maximum curvature?

Answer: At $(0, 0, 1)$, $\kappa = a$

13. At what point does the curve $\mathbf{r}(t) = \langle \sqrt{2}t, e^t, e^{-t} \rangle$ have minimum curvature? What is the minimum curvature?

Answer: At $(0, 1, 1)$, $\kappa = \frac{\sqrt{2}}{4}$

14. Find the arc length of the curve given by $\mathbf{r}(t) = \langle t^2, t^3 \rangle$, $0 \le t \le 1$.

Answer: $\frac{1}{27}\left(13\sqrt{13} - 8\right)$

15. Suppose C is the curve given by the vector function $\mathbf{r}(t) = \langle t, t^2, 1 - t^2 \rangle$. Find the unit tangent vector, the unit normal vector, and the curvature of C at the point where $t = 1$.

Answer: $\mathbf{T}(1) = \frac{1}{3}\langle 1, 2, -2 \rangle$, $\mathbf{N}(1) = \frac{1}{\sqrt{18}}\langle -4, 1, -1 \rangle$, $\kappa = \frac{2\sqrt{2}}{27}$

16. A picture of a helix is given below. The helix has radius 5 and height 6, and makes 4 revolutions. Find parametric equations of this helix. What is the arc length of the helix?

Answer: $\mathbf{r}(t) = \langle 5\cos 2\pi t, 5\sin 2\pi t, \frac{3}{2}t \rangle$, $0 \le t \le 4$; $L = \sqrt{36 + (40\pi)^2} \approx 125.8$

17. Find the length of the circular helix described by $x = 2\cos t$, $y = 2\sin t$, $z = \sqrt{5}t$, $0 \le t \le 2\pi$.

Answer: 6π

18. Find the center of the osculating circle of the parabola $y = x^2$ at the origin.

Answer: $\left(0, \frac{1}{2}\right)$

19. Find the center of the osculating circle of the curve described by $x = 4\sin t$, $y = 3t$, $z = 4\cos t$ at $(0, 0, 4)$.

Answer: $(0, 0, -2.25)$

20. Consider $\mathbf{r}(t)$, the vector function describing the curve shown below. Put the curvatures at A, B, and C in order from smallest to largest.

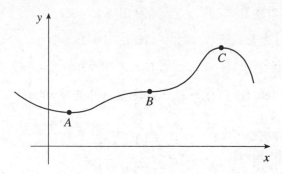

Answer: B, A, C

21. Show that if $\mathbf{r}'(t)$ and $\mathbf{r}''(t)$ are parallel at some point on the curve described by $\mathbf{r}(t)$, then the curvature at that point is 0. Give an example of a curve $\mathbf{r}(t)$ for which $\mathbf{r}'(t)$ and $\mathbf{r}''(t)$ are *always* parallel.

Answer: $\mathbf{r}'$ and $\mathbf{r}''$ are parallel $\Rightarrow$ $\mathbf{r}' \times \mathbf{r}'' = 0$ $\Rightarrow$ $\kappa = \dfrac{|\mathbf{r}' \times \mathbf{r}''|}{|\mathbf{r}'|^3} = 0$. Example: $\mathbf{r} = \langle t, t, t \rangle$

22. Consider $y = \sin x$, $-\pi < x < \pi$. Determine graphically where the curvature is maximal and minimal.

Answer: Minimal at $x = 0$, maximal at $x = \pm\frac{\pi}{2}$

23. Find the equation of the plane normal to $\mathbf{r}(t) = \left\langle e^t \sin \frac{\pi}{2}t, e^t \cos \frac{\pi}{2}t, t^2 \right\rangle$ when $t = 1$.

Answer: $ex - \frac{\pi}{2}y + 2z = e^2 + 2$.

10.4 Motion in Space

1. Let the position function of a particle be $\mathbf{r}(t) = \langle t^2, 2t, e^t \rangle$. Find the velocity of the particle when $t = 1$.

(A) $\langle 2, 2, 1 \rangle$ (B) $\langle 2, 2, e \rangle$ (C) $\langle 2, 0, 1 \rangle$ (D) $\langle 2, 0, e \rangle$

(E) $\langle 1, 1, 1 \rangle$ (F) $\langle 1, 1, e \rangle$ (G) $\langle 1, 0, 1 \rangle$ (H) $\langle 1, 0, e \rangle$

Answer: (B)

2. Let the position function of a particle be $\mathbf{r}(t) = \langle t^2, 2t, e^t \rangle$. Find the acceleration of the particle when $t = 0$.

(A) $\langle 2, 2, 1 \rangle$ (B) $\langle 2, 2, e \rangle$ (C) $\langle 2, 0, 1 \rangle$ (D) $\langle 2, 0, e \rangle$

(E) $\langle 1, 1, 1 \rangle$ (F) $\langle 1, 1, e \rangle$ (G) $\langle 1, 0, 1 \rangle$ (H) $\langle 1, 0, e \rangle$

Answer: (C)

3. Let the position function of a particle be $\mathbf{r}(t) = \langle 3\sin 2t, 2\cos 2t, -\sin 4t \rangle$. Find the speed of the particle when $t = \frac{\pi}{4}$.

(A) 1 (B) 4 (C) 3 (D) $4\sqrt{2}$

(E) $\sqrt{8}$ (F) $\sqrt{10}$ (G) $\sqrt{13}$ (H) $\sqrt{14}$

Answer: (D)

4. Let the acceleration of a particle be $\mathbf{a}(t) = \mathbf{i} + \mathbf{k}$, and let its velocity when $t = 0$ be $\mathbf{v}(0) = \mathbf{j}$. Find its velocity when $t = 1$.

(A) $\frac{1}{2}\mathbf{i} + \mathbf{k}$ (B) $2\mathbf{i} + \mathbf{k}$ (C) $3\mathbf{i} + \mathbf{k}$ (D) $\mathbf{i} + \mathbf{k}$

(E) $\frac{1}{2}\mathbf{i}$ (F) $\mathbf{i} + \mathbf{k}$ (G) $\mathbf{i} + \mathbf{j} + \mathbf{k}$ (H) $\mathbf{j} + \mathbf{k}$

Answer: (G)

5. Let the acceleration of a particle be $\mathbf{a}(t) = t\mathbf{i}$, and let its velocity when $t = 0$ be $\mathbf{v}(0) = \mathbf{i} + \mathbf{k}$. Find its speed when $t = 2$.

(A) $\sqrt{5}$ (B) $\sqrt{6}$ (C) $\sqrt{7}$ (D) $\sqrt{8}$

(E) 3   (F) $\sqrt{10}$ (G) $\sqrt{11}$ (H) $\sqrt{12}$

Answer: (F)

6. Let the velocity of a particle be $\mathbf{v}(t) = \mathbf{i} + t\mathbf{j}$, and let its position when $t = 0$ be $\mathbf{r}(0) = \mathbf{j} + 2\mathbf{k}$. Find its position when $t = 2$.

(A) $3\mathbf{i} + 3\mathbf{j} + 2\mathbf{k}$ (B) $2\mathbf{i} + 3\mathbf{j} + 2\mathbf{k}$ (C) $3\mathbf{i} + 2\mathbf{j} + 2\mathbf{k}$ (D) $3\mathbf{i} + 3\mathbf{j} + 2\mathbf{k}$

(E) $3\mathbf{i} + 4\mathbf{j} + 2\mathbf{k}$ (F) $2\mathbf{i} + 4\mathbf{j} + 2\mathbf{k}$ (G) $4\mathbf{i} + 2\mathbf{j} + 2\mathbf{k}$ (H) $4\mathbf{i} + 3\mathbf{j} + 2\mathbf{k}$

Answer: (B)

7. Let the position function of a particle be $\mathbf{r}(t) = \sin 3t\,\mathbf{i} + \cos 3t\,\mathbf{j} + \sin 4t\,\mathbf{k}$. Find the smallest value of its speed.

(A) 1   (B) 2   (C) 9   (D) $\sqrt{3}$

(E) 0   (F) $\sqrt{10}$ (G) $\sqrt{2}$ (H) 3

Answer: (H)

8. Let the position function of a particle be $\mathbf{r}(t) = \langle t^2, 1 - 2t, t \rangle$. Find the smallest value of its speed.

(A) 0   (B) 1   (C) $\sqrt{2}$ (D) $\sqrt{3}$

(E) 2   (F) $\sqrt{5}$ (G) $\sqrt{6}$ (H) $\sqrt{7}$

Answer: (F)

9. Let the position function of a particle be $\mathbf{r}(t) = t\,\mathbf{i} + t^2\,\mathbf{j}$. Find the tangential component of the acceleration vector when $t = 1$.

(A) $\frac{1}{\sqrt{5}}$ (B) $\frac{2}{\sqrt{5}}$ (C) $\frac{3}{\sqrt{5}}$ (D) $\frac{4}{\sqrt{5}}$

(E) $\sqrt{5}$ (F) $\frac{6}{\sqrt{5}}$ (G) $\frac{7}{\sqrt{5}}$ (H) $\frac{8}{\sqrt{5}}$

Answer: (D)

10. Let the position function of a particle be $\mathbf{r}(t) = t\mathbf{i} + t^2\mathbf{j}$. Find the normal component of the acceleration vector when $t = 1$.

(A) $\frac{1}{\sqrt{5}}$ (B) $\frac{2}{\sqrt{5}}$ (C) $\frac{3}{\sqrt{5}}$ (D) $\frac{4}{\sqrt{5}}$

(E) $\sqrt{5}$ (F) $\frac{6}{\sqrt{5}}$ (G) $\frac{7}{\sqrt{5}}$ (H) $\frac{8}{\sqrt{5}}$

Answer: (B)

11. Suppose a particle moves in the plane according to the vector-valued function $\mathbf{r}(t) = 2e^t\mathbf{i} + e^{-t}\mathbf{j}$, where t represents time. Find $\mathbf{v}(t)$, $|\mathbf{v}(t)|$, and $\mathbf{a}(t)$, and sketch a graph showing the path taken by the particle indicating the direction of motion.

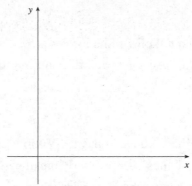

Answer: $\mathbf{v}(t) = 2e^t\mathbf{i} - e^{-t}\mathbf{j}$, $|\mathbf{v}(t)| = \sqrt{4e^{2t} + e^{-2t}}$, $\mathbf{a}(t) = 2e^t\mathbf{i} + e^{-t}\mathbf{j}$

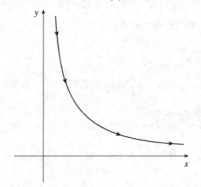

12. Is it possible for the velocity of a particle to be zero at the same time its acceleration is not zero? Explain.
Answer: Yes

13. Suppose a particle is moving in the xy-plane so that its position vector at time t is given by $\mathbf{r}(t) = \langle t^3 - t, t - t^2 \rangle$. Find the velocity, speed, and acceleration of the particle at time $t = 2$.
Answer: $\mathbf{v}(2) = \langle 11, -3 \rangle$; speed$= \sqrt{130}$; $\mathbf{a}(2) = \langle 12, -2 \rangle$

14. Let $\mathbf{a}(t)$, $\mathbf{v}(t)$, and $\mathbf{r}(t)$ denote the acceleration, velocity, and position at time t of an object moving in the xy-plane. Find $\mathbf{r}(t)$, given that $\mathbf{a}(t) = \langle e^{2t} + 2t, e^{2t} - 3 \rangle$, $\mathbf{v}(0) = \langle \frac{3}{2}, \frac{7}{2} \rangle$, and $\mathbf{r}(0) = \langle \frac{5}{4}, \frac{9}{4} \rangle$.
Answer: $\mathbf{r}(t) = \langle \frac{1}{4}e^{2t} + \frac{1}{3}t^3 + t + 1, \frac{1}{4}e^{2t} - \frac{3}{2}t^2 + 3t + 2 \rangle$

15. A paper carrier is traveling 60 miles per hour down a straight road in the direction of the vector $\mathbf{i}$ when he throws a paper out the car window with a velocity (relative to the car) in the direction of $\mathbf{j}$ and of magnitude 10 miles per hour.
(a) Find the velocity of the paper relative to the ground when the paper carrier releases it.
(b) Find the speed of the paper at that time.
Answer: (a) $\mathbf{v} = 60\mathbf{i} + 10\mathbf{j}$; (b) $\sqrt{3700} \approx 60.83$ miles per hour

16. A particle is traveling along a helix whose vector equation is given by $\mathbf{r}(t) = \langle R\cos\alpha t, R\sin\alpha t, \beta t \rangle$. Show that its velocity and acceleration are orthogonal at all times.

17. A cannon sits on top of a vertical tower 264 feet tall. It fires a cannonball at 80 ft/s. If the barrel of the cannon is elevated 30 degrees from the horizontal, find how far from the base of the tower the cannonball will land (assuming the ground around the tower is level).

Answer: $220\sqrt{3}$ ft

18. A person is standing 80 feet from a tall cliff. She throws a rock at 80 feet per second at an angle of $45°$ from the horizontal. Neglecting air resistance and discounting the height of the person, how far up the cliff does it hit?

Answer: 48 ft

19. Floyd Thunderfoot is a punter for the Vikings. Today the Vikings are playing the Bears in the Metrodome. The Bears stop the Vikings at the Vikings' 40 yard line (line of scrimmage), and Floyd is called in to punt. Floyd needs to kick from 10 yards behind the line of scrimmage in order to get the punt off in time. If the ball has a hang time of 4 seconds and lands at the Bears' 10 yard line, at what angle did Floyd kick the ball, and at what speed? (Ignore air resistance.)

Answer: $\theta \approx 55°$, $|\mathbf{v}(0)| \approx 78$ ft/s

20. For $\mathbf{r}(t) = t^2\mathbf{i} + t\mathbf{j}$, find $\mathbf{a}_T$ and $\mathbf{a}_N$, the tangential and normal components of acceleration.

Answer: $\mathbf{a}_T = \dfrac{4t}{\sqrt{4t^2 + 1}}$; $\mathbf{a}_N = \dfrac{-2}{\sqrt{4t^2 + 1}}$

21. If a particle moves in a plane with constant acceleration, show that its path is a straight line or a parabola.

22. A particle is moving along the curve described by the parametric equations $x = 5t$, $y = 2t^3$, $z = \frac{3}{5}t^5$. Determine the velocity and acceleration vectors as well as the speed of the particle when $t = 3$.

Answer: $\mathbf{v}(3) = 5\mathbf{i} + 54\mathbf{j} + 243\mathbf{k}$; $\mathbf{a}(3) = 36\mathbf{j} + 324\mathbf{k}$; $|\mathbf{v}(3)| = \sqrt{61,990}$

23. A particle is traveling along a helix whose vector equation is given by $\mathbf{r}(t) = \langle R_1 \cos \alpha t, R_2 \sin \alpha t, \beta t \rangle$, where $R_1 \geq R_2$. Find its maximum and minimum speeds.

Answer: Maximum speed $\sqrt{R_1^2\alpha^2 + \beta^2}$, minimum speed $\sqrt{R_2^2\alpha^2 + \beta^2}$

24. If $\mathbf{r}(t) = t^2\mathbf{i} + 3t\mathbf{j} + e^t\mathbf{k}$, find the acceleration vector and the tangential component of the acceleration vector.

Answer: $\mathbf{a}(t) = 2\mathbf{i} + e^t\mathbf{k}$; $a_T = \dfrac{4t + e^{2t}}{\sqrt{4t^2 + 9 + e^{2t}}}$

25. Let $\mathbf{r}(t) = \langle 5t, \sin 3t, \cos 3t \rangle$. Show that the velocity vector is perpendicular to the acceleration vector.

Answer: $\mathbf{v}(t) = \langle 5, 3\cos 3t, -3\sin 3t \rangle$; $\mathbf{r}(t) \cdot \mathbf{v}(t) = 0$

26. Let $\mathbf{r}(t) = \cos 2t\,\mathbf{i} + 2t\,\mathbf{j} + \sin 2t\,\mathbf{k}$. Show that the acceleration vector is parallel to the normal vector $\mathbf{N}(t)$.

Answer: $v(t) = |\mathbf{v}(t)| = \sqrt{4(\cos^2 2t + \sin^2 2t) + 2} = \sqrt{6}$, so $a_T = v'(t) = 0$ and thus $\mathbf{a}(t) = a_N\mathbf{N}$ is parallel to $\mathbf{N}$.

10.5 Parametric Surfaces

1. Find a parametric representation for the surface consisting of the upper half of the ellipsoid $x^2 + 5y^2 + z^2 = 1$.

   (A) $x = x, y = y, z = \sqrt{1 + x^2 + 5y^2}$ (B) $x = x, y = y, z = \sqrt{1 + x^2 - 5y^2}$

   (C) $x = x, y = y, z = \sqrt{1 - x^2 + 5y^2}$ (D) $x = x, y = y, z = \sqrt{1 - x^2 - 5y^2}$

   (E) $x = x, y = y, z = \sqrt{x^2 + 5y^2 - 1}$ (F) $x = x, y = y, z = \sqrt{x^2 - 5y^2 - 1}$

   (G) $x = x, y = y, z = \sqrt{-x^2 + 5y^2 - 1}$ (H) $x = x, y = y, z = \sqrt{-x^2 - 5y^2 - 1}$

   Answer: (D)

2. Find a parametric representation for the surface $z = x^2 + y^2$.

   (A) $x = r \sin \theta, y = r \sin \theta, z = r$ (B) $x = r \sin \theta, y = r \sin \theta, z = r^2$

   (C) $x = r \cos \theta, y = r \cos \theta, z = r$ (D) $x = r \cos \theta, y = r \cos \theta, z = r^2$

   (E) $x = \cos \theta, y = \sin \theta, z = r$ (F) $x = \cos \theta, y = \sin \theta, z = r^2$

   (G) $x = r \cos \theta, y = r \sin \theta, z = r$ (H) $x = r \cos \theta, y = r \sin \theta, z = r^2$

   Answer: (H)

3. Find a parametric representation for the surface consisting of that part of the hyperboloid $-x^2 - y^2 + z^2 = 1$ that lies below the rectangle $[-1, 1] \times [-3, 3]$.

   Answer: $x = x, y = y, z = -\sqrt{1 + x^2 + y^2}$ where $-1 \leq x \leq 1$ and $-3 \leq y \leq 3$.

4. Find a parametric representation for the surface consisting of that part of the elliptic paraboloid $x + y^2 + 2z^2 = 4$ that lies in front of the plane $x = 0$.

   Answer: $x = 4 - y^2 - 2z^2, y = y, z = z$ where $y^2 + 2z^2 \leq 4$ since $x \geq 0$.

5. Find a parametric representation for the surface consisting of that part of the cylinder $x^2 + z^2 = 1$ that lies between the planes $y = -1$ and $y = 3$.

   Answer: $x = \sin \theta, y = y, z = \cos \theta, 0 \leq \theta \leq 2\pi, -1 \leq y \leq 3$.

6. Find a parametric representation for the surface consisting of that part of the plane $z = x + 3$ that lies inside the cylinder $x^2 + y^2 = 1$.

   Answer: $x = x, y = y, z = x + 3$, where $0 \leq x^2 + y^2 \leq 1$.

7. Identify the surface with the vector equation $\mathbf{r}(u, v) = \cos u \sin v \, \mathbf{i} + \sin u \sin v \, \mathbf{j} + \cos v \, \mathbf{k}, 0 \leq u \leq 2\pi, 0 \leq v \leq \frac{\pi}{2}$. (*Hint:* First consider $x^2 + y^2$.)

   Answer: Top half of the unit sphere

8. Identify the surface with the vector equation $\mathbf{r}(u, v) = (1 + 2u + 3v)\mathbf{i} + (5 - u + 4v)\mathbf{j} + (3 + 5u - 7v)\mathbf{k}$.

   Answer: Plane

9. Find a parametric representation for the surface consisting of that part of the hyperboloid $-x^2 - y^2 + z^2 = 1$ that lies below the disk $\{(x, y) \mid x^2 + y^2 \leq 4\}$.

   Answer: $x = r \cos \theta, y = r \sin \theta, z = -\sqrt{1 + r^2}, 0 \leq \theta \leq 2\pi, 0 \leq r \leq 2$

10. Are the two planes $\mathbf{r}_1\left(s,t\right) \ = \ \langle 1+s+t, s-t, 1+2s\rangle$ and $\mathbf{r}_2\left(s,t\right) \ = \ \langle 2+s+2t, 3+t, s+3t\rangle$ parallel? Justify your answer.

Answer: Yes

11. A picture of a circular cylinder with radius a and height h is given below. Find a parametric representation of the cylinder.

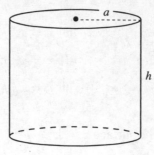

Answer: $\mathbf{r}\left(s,t\right) = \langle a\cos s, a\sin s, t\rangle, 0 \leq s \leq 2\pi, 0 \leq t \leq h$. Other answers are possible.

11 Partial Derivatives

11.1 Functions of Several Variables

1. Let $f(x,y) = x \sin y$. Find $f\left(2, \frac{\pi}{3}\right)$.

   (A) $\sqrt{3}$ (B) $\sqrt{2}$ (C) $\frac{\sqrt{3}}{2}$ (D) $\frac{\sqrt{2}}{2}$

   (E) $\frac{1}{2}$ (F) $\frac{1}{3}$ (G) 1 (H) 0

   Answer: (A)

2. Let $f(x,y) = x^2 + 2xy + y^2$. If $x = 2$, find $f(x, 2x)$.

   (A) 12 (B) 16 (C) 24 (D) 28

   (E) 32 (F) 36 (G) 42 (H) 48

   Answer: (F)

3. Let $f(x,y,z) = x^3 y^2 z + 1$. If $x = 1$, find $f(x, x^2, -x)$.

   (A) 3 (B) 2 (C) 4 (D) -1

   (E) -3 (F) -2 (G) 1 (H) 0

   Answer: (H)

4. Let $f(x,y) = \left(x^2 + y\right)^3$. If $x = 1$, find $f(x, 2x)$.

   (A) 1 (B) 2 (C) 3 (D) 4

   (E) 8 (F) 9 (G) 16 (H) 27

   Answer: (H)

5. Find the domain of the function $f(x,y) = \sqrt{x - y^2}$.

   (A) All points on or to the left of $x = y^2$ (B) All points on or to the right of $x = y^2$

   (C) All points to the left of $x = y^2$ (D) All points to the right of $x = y^2$

   (E) All points on or to the left of $x = 0$ (F) All points on or to the right of $x = 0$

   (G) All points to the left of $x = 0$ (H) All points in the xy-plane

   Answer: (B)

6. Find the range of the function $f(x,y) = \sqrt{x - y^2}$.

   (A) $(0, \infty)$ (B) $[0, \infty)$ (C) $(-\infty, 0)$ (D) $(-\infty, \infty)$

   (E) $(1, \infty)$ (F) $[1, \infty)$ (G) $(\sqrt{2}, \infty)$ (H) $\left[\sqrt{2}, \infty\right)$

   Answer: (B)

7. Find the domain of the function $f(x, y) = e^{x - y^2}$.

(A) All points on or to the left of $x = y^2$ (B) All points on or to the right of $x = y^2$

(C) All points to the left of $x = y^2$ (D) All points to the right of $x = y^2$

(E) All points on or to the left of $x = 0$ (F) All points on or to the right of $x = 0$

(G) All points to the left of $x = 0$ (H) All points in the xy-plane

Answer: (H)

8. Find the range of the function $f(x, y) = e^{x - y^2}$.

(A) $(0, \infty)$ (B) $[0, \infty)$ (C) $(-\infty, \infty)$ (D) $(-\infty, 0)$

(E) $(1, \infty)$ (F) $[1, \infty)$ (G) $(\sqrt{2}, \infty)$ (H) $[\sqrt{2}, \infty)$

Answer: (A)

9. Find the domain of the function $f(x, y) = \ln(x - y^2)$.

(A) All points on or to the left of $x = y^2$ (B) All points on or to the right of $x = y^2$

(C) All points to the left of $x = y^2$ (D) All points to the right of $x = y^2$

(E) All points on or to the left of $x = 0$ (F) All points on or to the right of $x = 0$

(G) All points to the left of $x = 0$ (H) All points in the x-y plane

Answer: (D)

10. Find the range of the function $f(x, y) = \ln(x - y^2)$.

(A) $(0, \infty)$ (B) $[0, \infty)$ (C) $(-\infty, \infty)$ (D) $(-\infty, 0)$

(E) $(1, \infty)$ (F) $[1, \infty)$ (G) $(\sqrt{2}, \infty)$ (H) $[\sqrt{2}, \infty)$

Answer: (C)

11. Describe the level curves of the function $f(x, y) = x^2 + y^2 + 3x - 4y + 73$.

(A) Concentric circles   (B) Non-concentric circles

(C) Concentric ellipses (not circles)   (D) Non-concentric ellipses (not circles)

(E) Parabolas with the same vertex   (F) Parabolas with the same focus

(G) Hyperbolas with the same vertices   (H) Hyperbolas with the same foci

Answer: (A)

12. Describe the level curves of the function $f(x, y) = \sqrt{1 - x^2 - 2y^2}$.

(A) Concentric circles   (B) Non-concentric circles

(C) Concentric ellipses (not circles)   (D) Non-concentric ellipses (not circles)

(E) Parabolas with the same vertex   (F) Parabolas with the same focus

(G) Hyperbolas with the same vertices   (H) Hyperbolas with the same foci

Answer: (C)

13. Identify the graph of the function $f(x, y) = 3 - x^2 - y^2$.

    (A) Cone

    (B) Paraboloid

    (C) Ellipsoid

    (D) Hyperboloid of one sheet

    (E) Hyperboloid of two sheets

    (F) Hyperbolic cylinder

    (G) Elliptic cylinder

    (H) Parabolic cylinder

    Answer: (B)

14. Describe the level curves of the function $f(x, y) = \dfrac{y}{x^2}$.

    (A) Concentric circles

    (B) Non-concentric circles

    (C) Concentric ellipses (not circles)

    (D) Non-concentric ellipses (not circles)

    (E) Parabolas with the same vertex

    (F) Parabolas with the same focus

    (G) Hyperbolas with the same vertices

    (H) Hyperbolas with the same foci

    Answer: (E)

15. Describe the level curves of the function $f(x, y) = \sqrt{x^2 + (y-1)^2} - y$.

    (A) Concentric circles

    (B) Non-concentric circles

    (C) Concentric ellipses (not circles)

    (D) Non-concentric ellipses (not circles)

    (E) Parabolas with the same vertex

    (F) Parabolas with the same focus

    (G) Hyperbolas with the same vertices

    (H) Hyperbolas with the same foci

    Answer: (F)

16. Identify the graph of the function $f(x, y) = \sqrt{3 - x^2 + y^2}$.

    (A) Cone

    (B) Paraboloid

    (C) Ellipsoid

    (D) Hyperboloid of one sheet

    (E) Hyperboloid of two sheets

    (F) Hyperbolic cylinder

    (G) Elliptic cylinder

    (H) Parabolic cylinder

    Answer: (D)

17. The temperature at a point (x, y) of a flat metal plate is $T(x, y) = 9x^2 + 16y^2$ where $T(x, y)$ is measured in degrees. Draw the isothermals for $T(x, y) = 0, 9, 16$, and 144 degrees.

    Answer:

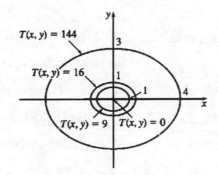

18. Sketch the domain of the function $z = \sqrt{x^2 + y^2 - 1}$.

Answer:

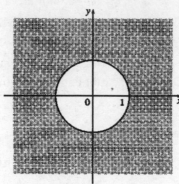

19. For the function $z = \sqrt{x^2 + y^2 - 1}$, sketch the level curves $z = k$ for $k = 0, 1, 2,$ and 3.

Answer:

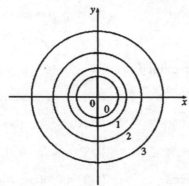

20. For the function $z = \sqrt{x^2 + y^2 - 1}$, sketch the portion of the surface in the first octant.

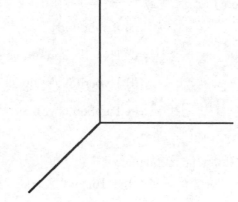

Answer:

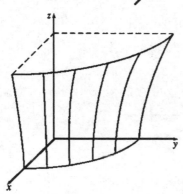

21. Suppose the point $(2,3)$ is on a curve C which is a level curve of the surface $z = x^2 + 2y$. Can it be concluded that the point $(4,-3)$ is also on C? Explain.

Answer: Yes, given that C is a level curve of $z = x^2 + 2y$ means C has equation $x^2 + 2y = k$ for some constant k. The fact that $(2,3)$ lies on C gives $k = 10$, so C has equation $x^2 + 2y = 10$ which does contain the point $(4,-3)$.

22. Describe the level surfaces of the function $f(x,y,z) = z - x^2 - y^2$.

Answer: Paraboloids with vertices along the z-axis

23. Describe the level surfaces of the function $f(x,y,z) = z - 2x - 3y$.

Answer: Parallel planes

24. Find the domain of the function $f(x,y,z) = \dfrac{1}{\sqrt{3x + y - z}}$.

(A) All points above $3x + y - z = 0$

(B) All points below $3x + y - z = 0$

(C) All points above $3x + y - z = 1$

(D) All points below $3x + y - z = 1$

(E) All points below $3x + y - z = 0$ but not above the plane $3x + y - z = 1$

(F) All points above $3x + y - z = 1$ but not above the plane $3x + y - z = 0$

(G) All points below $3x + y - z = 1$ or between $3x + y - z = 0$ and $3x + y - z = 1$

(H) All points in the xy-plane

Answer: (E)

25. Describe the difference between the horizontal trace in $z = k$ for the function $z = f(x,y)$ and the contour curve $f(x,y) = k$.

Answer: The contour curve $f(x,y) = k$ is the horizontal trace of $z = f(x,y)$ in $z = k$ projected down to the xy-plane.

26. Describe the vertical traces $x = k$ and $y = k$ and the horizontal traces $z = k$ for the function $f(x,y) = x^2 - y^2$.

Answer: $x = k$: $z = k^2 - y^2$, parabola; $y = k$: $z = x^2 - k^2$, parabola; $z = k$: $x^2 - y^2 = k$, hyperbola

27. Describe the level surfaces $k = 1$, $k = 0$, $k = -1$ for the function $f(x,y,z) = 1 - x^2 - \frac{1}{2}y^2 - \frac{1}{3}z^2$.

Answer: $k = 1$: point $(0,0,0)$; $k = 0$: ellipsoid $x^2 + \frac{1}{2}y^2 + \frac{1}{3}z^2 = 1$; $k = -1$: ellipsoid $x^2 + \frac{1}{2}y^2 + \frac{1}{3}z^2 = 2$

28. Describe how the graph of $g(x,y) = 2f(x-1,y-1)$ is obtained from the graph of $z = f(x,y)$.

Answer: The graph of g is the graph of f shifted 1 unit in the positive x-direction, shifted 1 unit in the positive y-direction, and stretched vertically (that is, in the z-direction) by a factor of 2.

29. Let $f(x,y) = x^2 - 2y$.

(a) Sketch the level curves for f.

(b) Find a formula for the level curve that passes through the point $(3,1)$.

Answer:

(a)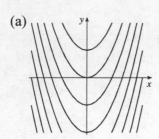

(b) $y = \frac{1}{2}x^2 - \frac{7}{2}$

30. The graph of level curves of $f(x, y)$ is given. Find a possible formula for $f(x, y)$ and sketch the surface $z = f(x, y)$.

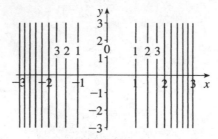

Answer: $z = x^2$. There are other possible answers.

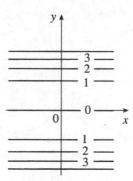

31. The graph of level curves of $f(x, y)$ is given. Find a possible formula for $f(x, y)$ and sketch the surface $z = f(x, y)$.

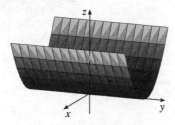

Answer: $z = y^2$. There are other possible answers.

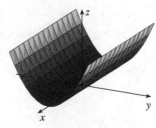

32. The graph of level curves of $f(x, y)$ is given. Find a possible formula for $f(x, y)$ and sketch the surface $z = f(x, y)$.

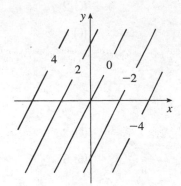

Answer: $z = y - 2x$

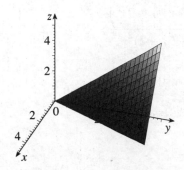

11.2   Limits and Continuity

1. Evaluate $\lim_{(x,y)\to(1,2)} (x^2 + 2xy)$.

(A) 0　　　　　　(B) 1　　　　　　(C) 2　　　　　　(D) 3

(E) 4　　　　　　(F) 5　　　　　　(G) 6　　　　　　(H) Does not exist

Answer: (F)

2. Evaluate $\lim_{(x,y)\to(1,2)} \dfrac{2x^2 + y^2}{xy}$.

(A) 1　　　　　　(B) 2　　　　　　(C) 3　　　　　　(D) 4

(E) 8　　　　　　(F) 9　　　　　　(G) 16　　　　　(H) Does not exist

Answer: (C)

3. Evaluate $\lim_{(x,y)\to(0,0)} x \sin y$.

(A) 0　　　　　　(B) 1　　　　　　(C) 2　　　　　　(D) 3

(E) 4　　　　　　(F) 5　　　　　　(G) 6　　　　　　(H) Does not exist

Answer: (A)

4. Evaluate $\lim\limits_{(x,y)\to(0,0)} \dfrac{x}{\sin y}$.

(A) 0   (B) 1   (C) 2   (D) 3

(E) 4   (F) 5   (G) 6   (H) Does not exist

Answer: (H)

5. Evaluate $\lim\limits_{(x,y)\to(0,0)} \dfrac{\sin(x^2+y^2)}{x^2+y^2}$.

(A) 0   (B) 1   (C) 2   (D) 3

(E) 4   (F) 5   (G) 6   (H) Does not exist

Answer: (B)

6. Evaluate $\lim\limits_{(x,y)\to(2,2)} \dfrac{\tan\left((x-2)^2+(y-2)^2\right)}{(x-2)^2+(y-2)^2}$.

(A) 0   (B) 1   (C) 2   (D) 3

(E) 4   (F) 5   (G) 6   (H) Does not exist

Answer: (B)

7. Evaluate $\lim\limits_{(x,y)\to(0,0)} \dfrac{xy}{x^2+xy+y^2}$.

(A) 0   (B) 1   (C) $\frac{1}{2}$ (D) $\frac{1}{3}$

(E) $\frac{1}{4}$ (F) $\frac{1}{5}$ (G) $\frac{1}{6}$ (H) Does not exist

Answer: (H)

8. Evaluate $\lim\limits_{(x,y)\to(0,0)} \dfrac{x^2-y^2}{x^2+y^2}$.

(A) 0   (B) 1   (C) -1 (D) $\frac{1}{2}$

(E) $-\frac{1}{2}$ (F) $\frac{1}{3}$ (G) $-\frac{1}{3}$ (H) Does not exist

Answer: (H)

9. Evaluate $\lim\limits_{(x,y)\to(0,0)} \dfrac{x^2y}{x^2+y^2}$.

(A) 1   (B) 0   (C) $\frac{1}{2}$ (D) ∞

(E) 2   (F) 4   (G) 8   (H) Does not exist

Answer: (B)

10. Evaluate $\lim\limits_{(x,y)\to(0,0)} \dfrac{x^2-3xy+y^2}{x^2+2y^2}$.

(A) 0   (B) ∞ (C) $-\infty$ (D) 1

(E) $\frac{1}{2}$ (F) $\frac{1}{3}$ (G) $\frac{1}{4}$ (H) Does not exist

Answer: (H)

11. Let $f(x, y) = \dfrac{xy}{x^2 + y^2}$ and let C_m be the curve with equation $y = mx$, where m is a constant. The value of the limit of $F(x, y)$ as (x, y) approaches $(0, 0)$ along C_m is

A) 0   B) $\dfrac{1}{2}$ C) 1   D) $\dfrac{m}{1 + m^2}$ E) $\dfrac{m^2}{1 + m^2}$

Answer: **(D)**

12. Let $f(x, y) = \begin{cases} \dfrac{x^4 + y^4}{(x^2 + y^2)^2} & \text{if } (x, y) \neq (0, 0) \\ 0 & \text{if } (x, y) = (0, 0) \end{cases}$ Does this function have a limit at the origin? If so, prove it. If not, demonstrate why not.

Answer: Approaching the origin along $y = 0$, the limit equals 1; approaching the origin along $y = x$, the limit equals $\frac{1}{2}$. Thus, this function does not have a limit at the origin.

13. Prove that the following limit does not exist: $\displaystyle\lim_{(x,y)\to(0,0)} f(x, y)$, where $f(x, y) = \dfrac{xy}{x^2 + y^4}$.

Answer: f is defined everywhere in $\mathbb{R}^2$ except at $(0, 0)$. Let $S_1 = \{(0, y)\}$; then $(0, 0) \in S_1$, and taking the limit of f as $y \to 0$ gives 0. Let $S_2 = \{(x, x)\}$; then $(0, 0) \in S_2$ and taking the limit of f as $x \to 0$ gives 1. Since these limits are not equal, the limit does not exist.

14. Show that the limit $\displaystyle\lim_{(x,y)\to(0,0)} \dfrac{2x^2 - y^2}{x^2 + 2y^2}$ does not exist.

Answer: Approaching $(0, 0)$ along the x-axis, we have $y = 0$, so the limit (if it exists) equals 2. Approaching $(0, 0)$ along the y-axis we have $x = 0$, so the limit (if it exists) equals $-\frac{1}{2}$. Since these limits are different, the limit does not exist.

15. If $f(x, y) = \dfrac{xy}{x^2 + y^2}$ then $\displaystyle\lim_{(x,y)\to(0,0)} f(x, y)$

(A) exists   (B) does not exist   (C) is equal to 0   (D) is equal to $\frac{1}{2}$ (E) is equal to 1

Answer: **(B)**

16. Determine if $f(x, y) = \begin{cases} \dfrac{x^2 + xy}{x^2 + y^2} & \text{if } (x, y) \neq (0, 0) \\ 1 & \text{if } (x, y) = (0, 0) \end{cases}$ is everywhere continuous, and if not, locate the point(s) of discontinuity.

Answer: f is continuous everywhere its denominator does not equal zero. The limit does not exist at $(0, 0)$, and thus f is discontinuous at $(0, 0)$.

17. Determine whether $f(x, y) = \begin{cases} \dfrac{3x^2 - 2y^2}{x^2 + y^2} & \text{if } (x, y) \neq (0, 0) \\ 0 & \text{if } (x, y) = (0, 0) \end{cases}$ is continuous at $(0, 0)$.

Answer: The function is discontinuous at $(0, 0)$

18. Consider $f(x, y) = \begin{cases} \dfrac{x^4 - y^4}{x^2 + y^2} & \text{if } (x, y) \neq (0, 0) \\ 0.1 & \text{if } (x, y) = (0, 0) \end{cases}$ Where is f continuous?

Answer: Continuous everywhere except at $(0, 0)$

19. Let $f(x,y) = \begin{cases} \dfrac{x^4 - y^4}{x^2 + y^2} & \text{if } (x,y) \neq (0,0) \\ 0 & \text{if } (x,y) = (0,0) \end{cases}$ Where is f continuous?

Answer: Continuous everywhere

20. Let $f(x,y) = \begin{cases} \dfrac{x^3 y^2}{x^4 + y^4} & \text{if } (x,y) \neq (0,0) \\ 0 & \text{if } (x,y) = (0,0) \end{cases}$ Where is f continuous?

Answer: Continuous everywhere

21. Find $\displaystyle\lim_{(x,y)\to(1,1)} \frac{x - y^4}{x^3 - y^4}$ if it exists, or show that the limit does not exist.

Answer: Along $y = 1$, $\displaystyle\lim_{(x,y)\to(1,1)} \frac{x - y^4}{x^3 - y^4} = \lim_{x\to 1} \frac{x - 1}{x^3 - 1} = \frac{1}{3}$ (if the limit exists). Along $x = 1$,

$\displaystyle\lim_{(x,y)\to(1,1)} \frac{x - y^4}{x^3 - y^4} = \lim_{y\to 1} \frac{1 - y^4}{1 - y^4} = 1$ (if the limit exists). Because these limits are different,

$\displaystyle\lim_{(x,y)\to(1,1)} \frac{x - y^4}{x^3 - y^4}$ does not exist.

11.3 Partial Derivatives

1. Let $f(x,y) = x^2 y^3$. Find the value of the partial derivative $f_x(1,1)$.

(A) 0   (B) 1   (C) 2   (D) 3

(E) 4   (F) 5   (G) 6   (H) 7

Answer: (C)

2. Let $f(x,y) = \dfrac{3x - y}{x + y}$. Find the value of the partial derivative $f_y(1,1)$.

(A) -4 (B) 1   (C) 2   (D) 3

(E) 4   (F) -1 (G) -2 (H) -3

Answer: (F)

3. Let $f(x,y,z) = 3\sqrt{x^2 + 4y^2 + z^2}$. Find $f_z(2,1,1)$.

(A) 0   (B) 1   (C) $\frac{1}{2}$ (D) 3

(E) 4   (F) -1 (G) $-\frac{1}{2}$ (H) -3

Answer: (B)

4. Let $f(x,y) = \int_0^{xy} \sin(t^2)\, dt$. Find $f_x\left(1, \sqrt{\frac{\pi}{2}}\right)$.

(A) 0   (B) $\sqrt{\frac{\pi}{2}}$ (C) $\frac{\pi}{2}$ (D) 3

(E) 4   (F) -1 (G) $-\sqrt{\frac{\pi}{2}}$ (H) -3

Answer: (C)

5. Let $f(x, y, z) = 2z \ln(x^2 y z)$. Find $f_z\left(\frac{1}{2}, 1, 4\right)$.

(A) 0   (B) $2 \ln 2$ (C) 12   (D) 2

(E) 4   (F) $\ln 2$ (G) 16   (H) 8

Answer: (D)

6. Let $f(x, y) = \sin(2x + y)$. Find the value of the partial derivative $f_{xy}\left(\pi, \frac{\pi}{2}\right)$.

(A) $\sqrt{2}$ (B) $-\sqrt{2}$ (C) $2\sqrt{2}$ (D) $-2\sqrt{2}$

(E) $\frac{\sqrt{2}}{2}$ (F) -2 (G) 2   (H) 0

Answer: (F)

7. Let $f(x, y) = e^{2x + y^2}$. Find the value of the partial derivative $f_{xyy}(0, 0)$.

(A) 1   (B) 2   (C) 4   (D) $2e$

(E) $4e$ (F) e^2 (G) $2e^2$ (H) $4e^2$

Answer: 4

8. How many third-order partial derivatives does a function $f(x, y)$ have?

(A) 3   (B) 4   (C) 5   (D) 6

(E) 7   (F) 8   (G) 9   (H) 10

Answer: (F)

9. If all the third-order partial derivatives of $f(x, y)$ are continuous, what is the largest number of them that can be distinct?

(A) 3   (B) 4   (C) 5   (D) 6

(E) 7   (F) 8   (G) 9   (H) 10

Answer: (B)

10. Let $f(x, y) = \left(x^3 + y^4\right)^5$. Find the value of $f_{xy} - f_{yx}$ at the point $(1, 2)$.

(A) -32 (B) -16 (C) -8 (D) -4

(E) 0   (F) 4   (G) 8   (H) 16

Answer: (E)

11. Let $f(x, y) = x e^{y/x}$. Find the value of the partial derivative $f_x(2, 4)$.

(A) $-2e^2$ (B) $-e^2$ (C) 0   (D) $e/2$

(E) $e^2/2$ (F) e^2 (G) $2e^2$ (H) $4e^2$

Answer: (B)

12. Let $f(x, y) = \tan^{-1}(x/y)$. Find the value of the partial derivative $f_y(1, 2)$.

(A) -1 (B) $-\frac{1}{2}$ (C) $-\frac{1}{3}$ (D) $-\frac{1}{5}$

(E) $\frac{1}{5}$ (F) $\frac{1}{3}$ (G) $\frac{1}{2}$ (H) 1

Answer: (D)

13. Let $f(x, y, z) = z^{xy}$, $z > 0$. Find the value of the partial derivative $f_y(2, 1, e)$.

(A) 0   (B) 1   (C) e (D) $2e$

(E) $2e^2$ (F) $\frac{1}{2}$ (G) $\ln 2$ (H) 2

Answer: (E)

14. Let $f(x, y, z) = x^{yz}$, $x > 0$. Find the value of the partial derivative $f_z(2, 3, 0)$.

(A) 0   (B) 2   (C) 3   (D) 8

(E) $\ln 2$ (F) $\ln 3$ (G) $2\ln 2$ (H) $3\ln 2$

Answer: (H)

15. If $f(r, \theta) = r\sin\theta + r^2\tan^2\theta$, find the partial derivative of f with respect to r and the partial derivative with respect to θ, both at the point $\left(-4, \frac{\pi}{6}\right)$.

Answer: $\left.\dfrac{\partial f}{\partial r}\right|_{(-4,\pi/6)} = \dfrac{-13}{6}$; $\left.\dfrac{\partial f}{\partial \theta}\right|_{(-4,\pi/6)} = \dfrac{110}{9}\sqrt{3}$

16. Let $f(x, y) == \begin{cases} \dfrac{x^2}{x + y} & \text{if } (x, y) \neq (0, 0) \\ 0 & \text{if } (x, y) = (0, 0) \end{cases}$

(a) Find $\dfrac{\partial f}{\partial x}$ and $\dfrac{\partial f}{\partial y}$.

(b) Find the values of the above derivatives at $(0, 0)$, if they exist.

Answer: (a) $\dfrac{\partial f}{\partial x} = \dfrac{x^2 + 2xy}{(x + y)^2}$, $\dfrac{\partial f}{\partial y} = \dfrac{-x^2}{(x + y)^2}$ (b) $f_x(0, 0) = 1$, $f_y(0, 0) = 0$

17. Find both partial derivatives if $f(x, y) = \dfrac{2x - 3y}{3x - 2y}$.

Answer: $\dfrac{\partial f}{\partial x} = \dfrac{5y}{(3x - 2y)^2}$; $\dfrac{\partial f}{\partial y} = \dfrac{-5x}{(3x - 2y)^2}$

18. If $w = x^2z + xy^2 - yz^2$, find $\dfrac{\partial w}{\partial x}$, $\dfrac{\partial w}{\partial y}$, and $\dfrac{\partial w}{\partial z}$.

Answer: $\dfrac{\partial w}{\partial y} = 2zx + y^2$, $\dfrac{\partial w}{\partial y} = 2xy - z^2$, $\dfrac{\partial w}{\partial z} = x^2 - 2yz$

19. Given $f(x, y) = 2x^3y^2 - 3x^3 + 8y^4$, find f_x and f_y and evaluate each at $(1, 2)$.

Answer: $f_x = 6x^2y^2 - 9x^2$, $f_x(1, 2) = 15$; $f_y = 4x^3y + 32y^3$, $f_y(1, 2) = 264$

20. Let $f(x, y, z) = x^2y^3 - \dfrac{x}{z} + e^x\ln y$. Find f_x, f_y, and f_z.

Answer: $f_x = 2xy^3 - \dfrac{1}{z} + e^x\ln y$, $f_y = 3x^2y^2 + \dfrac{e^x}{y}$, $f_z = \dfrac{x}{z^2}$

21. Given $f(x, y) = x^2\sin(xy)$, find f_x, f_y, and f_{xy}.

Answer: $f_x = 2x\sin(xy) + x^2y\cos(xy)$; $f_y = x^3\cos(xy)$; $f_{xy} = 3x^2\cos(xy) - x^3y\sin(xy)$

22. Let $f(x, y, z) = (xyz)^2$. Find all second-order partial derivatives of f.

Answer: $f_{xy} = 4xyz^2$, $f_{yx} = 4xyz^2$, $f_{zx} = 4xy^2z$, $f_{xz} = 4xy^2z$, $f_{yz} = 4x^2yz$, $f_{zy} = 4x^2yz$, $f_{xx} = 2y^2z^2$, $f_{yy} = 2x^2z^2$, $f_{zz} = 2x^2y^2$

23. Find f_{xx}, f_{yy}, and f_{yx} if $f(x,y) = \sin x^2 y$.

Answer: $f_{xx} = 2y \cos x^2 y - 4x^2 y^2 \sin x^2 y$; $f_{yy} = -x^4 \sin x^2 y$; $f_{xy} = 2x \cos x^2 y - 2x^3 y \sin x^2 y$

24. If $f(x,y,z) = x \ln(yz^2)$, find f_{xy}, f_{xz}, and f_{yz}.

Answer: $f_{xy} = \dfrac{1}{y}$, $f_{xz} = \dfrac{2}{z}$, $f_{yz} = 0$

25. If $z = x^2 \sin y + ye^x$, find $\dfrac{\partial z}{\partial x}$, $\dfrac{\partial z}{\partial y}$, $\dfrac{\partial^2 z}{\partial x^2}$, $\dfrac{\partial^2 z}{\partial x \partial y}$, and $\dfrac{\partial^2 z}{\partial y^2}$.

Answer: $\dfrac{\partial z}{\partial x} = 2x \sin y + ye^x$, $\dfrac{\partial z}{\partial y} = x^2 \cos y + e^x$, $\dfrac{\partial^2 z}{\partial x^2} = 2 \sin y + ye^x$, $\dfrac{\partial^2 z}{\partial x \partial y} = 2x \cos y + e^x$, $\dfrac{\partial^2 z}{\partial y^2} = -x^2 \sin y$

26. Let $f(xy) = x^3 y - xy^2 + y^4 + x$. Find $\dfrac{\partial^2 f}{\partial y \partial x}\bigg|_{(2,3)}$.

Answer: 6

27. Show that $f(x,y) = e^y \cos x - 2xy$ satisfies Laplace's Equation $f_{xx} + f_{yy} = 0$.

Answer: $f_x = -e^y \sin x - 2y$, $f_y = e^y \cos x - 2x$ $\Rightarrow$ $f_{xx} = -e^y \cos x$, $f_{yy} = e^y \cos x$ $\Rightarrow$ $f_{xx} + f_{yy} = 0$

28. If $g(x,y) = \begin{cases} \dfrac{x^4 + y^2}{x^2 + y^4} & \text{if } (x,y) \neq (0,0) \\ 0 & \text{if } (x,y) = (0,0) \end{cases}$ find $\dfrac{\partial g}{\partial x}(1,0)$ and $\dfrac{\partial g}{\partial y}(1,0)$.

Answer: $\dfrac{\partial g}{\partial x}(1,0) = 2$, $\dfrac{\partial g}{\partial y}(1,0) = 0$

29. If g is a differentiable function and $f(x,y) = g(x^2 + y^2)$, show that $yf_x - xf_y = 0$.

Answer: $f_x = g'(x^2 + y^2)(2x)$, $f_y = g'(x^2 + y^2)2y$ $\Rightarrow$ $yf_x - xf_y = 0$

30. If $f(x,y) = 6 - 2x^2 - y^2$, find $f_x(1,1)$ and $f_y(1,1)$ and interpret these numbers as slopes. Illustrate with sketches.

Answer: $f_x(1,1) = -4$, $f_y(1,1) = -2$

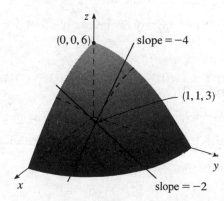

31. If $f(x, y) = 4 - x^2$, find $f_x(1, 1)$ and $f_y(1, 1)$ and interpret these numbers as slopes. Illustrate with sketches.

Answer: $f_x(1, 1) = -2$, $f_y(1, 1) = 0$

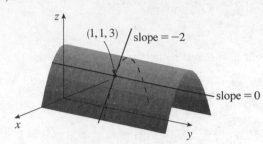

32. Consider a function of three variables $P = f(A, r, N)$, where P is the monthly mortgage payment in dollars, A is the amount borrowed in dollars, r is the annual interest rate, and N is the number of years before the mortgage is paid off.

   (a) Suppose $f(180{,}000, 6, 30) = 1080$. What does this tell you in financial terms?

   (b) Suppose $\dfrac{\partial f}{\partial r}(180{,}000, 6, 30) = 115.73$. What does this tell you in financial terms?

   (c) Suppose $\dfrac{\partial f}{\partial N}(180{,}000, 6, 30) = -12.86$. What does this tell you in financial terms?

Answer:

   (a) If you borrow \$180,000 with annual interest rate 6% and 30 year amortization, then your monthly payment is \$1080.

   (b) If you borrow \$180,000 with annual interest rate 6% and 30 year amortization, then your monthly payment increases by \$115.73 per 1% increase in interest rate.

   (c) If you borrow \$180,000 with annual interest rate 6% and 30 year amortization, then your monthly payment decreases by \$12.86 for each additional year of amortization.

33. Find all solutions to the partial differential equation $\dfrac{\partial^2 f}{\partial y \partial x} = 0$.

   Answer: $F(x) + G(y)$, where F and G are any differentiable functions.

34. Find all solutions to the partial differential equation $\dfrac{\partial^2 f}{\partial x \partial x} = 0$.

   Answer: $F(y) + xG(y)$, where G and H are any differentiable functions.

11.4   Tangent Planes and Linear Approximations

1. Find an equation of the tangent plane to the surface $z = x^2$ at the point $(1, 2, 1)$.

   (A) $z = x$ (B) $z = x + 2y - 4$ (C) $z = 2x - 1$ (D) $z = 2x + 2y - 5$

   (E) $z = x + y - 1$ (F) $z = 2x + y - 3$ (G) $z = 2x - y + 1$ (H) $z = 2x - 2y + 3$

   Answer: (C)

2. Find an equation of the tangent plane to the surface $z = x^2 + 2y^2$ at the point $(1, 1, 3)$.

(A) $z = x + y + 1$ (B) $z = x + 2y$ (C) $z = x - y + 3$ (D) $z = x - 2y + 4$

(E) $z = 2x + 2y - 1$ (F) $z = 2x + 4y - 3$ (G) $z = 2x - 2y + 3$ (H) $z = 2x - 4y + 5$

Answer: (F)

3. Find an equation of the tangent plane to the surface $z = e^{x+y}$ at the point $(0, 0, 1)$.

(A) $z = x + y + 1$ (B) $z = ex + ey - 2e + 1$

(C) $z = 2x + 2y + 1$ (D) $z = 2ex + 2ey - 4e + 1$

(E) $z = 4x + 4y - 7$ (F) $z = e^2 x + e^2 y - 2e^2 + 1$

(G) $z = 2e^2 x + 2e^2 y - 4e^2 + 1$ (H) $z = 4ex + 4ey - 8e + 1$

Answer: (A)

4. Find an equation of the tangent plane to the surface $z = e^{2x+2y}$ at the point $(0, 0, 1)$.

(A) $z = x + y + 1$ (B) $z = ex + ey - 2e + 1$

(C) $z = 2x + 2y + 1$ (D) $z = 2ex + 2ey - 4e + 1$

(E) $z = 4x + 4y - 7$ (F) $z = e^2 x + e^2 y - 2e^2 + 1$

(G) $z = 2e^2 x + 2e^2 y - 4e^2 + 1$ (H) $z = 4ex + 4ey - 8e + 1$

Answer: (C)

5. Find the differential of $z = 3x + 2y$.

(A) $3x\,dx + 2y\,dy$ (B) $3x^2\,dx + 2y^2\,dy$ (C) $2x\,dx + 3y\,dy$ (D) $2x^2\,dx + 3y^2\,dy$

(E) $3y\,dx + 2x\,dy$ (F) $2y\,dx + 3x\,dy$ (G) $2\,dx + 3\,dy$ (H) $3\,dx + 2\,dy$

Answer: (H)

6. Find the differential of $z = 3x + y^2$.

(A) $3\,dx + 2y\,dy$ (B) $3x\,dx + 2y^2\,dy$ (C) $2\,dx + 3y\,dy$ (D) $2x\,dx + 3y^2\,dy$

(E) $3y\,dx + 2x\,dy$ (F) $2y\,dx + 3x\,dy$ (G) $2\,dx + 3\,dy$ (H) $3\,dx + 2\,dy$

Answer: (A)

7. Find the differential of $z = \dfrac{1}{x + y^2}$ at the point $(x, y) = (1, 1)$.

(A) $-dx - dy$ (B) $-\frac{1}{4}\,dx - \frac{1}{2}\,dy$ (C) $-dx - \frac{1}{2}\,dy$ (D) $-\frac{1}{2}\,dx - dy$

(E) $dx + dy$ (F) $\frac{1}{4}\,dx + \frac{1}{2}\,dy$ (G) $dx + \frac{1}{2}\,dy$ (H) $\frac{1}{2}\,dx + dy$

Answer: (B)

8. Find the differential of $w = xe^{y\sin z}$ at the point $(x, y, z) = (1, 1, 0)$.

(A) dx (B) dy (C) dz (D) $dy + dz$

(E) $dx + dz$ (F) $dx + dy$ (G) $dx + dy + dz$ (H) 0

Answer: (E)

9. Use differentials to approximate $\sqrt{26}$.

(A) 5.05   (B) 5.06   (C) 5.07   (D) 5.08

(E) 5.09   (F) 5.10   (G) 5.11   (H) 5.12

Answer: (F)

10. Use differentials to approximate $\sqrt{24} + \sqrt{5}$.

(A) 6.85   (B) 6.90   (C) 6.95   (D) 7.00

(E) 7.05   (F) 7.10   (G) 7.15   (H) 7.20

Answer: (G)

11. Use differentials to approximate $\dfrac{\sqrt[3]{28}}{\sqrt{10}}$.

(A) $\frac{154}{162}$ (B) $\frac{155}{162}$ (C) $\frac{156}{162}$ (D) $\frac{157}{162}$

(E) $\frac{158}{162}$ (F) $\frac{159}{162}$ (G) $\frac{160}{162}$ (H) $\frac{161}{162}$

Answer: (B)

12. A boundary stripe 3 inches wide is painted around a rectangle whose dimensions are 100 feet by 200 feet. Use differentials to approximate the number of square feet of paint in the stripe.

(A) 120   (B) 130   (C) 140   (D) 150

(E) 160   (F) 170   (G) 180   (H) 190

Answer: (D)

13. Use differentials to estimate the amount of metal in a closed cylindrical can that is 10 cm high and 4 cm in diameter if the metal in the wall is 0.05 cm thick and the metal in the top and bottom is 0.1 cm thick.

(A) 2.0π (B) 2.4π (C) 2.8π (D) 3.2π

(E) 3.6π (F) 4.0π (G) 4.4π (H) 4.8π

Answer: (C)

14. Find an equation of the tangent plane to the surface $z = \ln(2x + y)$ at the point $(-1, 3, 0)$.

(A) $2x + y - z = 1$ (B) $x + 2y + z = 5$ (C) $x - 2y + z = 7$ (D) $3x + 2y + z = 3$

(E) $2x + 3y + z = 7$ (F) $x + 2y + 3z = 5$ (G) $3x + y - z = 0$ (H) $x + 3y + 2z = 8$

Answer: (A)

15. Find an equation of the tangent plane to the surface $z = \tan^{-1}(y/x)$ at the point $\left(-2, 2, -\frac{\pi}{4}\right)$.

(A) $x + y + z = \pi$ (B) $x + y + 4z + \pi = 0$

(C) $4x + 4y + z + \pi = 0$ (D) $2x - 2y + z = \frac{\pi}{4}$

(E) $2x - 2y + 4z = \pi$ (F) $4x - 2y - z + \pi = 0$

(G) $x + 2y + 4z = 2 - \pi$ (H) $x + 2y - 4z = 2 + \pi$

Answer: (B)

16. A right triangle has leg A with length 4, leg B with length 3, and hypotenuse with length 5. Use a total differential to approximate the length of the hypotenuse if leg A had length 4.2 and leg B had length 2.9.

Answer: 5.10

17. Find the total differential of w if $w = f(x, y, z) = xy^2z^3 - e^{xz}y$.

    Answer: $dw = \left(y^2z^3 - yze^{xz}\right) dx + \left(2xyz^3 - e^{xz}\right) dy + \left(3xy^2z^2 - xye^{xz}\right) dz$

18. Use the total differential to approximate $\sqrt[3]{25}\sqrt[4]{17}$.

    Answer: 5.95

19. Find an equation of the plane tangent to the surface $xyz = 2$ at $(1, -1, -2)$.

    Answer: $2x - 2y - z = 6$

20. If $f(x, y) = ye^{xy}$, find the values x_0 for which $f(x_0, 5) = 5$, and then find an equation of the plane tangent to the graph of f at $(x_0, 5, 5)$.

    Answer: $x_0 = 0$; $z = 25x + y$

21. Find an equation of the tangent plane to the parametric surface $x = u$, $y = v$, $z = u^2 + v$ at the point $(1, 2, 3)$.

    (A) $x + y + z = 6$ (B) $x + y - z = 0$ (C) $x + y + 2z = 9$ (D) $x + y - 2z = -3$

    (E) $x + 2y + z = 8$ (F) $x - 2y + z = 0$ (G) $2x + y + z = 7$ (H) $2x + y - z = 1$

    Answer: **(H)**

22. Find an equation of the tangent plane to the parametric surface $x = u - v$, $y = u + v$, $z = u^2$ at the point $(0, 2, 1)$.

    (A) $x + y + z = 3$ (B) $x + y - z = 1$ (C) $x + y + 2z = 4$ (D) $x + y - 2z = 0$

    (E) $x + 2y + z = 5$ (F) $x - 2y + z = -3$ (G) $2x + y + z = 3$ (H) $2x + y - z = 1$

    Answer: **(B)**

23. Find an equation of the tangent plane to the parametric surface $x = u^2$, $y = u - v^2$, $z = v^2$ at the point $(1, 0, 1)$.

    Answer: $x - 2y - 2z + 1 = 0$

24. Find an equation of the tangent plane to the surface given by $\mathbf{r}(u, v) = (u + v)\mathbf{i} + u\cos v\,\mathbf{j} + v\sin u\,\mathbf{k}$ at the point $(1, 1, 0)$.

    Answer: $(\sin 1)\,x - (\sin 1)\,y - z = 0$

25. Find an equation of the tangent plane to the surface with parametric equations $x = \cos u \sin v$, $y = \sin u \sin v$, $z = \cos v$ at the point $\left(\frac{1}{2}, \frac{1}{2}, \frac{1}{\sqrt{2}}\right)$.

    Answer: $x + y + \sqrt{2}z = 2$

26. Find an equation of the tangent plane to the surface with parametric equations $x = 1 + 2u + 3v$, $y = 5 - u + 4v$, $z = 3 + 5u - 7v$ at the point $(3, 4, 8)$.

    Answer: $-13x + 29y + 11z = 165$

27. Find a normal vector to the surface with parametric equations $x = 2uv$, $y = u^2 - v^2$, $z = u^2 + v^2$ at the point $(1, 0, 1)$.

    Answer: $\left\langle \frac{1}{\sqrt{2}}, 0, -\frac{1}{\sqrt{2}} \right\rangle$

28. Find the linear approximation to the function $f(x, y) = 2x^2 + y^2$ at $(1, 1)$ and use it to approximate $f(1.1, 1.1)$.

    Answer: $z = 4x + 2y - 3$, $f(1.1, 1.1) \approx 3.6$

29. Find the linear approximation to the function $f(x, y) = \ln(3x - y)$ at $(1, 2)$ and use it to approximate $f(0.95, 2.03)$.

   Answer: $z = 3x - y - 1$, $f(0.95, 2.03) \approx -0.18$

30. Suppose you want to give a closed cylindrical tank of radius 20 feet and height 15 feet a coat of paint 0.01 inch thick. Use the differential of the volume of the tank to estimate how many gallons of paint will be required. (1 gallon is approximately 231 cubic inches.)

   Answer: 27.42 gallons.

31. The dimensions of a closed rectangular box are measured to be 60 cm, 40 cm, and 30 cm. The ruler that is used has a possible error in measurement of at most 0.1 cm. Use differentials to estimate the maximum error in the calculated volume of the box.

   Answer: 540 cm^3

32. Find an equation of the tangent plane to the surface $x + yz^2 = x^2z + y^3$ at the point $(-1, 1, 2)$.

   Answer: $5x + y + 3z = 2$

33. Find the acute angle of intersection between the plane $x + y + z = 8$ and the paraboloid $z = x^2 + y^2$ at the point $(1, 2, 5)$.

   Answer: $\theta \approx 51°$

11.5   The Chain Rule

1. Let $z = xy$, and let x and y be functions of t with $x(1) = 1$, $y(1) = 2$, $x'(1) = 3$, and $y'(1) = 4$. Find dz/dt when $t = 1$.

   (A) 5   (B) 6   (C) 7   (D) 8

   (E) 9   (F) 10   (G) 11   (H) 12

   Answer: (F)

2. Let $z = \ln(2x^2 + y)$, and let x and y be functions of t with $x(1) = 1$, $y(1) = 2$, $x'(1) = 3$, and $y'(1) = 4$. Find dz/dt when $t = 1$.

   (A) 3   (B) 4   (C) 6   (D) 8

   (E) 9   (F) 10   (G) 12   (H) 16

   Answer: (B)

3. Let $z = \sin(xy)$, and let x and y be functions of t with $x(1) = 0$, $y(1) = 1$, $x'(1) = 2$, and $y'(1) = 3$. Find dz/dt when $t = 1$.

   (A) 0   (B) 1   (C) 2   (D) 3

   (E) 4   (F) 5   (G) 6   (H) 12

   Answer: (C)

4. Let $z = \sqrt{1 + 2x + xy}$, and let x and y be functions of t with $x(1) = 2$, $y(1) = 2$, $x'(1) = 3$, and $y'(1) = -6$. Find dz/dt when $t = 1$.

(A) 0   (B) -2 (C) 4   (D) -4

(E) 2   (F) 1   (G) -1 (H) $\frac{2}{3}$

Answer: (A)

5. Let $z = e^{x^2} \sin y$, and let x and y be functions of t with $x(1) = 0$, $y(1) = 0$, $x'(1) = 3$, and $y'(1) = 4$. Find dz/dt when $t = 1$.

(A) 0   (B) 1   (C) 2   (D) 3

(E) 4   (F) 5   (G) 6   (H) 7

Answer: (E)

6. Let $z = x + y$, and let x and y be functions of s and t with $x(0,0) = 1$, $y(0,0) = 2$, $\partial x / \partial s = 3$, and $\partial y / \partial s = 4$ at $(s, t) = (0, 0)$. Find $\partial z / \partial s$ when $(s, t) = (0, 0)$.

(A) 5   (B) 6   (C) 7   (D) 8

(E) 9   (F) 10   (G) 11   (H) 12

Answer: (C)

7. Let $z = xy + x^2 y$, and let x and y be functions of s and t with $x(0,0) = 1$, $y(0,0) = 2$, $\partial x / \partial s = 3$, and $\partial y / \partial s = 4$ at $(s, t) = (0, 0)$. Find $\partial z / \partial s$ when $(s, t) = (0,0)$.

(A) 21   (B) 22   (C) 23   (D) 24

(E) 25   (F) 26   (G) 27   (H) 28

Answer: (F)

8. Let $z = e^x \sin y$, and let x and y be functions of s and t with $x(0,0) = 0$, $y(0,0) = 0$, $\partial x / \partial s = 3$, and $\partial y / \partial s = 4$ at $(s, t) = (0, 0)$. Find $\partial z / \partial s$ when $(s, t) = (0, 0)$.

(A) 0   (B) 1   (C) 2   (D) 3

(E) 4   (F) 5   (G) 6   (H) 7

Answer: (E)

9. Let $x^3 + y^2 = x^2 z^3$. Use implicit differentiation to find $\partial z / \partial x$ when $(x, y, z) = (1, -2, 1)$.

(A) $-\frac{1}{3}$ (B) $\frac{1}{3}$ (C) $-\frac{1}{2}$ (D) $\frac{1}{2}$

(E) -1 (F) 1   (G) $-\frac{4}{3}$ (H) $\frac{4}{3}$

Answer: (B)

10. Let $e^x = 3 \sin y$. Use implicit differentiation to find dy/dx when $(x, y) = (1, 0)$.

(A) $-\frac{1}{3}e$ (B) $\frac{1}{3}e$ (C) $-\frac{1}{2}e$ (D) $\frac{1}{2}e$

(E) $-e$ (F) e (G) $-2e$ (H) $2e$

Answer: (B)

11. Let $x + y + z - \sin(xyz) = 3$. Use implicit differentiation to find $\partial z / \partial y$ when $(x, y, z) = (1, 0, 2)$.

(A) -3 (B) -2 (C) -1 (D) 0

(E) 1 (F) 2 (G) 3 (H) 4

Answer: (E)

12. Use implicit differentiation to find $\dfrac{\partial z}{\partial x}$ on the surface given by $x^3 y + y^2 z^2 + xz^3 = 3$.

Answer: $-\dfrac{3x^2 y + z^3}{2y^2 z + 3xz^2}$

13. If $z^3 + xz - y = 0$, find $\dfrac{\partial^2 z}{\partial x \partial y}$ in terms of x, y and z.

Answer: $\dfrac{3z^2 - x}{\left(3z^2 + x\right)^3}$

14. One side of a rectangle is increasing at 4 ft/min and another at 7 ft/min. At the time when the first side is 24 ft long and the second is 32 ft long, find

(a) how fast the area is changing.

(b) how fast the diagonal is changing.

Answer: (a) 296 ft^2/min (b) 8 ft/min

15. Suppose that $z = u^2 + uv + v^3$, and that $u = 2x^2 + 3xy$ and $v = 2x - 3y + 2$. Find $\dfrac{\partial z}{\partial x}$ at $(x, y) = (1, 2)$.

Answer: 180

16. Given $f = x^2 y^3$, $x = u^2 + v^2$, and $y = 2u + 3v$, the partial derivative of f with respect to v is

(A) $\left(14u^2 + 29v^2 + 36uv\right)(2v + 3)$

(B) $\left(u^2 + v^2\right)(2u + 3v)^2 \left(8uv + 21v^2 + 9u^2\right)$

(C) $2\left[\left(u^2 + v^2\right)(2u + 3v)^3 + v\right] + 3\left[\left(u^2 + v^2\right)^2 (2u + 3v)^2 + 1\right]$

(D) $2v(2u + 3v)^3 + 3\left(u^2 + v^2\right)^2$

(E) $4\left(u^2 + v^2\right)(2u + 3v)^3 u + 6\left(u^2 + v^2\right)^2 (2u + 3v)^2$

Answer: (B)

17. If f is a function of x and y, and y is a function of x, then indirectly f depends only on x: $g(x) = f(x, y(x))$. Use the Chain Rule to write an expression for $\dfrac{dg}{dx}$ in terms of $\dfrac{\partial f}{\partial x}$ and $\dfrac{\partial f}{\partial y}$.

Answer: $\dfrac{\partial g}{\partial x} = \dfrac{\partial f}{\partial x} + \dfrac{\partial f}{\partial y}\dfrac{dy}{dx}$

18. If f is a function of x and y, and y is a function of x, then indirectly f depends only on x: $g(x) = f(x, y(x))$. If $f(x, y) = \sin x + \sqrt{1 - y^2}$ and $y(x) = \cos x$, calculate $\dfrac{dg}{dx}$.

Answer: $\dfrac{dg}{dx} = 2\cos x$

19. Suppose that $z = x - y$, $x = 4\left(t^3 - 1\right)$, and $y = \ln t$. Find $\dfrac{dz}{dt}$.

Answer: $12t^2 - \dfrac{1}{t}$

20. The radius of a right circular cylinder is increasing at a rate of 2 cm/min and its height is decreasing at 4 cm/min. At what rate is the volume changing at the instant when the radius is 4 cm and the height is 10 cm?

    Answer: 96π cm^3/min

21. Where does the equation $x^2 + \frac{1}{2}y^2 + \frac{1}{3}z^2 = 1$ define z as a function of x and y?

    Answer: On or inside the ellipse $x^2 + \frac{1}{2}y^2 = 1$

22. Show that at $\left(\frac{1}{\sqrt{2}}, 0\right)$, the equation $x^2 + \frac{1}{2}y^2 + \frac{1}{3}z^2 = 1$ defines z implicitly as a function of x and y, and then compute $\dfrac{\partial z}{\partial x}\left(\frac{1}{\sqrt{2}}, 0, \sqrt{\frac{3}{2}}\right)$ and $\dfrac{\partial z}{\partial y}\left(\frac{1}{\sqrt{2}}, 0, \sqrt{\frac{3}{2}}\right)$.

    Answer: $z = \sqrt{3\left(1 - x^2 - \frac{1}{2}y^2\right)}$ for $1 - x^2 - \frac{1}{2}y^2 \geq 0$, which is true at $\left(\frac{1}{\sqrt{2}}, 0\right)$. $\dfrac{\partial z}{\partial x} = -\sqrt{3}, \dfrac{\partial z}{\partial y} = 0$

23. Find $\partial z/\partial x$ and $\partial z/\partial y$ given that z is defined implicitly as a function of x and y by the equation $\sin xyz + \ln\left(x^2 + y^2 + z^2\right) = 0$.

    Answer: $\dfrac{\partial z}{\partial x} = \dfrac{-\left(x^2yz + y^3z + yz^3\right)\cos xyz - 2x}{\left(x^3y + xy^3 + xyz^2\right)\cos xyz + 2z}, \dfrac{\partial z}{\partial y} = \dfrac{-\left(x^3z + xy^2z + xz^3\right)\cos xyz - 2y}{\left(x^3y + xy^3 + xyz^2\right)\cos xyz + 2z}$

24. If $z = f(x, y)$ has continuous partial derivatives, $x = s + 2t$, and $y = s - 2t$, show that

    $$\frac{\partial z}{\partial s}\frac{\partial z}{\partial t} = 2\left(\frac{\partial z}{\partial x}\right)^2 - 2\left(\frac{\partial z}{\partial y}\right)^2$$

25. If $w = f(x, y, z)$ has continuous partial derivatives, $x = s + t, y = s^2 - t^2$, and $z = st$, show that

    $$s\frac{\partial w}{\partial s} + t\frac{\partial w}{\partial t} = x\frac{\partial w}{\partial x} + 2y\frac{\partial w}{\partial y} + 2z\frac{\partial w}{\partial z}$$

26. If $z = f(x, y)$ has continuous second partial derivatives, $x = 2u + v$, and $y = u - 3v$, express $\dfrac{\partial^2 z}{\partial u \partial v}$ in terms of $\dfrac{\partial^2 z}{\partial x^2}, \dfrac{\partial^2 z}{\partial x \partial y}$, and $\dfrac{\partial^2 z}{\partial y^2}$.

    Answer: $\dfrac{\partial^2 z}{\partial u \partial v} = 2\dfrac{\partial^2 z}{\partial x^2} - 5\dfrac{\partial^2 z}{\partial x \partial y} - 3\dfrac{\partial^2 z}{\partial y^2}$

27. Suppose that $z = x^3y^2$, where both x and y are changing with time. At a certain instant when $x = 1$ and $y = 2$, x is decreasing at the rate of 2 units/s and y is increasing at the rate of 3 units/s. How fast is z changing at this instant? Is z increasing or decreasing?

    Answer: $\dfrac{dz}{dt} = -12$, z is decreasing.

28. The pressure P (in kilopascals), volume V (in liters), and temperature T (in °K) of a mole of an ideal gas are related by the equation $P = \dfrac{8.31T}{V}$. Find the rate at which the pressure is changing when the temperature is 300° K and increasing at a rate of 0.1° K/s and the volume is 100 L and increasing at a rate of 0.2 L/s.

    Answer: $\dfrac{dP}{dt} = -0.04155$ kPa/s

11.6 Directional Derivatives and the Gradient Vector

1. Find the directional derivative of the function $f(x, y) = x^2 + y^2$ at the point $(1, 2)$ in the direction $\theta = \frac{\pi}{2}$.

(A) 0   (B) 1   (C) 2   (D) 3

(E) 4   (F) 5   (G) 6   (H) 7

Answer: (E)

2. Find the directional derivative of the function $f(x, y) = x^2 + y^2$ at the point $(1, 1)$ in the direction $\theta = \frac{\pi}{4}$.

(A) $\sqrt{2}$ (B) $2\sqrt{2}$ (C) $4\sqrt{2}$ (D) $\frac{1}{\sqrt{2}}$

(E) 1   (F) 2   (G) 4   (H) $\frac{1}{2}$

Answer: (B)

3. Find the directional derivative of the function $f(x, y) = y^2 \ln x$ at the point $(1, 2)$ in the direction $\langle 3, 4 \rangle$.

(A) $\frac{5}{16}$ (B) 0   (C) $\frac{12}{5}$ (D) 12

(E) 1   (F) $\frac{16}{5}$ (G) $\frac{5}{12}$ (H) $\frac{1}{12}$

Answer: (C)

4. Let $f(x, y) = 3x + 2y$. Find the gradient vector ∇f.

(A) $3x\mathbf{i} + 2y\mathbf{j}$ (B) $3x^2\mathbf{i} + 2y^2\mathbf{j}$ (C) $2x\mathbf{i} + 3y\mathbf{j}$ (D) $2x^2\mathbf{i} + 3y^2\mathbf{j}$

(E) $3y\mathbf{i} + 2x\mathbf{j}$ (F) $2y\mathbf{i} + 3x\mathbf{j}$ (G) $2\mathbf{i} + 3\mathbf{j}$ (H) $3\mathbf{i} + 2\mathbf{j}$

Answer: (H)

5. Let $f(x, y) = \dfrac{x}{y} + \dfrac{y}{x}$. Find the gradient vector ∇f.

(A) $2x\,\mathbf{i} + 2y\,\mathbf{j}$ (B) $2y\,\mathbf{i} + 2x\,\mathbf{j}$

(C) $-\dfrac{y}{x^2}\,\mathbf{i} - \dfrac{x}{y^2}\,\mathbf{j}$ (D) $\dfrac{1}{y}\,\mathbf{i} + \dfrac{1}{x}\,\mathbf{j}$

(E) $x\,\mathbf{i} + y\,\mathbf{j}$ (F) $y\,\mathbf{i} + x\,\mathbf{j}$

(G) $\dfrac{y}{x^2}\,\mathbf{i} + \dfrac{x}{y^2}\,\mathbf{j}$ (H) $\left(\dfrac{1}{y} - \dfrac{y}{x^2}\right)\mathbf{i} + \left(\dfrac{1}{x} - \dfrac{x}{y^2}\right)\mathbf{j}$

Answer: (B)

6. Let $f(x, y) = \dfrac{1}{x + y^2}$. Find the gradient vector $\nabla f(1, 1)$ at the point $(x, y) = (1, 1)$.

(A) $-\mathbf{i} - \mathbf{j}$ (B) $-\frac{1}{4}\mathbf{i} - \frac{1}{2}\mathbf{j}$ (C) $-\mathbf{i} - \frac{1}{2}\mathbf{j}$ (D) $-\frac{1}{2}\mathbf{i} - \mathbf{j}$

(E) $\mathbf{i} + \mathbf{j}$ (F) $\frac{1}{4}\mathbf{i} + \frac{1}{2}\mathbf{j}$ (G) $\mathbf{i} + \frac{1}{2}\mathbf{j}$ (H) $\frac{1}{2}\mathbf{i} + \mathbf{j}$

Answer: (B)

7. Let $f(x, y, z) = xe^{y} \sin z$. Find the gradient $\nabla f(1, 1, 0)$ at the point $(x, y, z) = (1, 1, 0)$.

(A) $\mathbf{i}$ (B) $\mathbf{j}$ (C) $\mathbf{k}$ (D) $\mathbf{j} + \mathbf{k}$

(E) $\mathbf{i} + \mathbf{k}$ (F) $\mathbf{i} + \mathbf{j}$ (G) $\mathbf{i} + \mathbf{j} + \mathbf{k}$ (H) 0

Answer: (E)

8. Find the largest value of the directional derivative of the function $f(x, y) = \dfrac{y}{x+y}$ at the point $(x, y) = (1, 2)$.

(A) $\sqrt{5}$ (B) $\frac{5}{9}$ (C) $-\sqrt{5}$ (D) $-\frac{5}{9}$

(E) $\frac{\sqrt{5}}{3}$ (F) $\frac{\sqrt{5}}{9}$ (G) $-\frac{\sqrt{5}}{3}$ (H) $-\frac{\sqrt{5}}{9}$

Answer: (F)

9. Find the direction θ in which the directional derivative of the function $f(x, y) = xy + y^2$ at the point $(1, 1)$ is maximum.

(A) $\cot^{-1} 2$ (B) $\cot^{-1} 3$ (C) $\cos^{-1} \frac{1}{2}$ (D) $\cos^{-1} \frac{1}{3}$

(E) $\sin^{-1} \frac{1}{2}$ (F) $\sin^{-1} \frac{1}{3}$ (G) $\tan^{-1} 2$ (H) $\tan^{-1} 3$

Answer: (H)

10. Find a normal vector to the surface $xyz = 8$ at the point $(1, 2, 4)$.

(A) $2\mathbf{i} + 4\mathbf{j} + \mathbf{k}$ (B) $\mathbf{i} + 4\mathbf{j} + 2\mathbf{k}$ (C) $4\mathbf{i} + 2\mathbf{j} + \mathbf{k}$ (D) $\mathbf{i} + 2\mathbf{j} + 4\mathbf{k}$

(E) $4\mathbf{i} + \mathbf{j} + 2\mathbf{k}$ (F) $2\mathbf{k} + \mathbf{j} + 4\mathbf{i}$ (G) $\mathbf{i} + \mathbf{j} + \mathbf{k}$ (H) $\mathbf{i} + 2\mathbf{j} + 2\mathbf{k}$

Answer: (C)

11. Find an equation of the tangent plane to the surface $x^2 + y^2 + z^2 = 9$ at the point $(1, 2, 2)$.

(A) $2x + y + z = 4$ (B) $x + y + z = 5$

(C) $x + 2y + 2z = 9$ (D) $x + 4y + 4z = 17$

(E) $2x^2 + y^2 + z^2 = 10$ (F) $x^2 + y^2 + z^2 = 9$

(G) $x^2 + 2y^2 + 2z^2 = 17$ (H) $x^2 + 4y^2 + 4z^2 = 33$

Answer: (C)

12. Find the directional derivative of the function $f(x, y, z) = \sqrt{xyz}$ at the point $(2, 4, 2)$ in the direction of the vector $\langle 4, 2, -4 \rangle$.

(A) $-\frac{1}{6}$ (B) $-\frac{1}{4}$ (C) $-\frac{1}{2}$ (D) 0

(E) $\frac{1}{2}$ (F) $\frac{1}{4}$ (G) $\frac{1}{6}$ (H) $\frac{1}{8}$

Answer: (G)

13. Find the directional derivative of the function $f(x, y, z) = xe^{xy/z}$ at the point $P(3, 0, 1)$ in the direction from P toward the point $(2, 2, 3)$.

(A) $\frac{17}{3}$ (B) 6 (C) $\frac{19}{3}$ (D) $\frac{20}{3}$

(E) 7 (F) $\frac{22}{3}$ (G) $\frac{23}{3}$ (H) 8

Answer: (A)

14. Find the direction of maximum increase of the function $f(x, y, z) = xe^{-y} + 3z$ at the point $(1, 0, 4)$.

(A) $\langle 1, 1, 3 \rangle$ (B) $\langle -1, -1, 3 \rangle$ (C) $\langle -1, 1, 3 \rangle$ (D) $\langle 1, -1, 4 \rangle$

(E) $\langle 1, 3, 3 \rangle$ (F) $\langle 1, -3, 3 \rangle$ (G) $\langle 1, -1, 3 \rangle$ (H) $\langle -1, 1, 4 \rangle$

Answer: (G)

15. Find the direction of maximum increase of the function $f(x, y, z) = x^2 - 2xy + z^2$ at the point $(1, 1, 2)$.

   (A) $\langle 1, 0, -2 \rangle$ **(B)** $\langle 4, 1, 2 \rangle$ **(C)** $\langle 2, 1, -4 \rangle$ **(D)** $\langle 0, -2, 4 \rangle$

   (E) $\langle 2, 0, 3 \rangle$ **(F)** $\langle 3, 1, 2 \rangle$ **(G)** $\langle 0, 2, 1 \rangle$ **(H)** $\langle 5, -1, 6 \rangle$

   Answer: **(D)**

16. Find an equation of the tangent plane to the hyperboloid $x^2 + y^2 - z^2 - 2xy + 4xz = 4$ at the point $(1, 0, 1)$.

   (A) $3x - y + z = 4$ **(B)** $2x - 4y + z = 3$ **(C)** $x + 2y + 3z = 4$ **(D)** $2x + y - z = 1$

   (E) $3x + 2y - z = 2$ **(F)** $4x - y + 2z = 6$ **(G)** $x + y - z = 0$ **(H)** $5x + 3y - 2z = 3$

   Answer: **(A)**

17. Find an equation of the tangent plane to the surface $\sqrt{x} + \sqrt{y} + \sqrt{z} = 4$ at the point $(4, 1, 1)$.

   (A) $2x + y - z = 1$ **(B)** $x + 2y + 3z = 9$ **(C)** $x - 2y + 4z = 0$ **(D)** $4x - y + 6z = 1$

   (E) $x + 2y + 2z = 8$ **(F)** $3x + 2y + z = 1$ **(G)** $x + y + z = 6$ **(H)** $2x + y + z = 10$

   Answer: **(E)**

18. Find the directional derivative of $f(x, y) = x^2 - 3xy + 2y^2$ at $(-1, 2)$ in the direction of $\mathbf{i} + \sqrt{3}\mathbf{j}$.

   Answer: $\frac{11\sqrt{3} - 8}{2}$

19. Let $f(x, y) = \sqrt{2x + 3y}$.

   (a) In which direction does f increase most rapidly at the point $(3, 1)$?

   (b) What is the maximum rate of change of f at the point $(3, 1)$?

   (c) Find a unit vector $\mathbf{u}$ such that $D_{\mathbf{u}}f = 0$ at $(3, 1)$.

   Answer: (a) $\langle \frac{1}{3}, \frac{1}{2} \rangle$ (b) $\frac{\sqrt{13}}{6}$ (c) $\pm \left\langle \frac{-3}{\sqrt{13}}, \frac{2}{\sqrt{13}} \right\rangle$

20. Let $f(x, y, z) = x^2y + y^3z + xz^3$ and let $P(2, 1, -1)$.

   (a) Find the directional derivative at P in the direction of $\langle 1, 2, 3 \rangle$.

   (b) In what direction does f increase most rapidly?

   (c) What is the maximum rate of change of f at the point P?

   Answer: (a) $\frac{26}{\sqrt{14}}$ (b) $\langle 3, 1, 7 \rangle$ (c) $\sqrt{59}$

21. For $f(x, y) = x^2y^3$, $\mathbf{u} = \langle \frac{3}{5}, -\frac{4}{5} \rangle$, the directional derivative of f in the direction u at the point (x, y) is

   (A) $\dfrac{6xy^3 - 12x^2y^2}{5}$ **(B)** $\dfrac{3x^2 - 4y^3}{5}$ **(C)** $\dfrac{6x - 12y^2}{5}$ **(D)** $2xy^3 + 3x^2y^2$ **(E)** $\sqrt{4x^2y^6 + 9x^4y^4}$

   Answer: **(A)**

22. Find the directional derivative of $f(x, y, z) = x^2 + y^2 - z$ at the point $(1, 3, 5)$ in the direction of $\mathbf{a} = 2\mathbf{i} - \mathbf{j} + 4\mathbf{k}$.

   Answer: $\frac{-2\sqrt{21}}{7}$

23. Let the temperature in a flat plate be given by the function $T(x, y) = 3x^2 + 2xy$. What is the value of the directional derivative of this function at the point $(3, -6)$ in the direction $\mathbf{v} = 4\mathbf{i} - 3\mathbf{j}$? In what direction is the plate cooling most rapidly at $(3, -6)$?

   Answer: $\frac{6}{5}$; the plate is cooling most rapidly in the direction $-\mathbf{i} - \mathbf{j}$

24. Find the directional derivative of $f(x, y) = x^3 + xy^2$ at the point $(1, -2)$ in the direction toward the origin.

Answer: $-3\sqrt{5}$

25. Find the directional derivative of $f(x, y) = 3x^2 + xy - y^3$ in the direction $\theta = \frac{\pi}{3}$.

Answer: $\left(\frac{6+\sqrt{3}}{2}\right)x + \frac{1}{2}y - \frac{3\sqrt{3}}{2}y^2$

26. Let $f(x, y, z) = x^2 + y^2 + xz$. Find the directional derivative of f at $(1, 2, 0)$ in the direction of the vector $\mathbf{v} = \langle 1, -1, 1\rangle$.

Answer: $-\frac{1}{\sqrt{3}}$

27. Suppose that the equation $F(x, y, z) = 0$ defines z implicitly as a function of x and y. Let (a, b, c) be a point such that $F(a, b, c) = 0$ and $\nabla F(a, b, c) = \langle 2, -3, 4\rangle$. Find $\dfrac{\partial z}{\partial x}(a, b)$ and $\dfrac{\partial z}{\partial y}(a, b)$.

Answer: $\dfrac{\partial z}{\partial x}(a, b) = -\frac{1}{2}$, $\dfrac{\partial z}{\partial y}(a, b) = \frac{3}{4}$

28. Find $\lim\limits_{h \to 0} \dfrac{\ln\left((x+h)^2 y\right) - \ln\left(x^2 y\right)}{h}$.

Answer: $\dfrac{2}{x}$

29. Let $f(x, y, z) = \dfrac{x}{y} + \dfrac{y}{z} + \dfrac{z}{x}$. Find the rate of change of f at $P(1, -1, 1)$ in the direction from P toward $(2, 1, 0)$.

Answer: $-\dfrac{4}{\sqrt{6}}$

30. Find the directional derivative of $f(x, y) = x^2 y + \ln y$ $(y > 0)$ at the point $(1, 1)$ in the direction of the origin.

Answer: $-2\sqrt{2}$

31. A bug is crawling on the surface $z = x^2 + xy + 2y^2$. When he reaches the point $(2, 1, 8)$ he wants to avoid vertical change. In which direction should he head? (He wants the directional derivative in the z-direction to be zero.)

Answer: $\mathbf{u} = \pm\frac{1}{\sqrt{61}}\langle -6, 5\rangle$

32. Given $f(x, y) = x^2 y$, $P_0 = (3, 2)$, let $\mathbf{u}$ be the unit vector for which the directional derivative $D_{\mathbf{u}}f(P_0)$ has maximum value. This maximum value is

(A) $\frac{288}{5}$ $\qquad$ (B) 1 $\qquad$ (C) 6 $\qquad$ (D) $12\sqrt{3}$ $\qquad$ (E) 15

Answer: (E)

33. Let $f(x, y) = 3x^3 + y^2 - 9x + 4y$. Find the direction at the origin in which $f(x, y)$ is decreasing the fastest.

Answer: $9\mathbf{i} - 4\mathbf{j}$

34. Given $f(x, y) = \frac{1}{4}x^4 y^3$, at the point $(-1, 2)$. Find (a) the maximum value of the directional derivative and (b) the unit vector in the direction in which the directional derivative takes on its maximum value.

Answer: (a) $\sqrt{73}$; (b) $\left\langle -\frac{8}{\sqrt{73}}, \frac{3}{\sqrt{73}}\right\rangle$

35. If $f(x,y) = 2x^2 + 4y^2 - xy$, find the gradient at the point $(2,1)$. Also find the rate of change of $f(x,y)$ in the direction $\theta = \frac{\pi}{3}$ at $(2,1)$.

Answer: $\nabla f(2,1) = \langle 7, 6 \rangle$; $D_{\mathbf{u}}f(2,1) = \frac{7 + 6\sqrt{3}}{2}$

36. The surface of a certain lake is represented by a region in the xy-plane such that the depth under the point corresponding to (x,y) is $f(x,y) = 300 - 2x^2 - 3y^2$. Zeke the dog is at the point $(3,2)$.

    (a) In what direction should Zeke swim in order for the depth to decrease most rapidly?

    (b) In what direction would the depth remain the same?

    Answer: (a) $\mathbf{i} + \mathbf{j}$; (b) $\mathbf{i} - \mathbf{j}$ and $-\mathbf{i} + \mathbf{j}$

37. Find an equation of the tangent plane to the surface $4x^2 - y^2 + 3z^2 = 10$ at the point $(2, -3, 1)$.

    Answer: $16x + 6y + 6z = 20$

38. Find an equation of the tangent plane to the surface $z = f(x,y) = x^3 y^4$ at the point $(-1, 2, -16)$.

    Answer: $48x - 32y - z + 96 = 0$

39. Given $f(x,y) = xe^{-2y}$, at the point $(4,0)$ find the equation of the tangent plane to the graph of f. Also, find a normal vector to the graph of f.

    Answer: $z = x - 8y$; two normal vectors are $\langle 1, -8, -1 \rangle$ and $\langle -1, 8, 1 \rangle$

40. Consider the surface given by $z = xy^3 - x^2y$. Find an equation for the tangent plane to the surface at the point $(3, 2, 6)$. Also, find parametric equations for the normal line to the surface at the point $(3, 2, 6)$.

    Answer: tangent plane: $4x - 27y + z = -36$; normal line: $x = 3 - 4t$, $y = 2 + 27t$, $z = 6 - t$

41. The level curves of $f(x,y)$ are sketched below.

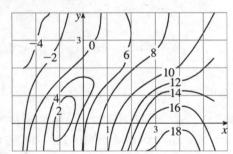

    (a) Find $f_x(2,1)$.

    (b) Find $f_y(2,1)$.

    (c) Sketch the gradient vector $\nabla f(2,1)$.

    Answer:

    (a) About 2.5   (b) About -2

    (c)

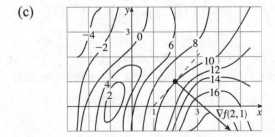

42. Find the directions in which the directional derivative of $f(x, y) = x^2y + x^3$ at the point $(-1, 2)$ has the value 1.

Answer: $\langle -1, 0 \rangle, \langle 0, 1 \rangle$

43. Consider the equation $x^2 + y^2 + z^2 = 49$.

   (a) Sketch this surface.

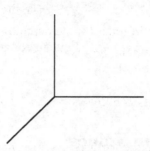

   (b) Find an equation of the tangent plane to the surface at the point $(6, 2, 3)$.

   (c) Find a symmetric equation of the line perpendicular to the tangent plane at the point $(6, 2, 3)$.

Answer:

   (a)

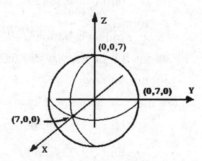

   The surface is a sphere with radius 7, centered at the origin.

   (b) $6x + 2y + 3z = 49$

   (c) $\dfrac{x - 6}{6} = \dfrac{y - 2}{2} = \dfrac{z - 3}{3}$

44. Let S be the surface $x^2y + 4xz^3 - yz = 0$. An equation of the tangent plane to S at $(1, 2, -1)$ is

   (A) $y + 5z = -3$ (B) $2x - 3y + z = 3$ (C) $x - 3z = 4$

   (D) $x - y + z = 1$ (E) $2x + y + 5z = -1$

Answer: (A)

45. Find the unit vectors $\mathbf{u}$ and $\mathbf{v}$ for $f(x, y) = x^3 + 3y^2$ which describe the direction of maximal and minimal increase at $(2, 1)$ on the level curve $f(x, y) = 11$.

Answer: $\mathbf{u} = \left\langle \dfrac{2}{\sqrt{5}}, \dfrac{1}{\sqrt{5}} \right\rangle, \mathbf{v} = \left\langle \dfrac{1}{\sqrt{5}}, -\dfrac{2}{\sqrt{5}} \right\rangle$

46. In what direction does the directional derivative for $f(x, y) = x^2y$ at $(1, 1)$ have value 1? Value -2? Is there a direction for which the value is 4?

Answer: Value 1 in direction of $\mathbf{u} = \langle 0, 1 \rangle$ and $\mathbf{u} = \langle \frac{4}{5}, -\frac{3}{5} \rangle$; value -2 in direction of $\mathbf{u} = \langle -1, 0 \rangle$ and $\mathbf{u} = \langle -\frac{3}{5}, \frac{4}{5} \rangle$; no

47. What is the direction of maximal decrease for $f(x, y, z) = xy + yz + xz$ at $(1, 1, 1)$?

Answer: Any vector $\mathbf{u}$ perpendicular to $\langle 2, 2, 2 \rangle$, for example, $\langle -1, -1, 2 \rangle$

48. Find the points on the hyperboloid of one sheet $x^2 + y^2 - z^2 = 1$ where the tangent plane is parallel to the plane $2x - y + z = 3$.

Answer: $\left(1, -\frac{1}{2}, -\frac{1}{2}\right), \left(-1, \frac{1}{2}, \frac{1}{2}\right)$

49. Given that the directional derivative of $f(x, y)$ at the point $(-1, 2)$ in the direction of $\langle 3, -4 \rangle$ is -10 and that $|\nabla f(-1, 2)| = 10$, find $\nabla f(-1, 2)$.

Answer: $\langle -6, 8 \rangle$

50. Let $z = f(x, y)$ such that $\nabla f(-1, 2) = \langle 3, -4 \rangle$. Find an equation of the tangent line to the level curve of $f(x, y)$ that passes through the point $(-1, 2)$.

Answer: $y - 2 = \frac{3}{4}(x + 1)$

11.7 Maximum and Minimum Values

1. The function $f(x, y) = x^2 - 2y^2$ has one critical point. Determine its location and type.

(A) $(2, 1)$, saddle point

(B) $(2, 1)$, minimum point

(C) $(2, 1)$, maximum point

(D) $(\sqrt{2}, 1)$, saddle point

(E) $(\sqrt{2}, 1)$, minimum point

(F) $(\sqrt{2}, 1)$, maximum point

(G) $(0, 0)$, saddle point

(H) $(0, 0)$, minimum point

Answer: (G)

2. The function $f(x, y) = x^2 + y^2 + xy$ has one critical point. Determine its location and type.

(A) $(2, 1)$, saddle point

(B) $(2, 1)$, minimum point

(C) $(2, 1)$, maximum point

(D) $(\sqrt{2}, 1)$, saddle point

(E) $(\sqrt{2}, 1)$, minimum point

(F) $(\sqrt{2}, 1)$, maximum point

(G) $(0, 0)$, saddle point

(H) $(0, 0)$, minimum point

Answer: (H)

3. The function $f(x, y) = x^2 + y^2 + 3xy$ has one critical point. Determine its location and type.

(A) $(2, 1)$, saddle point

(B) $(2, 1)$, minimum point

(C) $(2, 1)$, maximum point

(D) $(\sqrt{2}, 1)$, saddle point

(E) $(\sqrt{2}, 1)$, minimum point

(F) $(\sqrt{2}, 1)$, maximum point

(G) $(0, 0)$, saddle point

(H) $(0, 0)$, minimum point

Answer: (G)

4. The function $f(x, y) = 4 - x^2 - y^2 - xy - x$ has one critical point. Determine its location and type.

(A) $\left(-\frac{2}{3}, \frac{1}{3}\right)$, saddle point

(B) $\left(-\frac{2}{3}, \frac{1}{3}\right)$, minimum point

(C) $\left(-\frac{2}{3}, \frac{1}{3}\right)$, maximum point

(D) $\left(\frac{1}{3}, \frac{2}{3}\right)$, saddle point

(E) $\left(\frac{1}{3}, \frac{2}{3}\right)$, minimum point

(F) $\left(\frac{1}{3}, \frac{2}{3}\right)$, maximum point

(G) $\left(\frac{1}{3}, -\frac{2}{3}\right)$, saddle point

(H) $\left(\frac{1}{3}, -\frac{2}{3}\right)$, minimum point

Answer: (C)

5. Determine how many critical points the function $f(x,y) = x^2 + y^2 + 2x^2y + 3$ has.

(A) 0   (B) 1   (C) 2   (D) 3

(E) 4   (F) 5   (G) 6   (H) 7

Answer: **(D)**

6. Find the maximum value of the function $f(x,y) = 10x + 30y - x^2 - y^2 - 160$.

(A) 90   (B) 160   (C) 50   (D) 15

(E) 80   (F) 135   (G) 16   (H) 5

Answer: **(A)**

7. Find the minimum value of the function $f(x,y) = x^2 + \frac{9}{2}y^2 - 9y - 4xy + 50$.

(A) 8.5   (B) 18   (C) 19   (D) 10

(E) 10.5   (F) 9   (G) 9.5   (H) 50

Answer: **(G)**

8. Find the shortest distance from the origin to the surface $z^2 = 2xy + 2$.

(A) $\frac{1}{2}$ (B) $\frac{1}{\sqrt{2}}$ (C) 1   (D) $\sqrt{2}$

(E) 2   (F) $2\sqrt{2}$ (G) 4   (H) $4\sqrt{2}$

Answer: **(D)**

9. A cardboard box without a lid is to have volume 100 cubic inches, with total area of cardboard as small as possible. Find its height in inches.

(A) 2   (B) 5/2   (C) 4   (D) 5

(E) $25^{1/3}$ (F) $25^{2/3}$ (G) $200^{1/3}$ (H) $200^{2/3}$

Answer: **(E)**

10. Find the point at which the function $f(x,y) = xy - x^2y - xy^2$ has a local maximum.

(A) $(0,0)$ (B) $(1,1)$ (C) $(0,2)$ (D) $(2,0)$

(E) $(-1,0)$ (F) $(0,-1)$ (G) $\left(\frac{1}{3},\frac{1}{3}\right)$ (H) $\left(\frac{1}{2},\frac{1}{2}\right)$

Answer: **(G)**

11. Find the local maximum and minimum values and saddle points of the function $f(x,y) = 3x^3 + y^2 - 9x + 4y$.

Answer: $f(1,-2) = -10$ is a local minimum; $(-1,-2)$ is a saddle point.

12. A company estimates that its annual profit for next year will be $z = 6xy - y^3 - x^2$, where x represents investment in research and y represents investment in labor. All units are in tens of thousands of dollars. Determine the amount the company should spend on research and on labor to maximize its profit. What is the maximum profit?

Answer: $x = 18$ units or \$180,000, $y = 6$ units or \$60,000. The maximum profit is \$1,080,000.

13. The function $z = xy + (x+y)(120 - x - y)$ has a maximum. Find the values of x and y at which it occurs.

Answer: $x = y = 40$

14. Find the local maximum and minimum values and saddle points of the function $f(x, y) = x^3 - 3xy - y^3$.

Answer: $(0, 0)$ is a saddle point; $f(-1, 1) = 1$ is a local maximum

15. Use the level curves of $f(x, y)$ shown below to estimate the critical points of f. Indicate whether f has a saddle point or a local maximum or minimum at each of those points.

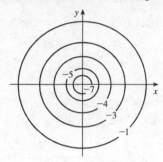

Answer: $f(0, 0)$ is a local minimum.

16. Use the level curves of $f(x, y)$ shown below to estimate the critical points of f. Indicate whether f has a saddle point or a local maximum or minimum at each of those points.

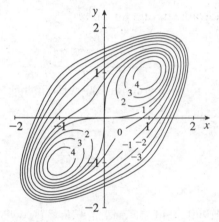

Answer: f has a saddle point at $(0, 0)$ and maximum points at $(-1, -1)$ and $(1, 1)$.

17. Find the local maximum and minimum values and saddle points of the function $f(x, y) = -x^4 + 4xy - 2y^2 + 1$.

Answer: $f(-1, -1) = 2$ is a local maximum; $(0, 0)$ is a saddle point; $f(1, 1) = 2$ is a local maximum

18. Find the local maximum and minimum values and saddle points of the function $f(x, y) = 2x^3 + 4y^3 + 3x^2 - 12x - 192y + 5$.

Answer: $f(-2, -4) = 537$ is a local maximum; $(-2, 4)$ is a saddle point; $(1, -4)$ is a saddle point; $f(1, 4) = -514$ is a local minimum

19. Find the local maximum and minimum values and saddle points of the function $f(x, y) = x^3 + y^3 - 3xy + 5$.

Answer: $(0, 0)$ is a saddle point; $f(1, 1) = 4$ is a local minimum

20. Find the local maximum and minimum values and saddle points of the function $f(x, y) = 4xy - x^4 - y^4 + \frac{1}{16}$.

Answer: $(0, 0)$ is a saddle point; $f(1, 1) = \frac{33}{16}$ is a local maximum; $f(-1, -1) = \frac{33}{16}$ is a local maximum

21. Find the absolute maximum and minimum values of $f(x, y) = x^2 + 2xy + 3y^2$ over the region D, where D is a closed triangular region with vertices $(-1, -2)$, $(-1, 1)$, and $(2, 1)$.

    Answer: Absolute minimum value $f(0, 0) = 0$, absolute maximum value $f(-1, -2) = 17$

22. Compute the minimum value of z and sketch a portion of the graph of $z = 3x^2 + 6x + 2y^2 - 8y$ near its lowest point.

    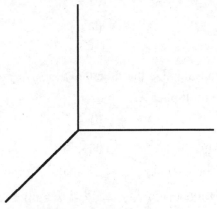

    Answer: $z(-1, 2) = -11$ is the absolute minimum value.

    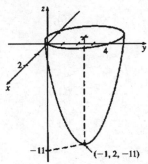

23. For each of the following functions, find the critical point, if there is one, and determine if it is a local maximum, local minimum, saddle point, or otherwise.

    (a) $f(x, y) = 4x^2 + 3x - 5y^2 - 8y + 7$

    (b) $f(x, y) = -2x^2 + 7x - 7y^2 + 4y + 9$

    (c) $f(x, y) = 3x^2 - 5y + 4y^2 + 12x - 11$

    (d) $f(x, y) = 2y^2 + 7x + 17y + 12$

    Answer: (a) $f\left(-\frac{3}{8}, -\frac{4}{5}\right) = \frac{771}{80}$ is a saddle point.

    (b) $f\left(\frac{7}{4}, \frac{2}{7}\right) = \frac{879}{56}$ is a local maximum.

    (c) $f\left(-2, \frac{5}{8}\right) = -\frac{393}{16}$ is a local minimum.

    (d) No critical point

24. Find the critical points (if any) for $f(x, y) = \dfrac{1}{x} + \dfrac{1}{y} + xy$ and determine if each is a local extreme value or a saddle point.

    Answer: $f(1, 1) = 3$ is a local minimum.

11.8 Lagrange Multipliers

1. In using Lagrange multipliers to minimize the function $f(x,y) = x^2 + y^2$ subject to the constraint that $x + y = 3$, what is the value of the multiplier λ?

(A) $\frac{1}{2}$ (B) 1   (C) $\frac{3}{2}$ (D) 2

(E) $\frac{5}{2}$ (F) 3   (G) $\frac{7}{2}$ (H) 4

Answer: (F)

2. In using Lagrange multipliers to minimize the function $f(x,y) = x^2 + y^2$ subject to the constraint that $xy = 2$, what is the value of the multiplier λ?

(A) $\frac{1}{2}$ (B) 1   (C) $\frac{3}{2}$ (D) 2

(E) $\frac{5}{2}$ (F) 3   (G) $\frac{7}{2}$ (H) 4

Answer: (D)

3. Find the minimum value of the function $f(x,y) = x^2 + y^2$ subject to the constraint that $xy = 2$.

(A) $\frac{1}{2}$ (B) 1   (C) $\frac{3}{2}$ (D) 2

(E) $\frac{5}{2}$ (F) 3   (G) $\frac{7}{2}$ (H) 4

Answer: (H)

4. Find the maximum value of the function $f(x,y) = 6 - 4x^2 - y^2$ subject to the constraint that $4x + y = 5$.

(A) $\frac{1}{2}$ (B) $\frac{1}{\sqrt{2}}$ (C) 1   (D) $\sqrt{2}$

(E) 2   (F) $2\sqrt{2}$ (G) 4   (H) $4\sqrt{2}$

Answer: (C)

5. Find the minimum value of the function $f(x,y) = xy$ subject to the constraint that $x^2 + y^2 = 2$.

(A) $\frac{1}{2}$ (B) 1   (C) $\frac{3}{2}$ (D) 2

(E) $-\frac{1}{2}$ (F) -1 (G) $-\frac{3}{2}$ (H) -2

Answer: (F)

6. Find the maximum value of the function $f(x,y) = xy$ subject to the constraint that $x^2 + y^2 = 2$.

(A) $\frac{1}{2}$ (B) 1   (C) $\frac{3}{2}$ (D) 2

(E) $-\frac{1}{2}$ (F) -1 (G) $-\frac{3}{2}$ (H) -2

Answer: (B)

7. Solve completely, using Lagrange multipliers: Find the dimensions of a box with volume 1000 which minimizes the total length of the 12 edges.

Answer: $x = y = z = 10$

8. Find the greatest product three numbers can have if the sum of their squares must be 48.

Answer: 64

9. Optimize $f(x,y) = x^2 + y^2 + 2$ subject to $xy = 4$.

Answer: $f(2,2) = 10$ is a local minimum; $f(-2,-2) = 10$ is also a local minimum

10. Find the point on the plane $x - 2y + z = 3$ where $x^2 + 4y^2 + 2z^2$ is minimum.

    Answer: $\left(\frac{6}{5}, -\frac{3}{5}, \frac{3}{5}\right)$

11. Compute the minimum value of $f(x, y, z) = x^2 + y + z^2$ subject to the condition that $g(x) = 2x + y + 4z = 6$.

    Answer: $f(1, -4, 2) = 1$

12. Find the maximum and minimum values of the function $f(x, y) = xy$ on the ellipse given by the equation $x^2 + \frac{y^2}{4} = 1$.

    Answer: Maximum value is 1, minimum value is -1

13. Find two positive numbers whose sum is eighteen and whose product is a maximum, using the method of Lagrange multipliers.

    Answer: 9 and 9

14. Use the method of Lagrange multipliers to find points on the surface $x^2 + y^2 + z^2 = 3$ where the function $f(x, y, z) = x + y + z$ has (a) a minimum, (b) a maximum.

    Answer: (a) $(-1, -1, -1)$; (b) $(1, 1, 1)$

15. Find the extreme values of $f(x, y) = xy + 2y^2 + x^4 - y^4$ on the circle $x^2 + y^2 = 1$.

    Answer: Maximum value is $f\left(-\frac{\sqrt{2}}{2}, -\frac{\sqrt{2}}{2}\right) = f\left(\frac{\sqrt{2}}{2}, \frac{\sqrt{2}}{2}\right) = \frac{3}{2}$, minimum value is $f\left(-\frac{\sqrt{2}}{2}, \frac{\sqrt{2}}{2}\right) = f\left(\frac{\sqrt{2}}{2}, -\frac{\sqrt{2}}{2}\right) = \frac{1}{2}$

16. What is the shortest distance from the origin to the surface $xyz^2 = 2$?

    Answer: 2

17. What point on the surface $\frac{1}{x} + \frac{1}{y} + \frac{1}{z} = 1$, $x > 0$, $y > 0$, $z > 0$ is closest to the origin?

    Answer: $(3, 3, 3)$

18. Find the maximum and minimum values of $f(x, y) = 2x + 3y + 4$ on the circle $x^2 + y^2 = 1$.

    Answer: Maximum value $\sqrt{13} + 4$, minimum value $-\sqrt{13} + 4$

19. The quantity Q of a good produced by a company is given by $Q = 10K^{0.6}L^{0.4}$, where K is the quantity of capital and L is the quantity of labor used. Capital costs are \$20 per unit, labor costs are \$10 per unit, and the company wants to keep costs for capital and labor combined to \$150.

    (a) What combination of labor and capital should be used to produce maximum quantity? What is the maximum value?

    (b) Draw the level curves of Q and the graph of the budget constraint on the same set of axes.

    (c) Compute the value of λ. What does λ represent?

Answer:

(a) $L = 6$, $K = 4.5$, $Q \approx 50.5$

(b)

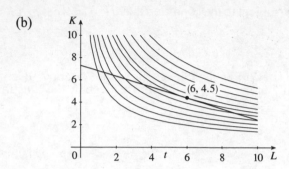

(c) $\lambda \approx 0.34 = \dfrac{dQ}{dc}\,(150)$, where c is the total cost of labor and capital.

20. Suppose that the quantity Q produced of a certain good depends on the number of units of labor L and the quantity of capital K according to the function $Q = 900L^{1/3}K^{2/3}$. Suppose also that labor costs \$100 per unit and that capital costs \$200 per unit.

   (a) What combination of labor and capital should be used to produce 36,000 units of the goods at minimum cost? What is that minimum cost?

   (b) Draw the level curves of C, the cost function, and the graph of the constraint on the same set of axes.

   (c) Compute the value of λ. What does λ represent?

Answer:

(a) $L = K = 40$ with cost \$12,000

(b)

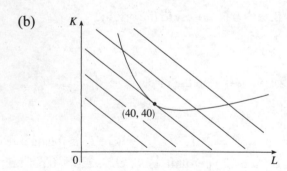

(c) $\lambda = \$0.33/\text{unit} = \dfrac{dC}{dQ}\,(36{,}000)$

21. A rancher with 300 ft of fence intends to enclose a rectangular corral, dividing it in half by a fence parallel to the short sides of the corral. What is the maximum area he can enclose? Compute the value of λ. What does λ represent?

Answer: Maximum area 3750 ft^2, $\lambda = \dfrac{dA}{df}\,(300) = 25$ ft^2/ft

22. A rancher intends to fence off a rectangular region along a river (which serves as a natural boundary requiring no fence). If the enclosed area is to be 1800 square yards, what is the least amount of fence needed? Compute the value of λ. What does λ represent?

Answer: Minimum fencing 120 yd, $\lambda = \dfrac{df}{dA}(1800) = \frac{1}{30}$ yd/yd^2

23. A rectangular area of 3200 ft^2 is to be fenced off. Two opposite sides will use fencing costing \$1 per foot and the remaining sides will use fencing costing \$2 per foot. Find the dimensions of the rectangle of least cost. Compute the value of λ. What does λ represent?

Answer: 80 ft × 40 ft, $\lambda = \dfrac{dC}{dA}(3200) = \$0.05/\text{ft}^2$

24. The level curves of a function $f(x,y)$ and a curve with equation $g(x,y) = c$ (c constant) are given below. Estimate the point where f has a maximum value and the point where f has a minimum value, subject to the constraint that $g(x,y) = c$. Indicate your answer in the figure.

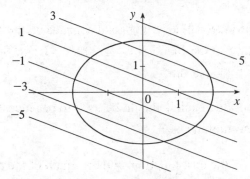

Answer: f has a maximum at about $(0.9, 1.8)$ and a minimum at about $(-0.9, -1.8)$.

12 Multiple Integrals

12.1 Double Integrals over Rectangles

1. Let $f(x,y) = x^2 y$, and let $R = \{(x,y) \mid 0 \le x \le 1,\ 0 \le y \le 1\}$. Let R be its own partition, and let (x_1^*, y_1^*) be the center of R. Calculate the double Riemann sum of f.

   (A) $\frac{3}{2}$ (B) $\frac{3}{4}$ (C) $\frac{3}{8}$ (D) $\frac{3}{16}$

   (E) $\frac{1}{2}$ (F) $\frac{1}{4}$ (G) $\frac{1}{8}$ (H) $\frac{1}{16}$

   Answer: (G)

2. Let $f(x,y) = x$, and let $R = \{(x,y) \mid 0 \le x \le 1,\ 0 \le y \le 1\}$. Let R be partitioned into two subrectangles by the line $x = \frac{1}{4}$, and let $\left(x_i^*, y_j^*\right)$ be the center of R_{ij}. Calculate the double Riemann sum of f.

   (A) $\frac{3}{16}$ (B) $\frac{1}{4}$ (C) $\frac{5}{16}$ (D) $\frac{3}{8}$

   (E) $\frac{7}{16}$ (F) $\frac{1}{2}$ (G) $\frac{9}{16}$ (H) $\frac{3}{4}$

   Answer: (F)

3. Let $f(x,y) = x^2$, and let $R = \{(x,y) \mid 0 \le x \le 1,\ 0 \le y \le 1\}$. Let R be partitioned into two subrectangles by the line $x = \frac{1}{2}$, and let $\left(x_i^*, y_j^*\right)$ be the center of R_{ij}. Calculate the double Riemann sum of f.

   (A) $\frac{3}{16}$ (B) $\frac{1}{4}$ (C) $\frac{5}{16}$ (D) $\frac{3}{8}$

   (E) $\frac{7}{16}$ (F) $\frac{1}{2}$ (G) $\frac{9}{16}$ (H) $\frac{3}{4}$

   Answer: (C)

4. Let $f(x,y) = xy$, and let $R = \{(x,y) \mid 0 \le x \le 1,\ 0 \le y \le 1\}$. Let R be partitioned into four subrectangles by the lines $x = \frac{1}{2}$ and $y = \frac{1}{2}$, and let $\left(x_i^*, y_j^*\right)$ be the upper right corner of R_{ij}. Calculate the double Riemann sum of f.

   (A) $\frac{3}{16}$ (B) $\frac{1}{4}$ (C) $\frac{5}{16}$ (D) $\frac{3}{8}$

   (E) $\frac{7}{16}$ (F) $\frac{1}{2}$ (G) $\frac{9}{16}$ (H) $\frac{5}{8}$

   Answer: (G)

5. Let $f(x,y) = xy$, and let $R = \{(x,y) \mid 0 \le x \le 1,\ 0 \le y \le 1\}$. Let R be partitioned into four subrectangles by the lines $x = \frac{1}{2}$ and $y = \frac{1}{2}$, and let $\left(x_i^*, y_j^*\right)$ be the upper left corner of R_{ij}. Calculate the double Riemann sum of f.

   (A) $\frac{3}{16}$ (B) $\frac{1}{4}$ (C) $\frac{5}{16}$ (D) $\frac{3}{8}$

   (E) $\frac{7}{16}$ (F) $\frac{1}{2}$ (G) $\frac{9}{16}$ (H) $\frac{5}{8}$

   Answer: (A)

6. Calculate the double Riemann sum of f for the partition of R given by the indicated lines and the given choice of $\left(x_{ij}^*, y_{ij}^*\right)$. $f(x, y) = x^2 + 4y$, $R = \{(x, y) \mid 0 \le x \le 2, \ 0 \le y \le 3\}$, $x = 1$, $y = 1$, $y = 2$; $\left(x_{ij}^*, y_{ij}^*\right) = \text{center of } R_{ij}$.

Answer: $\frac{87}{2}$

7. Calculate the double Riemann sum of f for the partition of R given by the indicated lines and the given choice of $\left(x_{ij}^*, y_{ij}^*\right)$. $f(x, y) = 2x + x^2 y$, $R = \{(x, y) \mid -2 \le x \le 2, \ -1 \le y \le 1\}$, $x = -1$, $x = 0$, $x = 1$, $y = -\frac{1}{2}$, $y = 0$, $y = \frac{1}{2}$; $\left(x_{ij}^*, y_{ij}^*\right) = \text{lower left corner of } R_{ij}$.

Answer: -11

8. Use the Midpoint Rule to estimate $\iint_R \left(x^2 + y^2\right) dA$ over $R = \{(x, y) \mid 0 \le x \le 2, 0 \le y \le 2\}$ partitioned by the lines $x = 1$ and $y = 1$. Then estimate the average value of $f(x, y) = x^2 + y^2$ over R.

Answer: $\iint_R \left(x^2 + y^2\right) dA \approx 10$; average value $\approx \frac{10}{4}$

9. Give an example of a non-constant function $f(x, y)$ such that the average value of f over $R = \{(x, y) \mid -1 \le x \le 1, -1 \le y \le 1\}$ is 0.

Answer: Possible functions include $f(x, y) = x$ and $f(x, y) = y$. Any linear function of x and y with no constant term will work, as will many other functions.

10. Use the Midpoint Rule to estimate $\iint_R (7 - 2x - y) \, dA$ over $R = \{(x, y) \mid -1 \le x \le 2, -1 \le y \le 2\}$ partitioned by the lines $x = 0$, $x = 1$, $y = 0$, and $y = 1$ into nine subrectangles.

Answer: 49.5

12.2 Iterated Integrals

1. Evaluate the iterated integral $\int_0^1 \int_0^1 x^2 y \, dx \, dy$.

(A) $\frac{1}{2}$ (B) $\frac{1}{3}$ (C) $\frac{1}{4}$ (D) $\frac{3}{4}$

(E) $\frac{2}{3}$ (F) $\frac{1}{6}$ (G) $\frac{5}{6}$ (H) 1

Answer: (F)

2. Evaluate the iterated integral $\int_0^1 \int_0^2 (x + y) \, dx \, dy$.

(A) $\frac{1}{2}$ (B) 2 (C) $\frac{3}{2}$ (D) 2

(E) $\frac{5}{2}$ (F) 3 (G) $\frac{7}{2}$ (H) 4

Answer: (F)

3. Evaluate the iterated integral $\int_0^1 \int_0^1 \left(x^2 + y\right) dx \, dy$.

(A) $\frac{1}{2}$ (B) $\frac{1}{3}$ (C) $\frac{1}{4}$ (D) $\frac{3}{4}$

(E) $\frac{2}{3}$ (F) $\frac{1}{6}$ (G) $\frac{5}{6}$ (H) 1

Answer: (G)

4. Evaluate the iterated integral $\int_0^\pi \int_0^1 x \sin y \, dx \, dy$.

(A) $\frac{1}{2}$ (B) $-\frac{1}{2}$ (C) $\frac{1}{4}$ (D) $-\frac{1}{4}$

(E) 2 (F) -2 (G) 1 (H) -1

Answer: (G)

5. Evaluate the iterated integral $\int_2^5 \int_0^2 x\sqrt{4 - x^2} \, dx \, dy$.

(A) 2 (B) 3 (C) 4 (D) 6

(E) 9 (F) 8 (G) 18 (H) 24

Answer: (F)

6. Evaluate the double integral $\iint_R y^3 \sin x \cos x \, dA$, where $R = \{(x, y) \mid 0 \le x \le \frac{\pi}{2}, 0 \le y \le 1\}$.

(A) $\frac{1}{4}$ (B) $\frac{1}{2}$ (C) $\frac{\pi}{4}$ (D) $\frac{1}{8}$

(E) $\frac{5}{4}$ (F) $\frac{3}{2}$ (G) $\frac{\pi}{2}$ (H) 0

Answer: (D)

7. Evaluate the double integral $\iint_R \frac{y}{(x + 1)^2} \, dA$, where $R = \{(x, y) \mid 0 \le x \le 1, 0 \le y \le 1\}$.

(A) $\frac{1}{2}$ (B) $\frac{2}{3}$ (C) $\frac{1}{4}$ (D) $\frac{3}{4}$

(E) $\frac{2}{3}$ (F) $\frac{1}{6}$ (G) $\frac{5}{6}$ (H) $\frac{4}{3}$

Answer: (C)

8. Evaluate the double integral $\iint_R \frac{1}{(x + y)^2} \, dA$, where $R = \{(x, y) \mid 1 \le x \le 2, 1 \le y \le 2\}$.

(A) $\frac{9}{8}$ (B) $\frac{1}{2}$ (C) $-\ln \frac{1}{2}$ (D) $\ln \frac{9}{8}$

(E) $\frac{8}{9}$ (F) $\frac{3}{2}$ (G) $\ln \frac{3}{2}$ (H) $\ln \frac{8}{9}$

Answer: (D)

9. Evaluate the double integral $\iint_R (x + \sin y) \, dA$, where $R = \{(x, y) \mid 0 \le x \le 2, 0 \le y \le \pi\}$.

(A) $2 + \pi$ (B) $4 + \pi$ (C) $(2 + \pi)/2$ (D) $4 + 2\pi$

(E) $-2 - \pi$ (F) $-4 - \pi$ (G) $-(2 + \pi)/2$ (H) $-(4 + \pi)/2$

Answer: (D)

10. Evaluate the double integral $\iint_R e^{x - y} \, dA$, where $R = \{(x, y) \mid 0 \le x \le 1, 0 \le y \le 1\}$.

(A) $e^2 + e^{-2} + 2$ (B) $e^2 - e^{-2} + 2$ (C) $e^2 + e^{-2} - 2$ (D) $e^2 - e^{-2} - 2$

(E) $e + e^{-1} + 2$ (F) $e - e^{-1} + 2$ (G) $e + e^{-1} - 2$ (H) $e - e^{-1} - 2$

Answer: (G)

11. Evaluate the double integral $\iint_R y \cos(xy) \, dA$, where $R = \{(x, y) \mid 0 \le x \le 1, 0 \le y \le \pi\}$.

(A) -3 (B) -2 (C) -1 (D) 0

(E) 1 (F) 2 (G) 3 (H) 4

Answer: (F)

12. Find $\int_0^2 f(x, y) \, dy$ and $\int_0^1 f(x, y) \, dx$ for $f(x, y) = 2xy - 3x^2$.

Answer: $\int_0^2 f(x, y) \, dy = 4x - 6x^2$, $\int_0^1 f(x, y) \, dx = y - 1$

13. Calculate the iterated integral $\int_0^{\ln 3} \int_0^{\ln 7} e^{x-y} \, dx \, dy$.

    Answer: 4

14. Calculate the iterated integral $\int_1^2 \int_0^{\pi/2} y \sin{(xy)} \, dy \, dx$.

    Answer: 1

15. Calculate the iterated integral $\int_0^{\pi/2} \int_0^{\pi/2} \sin{(x+y)} \, dy \, dx$

    Answer: 2

16. Calculate the double integral $\iint_R \left(xy^2 + \frac{y}{x} \right) dA$, where $R = \{(x,y) \mid 2 \le x \le 3, \ -1 \le y \le 0\}$.

    Answer: $\frac{5}{6} + \ln\sqrt{\frac{2}{3}}$

17. Calculate the double integral $\iint_R \frac{1+x}{1+y} \, dA$, where $R = \{(x,y) \mid -1 \le x \le 2, \ 0 \le y \le 1\}$.

    Answer: $\frac{9}{2} \ln 2$

18. Compute the average value of $f(x,y) = x^2 + y^2$ over $R = \{(x,y) \mid 0 \le x \le 2, 0 \le y \le 2\}$.

    Answer: $\frac{8}{3}$

19. Show that the average value of $f(x,y) = ax + by$ over $R = \{(x,y) \mid -1 \le x \le 1, -1 \le y \le 1\}$ is 0 for all values of a and b.

    Answer: Average value $= \frac{1}{4} \int_{-1}^1 \int_{-1}^1 (ax + by) \, dy \, dx = \frac{1}{4} \int_{-1}^1 \left[axy + \frac{1}{2} by^2 \right]_{-1}^1 dx$

    $\qquad = \frac{1}{4} \int_{-1}^1 2ax \, dx = \frac{1}{4} \left[ax^2 \right]_{-1}^1 = 0$

20. Compute $\displaystyle\int_0^2 \int_{-1}^1 \frac{ye^{y^2}}{1+x^2} \, dx \, dy$.

    Answer: $\frac{1}{4}\pi \left(e^4 - 1 \right)$

21. Compute $\int_0^1 \int_0^1 xy^2 e^{xy^3} \, dx \, dy$.

    Answer: $\frac{1}{3}(e - 2)$

22. Describe the shape of the solid whose volume is given by the integral $\int_0^3 \int_{-2}^2 \sqrt{9 - y^2} \, dx \, dy$.

    Answer: Quarter-cylinder of radius 3 and height 4

23. A greenhouse is shown below. It is 10 ft wide and 20 ft long and has a flat roof that is 12 ft high at one corner and 10 ft high at each of the adjacent corners. Find the volume of the greenhouse.

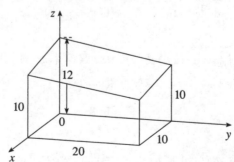

    Answer: 2000 ft^3

24. Sketch the solid whose volume is given by the iterated integral $\int_0^2 \int_0^3 (5 - x - y)\, dy\, dx$.

Answer:

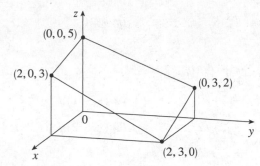

12.3 Double Integrals over General Regions

1. Evaluate the iterated integral $\int_0^1 \int_0^y dx\, dy$.

   (A) $\frac{1}{2}$ (B) $\frac{1}{3}$ (C) $\frac{1}{4}$ (D) $\frac{3}{4}$

   (E) $\frac{2}{3}$ (F) $\frac{1}{6}$ (G) $\frac{5}{6}$ (H) 1

   Answer: (A)

2. Evaluate the iterated integral $\int_0^1 \int_x^1 dy\, dx$.

   (A) $\frac{1}{2}$ (B) $\frac{1}{3}$ (C) $\frac{1}{4}$ (D) $\frac{3}{4}$

   (E) $\frac{2}{3}$ (F) $\frac{1}{6}$ (G) $\frac{5}{6}$ (H) 1

   Answer: (A)

3. Evaluate the iterated integral $\int_0^1 \int_0^y x\, dx\, dy$.

   (A) $\frac{1}{2}$ (B) $\frac{1}{3}$ (C) $\frac{1}{4}$ (D) $\frac{3}{4}$

   (E) $\frac{2}{3}$ (F) $\frac{1}{6}$ (G) $\frac{5}{6}$ (H) 1

   Answer: (F)

4. Evaluate the iterated integral $\int_0^1 \int_x^1 y\, dy\, dx$.

   (A) $\frac{1}{2}$ (B) $\frac{1}{3}$ (C) $\frac{1}{4}$ (D) $\frac{3}{4}$

   (E) $\frac{2}{3}$ (F) $\frac{1}{6}$ (G) $\frac{5}{6}$ (H) 1

   Answer: (B)

5. Evaluate the iterated integral $\int_0^2 \int_0^{x^2} (x + 3\sqrt{y})\, dy\, dx$.

   (A) 10   (B) 20   (C) 8   (D) 4

   (E) 12   (F) 6   (G) 7   (H) 14

   Answer: (E)

6. Evaluate the iterated integral $\int_0^1 \int_0^y y\, dx\, dy$.

   (A) $\frac{1}{2}$ (B) $\frac{1}{3}$ (C) $\frac{1}{4}$ (D) $\frac{3}{4}$

   (E) $\frac{2}{3}$ (F) $\frac{1}{6}$ (G) $\frac{5}{6}$ (H) 1

   Answer: (B)

7. Evaluate the iterated integral $\int_0^1 \int_0^y (x+y)\, dx\, dy$.

(A) $\frac{1}{2}$ (B) $\frac{1}{3}$ (C) $\frac{1}{4}$ (D) $\frac{3}{4}$

(E) $\frac{2}{3}$ (F) $\frac{1}{6}$ (G) $\frac{5}{6}$ (H) 1

Answer: (A)

8. Evaluate the iterated integral $\int_0^1 \int_0^y e^{y^2}\, dx\, dy$.

(A) $e - 1$ (B) $(e-1)/2$ (C) $(e-1)/3$ (D) $(e-1)/4$

(E) $e - 2$ (F) $(e-2)/2$ (G) $(e-2)/3$ (H) $(e-2)/4$

Answer: (B)

9. Evaluate the double integral $\iint_R (x+2y)\, dA$, where $R = \{(x,y) \mid 0 \le x \le 1,\ 0 \le y \le x\}$.

(A) $\frac{1}{4}$ (B) $\frac{1}{2}$ (C) $\frac{3}{4}$ (D) 1

(E) $\frac{1}{6}$ (F) $\frac{1}{3}$ (G) $\frac{2}{3}$ (H) $\frac{5}{6}$

Answer: (G)

10. Evaluate the double integral $\iint_R xy\, dA$, where $R = \{(x,y) \mid 0 \le x \le y,\ 0 \le y \le 2\}$.

(A) $\frac{1}{4}$ (B) $\frac{1}{2}$ (C) $\frac{3}{4}$ (D) 1

(E) $\frac{5}{4}$ (F) $\frac{3}{2}$ (G) $\frac{7}{4}$ (H) 2

Answer: (H)

11. Evaluate the double integral $\iint_R x\, dA$, where $R = \{(x,y) \mid 0 \le x \le 2,\ \frac{1}{2}x \le y \le 3 - x\}$.

(A) $\frac{2}{3}$ (B) $\frac{4}{3}$ (C) 2   (D) $\frac{8}{3}$

(E) $\frac{10}{3}$ (F) 4   (G) $\frac{14}{3}$ (H) $\frac{16}{3}$

Answer: (C)

12. Evaluate the double integral $\iint_R x\, dA$, where $R = \left\{(x,y) \mid y - 1 \le x \le \sqrt{1 - y^2},\ 0 \le y \le 1\right\}$.

(A) $\frac{1}{6}$ (B) $\frac{1}{4}$ (C) $\frac{1}{3}$ (D) $\frac{1}{2}$

(E) $\frac{2}{3}$ (F) $\frac{3}{4}$ (G) $\frac{5}{6}$ (H) 1

Answer: (A)

13. Find the volume under the paraboloid $z = x^2 + y^2$ above the region bounded by the x-axis, the y-axis, and the line $x + y = 1$.

(A) $\frac{1}{6}$ (B) $\frac{1}{4}$ (C) $\frac{1}{3}$ (D) $\frac{1}{2}$

(E) $\frac{2}{3}$ (F) $\frac{3}{4}$ (G) $\frac{5}{6}$ (H) 1

Answer: (A)

14. Find the volume under the paraboloid $z = 4x^2 + y^2$ above the triangle with vertices $(0,0,0)$, $(3,0,0)$, and $(3,1,0)$.

(A) $\frac{109}{4}$ (B) $\frac{55}{2}$ (C) $\frac{111}{4}$ (D) 28

(E) $\frac{113}{4}$ (F) $\frac{57}{2}$ (G) $\frac{115}{4}$ (H) 29

Answer: (A)

15. Express the integral $\int_0^2 \int_{x^2}^4 \left(xy^2 + x\right) dy\, dx$ as an equivalent integral with the order of integration reversed.

Answer: $\int_0^4 \int_0^{\sqrt{y}} \left(xy^2 + x\right) dx\, dy$

16. Evaluate $\int_0^1 \int_0^{x^3} \left(x^2 + y - y^2\right) dy\, dx$ and describe the region of integration.

Answer: $\frac{129}{630}$; R is bounded below by $y = 0$, above by $y = x^3$, on the left by $x = 0$ and on the right by $x = 1$.

17. Change the order of integration in the following integral and evaluate: $\int_0^9 \int_{\sqrt{y}}^3 \sin\left(\pi x^3\right) dx\, dy$

Answer: $\int_0^3 \int_0^{x^2} \sin\left(\pi x^3\right) dy\, dx = \frac{2}{3\pi}$

18. Evaluate the double integral of ye^{y^4} over the region bounded by $y = \sqrt{x}$, $y = 2$, and $x = 0$.

Answer: $\dfrac{e^{16} - 1}{4}$

19. Evaluate the double integral $\int_0^1 \int_x^1 \sin y^2 \, dy\, dx$.

Answer: $\frac{1}{2}\left(1 - \cos 1\right)$

20. Evaluate the following double integral: $\int_0^a \int_0^{\sqrt{a^2 - x^2}} \left(x + y\right) dy\, dx$, where $a > 0$

Answer: $\dfrac{2a^3}{3}$

21. Write $\int_0^{16} \int_0^{\sqrt{x}} f\left(x, y\right) dy\, dx$ with the order of integration reversed.

Answer: $\int_0^4 \int_{y^2}^{16} f\left(x, y\right) dx\, dy$

22. The region D in $\mathbb{R}^2$ shown below is bounded by $x = 1$, $y = e^x$, and $y = 1 - x^2$.

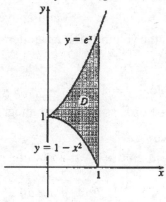

(a) Compute $\iint_R x\, dA$ by finding $\int_0^1 \int_{1 - x^2}^{e^x} x\, dy\, dx$.

(b) Write down the integral or integrals needed to compute $\iint_R x\, dA$ with the order of integration reversed.

Answer: (a) $\frac{3}{4}$ (b) $\int_0^1 \int_{\sqrt{1-y}}^1 x\, dx\, dy + \int_1^e \int_{\ln y}^1 x\, dx\, dy$

23. Evaluate $\displaystyle\int_1^2 \int_1^{x^2} \frac{x}{y}\, dy\, dx$.

Answer: $2 \ln 4 - \frac{3}{2}$

24. Evaluate $\int_0^1 \int_{2x}^2 \dfrac{1}{\sqrt{1+(2x/y)}} \, dy \, dx$.

Answer: $2\sqrt{2} - 2$

25. Evaluate $\int_0^1 \int_{x+1}^2 e^{x/(y-1)} \, dy \, dx$.

Answer: $\dfrac{e-1}{2}$

26. Find the volume under the surface $f(x,y) = xy$ over the region bounded by $y = 2x$, $x = 2y$, $x = 0$, and $x = 1$.

Answer: $\dfrac{15}{32}$

27. Use a double integral to find the volume of the solid bounded above by $y = 9 - x^2$, below by $z = 0$, and laterally by $y^2 = 3x$.

Answer: $\dfrac{432}{7}$

28. Find the volume of the solid in the first octant that is bounded by the plane $y + z = 4$, the cylinder $y = x^2$, and the xy- and yz-planes.

Answer: $\dfrac{128}{15}$

29. Find the volume of the solid bounded by $z = 4 - x^2$, $y^2 = 4x$, and the xy-plane.

Answer: $\dfrac{256}{21}\sqrt{2}$

30. Find the volume of the solid under the surface $z = x^2 + y^2$ and lying above the region $\{(x,y) \mid 0 \le x \le 1, \, x^2 \le y \le \sqrt{x}\}$.

Answer: $\dfrac{6}{35}$

31. Evaluate the iterated integral $\int_1^2 \int_0^{\pi/x} x^2 \sin xy \, dy \, dx$.

Answer: 3

32. Let E be the solid under the plane $x + y + z = 5$ and above the region in the xy-plane bounded by $x = 4 - y^2$ and $x + y = 2$. Express the volume of E as an iterated integral in rectangular coordinates.

Answer: $\int_{-1}^2 \int_{2-y}^{4-y^2} (5 - x - y) \, dx \, dy$

33. Let E be the solid under the paraboloid $z = 16 - x^2 - y^2$, above the xy-plane, and between the planes $x = 2$ and $x = 3$. Express the volume of E as an iterated integral in rectangular coordinates.

Answer: $\int_2^3 \int_{-\sqrt{16-x^2}}^{\sqrt{16-x^2}} (16 - x^2 - y^2) \, dy \, dx$

34. $\int_0^1 \int_0^x F(x,y) \, dy \, dx$ is equivalent to

(A) $\int_0^1 \int_y^1 F(x,y) \, dx \, dy$ (B) $\int_0^1 \int_1^y F(x,y) \, dx \, dy$ (C) $\int_0^1 \int_0^1 F(x,y) \, dx \, dy$

(D) $\int_0^1 \int_{-y}^y F(x,y) \, dx \, dy$ (E) $\int_0^1 \int_0^y F(x,y) \, dx \, dy$

Answer: (A)

35. Let S be the surface defined by $z = 1 - y - x^2$. Let V be the volume of the 3-dimensional region in the first octant bounded by S and the coordinate planes. Set up (but do not evaluate) the iterated integrals for V in two ways:

(a) Integrate first with respect to x and then with respect to y.

(b) Integrate first with respect to y and then with respect to x.

Answer: (a) $\int_0^1 \int_0^{\sqrt{1-y}} (1 - y - x^2) \, dx \, dy$; (b) $\int_0^1 \int_0^{1-x^2} (1 - y - x^2) \, dy \, dx$

36. Describe the region sketched below both as a type I and as a type II region.

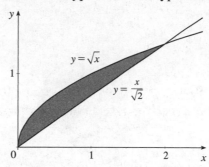

Answer: Type I: $0 \leq x \leq 2$, $\frac{1}{\sqrt{2}}x \leq y \leq \sqrt{x}$; type II: $0 \leq y \leq \sqrt{2}$, $y^2 \leq x \leq \sqrt{2}y$

37. Give good estimates of lower and upper bounds for $\int_1^2 \int_0^2 xy\sqrt{x^2 + y^2}\, dx\, dy$.

Answer: Lower bound: 0; upper bound: $16\sqrt{2}$

38. Evaluate the iterated integral $\int_0^1 \int_y^1 e^{x^2}\, dx\, dy$.

Answer: $\frac{1}{2}(e - 1)$

39. Rewrite $\iint_R f(x, y)\, dA$ as an iterated integral with y as the variable of integration in the outer integral, where R is the region shown below.

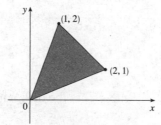

Answer: $\int_0^1 \int_{y/2}^{2y} f(x, y)\, dx\, dy + \int_1^2 \int_{y/2}^{3-y} f(x, y)\, dx\, dy$

40. Rewrite $\iint_R f(x, y)\, dA$ as an iterated integral with x as the variable of integration in the outer integral, where R is the region shown below.

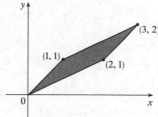

Answer: $\int_0^1 \int_{x/2}^{x} f(x, y)\, dy\, dx + \int_1^2 \int_{x/2}^{(x/2)+(1/2)} f(x, y)\, dy\, dx + \int_2^3 \int_{x-1}^{(x/2)+(1/2)} f(x, y)\, dy\, dx$

401

41. Rewrite $\iint_R f(x, y)\, dA$ as an iterated integral with y as the variable of integration in the outer integral, where R is the region shown below.

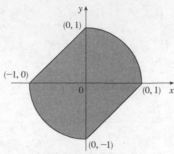

Answer: $\int_{-1}^{0} \int_{-\sqrt{1-y^2}}^{y+1} f(x, y)\, dx\, dy + \int_{0}^{1} \int_{y-1}^{\sqrt{1-y^2}} f(x, y)\, dx\, dy$

42. Rewrite $\iint_R f(x, y)\, dA$ as an iterated integral with x as the variable of integration in the outer integral, where R is the region shown below.

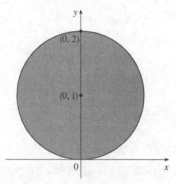

Answer: $\int_{-1}^{1} \int_{1-\sqrt{1-x^2}}^{1+\sqrt{1-x^2}} f(x, y)\, dy\, dx$

12.4 | Double Integrals in Polar Coordinates

1. Evaluate the integral $\iint_R (x^2 + y^2)\, dA$, where R is the disk with center the origin and radius 1.

(A) $\frac{\pi}{6}$ (B) $\frac{\pi}{4}$ (C) $\frac{\pi}{3}$ (D) $\frac{\pi}{2}$

(E) $\frac{2\pi}{3}$ (F) $\frac{3\pi}{4}$ (G) $\frac{5\pi}{6}$ (H) π

Answer: (D)

2. Use a double integral to find the area of the region enclosed by one loop of the curve $r = \cos 2\theta$.

(A) 1 (B) $\frac{\pi}{4}$ (C) $\frac{\pi}{16}$ (D) $\frac{46\pi}{27}$

(E) $\frac{5}{2}$ (F) $\frac{1}{2}$ (G) $\frac{\pi}{8}$ (H) $\frac{46}{27}$

Answer: (G)

3. Find the volume of the solid bounded by the paraboloid $z = x^2 + y^2$ and the plane $z = 4$.

(A) 4π (B) 8π (C) 12π (D) 16π

(E) 24π (F) 32π (G) 48π (H) 64π

Answer: (B)

4. Find the volume of the solid obtained by intersecting the two paraboloids $z = x^2 + y^2$ and $z = 1 - x^2 - y^2$.

(A) $\frac{\pi}{6}$ (B) $\frac{\pi}{4}$ (C) $\frac{\pi}{3}$ (D) $\frac{\pi}{2}$

(E) $\frac{2\pi}{3}$ (F) $\frac{3\pi}{4}$ (G) $\frac{5\pi}{6}$ (H) π

Answer: **(B)**

5. Find the volume of the solid obtained by intersecting the two cones $z = \sqrt{x^2 + y^2}$ and $z = 1 - \sqrt{x^2 + y^2}$.

(A) $\frac{\pi}{12}$ (B) $\frac{\pi}{6}$ (C) $\frac{\pi}{4}$ (D) $\frac{\pi}{3}$

(E) $\frac{\pi}{2}$ (F) $\frac{3\pi}{4}$ (G) $\frac{5\pi}{6}$ (H) π

Answer: **(A)**

6. Find the volume of the solid bounded by the paraboloid $z = 10 - 3x^2 - 3y^2$ and the plane $z = 4$.

(A) 14π (B) 10π (C) 5π (D) 6π

(E) 16π (F) 12π (G) 3π (H) π

Answer: **(D)**

7. Evaluate the integral $\iint_R \sqrt{x^2 + y^2}\, dA$, where R is the disk with center the origin and radius 2.

(A) $\frac{\pi}{3}$ (B) $\frac{2\pi}{3}$ (C) $\frac{4\pi}{3}$ (D) $\frac{8\pi}{3}$

(E) $\frac{16\pi}{3}$ (F) $\frac{32\pi}{3}$ (G) $\frac{64\pi}{3}$ (H) $\frac{128\pi}{3}$

Answer: **(E)**

8. If R is the region inside the circle $x^2 + y^2 = 4$, then $\iint_R x\sqrt{x^2 + y^2}\, dA$ is equal to

(A) $\int_0^2 \int_0^{2\pi} r^2\, d\theta\, dr$ (B) $\int_0^2 \int_0^{\pi/2} r^2 \cos\theta\, d\theta\, dr$ (C) $4\int_0^2 \int_0^{2\pi} r^3 \sin\theta\, d\theta\, dr$

(D) $\int_0^2 \int_0^{2\pi} r^3 \cos\theta\, d\theta\, dr$ (E) $\int_{-2}^2 \int_{-2}^2 x\sqrt{x^2 + y^2}\, dy\, dx$

Answer: **(D)**

9. Find the area inside the circle $r = 2\cos\theta$ and outside the circle $r = 1$.

Answer $\frac{\pi}{3} + \frac{\sqrt{3}}{2}$

10. Use polar coordinates to evaluate $\int_0^1 \int_0^{\sqrt{1-x^2}} e^{-(x^2+y^2)}\, dy\, dx$.

Answer: $\dfrac{e-1}{4e}\pi$

11. Convert the integral $\displaystyle\int_0^2 \int_{-\sqrt{4-x^2}}^0 \frac{xy}{\sqrt{x^2+y^2}}\, dy\, dx$ to polar coordinates and evaluate it.

Answer: $-\frac{4}{3}$

12. Evaluate $\int_{-1}^0 \int_{-\sqrt{1-y^2}}^0 \cos\left(x^2 + y^2\right)\, dx\, dy$.

Answer: $\dfrac{(\sin 1)\,\pi}{4}$

13. A solid is bounded above by the paraboloid $z = 1 - x^2 - y^2$ and below by the xy-plane. Compute the volume of this solid using polar coordinates.

Answer: $V = \int_0^{2\pi} \int_0^1 \left(1 - r^2\right) r\, dr\, d\theta = \frac{\pi}{2}$

14. Evaluate $\int_{-2}^2 \int_0^{\sqrt{4-x^2}} \sqrt{9 - x^2 - y^2}\, dy\, dx$.

Answer: $\left(9 - \dfrac{5^{3/2}}{3}\right)\pi$

15. Use polar coordinates to find the area inside the circle $x^2 + y^2 = 4$ and to the right of the line $x = 1$.

   Answer: $\frac{2}{3}\pi - \frac{\sqrt{3}}{2}$

16. Evaluate $\iint_D \dfrac{1}{\sqrt{x^2 + y^2 + 1}}\, dA$, where D is the region that lies between the circles $x^2 + y^2 = 1$ and $x^2 + y^2 = 9$.

   Answer: $2\pi\left(\sqrt{10} - \sqrt{2}\right)$

17. Evaluate $\iint_D \cos\left(x^2 + y^2\right) dA$, where $D = \left\{(x, y) \mid x^2 + y^2 \le 1\right\}$, the unit disk.

   Answer: $\pi \sin 1$

18. Use polar coordinates to combine the sum

$$\int_{\sqrt{2}}^{2} \int_{\sqrt{4-x^2}}^{x} xy\, dy\, dx + \int_{2}^{2\sqrt{2}} \int_{0}^{x} xy\, dy\, dx + \int_{2\sqrt{2}}^{4} \int_{0}^{\sqrt{16-x^2}} xy\, dy\, dx$$

   into one double integral. Then evaluate the integral.

   Answer: $\int_0^{\pi/4} \int_2^4 r^3 \sin\theta \cos\theta\, dr\, d\theta = 15$

19. Evaluate $\iint_R \dfrac{1}{x}\, dA$, where R is the region bounded by the curves $x^2 + y^2 = 1$, $y = x$, $x = 2$, and $y = 0$.

   Answer: $2 - \ln\left(\sqrt{2} + 1\right)$

20. Write $\iint_R f(x, y)\ dA$ as an iterated integral in polar coordinates, where R is the region shown below.

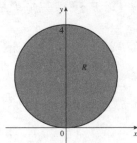

   Answer: $\int_0^\pi \int_0^{4\sin\theta} f(r\cos\theta, r\sin\theta)\, r\, dr\, d\theta$

21. Write $\iint_R f(x, y)\ dA$ as an iterated integral in polar coordinates, where R is the region shown below.

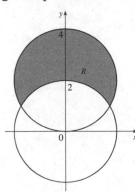

   Answer: $\int_{\pi/6}^{5\pi/6} \int_2^{4\sin\theta} f(r\cos\theta, r\sin\theta)\, r\, dr\, d\theta$

22. Write $\iint_R f(x, y)\, dA$ as an iterated integral in polar coordinates, where R is the region shown below.

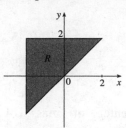

Answer: $\int_{\pi/4}^{3\pi/4} \int_0^{2/(\sin\theta)} f(r\cos\theta, r\sin\theta)\, r\, dr\, d\theta + \int_{3\pi/4}^{5\pi/4} \int_0^{-2/(\cos\theta)} f(r\cos\theta, r\sin\theta)\, r\, dr\, d\theta$

23. Write $\iint_R f(x, y)\, dA$ as an iterated integral in polar coordinates, where R is the region shown below.

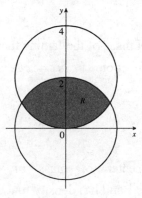

Answer:

$\int_0^{\pi/6} \int_0^{4\sin\theta} f(r\cos\theta, r\sin\theta)\, r\, dr\, d\theta + \int_{\pi/6}^{5\pi/6} \int_0^2 f(r\cos\theta, r\sin\theta)\, r\, dr\, d\theta$

$\qquad\qquad\qquad + \int_{5\pi/6}^{\pi} \int_0^{4\sin\theta} f(r\cos\theta, r\sin\theta)\, r\, dr\, d\theta$

12.5 Applications of Double Integrals

1. Find the mass of the lamina that occupies the region $D = \{(x, y) \mid 0 \le x \le 1, 0 \le y \le 1\}$ and has density function $\rho(x, y) = x$.

(A) $\frac{1}{6}$ (B) $\frac{1}{4}$ (C) $\frac{1}{3}$ (D) $\frac{1}{2}$

(E) $\frac{2}{3}$ (F) $\frac{3}{4}$ (G) $\frac{5}{6}$ (H) 1

Answer: (D)

2. Find the mass of the lamina that occupies the region $D = \{(x, y) \mid 0 \le x \le 1, 0 \le y \le 1\}$ and has density function $\rho(x, y) = xy$.

(A) $\frac{1}{6}$ (B) $\frac{1}{4}$ (C) $\frac{1}{3}$ (D) $\frac{1}{2}$

(E) $\frac{2}{3}$ (F) $\frac{3}{4}$ (G) $\frac{5}{6}$ (H) 1

Answer: (B)

CHAPTER 12 MULTIPLE INTEGRALS

3. Find the mass of the lamina that occupies the region $D = \{(x, y) \mid 0 \leq x \leq 1, x^2 \leq y \leq 1\}$ and has density function $\rho(x, y) = x + y$.

(A) 0.35   (B) 0.40   (C) 0.45   (D) 0.50

(E) 0.55   (F) 0.60   (G) 0.65   (H) 0.70

Answer: (G)

4. Find the y-coordinate of the center of mass of the lamina that occupies the region $D = \{(x, y) \mid 0 \leq x \leq 1, 0 \leq y \leq 1\}$ and whose density function at any point is the distance from that point to the y-axis.

(A) $\frac{1}{6}$ (B) $\frac{1}{4}$ (C) $\frac{1}{3}$ (D) $\frac{1}{2}$

(E) $\frac{2}{3}$ (F) $\frac{3}{4}$ (G) $\frac{5}{6}$ (H) 1

Answer: (D)

5. Find the x-coordinate of the center of mass of the lamina that occupies the part of the disk $x^2 + y^2 \leq 1$ in the first quadrant and has density function $\rho(x, y) = xy$.

(A) $\frac{15}{8}$ (B) $\frac{1}{5}$ (C) $\frac{1}{3}$ (D) $\frac{1}{2}$

(E) $\frac{8}{15}$ (F) $\frac{1}{8}$ (G) $\frac{5}{6}$ (H) 1

Answer: (E)

6. Find the x-coordinate of the center of mass of the lamina that occupies the region $D = \{(x, y) \mid 0 \leq x \leq 1, x^2 \leq y \leq 1\}$ and has density function $\rho(x, y) = x + y$.

(A) $\frac{6}{13}$ (B) $\frac{7}{13}$ C) $\frac{8}{13}$ (D) $\frac{9}{13}$

(E) $\frac{6}{11}$ (F) $\frac{7}{11}$ (G) $\frac{8}{11}$ (H) $\frac{9}{11}$

Answer: (A)

7. Find the moment of inertia I_y of the lamina that occupies the region $D = \{(x, y) \mid 0 \leq x \leq 1, 0 \leq y \leq 1\}$ and whose density function at any point is the distance from that point to the x-axis.

(A) $\frac{1}{24}$ (B) $\frac{1}{18}$ C) $\frac{1}{12}$ (D) $\frac{1}{9}$

(E) $\frac{1}{6}$ (F) $\frac{1}{4}$ (G) $\frac{1}{3}$ (H) $\frac{1}{2}$

Answer: (E)

8. Find the moment of inertia I_x of the lamina that occupies the region $D = \{(x, y) \mid 0 \leq x \leq 1, 0 \leq y \leq 1\}$ and has density function $\rho(x, y) = x$.

(A) $\frac{1}{24}$ (B) $\frac{1}{18}$ C) $\frac{1}{12}$ (D) $\frac{1}{9}$

(E) $\frac{1}{6}$ (F) $\frac{1}{4}$ (G) $\frac{1}{3}$ (H) $\frac{1}{2}$

Answer: (E)

9. Find the polar moment of inertia I_0 of the lamina that occupies the region $D = \{(x, y) \mid 0 \leq x \leq 1, 0 \leq y \leq 1\}$ and has density function $\rho(x, y) = 1$.

(A) $\frac{1}{6}$ (B) $\frac{1}{4}$ (C) $\frac{1}{3}$ (D) $\frac{1}{2}$

(E) $\frac{2}{3}$ (F) $\frac{3}{4}$ (G) $\frac{5}{6}$ (H) 1

Answer: (E)

406

10. A phonograph turntable is made in the shape of a circular disk of radius 6 inches with density function $\rho(x, y) = \sqrt{x^2 + y^2}$. Find the mass of the disk.

   (A) 60π (B) 96π (C) 108π (D) 120π

   (E) 144π (F) 180π (G) 192π (H) 240π

   Answer: (E)

11. A phonograph turntable is made in the shape of a circular disk of radius 6 inches with density function $\rho(x, y) = \sqrt{x^2 + y^2}$. Find the polar moment of inertia I_0 of the disk.

   (A) 2945.4π (B) 3110.4π (C) 3245.4π (D) 3362.4π

   (E) 3495.4π (F) 3560.4π (G) 3632.4π (H) 3775.4π

   Answer: (B)

12. Let R be the region bounded by $y = x^2$, $y = 0$, and $x = 1$. Find the center of mass of a lamina in the shape of R with density function $\rho(x, y) = xy$.

   Answer: $\left(\frac{6}{7}, \frac{1}{2}\right)$

13. Find the moment of inertia I_x about the x-axis and the moment of inertia I_y about the y-axis for the region in the first quadrant bounded by $y = x$ and $y^2 = x^3$, assuming $\rho = 1$.

   Answer: $I_x = \frac{1}{44}$; $I_y = \frac{1}{36}$

14. Electric charge is distributed over the unit disk $x^2 + y^2 \le 1$ so that the charge density at (x, y) is $\sigma(x, y) = 1 + x^2 + y^2$ (measured in coulombs per square meter). Find the total charge on the disk.

   Answer: $\frac{3\pi}{2}$ C

15. Find the mass and center of mass of the lamina that occupies the region $D = \{(x, y) \mid 0 \le x \le 2, 0 \le y \le 3\}$ and has density function $\rho(x, y) = y$.

   Answer: $m = 9$, $(\overline{x}, \overline{y}) = (1, 2)$

16. Find the mass and center of mass of the lamina that occupies the triangular region with vertices $(0, 0)$, $(1, 1)$, and $(4, 0)$, and has density function $\rho(x, y) = x$.

   Answer: $m = \frac{10}{3}$; $(\overline{x}, \overline{y}) = (2.1, 0.3)$

17. Find the center of mass of the lamina that occupies the part of the disk $x^2 + y^2 \le 1$ in the first quadrant if the density at any point is proportional to the square of its distance from the origin.

   Answer: $(\overline{x}, \overline{y}) = \left(\frac{8}{5\pi}, \frac{8}{5\pi}\right)$

18. Find the moments of inertia I_x, I_y, and I_0 for the lamina that occupies the region given by $D = \{(x, y) \mid 0 \le x \le 2, 0 \le y \le 3\}$.

   Answer: $I_x = 18$, $I_y = 8$, $I_0 = 26$

19. The average value of $f(x, y)$ over a region D in the plane with area $A(D)$ is $\dfrac{1}{A(D)} \iint\limits_D f(x, y)\, dA$.

   Find the average value of $f(x, y) = xy$ over the region $D = \{(x, y) \mid x^2 + y^2 \le 1, xy \ge 0\}$.

   Answer: $\frac{1}{2\pi}$

20. The centroid $(\overline{x}, \overline{y})$ of a planar region D is the center of mass with the density function $\rho(x, y) = 1$. Find the centroid of $D = \{(x, y) \mid x^2 + y^2 \le 4, x \ge 0, y \ge 0\}$.

   Answer $\left(\frac{8}{3\pi}, \frac{8}{3\pi}\right)$

21. Find the center of mass of $D = \{(x, y) \mid x^2 + y^2 \leq 4, x \geq 0, y \geq 0\}$ if $\rho(x, y) = \sqrt{x^2 + y^2}$.

Answer: $\left(\frac{3}{\pi}, \frac{3}{\pi}\right)$

22. Find the centroid of $D = \left\{(x, y) \mid \dfrac{x^2}{a^2} + \dfrac{y^2}{b^2} \leq 1, y \geq 0\right\}$, the region enclosed by the upper half of the

ellipse $\dfrac{x^2}{a^2} + \dfrac{y^2}{b^2} = 1$.

Answer: $\left(0, \dfrac{8b}{3\pi}\right)$

23. Find the y-coordinate of the centroid of the semiannular plane region given by $1 \leq x^2 + y^2 \leq 4$, $y \geq 0$.
Sketch the plane region and plot the centroid in the graph.

Answer: $\left(0, \frac{28}{9\pi}\right)$

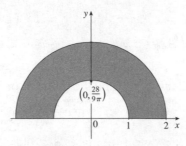

24. The joint density function for a pair of random variables X and Y is

$$f(x, y) = \begin{cases} C(x + y) & \text{if } 0 \leq x \leq y \leq 1 \\ 0 & \text{otherwise} \end{cases} \quad \text{Find the value of } C.$$

Answer: $C = 2$

25. The joint density function for a pair of random variables X and Y is $f(x, y) =$

$$\begin{cases} C\dfrac{x}{y} & \text{if } 0 \leq x \leq 1 \text{ and } 1 \leq y \leq 2 \\ 0 & \text{otherwise} \end{cases} \quad \text{Find the value of } C.$$

Answer: $C = \dfrac{2}{\ln 2}$

26. The joint density function for a pair of random variables X and Y is $f(x, y) =$

$$\begin{cases} C(x + 1) & \text{if } 0 \leq x \leq 1 \text{ and } 0 \leq y \leq 1 \\ 0 & \text{otherwise} \end{cases}$$

(a) Find the value of C.

(b) Find $P(X + Y \leq 1)$.

(c) Find $P(X \leq 2Y \leq 3X)$.

Answer: (a) $C = \frac{2}{3}$ (b) $\frac{4}{9}$ (c) $\frac{73}{162}$

12.6 Surface Area

1. Find the area of the part of the plane $x + z = 4$ that lies above the square with vertices $(0,0)$, $(1,0)$, $(0,1)$, and $(1,1)$.

   (A) 1   (B) $\sqrt{2}$ (C) $\sqrt{3}$ (D) 2

   (E) $\sqrt{5}$ (F) $\sqrt{6}$ (G) $\frac{\sqrt{5}}{2}$ (H) $\frac{\sqrt{6}}{2}$

   Answer: (B)

2. Find the area of the part of the plane $x + y + z = 6$ that lies above the square with vertices $(0,0)$, $(1,0)$, $(0,1)$, and $(1,1)$.

   (A) 1   (B) $\sqrt{2}$ (C) $\sqrt{3}$ (D) 2

   (E) $\sqrt{5}$ (F) $\sqrt{6}$ (G) $\frac{\sqrt{5}}{2}$ (H) $\frac{\sqrt{6}}{2}$

   Answer: (C)

3. Find the surface area of the part of the sphere $x^2 + y^2 + z^2 = 4$ that lies above the plane $z = 1$.

   (A) $\left(4 - 2\sqrt{2}\right)\pi$ (B) 2   (C) 2π (D) 4π

   (E) $\left(8 - 4\sqrt{3}\right)\pi$ (F) 6π (G) 8π (H) 16π

   Answer: (D)

4. Find the area of the part of the hemisphere $z = \sqrt{4 - x^2 - y^2}$ that lies above the area inside the circle $x^2 + y^2 = 1$.

   (A) $\left(4 - 2\sqrt{2}\right)\pi$ (B) $\left(6 - 3\sqrt{2}\right)\pi$ (C) $\left(8 - 4\sqrt{2}\right)\pi$ (D) $\left(6 - 3\sqrt{3}\right)\pi$

   (E) $\left(8 - 4\sqrt{3}\right)\pi$ (F) 6π (G) 8π (H) 16π

   Answer: (E)

5. Find the area of the surface with parametric equations $x = uv$, $y = u + v$, $z = u - v$, $u^2 + v^2 \le 1$.

   (A) $\frac{\sqrt{2}}{3}\pi$ (B) $\frac{\sqrt{6}}{3}\pi$ (C) $\frac{\sqrt{2}-1}{3}\pi$ (D) $\frac{\sqrt{6}-1}{3}\pi$

   (E) $\frac{2\sqrt{2}-1}{3}\pi$ (F) $\frac{6\sqrt{6}-8}{3}\pi$ (G) $\frac{10\sqrt{2}-1}{3}\pi$ (H) $\frac{10\sqrt{6}-9}{3}\pi$

   Answer: (F)

6. Find the area of the part of the surface $z = x + y^2$ that lies above the triangle with vertices $(0,0)$, $(1,1)$, and $(0,1)$.

   Answer: $\frac{3}{\sqrt{6}} - \frac{1}{3\sqrt{2}}$

7. Find the area of the part of the paraboloid $x = y^2 + z^2$ that lies inside the cylinder $y^2 + z^2 = 9$.

   Answer: $\frac{\pi}{6}\left(37\sqrt{37} - 1\right)$

8. Find the surface area of the surface $z = xy$ inside the cylinder $x^2 + y^2 = 1$.

   Answer: $\frac{2\pi}{3}\left(2\sqrt{2} - 1\right)$

9. Compute the area of that part of the graph of $3z = 5 + 2x^{3/2} + 4y^{3/2}$ which lies above the rectangular region in the first quadrant of the xy-plane bounded by the lines $x = 0$, $x = 3$, $y = 0$, and $y = 6$.

   Answer: $\frac{4}{15}\left(392\sqrt{7} - 789\right)$

10. Find the surface area of the part of the cone $z = \left(x^2 + y^2\right)^{1/2}$ lying inside the cylinder $x^2 - 2x + y^2 = 0$.

Answer: $\sqrt{2}\pi$

11. Set up, but do not evaluate, the integral to find the surface area of the portion of the sphere $x^2 + y^2 + z^2 = 16$ between the planes $z = 1$ and $z = 2$.

Answer: $\displaystyle\int_0^{2\pi} \int_{\sqrt{12}}^{\sqrt{15}} \sqrt{\frac{16}{16 - r^2}}\, r\, dr\, d\theta$

12. Find the area of the surface cut from the cone $z = 1 - \sqrt{x^2 + y^2}$ by the cylinder $x^2 + y^2 = y$.

Answer: $\frac{\pi\sqrt{2}}{4}$

13. Find the area of the portion of the surface $z = x^2 + y^2$ inside the cylinder $x^2 + y^2 = 4$.

Answer: $\frac{\pi}{6}\left(17\sqrt{17} - 1\right)$

14. Find the area of that part of the plane $2x + 3y - z + 1 = 0$ that lies above the rectangle $[1,4] \times [2,4]$.

Answer: $6\sqrt{14}$

15. Find the area of that part of the surface $z = x + y^2$ that lies above the triangle with vertices $(0,0)$, $(1,1)$, and $(0,1)$.

Answer: $\frac{1}{2}\sqrt{6} - \frac{1}{6}\sqrt{2}$

16. Find the area of that part of the paraboloid $z = 4 - x^2 - y^2$ that lies above the xy-plane.

Answer: $\frac{\pi}{6}\left(17\sqrt{17} - 1\right)$

17. Find the area of that part of the sphere $x^2 + y^2 + z^2 = 4$ that lies above the plane $z = 1$.

Answer: 4π

18. Find the area of that part of the sphere $x^2 + y^2 + z^2 = 4z$ that lies inside the paraboloid $z = x^2 + y^2$.

Answer: 4π

19. Find the surface area for the part of the plane $5z = 3x - 4y$ that lies inside the elliptic cylinder $x^2 + 2y^2 = 2$.

Answer: 2π

20. Find the area of the surface with vector equation $\mathbf{r}(s,t) = \langle s\cos t, s\sin t, s\rangle$, $1 \le s \le 5$, $0 \le t \le 2\pi$.

Answer: $24\sqrt{2}\pi$

21. Show that the surface areas for the functions $f(x,y) = 2x^2 + 2y^2$ and $g(x,y) = 4xy$ over the disk $D = \left\{(x,y) \mid x^2 + y^2 \le 1\right\}$ are equal.

Answer: $\dfrac{\partial f}{\partial x} = \dfrac{\partial g}{\partial y} = 4x$ and $\dfrac{\partial f}{\partial y} = \dfrac{\partial g}{\partial x} = 4y$, so the surface area integrals $\iint_D \sqrt{f_x^2 + f_y^2 + 1}\, dA$ and $\iint_D \sqrt{g_x^2 + g_y^2 + 1}\, dA$ are equal.

22. Find the area of the surface with vector equation $\mathbf{r}(u,v) = \langle u\cos v, u\sin v, u^2\rangle$, $0 \le u \le 2$, $0 \le v \le 2\pi$.

Answer: $\dfrac{\pi\left(17\sqrt{17} - 1\right)}{6}$

23. Find the area of the surface with vector equation $\mathbf{r}(u,v) = \langle u + 2v, u - 2v, u^2 + 2v^2\rangle$, $u^2 + v^2 \le 4$.

Answer: $\dfrac{104\pi}{3}$

12.7 Triple Integrals

1. Evaluate the iterated integral $\int_0^1 \int_0^z \int_0^y dx\, dy\, dz$.

(A) $\frac{1}{120}$ (B) $\frac{1}{90}$ (C) $\frac{1}{60}$ (D) $\frac{1}{48}$

(E) $\frac{1}{36}$ (F) $\frac{1}{24}$ (G) $\frac{1}{12}$ (H) $\frac{1}{6}$

Answer: (H)

2. Evaluate the iterated integral $\int_0^1 \int_0^z \int_0^y y\, dx\, dy\, dz$.

(A) $\frac{1}{120}$ (B) $\frac{1}{90}$ (C) $\frac{1}{60}$ (D) $\frac{1}{48}$

(E) $\frac{1}{36}$ (F) $\frac{1}{24}$ (G) $\frac{1}{12}$ (H) $\frac{1}{6}$

Answer: (G)

3. Evaluate the iterated integral $\int_0^1 \int_0^z \int_0^{y^2} dx\, dy\, dz$.

(A) $\frac{1}{120}$ (B) $\frac{1}{90}$ (C) $\frac{1}{60}$ (D) $\frac{1}{48}$

(E) $\frac{1}{36}$ (F) $\frac{1}{24}$ (G) $\frac{1}{12}$ (H) $\frac{1}{6}$

Answer: (G)

4. Evaluate the iterated integral $\int_0^1 \int_x^{3x} \int_{\sqrt{y}}^x 2z\, dz\, dy\, dx$.

(A) $-\frac{5}{12}$ (B) $-\frac{5}{6}$ (C) $-\frac{1}{12}$ (D) $-\frac{1}{6}$

(E) $\frac{5}{12}$ (F) $\frac{5}{6}$ (G) $\frac{1}{12}$ (H) $\frac{1}{6}$

Answer: (B)

5. Evaluate the triple integral $\iiint_E (x + 2y)\, dV$, where
$E = \{(x, y, z) \mid 0 \le x \le 1, 0 \le y \le 1, 0 \le z \le 1\}$.

(A) $\frac{1}{4}$ (B) $\frac{1}{2}$ (C) $\frac{3}{4}$ (D) 1

(E) $\frac{5}{4}$ (F) $\frac{3}{2}$ (G) $\frac{7}{4}$ (H) 2

Answer: (F)

6. Evaluate the triple integral $\iiint_E z\, dV$, where E is the wedge in the first octant bounded by $y^2 + z^2 = 1$, $y = x$, and the yz-plane.

(A) $\frac{1}{4}$ (B) $\frac{1}{8}$ (C) $\frac{1}{2}$ (D) $\frac{2}{3}$

(E) $\frac{3}{4}$ (F) 1 (G) $\frac{5}{4}$ (H) $\frac{4}{3}$

Answer: (B)

7. Evaluate the triple integral $\iiint_E x\, dV$, where $E = \{(x, y, z) \mid 0 \le x \le y, 0 \le y \le 1, 0 \le z \le 1\}$.

(A) $\frac{1}{6}$ (B) $\frac{1}{4}$ (C) $\frac{1}{3}$ (D) $\frac{1}{2}$

(E) $\frac{2}{3}$ (F) $\frac{1}{12}$ (G) $\frac{5}{6}$ (H) 1

Answer: (A)

8. Evaluate the triple integral $\iiint_E y\, dV$, where E is the solid bounded by the coordinate planes and the plane $2x + y + z = 4$.

(A) 1   (B) $\frac{3}{16}$ (C) $\frac{8}{3}$ (D) $\frac{3}{8}$

(E) $\frac{2}{3}$ (F) $\frac{16}{3}$ (G) $\frac{32}{3}$ (H) $\frac{3}{32}$

Answer: (F)

9. Find the mass of the solid that occupies the region $E = \{(x, y, z) \mid 0 \le x \le 1, 0 \le y \le 1, 0 \le z \le 1\}$ and has density function $\rho(x, y, z) = x$.

(A) $\frac{1}{6}$ (B) $\frac{1}{4}$ (C) $\frac{1}{3}$ (D) $\frac{1}{2}$

(E) $\frac{2}{3}$ (F) $\frac{3}{4}$ (G) $\frac{5}{6}$ (H) 1

Answer: (D)

10. Find $\iiint_R 2x\, dV$, where R is the region in the first octant bounded by the cylinders $z = 1 - y^2$ and $z = 1 - x^2$.

Answer: $\frac{2}{5}$

11. Find the volume, using triple integrals, of the region in the first octant beneath the plane $x + 2y + 3z = 6$.

Answer: 6

12. Find $\iiint_S x^2 y\, dV$, where S is the solid bounded by the cylinder $y = x^2$ and the planes $z = 0$, $y = 1$, and $z = y$.

Answer: $\frac{4}{27}$

13. Suppose the volume of a solid is given by $V = \int_0^3 \int_0^{(3-z)/2} \int_0^{4-x^2} dy\, dx\, dz$.

(a) Sketch the solid whose volume is given by V.

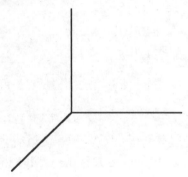

(b) Evaluate the integral to find the volume of the solid.

Answer: (a) 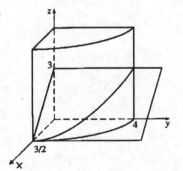   (b) $\frac{261}{32}$

14. Find the volume of the solid formed by the intersection of the cylinder $y = x^2$ and the two planes given by $z = 0$ and $y + z = 4$.

Answer: $\frac{256}{15}$

15. Evaluate $\int_0^1 \int_z^{2z} \int_{x+z}^{2x+2z} (x - 1)\, dy\, dx\, dz$.

Answer: $\frac{1}{8}$

16. Use the method of iterated integration in order to evaluate the triple integral $\iiint_N x\, dV$ where N is the region cut off from the first octant by the plane defined by $x + y + z = 3$.

Answer: $\frac{27}{8}$

17. Evaluate $\int_0^2 \int_0^{2z} \int_0^{xz} xyz^2\, dy\, dx\, dz$.

Answer: $\frac{1024}{9}$

18. Evaluate $\int_0^1 \int_{x^2}^1 \int_0^{3y} (y + 2x^2 z)\, dz\, dy\, dx$.

Answer: $\frac{32}{21}$

19. Set up the triple integral for $f(x, y, z) = \pi x^3$ over the solid E with vertices $(0,0,0)$, $(0,0,1)$, $(0,1,0)$, $(0,1,1)$, $(1,1,0)$, and $(1,1,1)$.

Answer: $\int_0^1 \int_0^1 \int_0^y \pi x^2\, dx\, dy\, dz$

20. The centroid $(\overline{x}, \overline{y}, \overline{z})$ of a region E in $\mathbb{R}^3$ is the center of mass with the density function $\rho(x, y, z) = 1$. Find the centroid of the tetrahedron bounded by the coordinate planes and the plane $x + y + z = 1$.

Answer: $\left(\frac{1}{4}, \frac{1}{4}, \frac{1}{4}\right)$

21. Find the average value of $f(x, y, z) = xy$ over the tetrahedron bounded by the coordinate planes and the plane $x + y + z = 1$.

Answer: $\frac{1}{20}$

22. Set up the volume integral for the solid cylinder $x^2 + y^2 \leq 1$, bounded above by $z = x^3 + y^2 = 9$ and below by $z = 2x + 3y + 3$.

Answer: $\int_{-1}^1 \int_{-\sqrt{1-x^2}}^{\sqrt{1-x^2}} (x^3 + y^4 - 2x - 3y + 6)\, dy\, dx$

23. (a) Sketch the solid whose volume is given by the iterated integral $\int_{-2}^2 \int_{x^2}^4 \int_0^{4-y} dz\, dy\, dx$.

  (b) Rewrite the integral in part (a) as an equivalent iterated integral (or integrals) in the order dx, dz, dy.

  (c) Rewrite the integral in part (a) as an equivalent iterated integral (or integrals) in the order dy, dz, dx.

Answer:

(a)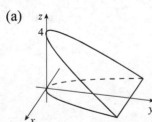

(b) $\int_0^4 \int_0^{4-y} \int_{-\sqrt{y}}^{\sqrt{y}} dx\, dz\, dy$

(c) $\int_{-2}^2 \int_0^{4-x^2} \int_{x^2}^{4-z} dy\, dz\, dx$

24. (a) Sketch the solid whose volume is given by the iterated integral $\int_0^2 \int_0^{2-y} \int_0^{4-y^2} dx\, dz\, dy$.

  (b) Rewrite the integral in part (a) as an equivalent iterated integral (or integrals) in the order dz, dx, dy.

  (c) Rewrite the integral in part (a) as an equivalent iterated integral (or integrals) in the order dy, dx, dz.

Answer:

(a)

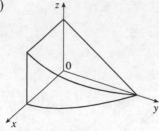

(b) $\int_0^2 \int_0^{4-y^2} \int_0^{2-y} dz\, dx\, dy$

(c) $\int_0^2 \int_0^{4z-z^2} \int_0^{2-z} dy\, dx\, dz + \int_0^2 \int_{4z-z^2}^4 \int_0^{\sqrt{4-x}} dy\, dx\, dz$

25. Sketch the solid whose volume is given by the triple integral $\int_0^1 \int_0^{\sqrt{1-x^2}} \int_0^{\sqrt{2-x^2-y^2}} dz\, dy\, dx$.

Answer:

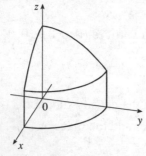

26. Let E be the solid under $z = 1 - y^2$ and above the region in the xy-plane bounded by $x + y = 1$ and $x + y = 2$. Sketch the solid, then express the volume of E as an iterated integral in rectangular coordinates.

Answer:
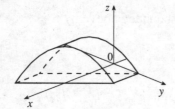
$\int_{-1}^1 \int_{1-y}^{2-y} \int_0^{1-y^2} dz\, dx\, dy$

27. Find the average value of the function $f(x,y,z) = xyz$ over the solid E bounded by planes $z = y$, $y = x$, $x = 1$, and $z = 0$.

Answer: $\frac{1}{8}$

28. Find the z-coordinate of the centroid of the solid E bounded by the cone $z = \sqrt{x^2 + y^2}$ and the plane $z = 2$.

Answer: $z = \frac{3}{2}$

12.8 Triple Integrals in Cylindrical and Spherical Coordinates

1. Evaluate the triple integral $\iiint_E 1 \, dV$ in cylindrical coordinates, where
   $E = \{(r, \theta, z) \mid 0 \le r \le 1, 0 \le \theta \le \pi, 0 \le z \le 1\}$.

   (A) $\frac{\pi}{4}$ (B) $\frac{\pi}{3}$ (C) $\frac{\pi}{2}$ (D) $\frac{2\pi}{3}$

   (E) $\frac{3\pi}{4}$ (F) π (G) $\frac{4\pi}{3}$ (H) 2π

   Answer: (C)

2. Evaluate the triple integral $\iiint_E r \, dV$ in cylindrical coordinates, where
   $E = \{(r, \theta, z) \mid 0 \le r \le 1, 0 \le \theta \le 2\pi, 0 \le z \le 1\}$.

   (A) $\frac{\pi}{4}$ (B) $\frac{\pi}{3}$ (C) $\frac{\pi}{2}$ (D) $\frac{2\pi}{3}$

   (E) $\frac{3\pi}{4}$ (F) π (G) $\frac{4\pi}{3}$ (H) 2π

   Answer: (D)

3. Evaluate the triple integral $\iiint_E 1 \, dV$ in spherical coordinates, where
   $E = \{(\rho, \theta, \phi) \mid 0 \le \rho \le 1, 0 \le \theta \le 2\pi, 0 \le \phi \le \pi\}$.

   (A) $\frac{\pi}{4}$ (B) $\frac{\pi}{3}$ (C) $\frac{\pi}{2}$ (D) $\frac{2\pi}{3}$

   (E) $\frac{3\pi}{4}$ (F) π (G) $\frac{4\pi}{3}$ (H) 2π

   Answer: (G)

4. Evaluate the triple integral $\iiint_E \sqrt{x^2 + y^2 + z^2} \, dV$ in spherical coordinates, where E is the solid
   bounded by the hemisphere $z = \sqrt{4 - x^2 - y^2}$ and the plane $z = 0$.

   (A) $\frac{\pi}{4}$ (B) 16π (C) $\frac{\pi}{2}$ (D) $\frac{2\pi}{3}$

   (E) $\frac{3\pi}{4}$ (F) 8π (G) $\frac{4\pi}{3}$ (H) 2π

   Answer: (F)

5. Evaluate the triple integral $\iiint_E (x^2 + y^2 + z^2) \, dV$ in spherical coordinates, where E is the solid in the
   first octant bounded by the sphere $x^2 + y^2 + z^2 = 4$ and the coordinate planes.

   (A) $\frac{32\pi}{5}$ (B) $\frac{4\pi}{5}$ (C) $\frac{\pi}{2}$ (D) $\frac{2\pi}{3}$

   (E) $\frac{16\pi}{5}$ (F) π (G) $\frac{4\pi}{3}$ (H) 2π

   Answer: (E)

6. Find the mass of the solid that occupies the region bounded by $x^2 + y^2 = 1$, $z = 2$, and $z = 0$ and has
   density function $\rho(x, y, z) = z$.

   (A) $\frac{\pi}{4}$ (B) $\frac{\pi}{3}$ (C) $\frac{\pi}{2}$ (D) $\frac{2\pi}{3}$

   (E) $\frac{3\pi}{4}$ (F) π (G) $\frac{4\pi}{3}$ (H) 2π

   Answer: (H)

7. Find the mass of the solid that occupies the region bounded by the paraboloid $z = x^2 + y^2$ and the plane $z = 1$ and has density function $\rho(x, y, z) = \sqrt{x^2 + y^2}$.

(A) $\frac{\pi}{4}$ (B) $\frac{\pi}{3}$ (C) $\frac{\pi}{2}$ (D) $\frac{2\pi}{3}$

(E) $\frac{3\pi}{4}$ (F) π (G) $\frac{4\pi}{15}$ (H) 2π

Answer: (G)

8. Evaluate the triple integral $\iiint_E (x^2 + y^2 + z^2) \, dV$, where $E = \{(x, y, z) \mid x^2 + y^2 + z^2 \le 1\}$.

(A) $\frac{2\pi}{3}$ (B) $\frac{2\pi}{5}$ (C) $\frac{4\pi}{3}$ (D) $\frac{4\pi}{5}$

(E) 2π (F) $\frac{6\pi}{5}$ (G) $\frac{8\pi}{3}$ (H) $\frac{8\pi}{5}$

Answer: (D)

9. Let E be the solid that lies below the sphere $x^2 + y^2 + z^2 = a^2$ and above the cone $\phi = \beta$, where $0 < \beta < \frac{\pi}{2}$. Find the value of the triple integral $\iiint_E z \, dV$.

(A) $\pi a^2 \sin \beta$ (B) $\frac{1}{2} \pi a^2 \sin \beta$ (C) $\pi a^2 \sin^2 \beta$ (D) $\frac{1}{2} \pi a^2 \sin^2 \beta$

(E) $\frac{1}{4} \pi a^2 \sin^2 \beta$ (F) $\frac{1}{2} \pi a^4 \sin^2 \beta$ (G) $\frac{1}{4} \pi a^4 \sin^2 \beta$ (H) $\pi a^4 \sin \beta$

Answer: (G)

10. Use cylindrical coordinates to find $\iiint_R z \, dV$, where R is the region bounded by $z = \sqrt{x^2 + y^2}$ and $z = x^2 + y^2$.

Answer: $\frac{\pi}{12}$

11. Find the volume bounded above by the surface $z = x^2 - y^2$, $x \ge 0$, below by the xy-plane, and laterally by the cylinder $x^2 + y^2 = 1$.

Answer: $\frac{1}{2}$

12. Find the volume of the region inside the cylinder $x^2 + y^2 = 7$ which is bounded below by the xy-plane and above by the sphere $x^2 + y^2 + z^2 = 16$.

Answer: $\frac{74\pi}{3}$

13. Evaluate $\iiint_E e^{(x^2+y^2+z^2)^{3/2}} \, dV$, where E is the solid bounded by the sphere $x^2 + y^2 + z^2 = 1$.

Answer: $\dfrac{4\pi(e-1)}{3}$

14. Find the volume of the region above the paraboloid $z = x^2 + y^2$ and below the hemisphere $z - 9 = \sqrt{9 - x^2 - y^2}$.

Answer: $\frac{117\pi}{2}$

15. Evaluate $\iiint_E e^{(x^2+y^2+z^2)^{3/2}} \, dV$, where E is the solid bounded by the sphere $x^2 + y^2 + z^2 = 1$ and the cone $z = \frac{1}{\sqrt{3}} \sqrt{x^2 + y^2}$.

Answer: $\dfrac{\pi(e-1)}{3}$

16. Evaluate $\displaystyle\int_{-5}^{5} \int_{0}^{\sqrt{25-x^2}} \int_{0}^{\sqrt{25-x^2-y^2}} (x^2 + y^2 + z^2)^{1/3} \, dz \, dy \, dx$ by changing to spherical coordinates.

Answer: $\frac{375}{11} \left(5^{2/3}\right) \pi$

17. A region W in $\mathbb{R}^3$ is described completely by $x \geq 0$, $y \geq 0$, $z \geq 0$, and $x^2 + y^2 + z^2 \leq 4$.

   (a) Describe or sketch this region.

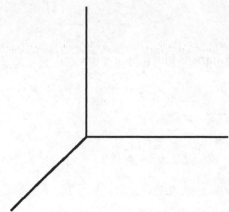

   (b) Write an integral in rectangular coordinates which gives the volume of W. Do not work out this integral.

   (c) Write an integral in spherical coordinates which gives the volume of W. Find the volume of W using this integral.

Answer:

   (a)

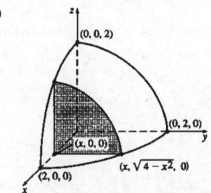

   (b) $\int_0^2 \int_0^{\sqrt{4-x^2}} \int_0^{\sqrt{4-x^2-y^2}} dz\,dy\,dx$

   (c) $\int_0^2 \int_0^{\pi/2} \int_0^{\pi/2} \rho^2 \sin\phi \, d\phi \, d\theta \, d\rho = \frac{4\pi}{3}$

18. Use a triple integral in spherical coordinates to find the volume of that part of the sphere $x^2 + y^2 + z^2 = 9$ which lies inside the cone $z = \sqrt{x^2 + y^2}$.

   Answer: $18\pi \left(1 - \frac{1}{\sqrt{2}}\right)$

19. Find the mass of that portion of the solid bounded above by the sphere $x^2 + y^2 + z^2 = 3$ which lies in the first octant, if the density varies as the distance from the center of the sphere.

   Answer: $\dfrac{9k\pi}{8}$

20. A sphere of radius k has a volume of $\frac{4}{3}\pi k^3$. Set up the iterated integrals in rectangular, cylindrical, and spherical coordinates to show this.

   Answer: Rectangular coordinates: $V = \int_{-k}^{k} \int_{-\sqrt{k^2-x^2}}^{\sqrt{k^2-x^2}} \int_{-\sqrt{k^2-x^2-y^2}}^{\sqrt{k^2-x^2-y^2}} dz\,dy\,dx$; cylindrical coordinates: $V = \int_0^{2\pi} \int_0^k \int_{-\sqrt{k^2-r^2}}^{\sqrt{k^2-r^2}} r\,dz\,dr\,d\theta$; spherical coordinates: $V = \int_0^{2\pi} \int_0^{\pi} \int_0^k \rho^2 \sin\phi \, d\rho \, d\phi \, d\theta$

21. Evaluate $\iiint_E z \left(x^2 + y^2\right) dV$, where E is the solid bounded by the cylinder $x^2 + y^2 = 4$, above by $z = 3$ and below by $z = 0$.

Answer: 36π

22. Sketch the region E whose volume is given by the integral $\int_0^{2\pi} \int_{\pi/6}^{5\pi/6} \int_{1/\sin\phi}^2 \rho^2 \sin\phi \, d\rho \, d\phi \, d\theta$.

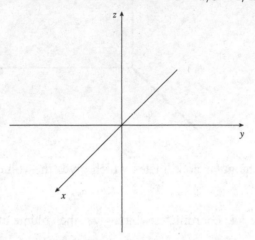

Answer: A sphere of radius 2 with a hole of radius 1 drilled through the center

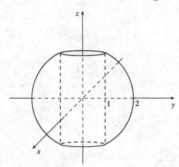

23. Find the mass of a solid ball of radius 2 if the density at each point (x, y, z) is $\dfrac{3}{1 + \sqrt{x^2 + y^2 + z^2}}$.

Answer: $12\pi \ln 3$

24. Give a geometric description of the solid S whose volume in spherical coordinates is given by $V = \int_0^{2\pi} \int_{\pi/4}^{\pi/2} \int_0^2 \rho^2 \sin\phi \, d\rho \, d\phi \, d\theta$.

Answer: A hemisphere with a cone cut out

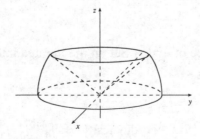

25. Give a geometric description of the solid S whose volume in cylindrical coordinates is given by $V = \int_0^{2\pi} \int_1^2 \int_{-\sqrt{3}}^{\sqrt{3}} r\, dz\, dr\, d\theta$.

Answer: A cylinder of radius 2 and height $2\sqrt{3}$ with a hole of radius 1 cut out in the center along the axis of the cylinder

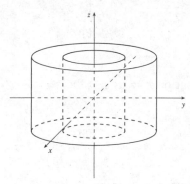

26. Let E be the solid bounded above by the sphere $x^2 + y^2 + z^2 = 1$ and below by the cone $z = \sqrt{x^2 + y^2}$.

   (a) Express the volume of E as an iterated integral in rectangular coordinates.

   (b) Express the volume of E as an iterated integral in cylindrical coordinates.

   (c) Express the volume of E as an iterated integral in spherical coordinates.

   Answer:

   (a) $\int_{-1/\sqrt{2}}^{1/\sqrt{2}} \int_{-\sqrt{(1/2)-x^2}}^{\sqrt{(1/2)-x^2}} \int_{\sqrt{x^2+y^2}}^{\sqrt{1-x^2-y^2}} dz\, dy\, dx$

   (b) $\int_0^{2\pi} \int_0^{1/\sqrt{2}} \int_r^{\sqrt{1-r^2}} r\, dz\, dr\, d\theta$

   (c) $\int_0^{2\pi} \int_0^{\pi/4} \int_0^1 \rho^2 \sin\phi\, d\rho\, d\phi\, d\theta$

27. Let E be the part of the solid ellipsoid $x^2 + y^2 + 4z^2 \leq 9$ that lies in the first octant above the plane $z = 1$.

   (a) Express the triple integral $\iiint_E \frac{y}{z}\, dV$ as an iterated integral in rectangular coordinates.

   (b) Express the triple integral $\iiint_E \frac{y}{z}\, dV$ as an iterated integral in cylindrical coordinates.

   (c) Express the triple integral $\iiint_E \frac{y}{z}\, dV$ as an iterated integral in spherical coordinates.

   Answer:

   (a) $\displaystyle\int_0^{\sqrt{5}} \int_0^{\sqrt{5-x^2}} \int_1^{(\sqrt{9-x^2-y^2})/2} \frac{y}{z}\, dz\, dy\, dx$

   (b) $\displaystyle\int_0^{\pi/2} \int_0^{\sqrt{5}} \int_1^{(\sqrt{9-r^2})/2} \frac{r^2 \sin\theta}{z}\, dz\, dr\, d\theta$

   (c) $\displaystyle\int_0^{\pi/2} \int_0^{\tan^{-1}(\sqrt{5})} \int_0^{3/(\sqrt{1+3\cos^2\phi})} \frac{\rho^2 \sin^2\phi \sin\theta}{\cos\phi}\, d\rho\, d\phi\, d\theta$

12.9 Change of Variables in Multiple Integrals

1. Find the Jacobian of the transformation $x = u + v$, $y = 2u - v$.

(A) 1   (B) 2   (C) 3   (D) 4

(E) -1 (F) -2 (G) -3 (H) -4

Answer: (G)

2. Find the Jacobian of the transformation $x = u$, $y = 2v$, $z = 3w$.

(A) 1   (B) 2   (C) 3   (D) 6

(E) -1 (F) -2 (G) -3 (H) -6

Answer: (D)

3. Find the Jacobian of the transformation $x = u^2$, $y = v^3$.

(A) uv^2 (B) $2uv^2$ (C) $3uv^2$ (D) $6uv^2$

(E) $-uv^2$ (F) $-2uv^2$ (G) $-3uv^2$ (H) $-6uv^2$

Answer: (D)

4. Find the Jacobian of the transformation $x = u \sin v$, $y = u \cos v$.

(A) $-u$ (B) $-u^2$ (C) u (D) u^2

(E) $-u^2 \sin v \cos v$ (F) $u^2 \sin v \cos v$ (G) $-2u^2 \sin v \cos v$ (H) $2u^2 \sin v \cos v$

Answer: (A)

5. Find the Jacobian of the transformation $x = 3u + v$, $y = u - 2w$, $z = v + w$.

(A) 1   (B) 6   (C) -5 (D) 4

(E) -1 (F) -6 (G) 5   (H) -4

Answer: (G)

6. Find the Jacobian of the transformation $x = u$, $y = 2v$, $z = 3w$ when $u = 1$, $v = -1$, and $w = \frac{1}{2}$.

(A) 1   (B) 2   (C) 3   (D) 6

(E) -1 (F) -2 (G) -3 (H) -6

Answer: (D)

7. Find the Jacobian of the transformation $x = u^2$, $y = v^3$ when $u = \frac{1}{2}$ and $v = 1$.

(A) 1   (B) 2   (C) 3   (D) 6

(E) -1 (F) -2 (G) -3 (H) -6

Answer: (C)

8. Find the Jacobian of the transformation $x = u \sin v$, $y = u \cos v$ when $u = 3$ and $v = 5$.

(A) 3   (B) 5   (C) 7.5   (D) 15

(E) -3 (F) -5 (G) -7.5 (H) -15

Answer: (E)

9. Under the transformation $x = u + v$, $y = v - 2u$, the image of the circle $x^2 + y^2 \leq 1$ is an ellipse. What is the area of that ellipse?

(A) $\frac{\pi}{4}$ (B) $\frac{\pi}{3}$ (C) $\frac{\pi}{2}$ (D) $\frac{2\pi}{3}$

(E) π (F) $\frac{3\pi}{2}$ (G) 2π (H) 3π

Answer: (B)

10. Find the area of the region whose image under the transformation $x = u + v$, $y = v - 2u$ is $D = \{(x,y) \mid -1 \leq x \leq 1, 0 \leq y \leq 1 - x^2\}$.

(A) $\frac{1}{9}$ (B) $\frac{2}{9}$ (C) $\frac{1}{3}$ (D) $\frac{4}{9}$

(E) $\frac{5}{9}$ (F) $\frac{2}{3}$ (G) $\frac{7}{9}$ (H) $\frac{8}{9}$

Answer: (D)

11. Evaluate the integral $\iint_R \frac{x+y}{x-y} \, dA$, where R is the triangular region with vertices $(1,0)$, $(0,-1)$, and $(0,0)$.

(A) 0 (B) $\frac{1}{4}$ (C) $\frac{1}{2}$ (D) $\frac{3}{4}$

(E) 1 (F) $\frac{3}{2}$ (G) 2 (H) -2

Answer: (A)

12. Evaluate the integral $\iint_R \sqrt{x^2 + 9y^2} \, dA$, where R is the region enclosed by the ellipse $\frac{x^2}{9} + y^2 = 1$.

(A) 24π (B) π (C) 12π (D) 3π

(E) 10π (F) 2π (G) 6π (H) 4π

Answer: (G)

13. Use the change of variables $u = 2x - y$, $v = x + y$ to evaluate $\iint_R (6x - 3y) \, dA$ where R is the region bounded by $2x - y = 1$, $2x - y = 3$, $x + y = 1$, and $x + y = 2$.

Answer: 4

14. Find the Jacobian of the transformation $x = u - v^2$, $y = u + v^2$.

Answer: $4v$

15. Find the Jacobian of the transformation $x = se^t$, $y = se^{-t}$.

Answer: $-2s$

16. Find the Jacobian of the transformation $x = 2u$, $y = 3v^2$, $z = 4w^3$.

Answer: $144vw^2$

17. Use the change of variables $x = 2u + 3v$, $y = 3u - 2v$ to evaluate $\iint_R (x + y) \, dA$, where R is the square with vertices $(0,0)$, $(2,3)$, $(5,1)$, and $(3,-2)$.

Answer: 39

18. Use the change of variables $x = \sqrt{2}u - \sqrt{\frac{2}{3}}v$, $y = \sqrt{2}u + \sqrt{\frac{2}{3}}v$ to evaluate $\iint_R (x^2 - xy + y^2) \, dA$, where R is the region bounded by the ellipse $x^2 - xy + y^2 = 2$.

Answer: $\frac{4\pi}{\sqrt{3}}$

19. Use the change of variables $u = xy$, $v = xy^2$ to evaluate $\iint_R y^2 \, dA$, where R is the region bounded by the curves $xy = 1$, $xy = 2$, $xy^2 = 1$, and $xy^2 = 2$.

Answer: $\frac{3}{4}$

20. Use the change of variables $x = au$, $y = bv$, $z = cw$ to evaluate $\iiint_E y \, dV$, where E is the solid enclosed by the ellipsoid $\dfrac{x^2}{a^2} + \dfrac{y^2}{b^2} + \dfrac{z^2}{c^2} = 1$.

Answer: 0

21. Evaluate $\iint_R \sin\left(9x^2 + 4y^2\right) dA$ by making an appropriate change of variables, where R is the region in the first quadrant bounded by the ellipse $9x^2 + 4y^2 = 1$.

Answer: $\frac{\pi}{24}\left(1 - \cos 1\right)$

22. Compute the Jacobian of the transformation T given by $x = \frac{1}{\sqrt{2}}\left(u - v\right)$, $y = \frac{1}{\sqrt{2}}\left(u + v\right)$, and find the image of $S = \{(u,v) \mid 0 \le u \le 1, 0 \le v \le 1\}$ under T.

Answer: $J = 1$, image of $S = \left\{(x,y) \mid -\frac{1}{\sqrt{2}} \le x \le \frac{1}{\sqrt{2}}, |x| \le y \le \sqrt{2} - |x|\right\}$

23. Compute the Jacobian of the transformation T given by $x = \sqrt{2}u - \frac{1}{\sqrt{2}}v$, $y = \frac{1}{\sqrt{2}}u + \sqrt{2}v$. Compute the area of the image of $S = \{(u,v) \mid 0 \le u \le 1, 0 \le v \le 1\}$ and compare it to the area of S.

Answer: $J = \frac{5}{2}$, area of image $= \frac{5}{2}$

24. Compute the Jacobian of the transformation T given by $x = v \cos 2\pi u$, $y = v \sin 2\pi u$. Describe the image of $S = \{(u,v) \mid 0 \le u \le 1, 0 \le v \le 1\}$, and compute its area.

Answer: $J = \pi$, image of $S = \left\{(x,y) \mid x^2 + y^2 \le 1\right\}$, area of image $= \pi$

25. Describe the image R of the set $S = \{(u,v) \mid 0 \le u \le 1, 0 \le v \le 1\}$ under the transformation $x = 3u + v$, $y = u + 2v$, and then compute $\iint_R \left(xy + y^2\right) dA$.

Answer: R is a parallelogram with vertices $(0,0)$, $(3,1)$, $(4,3)$, and $(1,2)$; $\iint_R \left(xy + y^2\right) dA = \frac{365}{12}$

26. Evaluate $\iint_R \sqrt{b^2x^2 + a^2y^2} \, dA$, where R is the region enclosed by the ellipse $\dfrac{x^2}{a^2} + \dfrac{y^2}{b^2} = 1$.

Answer: $\dfrac{2\pi \left(ab\right)^2}{3}$

27. Evaluate $\iiint_E z^2 \, dV$, where E is the solid bounded by the ellipsoid $\dfrac{x^2}{9} + \dfrac{y^2}{25} + z^2 = 1$.

Answer: 4π

28. Let T be the transformation given by $x = 2u + v$, $y = u + 2v$.

   (a) A region S in the uv-plane is given below. Sketch the image R of S in the xy-plane.

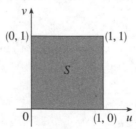

   (b) Find the inverse transformation T^{-1}.

   (c) Evaluate the double integral $\iint_R \left(-x + 2y\right)^2 \cos\left(2x - y\right) dA$.

Answer:

(a)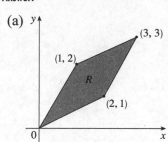

(b) $u = \frac{1}{3}(2x - y)$, $v = \frac{1}{3}(-x + 2y)$

(c) $3\sin 3$

29. Let T be the transformation given by $x = 2u + v$, $y = 3u$.

(a) A region S in the uv-plane is given below. Sketch the image R of S in the xy-plane.

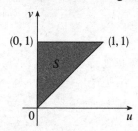

(b) Find the inverse transformation T^{-1}.

(c) Evaluate the double integral $\iint_R e^{y/(3x-2y)}\, dA$.

Answer:

(a)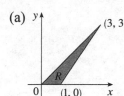

(b) $u = \frac{1}{3}y$, $v = x - \frac{2}{3}y$

(c) $-\frac{3}{2}(e - 1)$

13 Vector Calculus

13.1 Vector Fields

1. Find the gradient vector field of the function $f(x, y) = xy^2$.

(A) $\mathbf{i} + 2\mathbf{j}$ (B) $\mathbf{i} - 2\mathbf{j}$ (C) $x\mathbf{i} + y^2\mathbf{j}$ (D) $x\mathbf{i} - y^2\mathbf{j}$

(E) $\mathbf{i} + 2y\mathbf{j}$ (F) $\mathbf{i} - 2y\mathbf{j}$ (G) $y^2\mathbf{i} + 2xy\mathbf{j}$ (H) $y^2\mathbf{i} - 2xy\mathbf{j}$

Answer: (G)

2. Find the gradient vector field of the function $f(x, y) = x + y^2$.

(A) $2\mathbf{j}$ (B) $\mathbf{i} + 2\mathbf{j}$ (C) $\mathbf{i} + 2y\mathbf{j}$ (D) $x\mathbf{i} + 2y\mathbf{j}$

(E) $-2\mathbf{j}$ (F) $-\mathbf{i} - 2\mathbf{j}$ (G) $-\mathbf{i} - 2y\mathbf{j}$ (H) $-x\mathbf{i} - 2y\mathbf{j}$

Answer: (C)

3. Find the value of the gradient vector field of the function $f(x, y) = e^{xy^2}$ at the point $(1, 1)$.

(A) $e\mathbf{i}$ (B) $e\mathbf{j}$ (C) $2e\mathbf{i}$ (D) $2e\mathbf{j}$

(E) $e\mathbf{i} + e\mathbf{j}$ (F) $e\mathbf{i} + 2e\mathbf{j}$ (G) $2e\mathbf{i} + 2e\mathbf{j}$ (H) $2e\mathbf{i} + e\mathbf{j}$

Answer: (F)

4. Find the gradient vector field of the function $f(x, y, z) = x\sin y + z^2$.

(A) $\sin y\,\mathbf{i} + \cos y\,\mathbf{j} + 2\mathbf{k}$ (B) $\sin y\,\mathbf{i} + x\cos y\,\mathbf{j} + 2z\,\mathbf{k}$

(C) $x\sin y\,\mathbf{i} + \cos y\,\mathbf{j} + \mathbf{k}$ (D) $x\sin y\,\mathbf{i} + x\cos y\,\mathbf{j} + 2z\,\mathbf{k}$

(E) $\sin y\,\mathbf{i} - \cos y\,\mathbf{j} - 2\mathbf{k}$ (F) $\sin y\,\mathbf{i} - x\cos y\,\mathbf{j} + z\mathbf{k}$

(G) $x\sin y\,\mathbf{i} - \cos y\,\mathbf{j} + z\,\mathbf{k}$ (H) $x\sin y\,\mathbf{i} - x\cos y\,\mathbf{j} + z\,\mathbf{k}$

Answer: (B)

5. Find the value of the gradient vector field of the function $f(x, y, z) = x^2y^3z$ at the point $(1, 1, -1)$.

(A) $-2\mathbf{i} - 3\mathbf{j} + \mathbf{k}$ (B) $2\mathbf{i} + 3\mathbf{j} + \mathbf{k}$ (C) $3\mathbf{i} - 2\mathbf{j} + \mathbf{k}$ (D) $3\mathbf{i} + 2\mathbf{j} - \mathbf{k}$

(E) $6\mathbf{i} - 6\mathbf{j} + \mathbf{k}$ (F) $6\mathbf{i} + 6\mathbf{j} - \mathbf{k}$ (G) $\mathbf{i} - \mathbf{j} + \mathbf{k}$ (H) $\mathbf{i} + \mathbf{j} - \mathbf{k}$

Answer: (A)

6. Find the value of the gradient vector field of the function $f(x, y) = \dfrac{1}{x^2 + y^2}$ at the point $(1, 2)$.

(A) $0.08\mathbf{i} + 0.16\mathbf{j}$ (B) $-0.08\mathbf{i} - 0.16\mathbf{j}$ (C) $0.04\mathbf{i} + 0.08\mathbf{j}$ (D) $-0.04\mathbf{i} - 0.08\mathbf{j}$

(E) $0.02\mathbf{i} + 0.04\mathbf{j}$ (F) $-0.02 - 0.04\mathbf{j}$ (G) $0.01\mathbf{i} + 0.02\mathbf{j}$ (H) $-0.01\mathbf{i} - 0.02\mathbf{j}$

Answer: (B)

7. Sketch the vector field **F** where $\mathbf{F}(x, y) = x\mathbf{i} - y\mathbf{j}$.

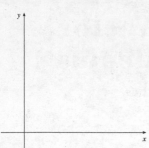

Answer:

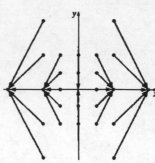

8. Sketch the vector field **F** where $\mathbf{F}(x, y) = \dfrac{y\mathbf{i} - x\mathbf{j}}{\sqrt{x^2 + y^2}}$.

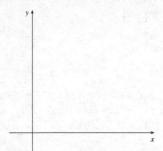

Answer:

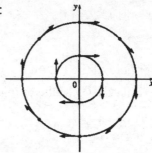

9. Sketch the vector field **F** where $\mathbf{F}(x, y, z) = z\mathbf{k}$.

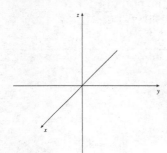

Answer:

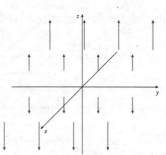

10. Sketch the vector field **F** where $\mathbf{F}(x, y, z) = \mathbf{j} + \mathbf{k}$.

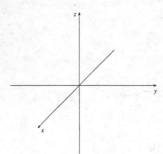

Answer:

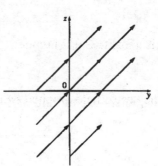

11. Find the gradient vector field of $f(x, y) = \sin(2x + 3y)$.

Answer: $\nabla f = 2\cos(2x + 3y)\mathbf{i} + 3\cos(2x + 3y)\mathbf{j}$

12. Find the gradient vector field of $f(x, y, z) = xyz$.

Answer: $\nabla f = \langle yz, xz, xy \rangle$

13. Find the gradient vector field of $f(x, y, z) = x\ln(y - z)$.

Answer: $\nabla f = \langle \ln(y - z), x/(y - z), -x/(y - z) \rangle$

426

14. Sketch the vector field $\mathbf{F}(x, y) = -x\mathbf{i} + y\mathbf{j}$.

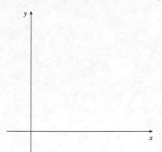

Answer:

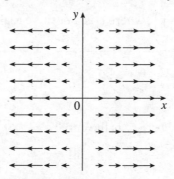

15. Find the function $f(x, y)$ for which $\mathbf{F}(x, y) = (2x + y^2)\mathbf{i} + 2xy\mathbf{j}$ is the gradient field, that is, for which $\mathbf{F}(x, y) = \nabla f(x, y)$.

Answer: $f(x, y) = x^2 + xy^2$

16. Determine the points (x, y, z) where the gradient field $\nabla f(x, y, z)$ for $f(x, y, z) = xy + xz + yz$ has z-component 0.

Answer: All points of the form $(a, -a, b)$

17. Find a formula for the vector field graphed below. (There are many possible answers.)

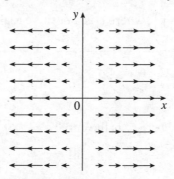

Answer: $ax\,\mathbf{i}$, where a is a positive real number.

18. Find a formula for the vector field graphed below. (There are many possible answers.)

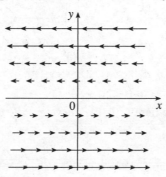

Answer: $-ay\,\mathbf{i}$, where a is a positive real number.

19. Find a formula for the vector field graphed below. (There are many possible answers.)

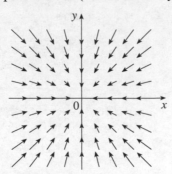

Answer: $a\left(-x\,\mathbf{i} - y\,\mathbf{j}\right)$, where a is a positive real number.

20. Find a formula for the vector field graphed below. (There are many possible answers.)

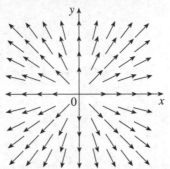

Answer: $a\left(\dfrac{x}{\sqrt{x^2+y^2}}\mathbf{i} + \dfrac{y}{\sqrt{x^2+y^2}}\mathbf{j}\right)$, where a is a positive real number.

13.2 Line Integrals

1. Evaluate the line integral $\int_C x\,ds$, where C is the curve $x = t$, $y = t$, $0 \le t \le 1$.

(A) $\frac{1}{3}$ (B) $\frac{1}{2}$ (C) $\frac{1}{\sqrt{3}}$ (D) $\frac{1}{\sqrt{2}}$

(E) 1   (F) $\sqrt{2}$ (G) $\sqrt{3}$ (H) 2

Answer: (D)

2. Evaluate the line integral $\int_C x\,ds$, where C is the curve $x = t$, $y = t^2$, $0 \le t \le 1$.

(A) $\dfrac{\sqrt{5}-1}{12}$ (B) $\dfrac{\sqrt{125}-1}{12}$ (C) $\dfrac{\sqrt{5}-1}{6}$ (D) $\dfrac{\sqrt{125}-1}{6}$

(E) $\dfrac{\sqrt{5}-1}{4}$ (F) $\dfrac{\sqrt{125}-1}{4}$ (G) $\dfrac{\sqrt{5}-1}{3}$ (H) $\dfrac{\sqrt{125}-1}{3}$

Answer: (B)

3. Evaluate the line integral $\int_C x\,dx$, where C is the curve $x = t$, $y = t$, $0 \le t \le 1$.

(A) $\frac{1}{3}$ (B) $\frac{1}{2}$ (C) $\frac{1}{\sqrt{3}}$ (D) $\frac{1}{\sqrt{2}}$

(E) 1   (F) $\sqrt{2}$ (G) $\sqrt{3}$ (H) 2

Answer: (B)

4. Evaluate the line integral $\int_C y\,dx$, where C is the curve $x = t, y = t^2, 0 \le t \le 1$.

   (A) $\frac{1}{3}$ (B) $\frac{1}{2}$ (C) $\frac{1}{\sqrt{3}}$ (D) $\frac{1}{\sqrt{2}}$

   (E) 1 (F) $\sqrt{2}$ (G) $\sqrt{3}$ (H) 2

   Answer: (A)

5. Evaluate the line integral $\int_C x\,dx + y\,dy$, where C is the curve $x = t, y = t^3, 1 \le t \le 2$.

   (A) 15   (B) 18   (C) 21   (D) 24

   (E) 27   (F) 30   (G) 33   (H) 36

   Answer: (G)

6. Evaluate the line integral $\int_C y\,dx + x\,dy$, where C is the curve $x = t, y = t^3, 1 \le t \le 2$.

   (A) 15   (B) 18   (C) 21   (D) 24

   (E) 27   (F) 30   (G) 33   (H) 36

   Answer: (A)

7. Evaluate the line integral $\int_C \mathbf{F} \cdot d\mathbf{r}$, where $\mathbf{F}(x, y) = xy^2\,\mathbf{i} + y\,\mathbf{j}$ and the curve C is the straight line from $(0, 0)$ to $(1, 1)$.

   (A) $\frac{1}{2}$ (B) $\frac{1}{3}$ (C) $\frac{1}{4}$ (D) $\frac{1}{6}$

   (E) $\frac{3}{4}$ (F) 1 (G) $\frac{2}{3}$ (H) $\frac{5}{6}$

   Answer: (E)

8. Evaluate the line integral $\int_C \mathbf{F} \cdot d\mathbf{r}$, where $\mathbf{F}(x, y) = xy^2\,\mathbf{i} + y\,\mathbf{j}$ and the curve C is the shortest path from $(0, 0)$ to $(0, 1)$ to $(1, 1)$.

   (A) $\frac{1}{2}$ (B) $\frac{1}{3}$ (C) $\frac{1}{4}$ (D) $\frac{1}{6}$

   (E) $\frac{3}{4}$ (F) 1 (G) $\frac{2}{3}$ (H) $\frac{5}{6}$

   Answer: (F)

9. Find the work done by the force field $\mathbf{F}(x, y) = xy^2\,\mathbf{i} + y\,\mathbf{j}$ on a particle that moves along the curve $y = x^2$ from $(0, 0)$ to $(1, 1)$.

   (A) $\frac{1}{2}$ (B) $\frac{1}{3}$ (C) $\frac{1}{4}$ (D) $\frac{1}{6}$

   (E) $\frac{3}{4}$ (F) 1 (G) $\frac{2}{3}$ (H) $\frac{5}{6}$

   Answer: (G)

10. Find the work done by the force field $\mathbf{F}(x, y) = xy\,\mathbf{i} + x^2\,\mathbf{j}$ on a particle that moves along the curve $x = y^2$ from $(0, 0)$ to $(1, 1)$.

   (A) $\frac{1}{2}$ (B) $\frac{1}{3}$ (C) $\frac{1}{4}$ (D) $\frac{1}{6}$

   (E) $\frac{3}{4}$ (F) 1 (G) $\frac{2}{3}$ (H) $\frac{3}{5}$

   Answer: (H)

11. Evaluate the line integral $\int_C \mathbf{F} \cdot d\mathbf{r}$, where $\mathbf{F}(x, y) = 2xy\mathbf{i} + x^2\mathbf{j} + \mathbf{k}$, and the curve C is given by the vector function $\mathbf{r}(t) = t^2\mathbf{i} + t^3\mathbf{j} + t\mathbf{k}$, $0 \le t \le 1$.

   (A) $\frac{1}{4}$ (B) $\frac{1}{2}$ (C) $\frac{3}{4}$ (D) 1

   (E) $\frac{5}{4}$ (F) $\frac{3}{2}$ (G) $\frac{7}{4}$ (H) 2

   Answer: (H)

12. Evaluate the line integral $\int_C \mathbf{F} \cdot d\mathbf{r}$, where $\mathbf{F}(x, y, z) = yz\mathbf{i} + xz\mathbf{j} + xy\mathbf{k}$, and the curve C is given by the vector function $\mathbf{r}(t) = t^2\mathbf{i} + t\mathbf{j} + t^3\mathbf{k}$, $0 \le t \le 1$.

   (A) -3 (B) -2 (C) -1 (D) 0

   (E) 1   (F) 2   (G) 3   (H) 4

   Answer: 1

13. Evaluate the line integral $\int_C xy \, dx - x \, dy$ over the curve $y = 1 - x^2$ from the point $(1, 0)$ to the point $(0, 1)$.

   Answer: $-\frac{11}{12}$

14. Find the work done by the force $\mathbf{F} = (2x + y)\mathbf{i} + (xy)\mathbf{j}$ in moving an object from $(1, 0)$ to $(2, 3)$ along the path C given by $x = t + 1$, $y = 3t$.

   Answer: 12

15. Evaluate the line integral $\int_C xy \, dx + (x + y) \, dy$ where C is the curve $x = t^2$, $y = t^3$, $0 \le t \le 1$.

   Answer: $\frac{97}{70}$

16. Evaluate the line integral $\int_C xy \, ds$ where C is the line segment joining $(-1, 1)$ to $(2, 3)$.

   Answer: $\frac{3\sqrt{13}}{2}$

17. Evaluate the line integral $\int_C \sin x \, dx$ where C is the arc of the curve $x = y^4$ from $(1, -1)$ to $(1, 1)$.

   Answer: 0

18. Evaluate the line integral $\int_C x^2 z \, ds$ where C is the curve $x = \sin 2t$, $y = 3t$, $z = \cos 2t$, $0 \le t \le \frac{\pi}{4}$.

   Answer: $\frac{\sqrt{13}}{6}$

19. A wire in the shape of the curve $x = t^3$, $y = 2t^{3/2}$, $z = 3t + 1$, $0 \le t \le 1$ has density function $\rho(x, y, z) = y^2 + 1$. Find the mass of the wire.

   Answer: $6\sqrt{3} - 2$

20. Evaluate the line integral $\int_C yz \, dy + xy \, dz$, where C is the curve $x = \sqrt{t}$, $y = t$, $z = t^2$, $0 \le t \le 1$.

   Answer: $\frac{23}{28}$

21. Evaluate the line integral $\int_C yz \, dx + xz \, dy + xy \, dz$, where C consists of line segments from $(0, 0, 0)$ to $(2, 0, 0)$, from $(2, 0, 0)$ to $(1, 3, -1)$, and from $(1, 3, -1)$ to $(1, 3, 0)$.

   Answer: 0

22. Evaluate the line integral $\int_C \mathbf{F} \cdot d\mathbf{r}$, where $\mathbf{F}(x, y) = e^x\mathbf{i} + xy\mathbf{j}$, and the curve C is given by the vector function $\mathbf{r}(t) = t^2\mathbf{i} + t^3\mathbf{j}$, $0 \le t \le 1$.

   Answer: $\dfrac{8e - 5}{8}$

23. Evaluate the line integral $\int_C \mathbf{F} \cdot d\mathbf{r}$, where $\mathbf{F}(x, y, z) = (y + z)\mathbf{i} - x^2\mathbf{j} - 4y^2\mathbf{k}$, and the curve C is given by the vector function $\mathbf{r}(t) = t\mathbf{i} + t^2\mathbf{j} + t^4\mathbf{k}$, $0 \leq t \leq 1$.

    Answer: $\frac{-59}{30}$

24. Evaluate the line integral $\int_C \mathbf{F} \cdot d\mathbf{r}$, where $\mathbf{F}(x, y, z) = x^2\mathbf{i} + xy\mathbf{j} + z^2\mathbf{k}$, and the curve C is given by the vector function $\mathbf{r}(t) = \sin t\,\mathbf{i} + \cos t\,\mathbf{j} + t^2\mathbf{k}$, $0 \leq t \leq \frac{\pi}{2}$.

    Answer: $\frac{\pi^6}{192}$

25. Find the mass and center of mass of a thin wire in the shape of a quarter-circle $x^2 + y^2 = r^2$, $x \geq 0$, $y \geq 0$, if the density function is $\rho(x, y) = x + y$.

    Answer: $m = 2r^2$; $(\overline{x}, \overline{y}) = \left(\dfrac{r(\pi + 2)}{8}, \dfrac{r(\pi + 2)}{8} \right)$

26. Find the work done by the force field $\mathbf{F}(x, y) = x \sin y\,\mathbf{i} + y\mathbf{j}$ on a particle that moves along the parabola $y = x^2$ from $(-1, 1)$ to $(2, 4)$.

    Answer: $\dfrac{15 + \cos 1 - \cos 4}{2}$

27. Evaluate the line integral $\int_C y\,ds$, where C is the curve $x = \cos^3 t$, $y = \sin^3 t$, $0 \leq t \leq \frac{\pi}{2}$.

    Answer: $\frac{3}{5}$

28. Evaluate the line integral $\int_C xy^2\,dx + x^2y\,dy$:

    (a) if C is the curve $x = \cos t$, $y = \sin t$, $0 \leq t \leq \pi$, the top half of the unit circle from $(1, 0)$ to $(-1, 0)$.

    (b) if C is the line segment from $(1, 0)$ to $(-1, 0)$.

    Answer (a) 0   (b) 0

29. Evaluate the line integral $\int_C xy\,dx + yz\,dy + zx\,dx$:

    (a) if C is the line segment from $(1, 1, 1)$ to $(3, 3, 3)$.

    (b) if C is the line segment from $(3, 3, 3)$ to $(1, 1, 1)$.

    Answer (a) 26   (b) -26

30. Evaluate the line integral $\int_C e^{x^2 y^2 z^2}\,dx + \sin(xyz)\,dy + \ln(1 + xy)\,dz$ where C is the line segment from $(0, 0, 0)$ to $(0, 0, 1)$.

    Answer: 0

31. Find the work done by the force field $\mathbf{F}(x, y) = -\dfrac{y}{x^2 + y^2}\mathbf{i} + \dfrac{x}{x^2 + y^2}\mathbf{j}$ on a particle that moves along the quarter-circle C given in the figure below.

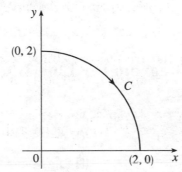

    Answer: $-\dfrac{\pi}{2}$

32. Find the work done by the force field $\mathbf{F}(x, y) = \dfrac{x}{(x^2 + y^2)^{\frac{3}{2}}}\mathbf{i} + \dfrac{y}{(x^2 + y^2)^{\frac{3}{2}}}\mathbf{j}$ on a particle that moves

along the curve C given in the figure below.

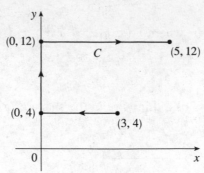

Answer: $\frac{8}{65}$

33. Evaluate the line integral $\int_C x\, dy$, where the curve C is given in the figure below.

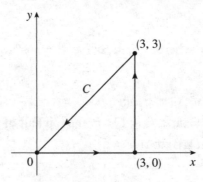

Answer: $\frac{9}{2}$

34. Evaluate the line integral $\int_C xy\, dx + z\, dy + y\, dz$, where the curve C is given in the figure below.

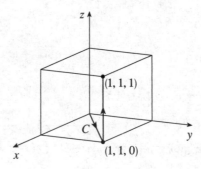

Answer: $\frac{4}{3}$

13.3 The Fundamental Theorem for Line Integrals

1. Find a function $f(x, y)$ such that $\nabla f = 2xy\mathbf{i} + x^2\mathbf{j}$.

(A) $x^3 y$ (B) $x^3 y^2$ (C) x^3/y (D) x^3/y^2

(E) $x^2 y$ (F) $2x^2 y$ (G) $2xy + x^2$ (H) $2xy + 2x^2$

Answer: (E)

2. Find a function $f(x, y)$ such that $\nabla f = (x^2 + y)\mathbf{i} + (x + y)\mathbf{j}$.

(A) $\frac{1}{3}x^3 + xy + y^2$ (B) $\frac{1}{3}x^3 + \frac{1}{2}xy + \frac{1}{2}y^2$

(C) $\frac{1}{3}x^3 + xy + \frac{1}{2}y^2$ (D) $\frac{1}{3}x^3 + \frac{1}{2}xy + y^2$

(E) $\frac{1}{2}x^3 + xy + y^2$ (F) $\frac{1}{2}x^3 + \frac{1}{2}xy + \frac{1}{2}y^2$

(G) $\frac{1}{2}x^3 + xy + \frac{1}{2}y^2$ (H) $\frac{1}{2}x^3 + \frac{1}{2}xy + y^2$

Answer: (C)

3. For what value of the constant b is there a function $f(x, y)$ such that $\nabla f = bx^2y^2\mathbf{i} + x^3y\mathbf{j}$?

(A) 0 (B) $\frac{1}{4}$ (C) $\frac{1}{2}$ (D) $\frac{3}{4}$

(E) 1 (F) $\frac{5}{4}$ (G) $\frac{3}{2}$ (H) $\frac{7}{4}$

Answer: (G)

4. Find the work done by the force field $\mathbf{F}(x, y) = 2xy\mathbf{i} + x^2\mathbf{j}$ on a particle that moves along the curve $\mathbf{r}(t) = t^2\mathbf{i} + t^3\mathbf{j}$, $1 \le t \le 2$.

(A) 127 (B) 128 (C) 63 (D) 64

(E) 31 (F) 32 (G) 15 (H) 16

Answer: (A)

5. Find the work done by the force field $\mathbf{F}(x, y) = (x + y)\mathbf{i} + x^2\mathbf{j}$ on a particle that moves from the point $(1, 0)$ to the point $(2, 2)$ along the parabola $y = x^2 - x$.

(A) $\frac{15}{4}$ (B) $\frac{15}{2}$ (C) $\frac{49}{6}$ (D) $\frac{49}{2}$

(E) 15 (F) $\frac{15}{8}$ (G) $\frac{49}{3}$ (H) 49

Answer: (B)

6. Find the work done by the force field $\mathbf{F}(x, y) = \nabla (x^2 + y^2)^{-1/2}$ on a particle that moves from the point $(3, 4)$ to the point $(0, 2)$.

(A) 0 (B) $\frac{1}{10}$ (C) $\frac{1}{5}$ (D) $\frac{3}{10}$

(E) $\frac{2}{5}$ (F) $\frac{1}{2}$ (G) $\frac{3}{5}$ (H) $\frac{7}{10}$

Answer: (D)

7. Evaluate the line integral $\int_C 3x^2y^2\, dx + 2x^3y\, dy$, where C is any path from $(1, 2)$ to $(2, 1)$.

(A) 2 (B) 4 (C) 6 (D) 8

(E) -2 (F) -4 (G) -6 (H) -8

Answer: (B)

8. Evaluate the line integral $\int_C (3x^2y^4 - 6xy)\, dx + (4x^3y^3 - 3x^2)\, dy$, where C is any path from $(1, 2)$ to $(2, 1)$.

(A) 12 (B) 14 (C) 16 (D) 18

(E) -12 (F) -14 (G) -16 (H) -18

Answer: (F)

9. For what value of the constant b is the vector field $\mathbf{F} = bxy^2\mathbf{i} + x^2y\mathbf{j}$ conservative?

(A) 0   (B) $\frac{1}{4}$ (C) $\frac{1}{2}$ (D) $\frac{3}{4}$

(E) 1   (F) $\frac{5}{4}$ (G) $\frac{3}{2}$ (H) No constant

Answer: (E)

10. Evaluate $\int_C z\,dx + 2yz\,dy + (x + y^2)\,dz$, where C is the line segment $x = 2 - t$, $y = 2t$, $z = 2t - 1$, $0 \le t \le 1$.

(A) 0   (B) 3   (C) 8   (D) 9

(E) 1   (F) 5   (G) 6   (H) 7

Answer: (H)

11. Determine whether or not $\mathbf{F}(x,y) = (3x^2 - 4y)\mathbf{i} + (4y^2 - 2x)\mathbf{j}$ is a conservative vector field. If it is, find a function f such that $\mathbf{F} = \nabla f$.

Answer: not conservative

12. Determine whether or not $\mathbf{F}(x,y) = (x^2 + y)\mathbf{i} + (y^2 + x)\mathbf{j}$ is a conservative vector field. If it is, find a function f such that $\mathbf{F} = \nabla f$.

Answer: $f(x,y) = \dfrac{x^3}{3} + xy + \dfrac{y^3}{3} + K$

13. Determine whether or not $\mathbf{F}(x,y) = (y\cos x - \cos y)\mathbf{i} + (\sin x + x\sin y)\mathbf{j}$ is a conservative vector field. If it is, find a function f such that $\mathbf{F} = \nabla f$.

Answer: $f(x,y) = y\sin x - x\cos y + K$

14. Determine whether or not $\mathbf{F}(x,y) = (ye^{xy} + 4x^3y)\mathbf{i} + (xe^{xy} + x^4)\mathbf{j}$ is a conservative vector field. If it is, find a function f such that $\mathbf{F} = \nabla f$.

Answer: $f(x,y) = e^{xy} + x^4y + K$

15. Determine whether or not $\mathbf{F}(x,y) = (x + y^2)\mathbf{i} + (2xy + y^2)\mathbf{j}$ is a conservative vector field. If it is, find a function f such that $\mathbf{F} = \nabla f$.

Answer: $f(x,y) = \dfrac{x^2}{2} + xy^2 + \dfrac{y^3}{3} + K$

16. Find a function f such that $\mathbf{F} = \nabla f$ and use it to evaluate $\int_C \mathbf{F} \cdot d\mathbf{r}$ along the curve C.

$\mathbf{F}(x,y) = y\mathbf{i} + x\mathbf{j}$; C is the arc of the curve $y = x^4 - x^3$ from $(1,0)$ to $(2,8)$.

Answer: $f(x,y) = xy$; 16

17. Find a function f such that $\mathbf{F} = \nabla f$ and use it to evaluate $\int_C \mathbf{F} \cdot d\mathbf{r}$ along the curve C.

$\mathbf{F}(x,y) = e^{2y}\mathbf{i} + (1 + 2xe^{2y})\mathbf{j}$; $C: \mathbf{r}(t) = te^t\mathbf{i} + (1+t)\mathbf{j}$; $0 \le t \le 1$

Answer: $f(x,y) = xe^{2y} + y$; $e^5 + 1$

18. Find a function f such that $\mathbf{F} = \nabla f$ and use it to evaluate $\int_C \mathbf{F} \cdot d\mathbf{r}$ along the curve C.

$\mathbf{F}(x,y,z) = 2xy^3z^4\mathbf{i} + 3x^2y^2z^4\mathbf{j} + 4x^2y^3z^3\mathbf{k}$; $C: x = t, y = t^2, z = t^3, 0 \le t \le 2$

Answer: $f(x,y,z) = x^2y^3z^4$; 2^{20}

19. Find a function f such that $\mathbf{F} = \nabla f$ and use it to evaluate $\int_C \mathbf{F} \cdot d\mathbf{r}$ along the curve C.

$\mathbf{F}(x,y,z) = 4xe^z\mathbf{i} + \cos y\mathbf{j} + 2x^2e^z\mathbf{k}$; $C: \mathbf{r}(t) = t\mathbf{i} + t^2\mathbf{j} + t^4\mathbf{k}$; $0 \le t \le 1$

Answer: $f(x,y,z) = 2x^2e^z + \sin y$; $2e + \sin 1$

20. Let $\phi(x, y) = 3x^2 y^3$. Note that $\nabla \phi = \langle 6xy^3, 9x^2 y^2 \rangle$. Evaluate the line integral $\int_C 6xy^3\, dx + 9x^2 y^2\, dy$ where C is the curve $x = te^{t^3 - 1}$, $y = (2t + 1)\cos(2\pi t)$, $0 \le t \le 1$.

Answer: 81

21. Evaluate $\int_C (e^x + \cos x + y)\, dx + \left(\dfrac{1}{1 + y^2} + ye^{y^2} + x \right) dy$ if C is the path starting at $(0, 0)$ and going along the line segment from $(0, 0)$ to $(1, 1)$, and then along the line segment from $(1, 1)$ to $(2, 0)$.

Answer: $e^2 + \sin 2 - 1$

22. Evaluate $\int_C \left[3x^2 y^2 + 2\cos(2x + y) \right] dx + \left[2x^3 y + \cos(2x + y) \right] dy$ if C is the closed path starting at $(0, 0)$ and moving clockwise around the square with vertices $(0, 0)$, $(1, 0)$, $(1, 1)$, and $(0, 1)$.

Answer: 0

23. Show that $\int_C 2x\, dx + 2y\, dy + 2z\, dz = \mathbf{a} \cdot \mathbf{a}$, where $\mathbf{a} = a_1 \mathbf{i} + a_2 \mathbf{j} + a_3 \mathbf{k}$, and C is any path from $(0, 0, 0)$ to (a_1, a_2, a_3).

Answer: $f(x, y, z) = x^2 + y^2 + z^2 \Rightarrow \nabla f(x, y, z) = \langle 2x, 2y, 2z \rangle$, so the integral is equal to $f(a_1, a_2, a_3) - f(0, 0, 0) = a_1^2 + a_2^2 + a_3^2 = \mathbf{a} \cdot \mathbf{a}$.

24. If $\mathbf{r} = x\mathbf{i} + y\mathbf{j} + z\mathbf{k}$ and $f(x, y, z) = \ln |\mathbf{r}|$, compute ∇f and determine where $f = 0$ and where $\nabla f = 0$. What is the domain of f?

Answer: $\nabla f = \dfrac{x}{x^2 + y^2 + z^2} \mathbf{i} + \dfrac{y}{x^2 + y^2 + z^2} \mathbf{j} + \dfrac{z}{x^2 + y^2 + z^2} \mathbf{k}$; $f(x, y, z) = 0$ where $|\mathbf{r}| = 1$, on the unit sphere; ∇f is nowhere 0; the domain of f is all of $\mathbb{R}^3$ except the origin.

25. Evaluate the line integral $\int_C \mathbf{F} \cdot d\mathbf{r}$, where $\mathbf{F}(x, y, z) = (2xy + \ln z)\,\mathbf{i} + (x^2 + 1 + z\cos yz)\,\mathbf{j} + \left(\dfrac{x}{z} + y\cos yz \right) \mathbf{k}$ and C is the curve $x = \sqrt{3\cos t + 1}$, $y = 2\sin^3 t$, $z = \sin t + \cos t$, $0 \le t \le \frac{\pi}{2}$.

Answer: $f(x, y, z) = x^2 y + y + \sin(yz) + x \ln z \Big|_{(2, 0, 1)}^{(1, 2, 1)} = \sin 2 + 4$

26. Evaluate the line integral $\int_C \mathbf{F} \cdot d\mathbf{r}$, where $\mathbf{F}(x, y) = (ye^{xy} + \sin y)\,\mathbf{i} + (xe^{xy} + x\cos y)\,\mathbf{j}$ and C is the curve $x = \sqrt{3\cos t + 1}$, $y = 2\sin^3 t$, $0 \le t \le \frac{\pi}{2}$.

Answer: $e^2 + \sin 2 - 1$

27. Evaluate the line integral $\int_C xy\, dx + (x - y)\, dy$, where C is the arc of the circle $x^2 + y^2 = 1$ from the point $(1, 0)$ to the point $(0, 1)$, followed by the line segment from the point $(0, 1)$ to the point $(4, 3)$.

Answer: $\frac{\pi}{4} + \frac{107}{6}$

28. Evaluate the line integral $\int_C (x + y)\, dx + x^2\, dy$, where C is the arc of the parabola $y = x^2 - x$ from the point $(1, 0)$ to the point $(2, 2)$.

Answer: $\frac{15}{2}$

29. Determine whether or not each of the following vector fields is conservative. Justify your answer.

(a) 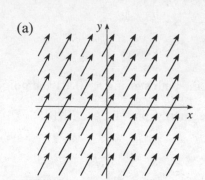 (b) 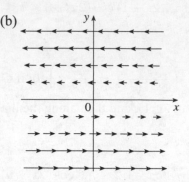 (c)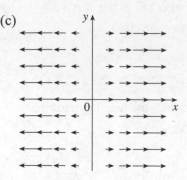

Answer: (a) Conservative   (b) Not conservative   (c) Conservative

13.4 Green's Theorem

1. According to Green's Theorem, the line integral $\int_C x^2\,dx + y^2\,dy$ over a positively oriented, piecewise-smooth, simple closed curve C is equal to the double integral $\iint_D f(x,y)\,dA$ over the region D bounded by C. Find the function $f(x,y)$.

(A) $2x - y$ (B) $x - 2y$ (C) $2x - 2y$ (D) 0

(E) 1 (F) $2x + y$ (G) $x + 2y$ (H) $2x + 2y$

Answer: (D)

2. According to Green's Theorem, the line integral $\int_C y\,dx + x\,dy$ over a positively oriented, piecewise-smooth, simple closed curve C is equal to a double integral $\iint_D f(x,y)\,dA$ over the region D bounded by C. Find the function $f(x,y)$.

(A) $2x - y$ (B) $x - 2y$ (C) $2x - 2y$ (D) 0

(E) 1 (F) $2x + y$ (G) $x + 2y$ (H) $2x + 2y$

Answer: (D)

3. According to Green's Theorem, the line integral $\int_C y^2\,dx + x^2\,dy$ over a positively oriented, piecewise-smooth, simple closed curve C is equal to a double integral $\iint_D f(x,y)\,dA$ over the region D bounded by C. Find the function $f(x,y)$.

(A) $2x - y$ (B) $x - 2y$ (C) $2x - 2y$ (D) 0

(E) 1 (F) $2x + y$ (G) $x + 2y$ (H) $2x + 2y$

Answer: (C)

4. Evaluate the line integral $\int_C x\,dy$ along the circle $x = \cos t$, $y = \sin t$, $0 \le t \le 2\pi$.

(A) $\frac{\pi}{2}$ (B) π (C) 2π (D) 4π

(E) $-\frac{\pi}{2}$ (F) $-\pi$ (G) -2π (H) -4π

Answer: (B)

5. Evaluate the line integral $\int_C y\,dx - x\,dy$ along the circle $x = 2\cos t$, $y = 3\sin t$, $0 \le t \le 2\pi$.

(A) 0   (B) -24π (C) -6π (D) -12π

(E) $-\frac{\pi}{2}$ (F) 24π (G) 6π (H) 12π

Answer: (D)

6. Evaluate the line integral $\int_C x\,dy$ along the triangular path consisting of the line segment from $(0,0)$ to $(2,3)$ followed by the line segment from $(2,3)$ to $(1,0)$ followed by the line segment from $(1,0)$ to $(0,0)$.

(A) $\frac{1}{2}$ (B) 1   (C) $\frac{3}{2}$ (D) 2

(E) $-\frac{1}{2}$ (F) -1 (G) $-\frac{3}{2}$ (H) -2

Answer: (G)

7. Evaluate the line integral $\int_C xe^{x^2}\,dx + y\sin y^2\,dy$ along the triangular path consisting of the line segment from $(0,0)$ to $(2,3)$ followed by the line segment from $(2,3)$ to $(1,0)$ followed by the line segment from $(1,0)$ to $(0,0)$.

(A) 0   (B) $\frac{25}{9}$ (C) $\frac{26}{9}$ (D) 3

(E) $-\frac{8}{3}$ (F) $-\frac{25}{9}$ (G) $-\frac{26}{9}$ (H) -3

Answer: (A)

8. Evaluate the line integral $\oint_C xy^2\,dx - yx^2\,dy$ around the triangle with vertices $(1,0)$, $(0,1)$, and $(0,0)$ with clockwise orientation.

Answer: $\frac{1}{6}$

9. Let C be the closed path from $(0,0)$ to $(2,4)$ along $y = x^2$ and back again from $(2,4)$ to $(0,0)$ along $y = 2x$. Evaluate $\int_C \left(x^3 + 2y\right)\,dx + \left(x - y^2\right)\,dy$ directly, and then using Green's Theorem.

Answer: $-\frac{4}{3}$

10. If R is the region enclosed by a simple closed positively-oriented curve C, then the area of R is given by

(A) $\int_C y\,dx + x\,dy$ (B) $\frac{1}{2}\int_C x\,dy - y\,dx$ (C) $\frac{1}{2}\int_C y\,dx + x\,dy$

(D) $\frac{1}{2}\int_C y\,dx - x\,dy$ (E) None of the above

Answer: (B)

11. Evaluate the line integral $\int_C \left(2xy^2 + \tan^{-1} x^3\right)\,dx + \left(x^2 y + \sqrt{y^3 + 1}\right)\,dy$, where C consists of the arc of the parabola $y = x^2$ from $(1,1)$ to $(2,4)$, followed by the line segments from $(2,4)$ to $(0,4)$, from $(0,4)$ to $(0,1)$ and from $(0,1)$ to $(1,1)$.

Answer: -21

12. Evaluate the line integral by two methods: directly and using Green's Theorem.

$\oint_C x\,dx - x^2 y^2\,dy$, where C is the triangle with vertices $(0,0)$, $(1,1)$, and $(0,1)$.

Answer: $-\frac{1}{5}$

13. Use Green's Theorem to evaluate the line integral along the given positively oriented curve:

$\int_C x^2 y\,dx + xy^5\,dy$, where C is the square with vertices $(\pm 1, \pm 1)$.

Answer: $-\frac{4}{3}$

14. Use Green's Theorem to evaluate the line integral along the given positively oriented curve:
$\int_C \left(y^2 - \tan^{-1} x \right) dx + (3x + \sin y) \, dy$, where C is the boundary of the region enclosed by the parabola $y = x^2$ and the line $y = 4$.
Answer: $-\frac{96}{5}$

15. Use Green's Theorem to evaluate the line integral along the given positively oriented curve:
$\int_C x^2 y \, dx - 3y^2 \, dy$, where C is the circle $x^2 + y^2 = 1$.
Answer: $-\frac{\pi}{4}$

16. Use Green's Theorem to evaluate the line integral along the given positively oriented curve:
$\int_C 2xy \, dx + x^2 \, dy$, where C is the cardioid $r = 1 + \cos\theta$.
Answer: 0

17. Use Green's Theorem to evaluate the line integral along the given positively oriented curve:
$\int_C \left(x^3 - y^3 \right) dx + \left(x^3 + y^3 \right) dy$, where C is the boundary of the region between the circles $x^2 + y^2 = 1$ and $x^2 + y^2 = 9$.
Answer: 120π

18. Use Green's Theorem to evaluate the line integral along the given positively oriented curve:
$\int_C \mathbf{F} \cdot d\mathbf{r}$, where $\mathbf{F}(x, y) = x^3 y \mathbf{i} + x^4 \mathbf{j}$ and C is the curve $x^4 + y^4 = 1$.
Answer: 0

19. Use Green's Theorem to find the area of the region formed by the intersection of $x^2 + y^2 \le 2$ and $y \ge 1$.
Answer: $\frac{\pi}{2} - 1$

20. Use Green's Theorem to find the area of the region interior to the ellipse $\dfrac{x^2}{9} + \dfrac{y^2}{16} = 1$.
Answer: 12π

21. Evaluate $\oint_C \left(x \cos x + e^{\sin x} + 3y \right) dx + \left[5x + \left(1 + y^2 \right)^3 + \cos \left(e^y + y^2 \right) \right] dy$ where C is the positively-oriented boundary of the half disk D: $x^2 + y^2 \le 2$, $y \ge 0$.
Answer: 2π

22. Evaluate $\oint_C \left(\frac{1}{4} y^4 - \frac{1}{2} x^3 \cos y^3 \right) dx + \left(xy^3 + x^2 + \frac{3}{8} x^4 y^2 \sin y^3 \right) dy$, if C is the path shown below.

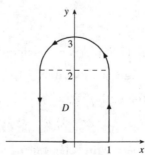

Answer: 0

23. Evaluate $\oint_C 0\,dx + 4x\,dy$, if C is the path shown below, starting and ending at $(1,1)$.

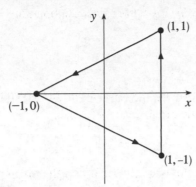

Answer: 8

24. Evaluate the line integral $\displaystyle\int_C \frac{xy}{1+x}\,dx - \ln(1+x)\,dy$, where C is the triangular path consisting of the line segment from $(0,0)$ to $(4,0)$, followed by the line segment from $(4,0)$ to $(0,2)$, followed by the line segment from $(0,2)$ to $(0,0)$.

Answer: -4

25. Use Green's Theorem to compute the area of the region enclosed by the curve $x = \cos^3 t$, $y = \sin^3 t$, $0 \le t \le 2\pi$.

Answer: $\frac{3\pi}{8}$

26. Evaluate the line integral $\int_C \left(y + x^2\right) dx + \left(2x + \sqrt[3]{\sin y^3 + e^{y^2}}\right) dy$, where C is the upper half of the circle $x^2 + y^2 = 1$ from $(1,0)$ to $(-1,0)$.

Answer: $\frac{\pi}{2} - \frac{2}{3}$

27. Find the work done by the force field $\mathbf{F}(x,y) = -\dfrac{y}{x^2 + y^2}\,\mathbf{i} + \dfrac{x}{x^2 + y^2}\,\mathbf{j}$ on a particle that moves along the circle C: $x = \cos t$, $y = \sin t$, $0 \le t \le 2\pi$.

Answer: 2π

28. Find the work done by the force field $\mathbf{F}(x,y) = -\dfrac{y}{x^2 + y^2}\,\mathbf{i} + \dfrac{x}{x^2 + y^2}\,\mathbf{j}$ on a particle that moves along the circle C: $x = 1 + \cos t$, $y = 1 + \sin t$, $0 \le t \le 2\pi$.

Answer: 0

13.5 | Curl And Divergence

1. Let $\mathbf{F}(x,y,z) = z\mathbf{i} + x\mathbf{j} + y\mathbf{k}$. Find the curl of $\mathbf{F}$.

(A) $\mathbf{i}$ (B) $\mathbf{j}$ (C) $\mathbf{k}$ (D) $\mathbf{i} + \mathbf{j} + \mathbf{k}$

(E) $-\mathbf{i}$ (F) $-\mathbf{j}$ (G) $-\mathbf{k}$ (H) $-\mathbf{i} - \mathbf{j} - \mathbf{k}$

Answer: (D)

2. Let $\mathbf{F}(x, y, z) = y\mathbf{i} - x\mathbf{j}$. Find the curl of $\mathbf{F}$.

(A) $2\mathbf{i}$ (B) $2\mathbf{j}$ (C) $2\mathbf{k}$ (D) $2\mathbf{i} + 2\mathbf{j} + 2\mathbf{k}$

(E) $-2\mathbf{i}$ (F) $-2\mathbf{j}$ (G) $-2\mathbf{k}$ (H) $-2\mathbf{i} - 2\mathbf{j} - 2\mathbf{k}$

Answer: (G)

3. Let $\mathbf{F}(x, y, z) = z^2\mathbf{i} + x^2\mathbf{j} + y^2\mathbf{k}$. Find the curl of $\mathbf{F}$.

(A) $2y\mathbf{i}$ (B) $2z\mathbf{j}$ (C) $2x\mathbf{k}$ (D) $2y\mathbf{i} + 2z\mathbf{j} + 2x\mathbf{k}$

(E) $2x\mathbf{i}$ (F) $2y\mathbf{j}$ (G) $2z\mathbf{k}$ (H) $2x\mathbf{i} + 2y\mathbf{j} + 2z\mathbf{k}$

Answer: (D)

4. Let $\mathbf{F}(x, y, z) = y^2\mathbf{i} + x\mathbf{j}$. Find the value of the curl of $\mathbf{F}$ at the point $(1, 1, 3)$.

(A) $\mathbf{i}$ (B) $\mathbf{j}$ (C) $\mathbf{k}$ (D) $\mathbf{i} + \mathbf{j} + \mathbf{k}$

(E) $-\mathbf{i}$ (F) $-\mathbf{j}$ (G) $-\mathbf{k}$ (H) $-\mathbf{i} - \mathbf{j} - \mathbf{k}$

Answer: (G)

5. Let $\mathbf{F}(x, y, z) = (z + y^2)\mathbf{i} + 2xy\mathbf{j} + (x + y)\mathbf{k}$. Find the value of the curl of $\mathbf{F}$ at the point $(1, 1, 1)$.

(A) $\mathbf{i}$ (B) $\mathbf{j}$ (C) $\mathbf{k}$ (D) $\mathbf{i} + \mathbf{j} + \mathbf{k}$

(E) $-\mathbf{i}$ (F) $-\mathbf{j}$ (G) $-\mathbf{k}$ (H) $-\mathbf{i} - \mathbf{j} - \mathbf{k}$

Answer: (A)

6. Let $\mathbf{F}(x, y, z) = z\mathbf{i} + x\mathbf{j} + y\mathbf{k}$. Find the divergence of $\mathbf{F}$.

(A) -2 (B) -1 (C) 0 (D) 1

(E) 2 (F) 3 (G) 4 (H) 5

Answer: (C)

7. Let $\mathbf{F}(x, y, z) = (z + y^2)\mathbf{i} + 2xy\mathbf{j} + (x + y)\mathbf{k}$. Find the value of the divergence of $\mathbf{F}$ at the point $(1, 2, 3)$.

(A) -2 (B) -1 (C) 0 (D) 1

(E) 2 (F) 3 (G) 4 (H) 5

Answer: (E)

8. For what value of the constant b is the vector field $\mathbf{F}(x, y, z) = 2x\mathbf{i} + z\mathbf{j} + bz\mathbf{k}$ incompressible?

(A) -3 (B) -2 (C) -1 (D) 0

(E) 1 (F) 2 (G) 3 (H) No constant

Answer: (B)

9. For what value of the constant b is the vector field $\mathbf{F} = bxy^2\mathbf{i} + x^2y\mathbf{j}$ irrotational?

(A) 0 (B) $\frac{1}{4}$ (C) $\frac{1}{2}$ (D) $\frac{3}{4}$

(E) 1 (F) $\frac{5}{4}$ (G) $\frac{3}{2}$ (H) No constant

Answer: (E)

10. For what value of the constant b is the vector field $\mathbf{F} = bxy\mathbf{i} + x^2y\mathbf{j}$ irrotational?

    (A) 0   (B) $\frac{1}{4}$ (C) $\frac{1}{2}$ (D) $\frac{3}{4}$

    (E) 1   (F) $\frac{5}{4}$ (G) $\frac{3}{2}$ (H) No constant

    Answer: (H)

11. Find the value of the Laplacian $\nabla^2 f$ of $f(x,y) = xy^3$ at the point $(1,1)$.

    (A) 0   (B) $\frac{11}{4}$ (C) 2   (D) 3

    (E) 4   (F) 5   (G) 6   (H) 9

    Answer: (G)

12. Find the value of the Laplacian $\nabla^2 f$ of $f(x,y,z) = z(x^2 + y^3)$ at the point $(1,2,3)$.

    (A) 24   (B) 30   (C) 36   (D) 42

    (E) 48   (F) 54   (G) 60   (H) 66

    Answer: (D)

13. What value of the constant a makes the vector field $\mathbf{F}(x,y,z) = 2xz\mathbf{i} + ay^2z\mathbf{j} + (x^2 + y^3)\mathbf{k}$ conservative?

    (A) -2 (B) -1 (C) 0   (D) 1

    (E) 2   (F) 3   (G) 4   (H) 5

    Answer: (F)

14. Let $\mathbf{F}(x,y,z) = (z - 4y\sin x)\mathbf{i} + xz\mathbf{j} + yz^2\mathbf{k}$. Find the value of the divergence of $\mathbf{F}$ at the point $(0,0,1)$.

    (A) -3 (B) -2 (C) -1 (D) 0

    (E) 1   (F) 2   (G) 3   (H) 4

    Answer: (D)

15. Find (a) the curl and (b) the divergence of the vector field $\mathbf{F}(x,y,z) = x^2y\mathbf{i} + yz^2\mathbf{j} + zx^2\mathbf{k}$.

    Answer: (a) $-(2yz\mathbf{i} + 2xz\mathbf{j} + x^2\mathbf{k})$ (b) $2xy + z^2 + x^2$

16. Find (a) the curl and (b) the divergence of the vector field $\mathbf{F}(x,y,z) = y^2z\mathbf{i} - x^2yz\mathbf{k}$.

    Answer: (a) $-x^2z\mathbf{i} + (y^2 + 2xyz)\mathbf{j} - 2yz\mathbf{k}$ (b) $-x^2y$

17. Find (a) the curl and (b) the divergence of the vector field $\mathbf{F}(x,y,z) = \sin x\mathbf{i} + \cos x\mathbf{j} + z^2\mathbf{k}$.

    Answer: (a) $-\sin x\,\mathbf{k}$ (b) $\cos x + 2z$

18. Find (a) the curl and (b) the divergence of the vector field $\mathbf{F}(x,y,z) = (x + 3y - 5z)\mathbf{i} + (z - 3y)\mathbf{j} + (5x + 6y - z)\mathbf{k}$.

    Answer: (a) $5\mathbf{i} - 10\mathbf{j} - 3\mathbf{k}$ (b) -3

19. Determine whether or not the vector field $\mathbf{F}(x,y,z) = x\mathbf{i} + y\mathbf{j} + x\mathbf{k}$ is conservative. If it is conservative, find a function f such that $\mathbf{F} = \nabla f$.

    Answer: Not conservative

20. Determine whether or not the vector field $\mathbf{F}(x,y,z) = z\mathbf{i} + 2yz\mathbf{j} + (x + y^2)\mathbf{k}$ is conservative. If it is conservative, find a function f such that $\mathbf{F} = \nabla f$.

    Answer: $f(x,y,z) = xz + y^2z + K$

21. Is there a vector field $\mathbf{G}$ on $\mathbb{R}^3$ such that $\operatorname{curl}\mathbf{G} = yz\mathbf{i} + xyz\mathbf{j} + xy\mathbf{k}$? Explain.

    Answer: No. Assume there is such a $\mathbf{G}$. Then div curl $\mathbf{G} = xz \neq 0$, which contradicts Theorem 13.5.11.

22. Consider the vector field $\mathbf{F}(x, y) = -\dfrac{y}{x^2 + y^2}\,\mathbf{i} + \dfrac{x}{x^2 + y^2}\,\mathbf{j}$.

    (a) Compute the curl of $\mathbf{F}$.

    (b) Compute the divergence of $\mathbf{F}$.

    Answer: (a) $\mathbf{0}$ (b) 0

23. Consider the vector field $\mathbf{F}(x, y, z) = \dfrac{x}{(x^2 + y^2 + z^2)^{3/2}}\,\mathbf{i} + \dfrac{y}{(x^2 + y^2 + z^2)^{3/2}}\,\mathbf{j} + \dfrac{z}{(x^2 + y^2 + z^2)^{3/2}}\,\mathbf{k}$.

    (a) Compute the curl of $\mathbf{F}$.

    (b) Compute the divergence of $\mathbf{F}$.

    Answer: (a) $\mathbf{0}$ (b) 0

24. Each vector field $\mathbf{F}$ graphed below is shown in the xy-plane and looks the same in all other horizontal planes. Is div $\mathbf{F}$ at the point P positive, negative or zero? Is curl $\mathbf{F}$ at the point P equal to $\mathbf{0}$? Explain.

(a) 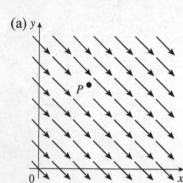   (b) 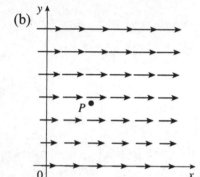   (c)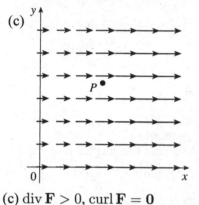

Answer: (a) div $\mathbf{F} = 0$, curl $\mathbf{F} = \mathbf{0}$ (b) div $\mathbf{F} = 0$, curl $\mathbf{F} \neq \mathbf{0}$ (c) div $\mathbf{F} > 0$, curl $\mathbf{F} = \mathbf{0}$

13.6   Surface Integrals

1. Evaluate the surface integral $\iint_S x\,dS$, where S is that part of the plane $z = x$ that lies above the square with vertices $(0, 0)$, $(1, 0)$, $(0, 1)$, and $(1, 1)$.

    (A) 1 (B) $\sqrt{2}$ (C) $\sqrt{3}$ (D) 2

    (E) $\dfrac{\sqrt{2}}{2}$ (F) $\dfrac{\sqrt{3}}{2}$ (G) $\dfrac{\sqrt{2}}{3}$ (H) $\dfrac{\sqrt{3}}{3}$

    Answer: (E)

2. Evaluate the surface integral $\iint_S x^2\,dS$, where S is that part of the plane $z = x$ that lies above the square with vertices $(0, 0)$, $(1, 0)$, $(0, 1)$, and $(1, 1)$.

    (A) 1 (B) $\sqrt{2}$ (C) $\sqrt{3}$ (D) 2

    (E) $\dfrac{\sqrt{2}}{2}$ (F) $\dfrac{\sqrt{3}}{2}$ (G) $\dfrac{\sqrt{2}}{3}$ (H) $\dfrac{\sqrt{3}}{3}$

    Answer: (G)

3. Evaluate the surface integral $\iint_S (x + y + z)\,dS$, where S is that part of the plane $z = x$ that lies above the square with vertices $(0, 0)$, $(1, 0)$, $(0, 1)$, and $(1, 1)$.

    (A) 1 (B) $\sqrt{2}$ (C) $\sqrt{3}$ (D) $\dfrac{3}{2}$

    (E) $\dfrac{\sqrt{2}}{2}$ (F) $\dfrac{\sqrt{3}}{2}$ (G) $\dfrac{\sqrt{2}}{3}$ (H) $\dfrac{3\sqrt{2}}{2}$

    Answer: (H)

4. Let $\mathbf{F}(x, y, z) = \mathbf{k}$. Evaluate the surface integral $\iint_S \mathbf{F} \cdot d\mathbf{S}$, where S is that part of the plane $z = x$ that lies above the square with vertices $(0, 0)$, $(1, 0)$, $(0, 1)$, and $(1, 1)$ and has upward orientation.

(A) 1   (B) $\sqrt{2}$ (C) $\sqrt{3}$ (D) 2

(E) $\frac{\sqrt{2}}{2}$ (F) $\frac{\sqrt{3}}{2}$ (G) $\frac{1}{2}$ (H) $\frac{1}{4}$

Answer: (A)

5. Let $\mathbf{F}(x, y, z) = x\mathbf{k}$. Evaluate the surface integral $\iint_S \mathbf{F} \cdot d\mathbf{S}$, where S is that part of the plane $z = x$ that lies above the square with vertices $(0, 0)$, $(1, 0)$, $(0, 1)$, and $(1, 1)$ and has upward orientation.

(A) 1   (B) $\sqrt{2}$ (C) $\sqrt{3}$ (D) 2

(E) $\frac{\sqrt{2}}{2}$ (F) $\frac{\sqrt{3}}{2}$ (G) $\frac{1}{2}$ (H) $\frac{1}{4}$

Answer: (G)

6. Evaluate the surface integral $\iint_S z \, dS$, where S is that part of the cylinder $z = \sqrt{1 - x^2}$ that lies above the square with vertices $(-1, -1)$, $(1, -1)$, $(-1, 1)$, and $(1, 1)$.

(A) $\sqrt{2}$ (B) 2   (C) $\sqrt{8}$ (D) 4

(E) π (F) 2π (G) 4π (H) 8π

Answer: (D)

7. Evaluate the surface integral $\iint_S z^2 \, dS$, where S is that part of the cylinder $z = \sqrt{1 - x^2}$ that lies above the square with vertices $(-1, -1)$, $(1, -1)$, $(-1, 1)$, and $(1, 1)$.

(A) $\sqrt{2}$ (B) 2   (C) $\sqrt{8}$ (D) 4

(E) π (F) 2π (G) 4π (H) 8π

Answer: (E)

8. Evaluate the surface integral $\iint_S \mathbf{F} \cdot d\mathbf{S}$, where $\mathbf{F} = x\mathbf{i} + y\mathbf{j} + x\mathbf{k}$ and S is the part of the plane $z = 1 - x - y$ in the first octant with downward orientation.

(A) $\frac{1}{3}$ (B) $\frac{1}{2}$ (C) $\frac{1}{4}$ (D) 1

(E) $-\frac{1}{3}$ (F) $-\frac{1}{2}$ (G) $-\frac{1}{4}$ (H) -1

Answer: (F)

9. Evaluate the surface integral $\iint_S xz \, dS$, where S is the triangle with vertices $(1, 0, 0)$, $(0, 1, 0)$, and $(0, 0, 1)$.

Answer: $\frac{1}{8\sqrt{3}}$

10. Evaluate the surface integral $\iint_S (y^2 + z^2) \, dS$, where S is the part of the paraboloid $x = 4 - y^2 - z^2$ that lies in front of the plane $x = 0$.

Answer: $\dfrac{\pi \left(391\sqrt{17} + 1\right)}{60}$

11. Evaluate the surface integral $\iint_S xyz \, dS$, where S is the part of the sphere $x^2 + y^2 + z^2 = 1$ that lies above the cone $z = \sqrt{x^2 + y^2}$.

Answer: 0

12. Evaluate the surface integral $\iint_S \mathbf{F} \cdot d\mathbf{S}$ for the vector field $\mathbf{F}(x, y, z) = x^2 y\mathbf{i} - 3xy^2\mathbf{j} + 4y^3\mathbf{k}$, where S is the part of the elliptic paraboloid $z = x^2 + y^2 - 9$ that lies below the square $0 \le x \le 1, 0 \le y \le 1$ and has downward orientation.

Answer: $-\frac{3}{2}$

13. Evaluate the surface integral $\iint_S \mathbf{F} \cdot d\mathbf{S}$ for the vector field $\mathbf{F}(x, y, z) = -x\mathbf{i} - y\mathbf{j} + z^2\mathbf{k}$, where S is part of the cone $z = \sqrt{x^2 + y^2}$ between the planes $z = 1$ and $z = 2$ with upward orientation.

Answer: $\frac{73\pi}{6}$

14. Evaluate the surface integral $\iint_S \mathbf{F} \cdot d\mathbf{S}$ for the vector field $\mathbf{F}(x, y, z) = -y\mathbf{i} + x\mathbf{j} + 3z\mathbf{k}$, where S is the hemisphere $z = \sqrt{16 - x^2 - y^2}$ with upward orientation.

Answer: 128π

15. Find the mass of a thin funnel in the shape of a cone $z = \sqrt{x^2 + y^2}$, $1 \le z \le 4$, is its density function is $\rho(x, y, z) = 10 - z$.

Answer: $108\sqrt{2}\,\pi$

16. A fluid has density 1500 and velocity field $\mathbf{v} = -y\mathbf{i} + x\mathbf{j} + 2z\mathbf{k}$. Find the rate of flow outward through the sphere $x^2 + y^2 + z^2 = 25$.

Answer: $500,000\pi$

17. Consider the top half of the ellipsoid $x^2 + y^2 + \frac{1}{4}z^2 = 1$, $z \ge 0$ parametrized by $x = \sin u \sin v$, $y = \cos u \sin v$, $z = 2\cos v$, $0 \le v \le \frac{\pi}{2}$. Find a normal vector $\mathbf{N}$ at the point determined by $u = \frac{\pi}{4}$, $v = \frac{\pi}{3}$, and determine if it is upward and/or outward.

Answer: $\left\langle \frac{3\sqrt{2}}{\sqrt{39}}, \frac{3\sqrt{2}}{\sqrt{39}}, \frac{\sqrt{3}}{\sqrt{39}} \right\rangle$; upward and outward

18. Compute the surface integral $\iint_S \mathbf{F} \cdot d\mathbf{S}$ if $\mathbf{F}(x, y, z) = z^2\mathbf{k}$ and S is the piece of the sphere $x^2 + y^2 + z^2 = 1$ in the second octant ($x \le 0, y \ge 0, z \ge 0$).

Answer: $\frac{\pi}{3}$

19. Evaluate $\iint_S \frac{x^2 + z}{x^2 + y^2}\, dS$, where S is the part of the surface $z = xy$ that lies between the cylinders $x^2 + y^2 = 1$ and $x^2 + y^2 = 4$.

Answer: $\frac{\pi}{3}\left(5\sqrt{5} - 2\sqrt{2}\right)$

20. Evaluate $\iint_S \mathbf{F} \cdot d\mathbf{S}$, where $\mathbf{F}(x, y, z) = y^2\mathbf{i} + x\mathbf{j} + z\mathbf{k}$ and S is the part of the surface $z = x + y^2$ that lies above the rectangle $0 \le x \le 1, 0 \le y \le 2$ and has upward orientation.

Answer: -1

21. Evaluate $\iint_S \mathbf{F} \cdot d\mathbf{S}$, where $\mathbf{F}(x, y, z) = x^2\mathbf{i} + xy\mathbf{j} + z\mathbf{k}$ and S is the part of the surface $z = x^2 + y^2$ below the plane $z = 1$, with upward orientation.

Answer: $\frac{\pi}{2}$

22. Evaluate $\iint_S \mathbf{F} \cdot d\mathbf{S}$, where $\mathbf{F}(x, y, z) = -y\mathbf{i} + x\mathbf{j} + 2z\mathbf{k}$ and S is the upper half of the sphere $x^2 + y^2 + z^2 = 25$, with upward orientation.

Answer: $\frac{1000\pi}{6}$

23. Evaluate the flux of the vector field $\mathbf{F} = 2\mathbf{i} + \mathbf{j} + 3\mathbf{k}$ through the plane region with the given orientation as shown below.

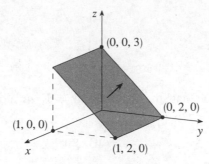

Answer: 9

24. Evaluate the flux of the vector field $\mathbf{F} = 2\mathbf{i} + \mathbf{j} + 3\mathbf{k}$ through the plane region with the given orientation as shown below.

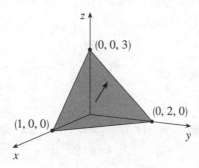

Answer: $\frac{21}{2}$

13.7 Stokes' Theorem

1. Let $\mathbf{F}(x, y, z) = x\mathbf{j}$. Evaluate the line integral $\int_C \mathbf{F} \cdot d\mathbf{r}$ along the rectangular path from $(0, 0, 0)$ to $(1, 0, 1)$ to $(1, 1, 1)$ to $(0, 1, 0)$ to $(0, 0, 0)$.

(A) 1   (B) $\sqrt{2}$ (C) $\sqrt{3}$ (D) 2

(E) $\frac{\sqrt{2}}{2}$ (F) $\frac{\sqrt{3}}{2}$ (G) $\frac{1}{2}$ (H) $\frac{1}{4}$

Answer: (A)

2. Let $\mathbf{F}(x, y, z) = x\mathbf{j}$. Evaluate the line integral $\int_C \mathbf{F} \cdot d\mathbf{r}$ along the elliptical path $\mathbf{r}(t) = \cos t\,\mathbf{i} + \sin t\,\mathbf{j} + \cos t\,\mathbf{k}$, $0 \le t \le 2\pi$.

(A) π (B) $\pi\sqrt{2}$ (C) $\pi\sqrt{3}$ (D) 2π

(E) $\frac{\sqrt{2}}{2}\pi$ (F) $\frac{\sqrt{3}}{2}\pi$ (G) $\frac{\pi}{2}$ (H) $\frac{\pi}{4}$

Answer: (A)

3. Let $\mathbf{F}(x, y, z) = -y\mathbf{i} + x\mathbf{j} + e^{z^2}\mathbf{k}$. Evaluate $\iint_S \text{curl } \mathbf{F} \cdot d\mathbf{S}$ over the surface S given by $z = \sqrt{1 - x^2 - y^2}$, with downward orientation.

(A) 2π (B) π (C) $\frac{\pi}{2}$ (D) 3π

(E) -2π (F) $-\pi$ (G) $-\frac{\pi}{2}$ (H) -3π

Answer: (E)

4. Let $\mathbf{F}(x, y, z) = 2xy^3z^4\,\mathbf{i} + 3x^2y^2z^4\,\mathbf{j} + 4x^2y^3z^3\,\mathbf{k}$. Evaluate the line integral $\int_C \mathbf{F} \cdot d\mathbf{r}$ along the elliptical path $\mathbf{r}(t) = \cos t\,\mathbf{i} + \sin t\,\mathbf{j} + \cos t\,\mathbf{k}$, $0 \le t \le 2\pi$.

   (A) π (B) $\pi\sqrt{2}$ (C) $\pi\sqrt{3}$ (D) 2π

   (E) $\frac{\sqrt{2}}{2}\pi$ (F) $\frac{\sqrt{3}}{2}\pi$ (G) $\frac{\pi}{2}$ (H) 0

   Answer: (H)

5. Let $\mathbf{F}(x, y, z) = z\mathbf{i} + x\mathbf{j} + y\mathbf{k}$. Evaluate the line integral $\int_C \mathbf{F} \cdot d\mathbf{r}$ along the rectangular path from $(0, 0, 0)$ to $(1, 0, 1)$ to $(1, 1, 1)$ to $(0, 1, 0)$ to $(0, 0, 0)$.

   (A) 1 (B) -1 (C) $\sqrt{2}$ (D) $-\sqrt{2}$

   (E) $\sqrt{3}$ (F) $-\sqrt{3}$ (G) 2 (H) 0

   Answer: (H)

6. Let $\mathbf{F}(x, y, z) = x^2\mathbf{j}$. Evaluate the line integral $\int_C \mathbf{F} \cdot d\mathbf{r}$ along the rectangular path from $(0, 0, 0)$ to $(1, 0, 1)$ to $(1, 1, 1)$ to $(0, 1, 0)$ to $(0, 0, 0)$.

   (A) 1 (B) $\sqrt{2}$ (C) $\sqrt{3}$ (D) 2

   (E) $\frac{\sqrt{2}}{2}$ (F) $\frac{\sqrt{3}}{2}$ (G) $\frac{1}{2}$ (H) $\frac{1}{4}$

   Answer: (A)

7. Evaluate the following line integral where the path C is the curve of intersection of the paraboloid $3z = x^2 + y^2$ with the plane $3x + 4y + z = 12$: $\oint_C \left(12x^2y^2 - 6yz^2\right) dx + \left(8x^3y - 6xz^2\right) dy - 12xyz\,dz$

   Answer: 0

8. Let $\mathbf{F}(x, y, z) = x^2y^2\mathbf{i} + x^2z^2\mathbf{j} + y^2z^2\mathbf{k}$. Let C be the rectangular path from $(1, 1, 2)$ to $(3, 1, 2)$ to $(3, 5, 2)$ to $(1, 5, 2)$ to $(1, 1, 2)$. Use Stokes' Theorem to evaluate the line integral $\int_C \mathbf{F} \cdot \mathbf{T}\,ds$, where $\mathbf{T}$ is the unit tangent vector to C.

   Answer: -80

9. Use Stokes' Theorem to evaluate $\iint_S \operatorname{curl}\mathbf{F} \cdot d\mathbf{S}$ where $\mathbf{F}(x, y, z) = y^2z\mathbf{i} + xz\mathbf{j} + x^2y^2\mathbf{k}$ and S is the part of the paraboloid $z = x^2 + y^2$ that lies inside the cylinder $x^2 + y^2 = 1$, oriented upward.

   Answer: π

10. Use Stokes' Theorem to evaluate $\iint_S \operatorname{curl}\mathbf{F} \cdot d\mathbf{S}$ where $\mathbf{F}(x, y, z) = \left(x + \tan^{-1}yz\right)\mathbf{i} + y^2z\mathbf{j} + z\mathbf{k}$ and S is the part of the hemisphere $x = \sqrt{9 - y^2 - z^2}$ that lies inside the cylinder $y^2 + z^2 = 4$, oriented in the direction of the positive x-axis.

    Answer: -4π

11. Use Stokes' Theorem to evaluate $\int_C \mathbf{F} \cdot d\mathbf{r}$ where $\mathbf{F}(x, y, z) = z^2\mathbf{i} + y^2\mathbf{j} + xy\mathbf{k}$ and C is the triangle with vertices $(1, 0, 0)$, $(0, 1, 0)$, and $(0, 0, 2)$.

    Answer: $\frac{4}{3}$

12. Use Stokes' Theorem to evaluate $\int_C \mathbf{F} \cdot d\mathbf{r}$ where $\mathbf{F}(x, y, z) = x^2z\mathbf{i} + xy^2\mathbf{j} + z^2\mathbf{k}$ and C is the curve of intersection of the plane $x + y + z = 1$ and the cylinder $x^2 + y^2 = 9$.

    Answer: $\frac{81\pi}{2}$

13. Let $\mathbf{F}(x,y,z) = \dfrac{x\mathbf{i} + y\mathbf{j} + z\mathbf{k}}{(x^2 + y^2 + z^2)^{3/2}}$. Evaluate the line integral $\int_C \mathbf{F} \cdot d\mathbf{r}$, where C is the curve of intersection of the paraboloid $x^2 + y^2 = 2z$ and the cylinder $x^2 + y^2 = 2x$.

(A) 1   (B) -1 (C) $\sqrt{2}$ (D) $-\sqrt{2}$

(E) $\sqrt{3}$ (F) $-\sqrt{3}$ (G) 2   (H) 0

Answer: (H)

14. Let S be the parametric surface $x = r\cos\theta$, $y = r\sin\theta$, $z = 0$, $0 \le r \le 1$, $0 \le \theta \le \frac{\pi}{2}$. Use Stokes' Theorem to evaluate $\iint_S \operatorname{curl}\mathbf{F} \cdot d\mathbf{S}$, where $\mathbf{F}(x,y,z) = -y\mathbf{i} + x\mathbf{j} + z\mathbf{k}$.

Answer: $\frac{\pi}{2}$

15. Consider the surfaces S_1: $\frac{1}{9}x^2 + \frac{1}{9}y^2 + \frac{1}{4}z^2 s = 1$, $z \ge 0$, and S_2: $4z = 9 - x^2 - y^2$, $z \ge 0$, and let $\mathbf{F}$ be a vector field with continuous partial derivatives everywhere. Why do we know that $\iint_{S_1} \operatorname{curl}\mathbf{F} \cdot d\mathbf{S} = \iint_{S_2} \operatorname{curl}\mathbf{F} \cdot d\mathbf{S}$?

Answer: The boundary curves C_1 and C_2 for S_1 and S_2 are the same

16. Parametrize the boundary curve C of the surface S: $\frac{1}{4}x^2 + \frac{1}{9}y^2 + \frac{1}{16}z^2 = 1$, $z \ge 0$, so that it has positive orientation with S.

Answer: $x = 2\cos\theta$, $y = 3\sin\theta$, $0 \le \theta \le 2\pi$

17. Use Stokes' Theorem to evaluate $\int_C xy\,dx + yz\,dy + zx\,dz$, where C is the triangle with vertices $(1,0,0)$, $(0,1,0)$, and $(0,0,1)$, oriented counterclockwise as viewed from above.

Answer: $-\frac{1}{2}$

18. Use Stokes' Theorem to evaluate $\int_C (xz + 2y)\,dx + (x^2 + 5yz)\,dy + (y^2 + z)\,dz$, where C is the curve of intersection of the paraboloid $z = x^2 + 5y^2$ and the cylinder $(x - 4)^2 + (y + 3)^2 = 16$, oriented counterclockwise as viewed from above.

Answer: -32π

13.8 | The Divergence Theorem

1. Let $\mathbf{F}(x,y,z) = \mathbf{i}$ and let S be the boundary surface of the solid $E = \{(x,y,z) \mid 0 \le x \le 1, 0 \le y \le 1, 0 \le z \le 1\}$. Evaluate the surface integral $\iint_S \mathbf{F} \cdot d\mathbf{S}$.

(A) 0   (B) $\frac{1}{4}$ (C) $\frac{1}{3}$ (D) $\frac{1}{2}$

(E) $\frac{2}{3}$ (F) $\frac{3}{4}$ (G) 1   (H) $\frac{3}{2}$

Answer: (A)

2. Let $\mathbf{F}(x,y,z) = x\mathbf{i}$ and let S be the boundary surface of the solid $E = \{(x,y,z) \mid 0 \le x \le 1, 0 \le y \le 1, 0 \le z \le 1\}$. Evaluate the surface integral $\iint_S \mathbf{F} \cdot d\mathbf{S}$.

(A) 0   (B) $\frac{1}{4}$ (C) $\frac{1}{3}$ (D) $\frac{1}{2}$

(E) $\frac{2}{3}$ (F) $\frac{3}{4}$ (G) 1   (H) $\frac{3}{2}$

Answer: (G)

3. Let $\mathbf{F}(x, y, z) = x^2\mathbf{i}$ and let S be the boundary surface of the solid
$E = \{(x, y, z) \mid 0 \le x \le 1, 0 \le y \le 1, 0 \le z \le 1\}$. Evaluate the surface integral $\iint_S \mathbf{F} \cdot d\mathbf{S}$.

(A) 0   (B) $\frac{1}{4}$ (C) $\frac{1}{3}$ (D) $\frac{1}{2}$

(E) $\frac{2}{3}$ (F) $\frac{3}{4}$ (G) 1   (H) $\frac{3}{2}$

Answer: (G)

4. Let $\mathbf{F}(x, y, z) = xy\mathbf{i}$ and let S be the boundary surface of the solid
$E = \{(x, y, z) \mid 0 \le x \le 1, 0 \le y \le 1, 0 \le z \le 1\}$. Evaluate the surface integral $\iint_S \mathbf{F} \cdot d\mathbf{S}$.

(A) 0   (B) $\frac{1}{4}$ (C) $\frac{1}{3}$ (D) $\frac{1}{2}$

(E) $\frac{2}{3}$ (F) $\frac{3}{4}$ (G) 1   (H) $\frac{3}{2}$

Answer: (D)

5. Let $\mathbf{F}(x, y, z) = xy^2\mathbf{i}$ and let S be the boundary surface of the solid
$E = \{(x, y, z) \mid 0 \le x \le 1, 0 \le y \le 1, 0 \le z \le 1\}$. Evaluate the surface integral $\iint_S \mathbf{F} \cdot d\mathbf{S}$.

(A) 0   (B) $\frac{1}{4}$ (C) $\frac{1}{3}$ (D) $\frac{1}{2}$

(E) $\frac{2}{3}$ (F) $\frac{3}{4}$ (G) 1   (H) $\frac{3}{2}$

Answer: (C)

6. Let $\mathbf{F}(x, y, z) = \sin(y^2 + z^2)\,\mathbf{i} + \cos(x^2 + z^2)\,\mathbf{j} + e^{x^2 + y^2}\,\mathbf{k}$ and let S be the boundary surface of the
solid $E = \{(x, y, z) \mid x^2 + y^2 + z^2 \le 1\}$. Evaluate the surface integral $\iint_S \mathbf{F} \cdot d\mathbf{S}$.

(A) 0   (B) $\frac{\pi}{4}$ (C) $\frac{\pi}{3}$ (D) $\frac{\pi}{2}$

(E) $\frac{2\pi}{3}$ (F) $\frac{3\pi}{4}$ (G) π (H) $\frac{3\pi}{2}$

Answer: (A)

7. Let $\mathbf{F}(x, y, z) = x\mathbf{i} + y\mathbf{j} + z\mathbf{k}$ and let S be the boundary surface of the solid
$E = \{(x, y, z) \mid x^2 + y^2 + z^2 \le 1\}$. Evaluate the surface integral $\iint_S \mathbf{F} \cdot d\mathbf{S}$.

(A) 0   (B) $\frac{\pi}{2}$ (C) π (D) $\frac{4\pi}{3}$

(E) $\frac{2\pi}{3}$ (F) $\frac{8\pi}{3}$ (G) 2π (H) 4π

Answer: (H)

8. Let $\mathbf{F}(x, y, z) = (x^3 + y\sin z)\,\mathbf{i} + (y^3 + z^2\sin z)\,\mathbf{j} + (z^3 + x)\,\mathbf{k}$ and let S be the boundary surface of
the solid E bounded by $z = \sqrt{4 - x^2 - y^2}$, $z = \sqrt{1 - x^2 - y^2}$, and $z = 0$. Evaluate the surface integral
$\iint_S \mathbf{F} \cdot d\mathbf{S}$.

(A) $\frac{62\pi}{5}$ (B) $\frac{\pi}{2}$ (C) π (D) $\frac{4\pi}{3}$

(E) $\frac{2\pi}{3}$ (F) $\frac{192\pi}{5}$ (G) $\frac{186\pi}{5}$ (H) 4π

Answer: (G)

9. Evaluate the flux integral $\iint_S (2x\mathbf{i} - y\mathbf{j} + 3z\mathbf{k}) \cdot \mathbf{n}\, dS$ over the boundary of the ball $x^2 + y^2 + z^2 \le 9$.

Answer: 144π

10. Evaluate $\iint_S \mathbf{F} \cdot \mathbf{n}\, dS$, where S is the cube bounded by the planes $x = \pm 1$, $y = \pm 1$, and $z = \pm 1$,
$\mathbf{F} = x^2 y\mathbf{i} + xy\mathbf{j} + y^2 z^3\mathbf{k}$, and $\mathbf{n}$ is the outward normal.

Answer: $\frac{8}{3}$

11. Define the vector function $\mathbf{F}$ by $\mathbf{F}(x, y, z) = (2x - z)\mathbf{i} + x^2 y\mathbf{j} + xz^2\mathbf{k}$. Use the Divergence Theorem to evaluate the surface integral $\iint_S \mathbf{F} \cdot d\mathbf{S}$, where S is the surface enclosing the unit cube with $\mathbf{n}$ the outward-pointing unit normal.

    Answer: $\frac{17}{6}$

12. Let $\mathbf{F}(x, y, z) = x^2 y\mathbf{i} - x^2 z\mathbf{j} + z^2 y\mathbf{k}$ and let S be the surface of the rectangular box bounded by the planes $x = 0$, $x = 3$, $y = 0$, $y = 2$, $z = 0$, and $z = 1$. Evaluate the surface integral $\iint_S \mathbf{F} \cdot d\mathbf{S}$.

    Answer: 24

13. Let $\mathbf{F}(x, y, z) = 3xy\mathbf{i} + y^2\mathbf{j} - x^2 y^4\mathbf{k}$ and let S be the surface of the tetrahedron with vertices $(0, 0, 0)$, $(1, 0, 0)$, $(0, 1, 0)$, and $(0, 0, 1)$. Evaluate the surface integral $\iint_S \mathbf{F} \cdot d\mathbf{S}$.

    Answer: $\frac{5}{24}$

14. Let $\mathbf{F}(x, y, z) = \left(x + e^{y \tan z}\right)\mathbf{i} + 3xe^{xz}\mathbf{j} + (\cos y - z)\mathbf{k}$ and let S be the surface with equation $x^4 + y^4 + z^4 = 1$. Evaluate the surface integral $\iint_S \mathbf{F} \cdot d\mathbf{S}$.

    Answer: 0

15. Let $\mathbf{F}(x, y, z) = x^3\mathbf{i} + 2xz^2\mathbf{j} + 3y^2 z\mathbf{k}$ and let S be the surface of the solid bounded by the paraboloid $z = 4 - x^2 - y^2$ and the xy-plane. Evaluate the surface integral $\iint_S \mathbf{F} \cdot d\mathbf{S}$.

    Answer: 32π

16. Let $\mathbf{F}(x, y, z) = \left(x^3 + yz\right)\mathbf{i} + x^2 y\mathbf{j} + xz^2\mathbf{k}$ and let S be the surface of the solid bounded by the spheres $x^2 + y^2 + z^2 = 4$ and $x^2 + y^2 + z^2 = 9$. Evaluate the surface integral $\iint_S \mathbf{F} \cdot d\mathbf{S}$.

    Answer: $\frac{3376\pi}{15}$

17. Let $\mathbf{F}(x, y, z) = \left(x^2 + ye^z\right)\mathbf{i} + \left(y^2 + ze^x\right)\mathbf{j} + \left(z^2 + xe^y\right)\mathbf{k}$ and let S be the boundary surface of the solid $E = \left\{(x, y, z) \mid x^2 + y^2 \le 1, 0 \le z \le x + 2\right\}$. Evaluate the surface integral $\iint_S \mathbf{F} \cdot d\mathbf{S}$.

    Answer: $\frac{19\pi}{4}$

18. Let $\mathbf{F}(x, y, z) = x\mathbf{i} + y\mathbf{j} + 2z\mathbf{k}$ and let S be the boundary surface of the solid $E = \left\{(x, y, z) \mid x^2 + y^2 \le z \le 4\right\}$. Evaluate the surface integral $\iint_S \mathbf{F} \cdot d\mathbf{S}$.

    Answer: 2π

19. Let $\mathbf{F}(x, y, z) = \dfrac{z\mathbf{i} + x\mathbf{j} + y\mathbf{k}}{\left(x^2 + y^2 + z^2\right)^{3/2}}$ and let S be the boundary surface of the solid $E = \left\{(x, y, z) \mid 1 \le x^2 + y^2 + z^2 \le 4\right\}$. Evaluate the surface integral $\iint_S \mathbf{F} \cdot d\mathbf{S}$.

    Answer: 0

20. Evaluate $\iint_S \mathbf{F} \cdot d\mathbf{S}$, where S is the boundary surface of the solid sphere E: $x^2 + y^2 + z^2 \le 4$ and $\mathbf{F} = 3x\mathbf{i} + 4y\mathbf{j} + 5z\mathbf{k}$.

    Answer: 96π

21. Evaluate $\iint_S \mathbf{F} \cdot d\mathbf{S}$, where S is the boundary surface of the region outside the sphere $x^2 + y^2 + z^2 = 1$ and inside the ball $x^2 + y^2 + z^2 \le 4$ and $\mathbf{F} = e^{y^2}\mathbf{i} + \left(5y + e^{x^2}\right)\mathbf{j} + (-3z + 2x)\mathbf{k}$.

    Answer: $\frac{56\pi}{3}$

22. Find the flux of $\mathbf{F}(x, y, z) = \left(x^2 z + \dfrac{1}{\ln(y + 3)}\right)\mathbf{i} + \left(xyz + \dfrac{1}{y + 3}\right)\mathbf{j} + \left(xz^2 + \dfrac{z}{(y + 3)^2}\right)\mathbf{k}$ across the surface of the solid $x^2 + y^2 + z^2 \le 1$.

    Answer: 0

23. Find the flux of $\mathbf{F}(x, y, z) = x^3\,\mathbf{i} + 2xz^2\,\mathbf{j} + 3y^2z\,\mathbf{k}$ across the surface of the solid bounded by the paraboloid $z = 4 - x^2 - y^2$ and the xy-plane.

Answer: 32π

24. Let S be the outwardly-oriented surface of a solid region E where the volume of E is 10 ft^3. If $\mathbf{r} = x\mathbf{i} + y\mathbf{j} + z\mathbf{k}$ and $r = |\mathbf{r}|$, evaluate the surface integral $\iint_S \nabla\left(r^2\right)\,d\mathbf{S}$.

Answer: 60 ft^3

25. Evaluate

$\iint_S \mathbf{F} \cdot d\mathbf{S}$, where $\mathbf{F}(x, y, z) = \dfrac{x}{\left(x^2 + y^2 + z^2\right)^{3/2}}\,\mathbf{i} + \dfrac{y}{\left(x^2 + y^2 + z^2\right)^{3/2}}\,\mathbf{j} + \dfrac{z}{\left(x^2 + y^2 + z^2\right)^{3/2}}\,\mathbf{k}$ and S is the sphere $x^2 + y^2 + z^2 = 9$.

Answer: 4π

26. Evaluate

$\iint_S \mathbf{F} \cdot d\mathbf{S}$, where $\mathbf{F}(x, y, z) = \dfrac{x}{\left(x^2 + y^2 + z^2\right)^{3/2}}\,\mathbf{i} + \dfrac{y}{\left(x^2 + y^2 + z^2\right)^{3/2}}\,\mathbf{j} + \dfrac{z}{\left(x^2 + y^2 + z^2\right)^{3/2}}\,\mathbf{k}$ and S is the sphere $x^2 + y^2 + (z - 5)^2 = 9$.

Answer: 0